THE HUMAN REALITY

THE HUMAN REALITY

*A Reinterpretation of our Origins
and Evolution*

Peter Prew

Illustrated by Perina Prew

Book Guild Publishing
Sussex, England

First published in Great Britain in 2006 by
The Book Guild Ltd
Pavilion View
19 New Road
Brighton, BN1 1UF

Typesetting in Garamond by
Keyboard Services, Luton, Bedfordshire

Printed in Great Britain by
Athenaeum Press, Gateshead

A catalogue record for this book is available from
The British Library

ISBN 1 84624 014 X

*In memory of
hunter-gatherers throughout Europe, Asia, Africa,
the Americas and Australia who were robbed of
the land, their rightful inheritance.*

All royalties from this First Edition go to Survival. Survival is a worldwide organization supporting tribal peoples. It stands for their right to decide their own future and helps them protect their lives, lands and human rights.

Survival International
6 Charterhouse Buildings
London
EC1M 7ET
United Kingdom
T: 020 7687 8700
F: 020 7687 8701
info@survival-international.org
www.survival-international.org

Contents

PART II: THE COMPOSITE ANIMAL

PART III: THE HISTORICAL IMPERATIVE

APPENDICES

Foreword and Acknowledgements

After 17 years service I retired from the Royal Navy in 1960, and subsequently trained for the ministry of the Church of England. For the first time in my life I was living in an atmosphere of intense intellectual discussion and also had the time to read widely. In the process I became disenchanted not only with the Church but with everything that passed for the civilized way of life. I decided to devote myself to the pursuit of philosophy in its original and broadest sense. I wanted somehow to get behind the dazzling images and seemingly unassailable tenets of the great religions, the sciences, the law and other intellectual disciplines and institutions that so dominate our lives, in order to discover not only the laws that underlie their origins and development, but also the reasons why the original and continuing pursuit of knowledge, wealth and power has so unquestionably devastated peoples and the natural environment.

This book is thus the product of a quest to discover the truth and reality of the human condition. It was born out of chaos, my own private chaos, when I had to set aside all my preconceived notions and all I had experienced and had been taught of life and humanity, in order to find out for myself the fundamental causes of man's inhumanity to man and to nature. Having no idea where to begin, I realized that I was passing through a personal crisis when, for months, I searched through the mass of research material I had accumulated. Then a friend said simply: 'Just start at the beginning!' So I did just that, since when I have had many beginnings, endlessly re-writing the book because I realized each time that I had not delved sufficiently deeply into the past, the better to reveal the present. Without the continued intervention and advice of that friend, Séan Doherty, and too without the constant encouragement and support of Angela, my wife, this book would not have been written at all. In addition, I owe a great debt of gratitude to the late Arthur Koestler and to Ian Player for their interest and letters of encouragement, particularly in the early stages of the work. I must thank too the rest of my family for their critical comments and help throughout. Finally, my thanks to Rosanne Sanders for her support and help with the book's diagrams, and to my daughter, Perina, for editing and illustrating the book; to Ralph Estling for his invaluable advice and comments on the work; and to Sara Maitland and Gareth Vaughan for their invaluable advice in editing the book.

Other acknowledgements relating to copyright material used in the book appear in *References and Bibliography* at the end of the book.

The book has been 40 years in the preparation and writing. All efforts possible have been made to eliminate or reveal borrowed material. Any remaining plagiarism is entirely unintentional. In the words of Sir Walter Scott, this book is 'entirely the composition of the author ... with the exception, always, of avowed quotations, and such unpremeditated and involuntary plagiarisms as can scarce be guarded against by any one who has read and written a great deal.' (The General Preface to the Waverley Novels – Edinburgh, Robert Cadell, 1829, p. xxxvi)

Prologue

PLANET EARTH IS 4,600 MILLION YEARS OLD
If we condense this inconceivable time-span into an understandable concept, we can liken Earth to a person of 46 years of age.

Nothing is known about the first 7 years of this person's life, and whilst only scattered information exists about the middle span, we know that only at the age of 42 did the Earth begin to flower.

Dinosaurs and the great reptiles did not appear until one year ago, when the planet was 45. Mammals arrived only 8 months ago; in the middle of the last week man-like apes evolved into ape-like men, and at the weekend the last ice age enveloped the Earth.

Modern Man has been around for 4 hours. During the last hour, Man discovered agriculture. The industrial revolution began a minute ago.

During those sixty seconds of biological time, Modern Man has made a rubbish tip of Paradise.

He has multiplied his numbers to plague proportions, caused the extinction of 500 species of animals, ransacked the planet for fuels and now stands like a brutish infant, gloating over his meteoric rise to ascendancy, on the brink of a war to end all wars and of effectively destroying this oasis of life in the solar system.

(From *Against All Odds*, by Greenpeace)

What does it mean to be human? We presume that we are men and women looking back at our hunter-gatherer ancestors, and tracing our evolutionary descent in an unbroken line from *Homo sapiens* hunter-gatherers to ourselves. We accept without question such ordered environmental states as city, social pyramid, nation, empire and civilization itself, as though their inception and development were proper and natural to our present and future well-being. Anthropologists and archaeologists would have us believe that *Homo sapiens* is, in the end, a civilized animal; while many scientists, lawyers, historians, prelates and politicians look forward to a spread of world government – one world, under one government, one law and one God. Yet, is civilization a real and inevitable stage in the evolution of *Homo sapiens*? After all, civilization, like all human culture at whatever level, is something artificial and man-made. And when measured against the two million years that humans have been on Earth, the 6–8,000 years of their civilizations is a very short period indeed. What, in fact, is the reality of civilization and why did it appear when it did in Sumeria, in Egypt, in India, in China and elsewhere?

Likewise, it is a truism that our society is based on different sorts of exploitation, but why is it so based? How and why is it that some civilized men should have such driving power, and opportunity, to sacrifice their fellows, either deliberately or by default? Every prolonged encounter with the inhuman, even if it does not destroy the victims, inevitably scars people, particularly when they have been subjected to humiliating conditions such as those experienced by aboriginal hunter-gatherers dispossessed of their lands, by slaves in the Americas, by the inmates of Stalin's Gulags and Hitler's concentration camps, and subsequently by the ethnic cleansing of Bosnia, Croatia, Kosovo and Rwanda, the bombing of the World Trade Center and the wars against Afghanistan and Iraq, experiences often conducive to utter despair. So who are we exactly, we who have perpetrated such thefts and atrocities, as well as seemingly endless wars, down the ages and throughout the world? For surely to describe as 'human' animals whose major preoccupations have so often involved the grossly inhuman is a contradiction in terms. Furthermore, the human species has multiplied itself faster and faster, as if to provide more and more victims for the sacrifice, while at the same time sacrificing wildlife and wilderness on the altar of development. Is this progress, or is the whole idea of progress a mental refuge, a comforting myth, in the face of an apparent historical inevitability?

For, whether we like it or not, there is a seemingly inevitable process at work in history. As Machiavelli put it:

> Nations pass from order to disorder, and afterwards from disorder to order, because Nature allows no stability in human affairs.

Paul Kennedy,[1] in an analysis of the forces behind the rise and fall of the Great Powers, recognized the drive on the part of nations to grow, to become both rich and strong. He argued that military power is usually needed to acquire and protect wealth, while wealth is usually needed to sustain military power. He portrayed an anarchic international scene in which states struggle for their share of wealth. In that struggle to acquire and to protect wealth, the tendency has been for states to overstretch themselves strategically, leading to their eclipse and to the ascendancy of new states, and so on *ad infinitum.*

This inexorable and seemingly inevitable process, and the associated suffering of those trampled underfoot, indicates, whatever the cause, an unreality and unreal activity of such proportions as to suggest that civilized peoples are irrevocably caught up in a long-drawn out nightmare and become like sleepwalkers, groping their 'eerie way down the corridors of history', seemingly incapable of halting their suicidal devastation of the planet.

In seeking to explain our apparently irresistible drift towards self-destruction, Arthur Koestler rightly intimated that the first step towards a possible therapy is a correct diagnosis of what went wrong with our species.

> There have been countless attempts at such a diagnosis, but none of them carried much conviction, because none started from the hypothesis that *Homo sapiens* may be an aberrant biological species, an evolutionary misfit.[2]

Are we? Or is it that only some of humankind became misfits, perhaps after a traumatic experience in our prehistoric past that has rendered us semi-invalid and a prey to haunting fears and delusions? In the words of George Steiner:

> Most history seems to carry on its back vestiges of paradise. At some point in more or less remote times, things were better, almost golden. A deep concordance lay between man and the natural setting. The myth of the Fall runs stronger than any particular religion. There is hardly a civilization, perhaps hardly an individual conscious-ness, that does not carry inwardly, and answer to, intimations of a sense of distant catastrophe. Somewhere a wrong turn was taken in that 'dark and sacred wood', after which man has had to labour, socially, psychologically, against the natural grain of being.[3]

I believe this was the result of the adaptation of certain hunter-gatherer groups to agriculture following the end of the Ice Age, when those who so adapted lost their ecological understanding and self-control as predatory wild animals, and were thus turned into failed animals confronted by powers that have remained alien and hostile just because of their own alienation and uncomprehending fear of the wilderness, their erstwhile home.

It is my contention that the overwhelming problems, the widespread violence, the suffering, and in particular the sense of impotence in the face of a ruthless destiny, are the outcome of a degeneration on the part of far ranging hunter-gatherers forced by environmental pressures to adapt to a primitive subsistence agriculture as a principal source of food. This was the real fall, when some people fell from a highly developed and relatively perfect state as hunter-gatherers to a grossly imperfect and environmentally insensitive state as primitive farmers imprisoned in a wilderness they could no longer freely enter nor understand; a fall which the myths of a Fall and Flood falsify and disguise.

The Mesolithic and early Neolithic introduced what may be described as a two-fold fall. First, in losing many of their characteristics as hunter-gatherers, and in suffering a fundamental socio-economic disintegration, disorientation and deculturation, these de-ranged people lost the basis of their identities and stable state, and the wilderness became a hostile environment to them. They were thereafter imprisoned in conflict with that world. This was the primary fall, which was followed by a secondary fall, when a few climbed, as it were, on the bent backs of their weaker fellows to escape their imprisoning circumstances and dearth, to create stratified societies of

Homo sapiens sapiens   agents
Homo sapiens non sapiens   workers

out of a wilderness – which had only yesterday been their beloved home – exploited and destroyed to that end. With the growth of stratified societies, not only were men and women humiliated in each generation as forcibly de-ranged hunter-gatherers, but further degraded as domesticated, or enslaved, animals to the lowly condition of peasant cultivators for a few elevated as Chiefs and Kings of stratified societies.

The two-fold fall thus involved both a primary and a secondary historical degeneration. I describe members of

Homo sapiens sapiens
Homo sapiens non sapiens

stratified societies as *Homo degener*, or degenerate human, in sharp contradistinction to *Homo sapiens*, or true human being. If *Homo sapiens* hunter-gatherers, in their relative physical and psychical perfection, may be regarded as a model of what it is to be human, *Homo degener*'s deviation from that model may be seen as a progressive degeneration into inhumanity and imperfection. In losing many of their characteristics as human beings, and in destroying their erstwhile home, *Homo degener* peoples were doubly deprived. They had changed out of all recognition, undergoing what may be described as a primary re-evolution: when a process of an infinitely slow evolutionary change and development of all humans made relatively perfect* in a limitless freedom of movement in the horizontal → as hunter-gatherers was turned into a process of accelerating anti-evolutionary change and development of degenerate sedentary people attempting to acquire power and improve their condition, thereby raising up hierarchical structures in the vertical ↑. Their stratified societies have subsequently grown through progressive revolutions on the original re-evolution.

However, this is only one major element of the re-evolution that occurred. For the second major aspect of the fall, which relates to the growth and spread of stratified societies as pyramids of power, may also be viewed as a growth and spread of composite animals across the world. History – or rather what may now be better described as bio-history – can also be seen as the story of the progressive development and growth of new (pioneer) species of composite animal comprising

> *Homo sapiens sapiens*   head and brain
> *Homo sapiens non sapiens* hands and feet

that are subject to a convergent evolution.

These animals could only survive in the world by cutting back the wilderness and cohering in groups in protected environments. As they slowly developed hierarchies of leaders and led, these groups began to multiply and grow up as composite animals comprising controlling head, fighting arms and cultivating hands and feet. They were characterized by a division of labour which made the whole greater than the sum of its individual parts: they resembled giant human beings. Their members faced the wilderness and world as corporate bodies of degenerate people to whom the outside world was a hostile environment. These composite animals now spread their prison-like protected environments outwards to engulf the wilderness, other composite animals and hunter-gatherer peoples. For whereas previously all men and women had belonged to one species – *Homo sapiens*, at home in a wilderness in which men and women occupied an equal economic and social status and obeyed the laws of nature that governed their behaviour – a majority now belonged to new species of composite animal at war with the world, whose principal concern has been to discover and pervert the laws of nature, and to

---

*See Part 1, Chapter 2, pp. 42, 43 for a definition of relative perfection.

exploit the land, to make the world as comfortable and safe as possible for their alien and exotic kind.

It has been shown that profound cultural change is a costly response to perturbation which, at best, may just permit an animal to survive. It is least costly and ultimately most adaptive to change as little as possible, particularly when, as in the case of the hunter-gatherers, their evolutionary adaptations had already proved enormously successful over tens of thousands of years. In the case of the adaptation to farming, I wish to show that the change was, and remains, catastrophic, mainly because it was a degenerative re-evolutionary adaptation that has required the ongoing destruction of the wilderness in order that farming cultures might not only survive but prosper.

Humanity was thus divided in two: on the one hand *Homo sapiens* hunter-gatherers still true to their evolutionary selves, and on the other failed degenerates separated from their true selves by their adaptation to agriculture. The highly developed hunter-gatherer is an evolutionary marvel; while those peoples alienated from their original evolutionary path by their adaptation to a primitive agriculture in order to survive became re-evolutionary outsiders or 'evolutionary misfits'.

Each nation is a protected environment of degenerate people fundamentally at war with the world. All the aggressive characteristics so conducive to the well-being of humans as hunter-gatherers evolving co-operatively in a freedom of movement in the horizontal within nature are redirected and perverted to serve static composite animals concerned to expand in the horizontal the better to grow in the vertical in competition with other similar exotic animals. It is this frustration and perversion of the true potential of humankind that makes for man's inhumanity to man, to women and to nature. The co-operative cultures of the hunter-gatherers gave way to rivalry, warfare and slavery. We are no longer evolving as true men and women integrated within the natural world. That we are true human beings is a fallacious belief which permeates all our intellectual disciplines and renders them nugatory. We are members of anti-evolutionary composite animals alienated from one another and from the natural world – hence the *angst,* loneliness and pain of humankind – and subject to an increasingly competitive convergent evolution that invites nemesis: it is propelling *Homo degener* both towards World Government and ultimate self-destruction.

It is this hypothesis, and its implications, that this book sets out to explore. It seeks to reveal the truth about the past in order to reinterpret the present. This is important because we are apt to interpret the past, and so too the present, in terms of our preconceptions. We think we are true human beings and look at the past in the light of that supposition, a preconception that I wish to show is a gross misconception. In particular, the book seeks to answer more truly than heretofore the perennial and fundamental questions of life: who and what am I, where have I come from, why am I here, and where am I going? In short, what is the meaning of life? More than that, the book seeks to probe the hidden laws which govern behaviour and hence change. It also seeks to reveal the true nature of the perennial problem of good and evil, and to reveal the basic causes of man's inhumanity to man and to nature, which have hitherto remained hidden beneath the gilded veneer of civilization.

The book is written from the evolutionary standpoint of the hunter-gatherer and of nature and its laws, using nature as the foundation and touchstone of the argument. It explores the scientific, spiritual and moral aspects of human societies as these evolved within the wilderness. And whilst any one theory or observation in it may be successfully challenged by a relevant authority, it is my aim to show that, taken cumulatively, the diverse ideas presented indicate an alternative explanation for the origin of civilizations and for their extraordinarily destructive effects on the natural environments of the world. The book is truly hopeful because it shows a ray of light at the end of the very dark tunnel of man's 12,000 years of inhumanity to man and to nature, a light that invites humankind to redeem itself through a love of the wilderness, and its resurrection under the guidance of the hunter-gatherer peoples who are at present threatened with extinction, yet who alone are capable of guiding humankind away from the brink of catastrophe and towards the recovery of their true evolutionary path and perfection.

PART I
THE FALL

'For they have sown the wind...'

Chapter 1

The Challenge of the Natural Flux

Ere land or water was, or circling sky,
Throughout the world Nature was uniform,
What men call Chaos, shapeless and obscure,
Where seethed the germs of things as yet to be.

Not yet the pure light of the sun shone down,
Nor yet the moon renewed her crescent horns;
No globe hung poised in the enfolding air,
Nor did the sea with its long arms embrace
The margent shores. Such was this vague, dark world:
Nor earth nor water yet, nor hot nor cold,
Nor soft nor hard, but indeterminate.

(Ovid)

The Earth itself, and life upon the Earth, were born as in a womb, in chaos within the greater order of the universe.

The gaseous birth of this planet occurred within the womb of the universe, during what is known as the Hadean Aeon, 4,600–3,900 million years ago. As it swung around the sun its gases condensed to a molten mass, and by about 3,900 million years ago the Earth's surface had cooled enough for a thin crust to form upon it. That crust was penetrated from above by huge meteorites and punctured from below by volcanic eruptions which spewed out water vapour and carbon dioxide, the original greenhouse gases. There followed what is known as the Archean Aeon, 3,900–2,500 million years ago (see Table 1.1). Torrential rains, falling for perhaps a hundred thousand years without stopping, began to form hot, shallow oceans on the cooling crust. The waters began to erode the rocky landscape, washing minerals and salts into the oceans. By now too the moon had condensed as Earth's satellite, pulling rhythmically on the oceans, creating

3

TABLE 1.1

GEOLOGICAL TIME SCALE

(Millions of years ago)

Aeons	Beginning of Aeon	Eras	Periods or Epochs		Evolutionary Events
Hadean	4,550				Formation of Earth (4,550)
Archean	3,900	Prephanerozoic	Pre-Cambrian		Oldest rocks (4,000) Prokaryotic cells (3,500)
Proterozoic	2,500				First free oxygen (2,000) Eukaryotic cells (2,000) First complex animals (800)
Phanerozoic	540	Palaeozoic 540–245	Cambrian	540–500	Diverse animals Jawless fish
			Ordovician	500–430	Land plants
			Silurian	430–410	
			Devonian	410–360	Amphibians on land
			Carboniferous	360–290	Reptiles
			Permian	290–245	
		Mesozoic 245–65	Triassic	245–200	Early dinosaurs and mammals
			Jurassic	200–145	First birds
			Cretaceous	145–65	Flowering plants
		Cenozoic 65–0	Tertiary	Paleocene 65–58	Whales, modern mammals
				Eocene 58–38	Prosimians
				Oligocene 38–25	Monkeys and apes
				Miocene 25–5	
				Pliocene 5–2	Early humans
	0		Quaternary	Pleistocene 2–0.01	
			Epoch	Holocene 0.01–	

tides. It was during this Archean Aeon that the first traces of life have been found, in the shape of single bacterial cells. And although an influx of carbon-based molecules from space might have played some part in the origin and evolution of life on Earth, I am assuming that life arose out of the environmental circumstances outlined above, either in the oceans or in freshwater ponds on land.

In the line of evolution from rock to sentient life there seems to be no break: in other words, there was little chemical difference between living cells and their immediate environment, between life and the inorganic realm of nonlife. Eventually, around 3,500 million years ago, a molecule which biologists describe as DNA, a *replicator*, with the property of being able to create copies of itself, came into being. In time these developed protective coats around themselves the better to survive: they evolved into the first simple cells, now known as prokaryotes. These survival machines included bacteria, within which the replicators now survived as colonies of genes made of DNA molecules. The live bacterium became capable of active self-maintenance against forces that might destroy it, responding to disturbances in its habitat by changing and renewing its component parts without changing its identity. Once it could do this its existence was assured. And when in addition reproduction guaranteed its expansion, the process of evolution was under way and the Earth's bacterial microcosm was created.

For the following billion years – from approximately 3,000–2,000 million years ago – the Earth was inhabited solely by prokaryotes, including bacterial microorganisms, until some began to evolve into a more elaborate kind of cell called a eukaryote. The significance of bacteria and their evolution is such that the fundamental division in life-forms on Earth is arguably between prokaryotes (organisms comprising cells with no nucleus, including bacteria) and eukaryotes (all other forms of life) rather than between animals and plants. Lynn Margulis and Dorion Sagan[1] aver that over their first two billion years on Earth, bacteria constantly changed the earth's atmosphere and surface. Covering the earth in a film of life, bacteria formed one world-wide organism capable of sharing genes on a planetary scale. They acquired motility and began behaviour, moving in search of light and acceptable habitats, developing simple systems of chemical sensing for detecting foods and avoiding poisons and other dangers. And they eventually helped create the biosphere, that extends from the mountain tops some six miles up into the ocean some five miles deep. Above all, they helped bring an order out of the original chaos that we now know as the 'balance of nature'. But it would be an order or balance maintained only by greater or lesser reversions to chaos, as when mass extinctions occur.

Plants, fungi and animals emerged from the bacterial microcosm. The first plants are descended from algal ancestors. Algae dwelt in wet, sunlit shallows. Occasionally these shallows dried up, and those algae that could remain wet on the inside while dry on the outside had the evolutionary edge. They survived and multiplied to become the early plants – low-lying forms without stems or leaves, related to modern-day mosses and liverworts, that could not support their own weight out of water. Algae became land plants by bringing water with them. Plant spores are known to have arrived ashore by about 460 million years ago. By 400 million years ago, vascular plants were already thriving. The first forests contained giant 'seed ferns', or cycads. These were trees that looked like overgrown ferns but which, unlike ferns, produced seeds. From 345 to 225 million years ago, when winged insects, dinosaurs and other animals were evolving, forests of great cycads spread over the vast expanses of land. Then, about 225 million years ago, the cycads gave way to the conifers, or cone-bearing plants, that were the principal diet of some of the first vegetarian dinosaurs.

Long before the evolution of plants, however, the evolution of the first complex animals occurred some 800 million years ago. The earliest animal fossils so far found are those of primitive water-dwelling invertebrates. It is thought that the creatures most nearly related to our line, through a common Proterozoic ancestor, were the spineless (echinodermata) sea-cucumbers, cystids and sea-urchins, uniting as they do the teeming kingdom of the pre-eminent spined group (chordata) comprising all the vertebrates from fish to man. Chordates always develop gill slits at some time during their life cycle – evidence of their origins in the sea. The subphylum of chordates to which we belong is the vertebrates.

The first of the vertebrate fish originated some 450 million years ago. In time, in addition to gills, some of these fish developed lungs. They probably evolved to be the first amphibians, venturing out on the land some 400–360 million years ago. It seems that this move was prompted by geological upheavals and the periodic receding of waters in which the animals lived. For the edge of the sea has been an area of unrest, with tides sweeping over the continents, receding and then returning. Only the most hardy and adaptable have survived in such a mutable region. This persistent restlessness and urgent command to adapt – a relentless drive that is inherent in every littoral and terrestrial living form through its origin in the seas – helped plants, invertebrate and vertebrate animals make the revolutionary change from water to air, encouraging an increasing development and use of lungs.

Already by the end of the Devonian Period, 360 million years ago, there were true amphibians, animals that lived largely on the land but enjoyed an aquatic infancy. These amphibians were not, of course, the only animals on Devonian lands. The invertebrates had already invaded the land in Silurian times, some 425 million years ago, ensuring the amphibians an entirely new source of food. They could crawl along the banks of streams and catch insects now living there. During the next 100 million years, such early amphibians spread widely and evolved into many different species. Their fossilized remains and imprints have been found in Europe, parts of Asia and North America. They now relied on their lungs and they had legs, but still returned to the water to lay their eggs.

> The step from water to land was the most significant stage in vertebrate history. Human beings are merely a highly derived subgroup of osteolepiform fishes, our Devonian ancestors...[2]

It was from the sea that we inherited our original strength and adaptability in flux, in a continual succession of changes, of challenges that demanded evolutionary responses that would eventually lead to *Homo sapiens*. The challenge of such changes – which may be described as 'the challenge of the natural flux' – has not only been the main driving force behind evolution but also the principal force behind the maintenance of Earth in a relative stability. It is necessary to examine the phenomenon of *the natural flux* in detail, because of its importance to the evolution of *Homo sapiens*.

Ever since the earliest widespread appearance of microbial life on Earth, the surface has been continuously regulated and maintained in a relatively stable and hospitable state. It has been argued not only that the environment is continually regulated by life, for life, but that, in their alliance with plants and animals, which could not live or evolve without them, it is the Earth's bacteria that have formed the necessary planetary regulating system, keeping Earth habitable. However, I believe that is only one aspect of the regulating system, and not even the most important one. The main control mechanism is what I describe as the natural flux, which is the sum total of flux and reflux, of alternations, rhythms and cataclysms and other forces of change that challenge the bacteria, plants and animals alike to adapt or die. In other words, in the regulation and maintenance of Earth in a dynamic equilibrium, the natural flux is *primus inter pares*. It is this challenge of environmental change that has not only brought life itself into being, but caused life-forms themselves to develop a variety of methods of adaptive changes to meet the challenges of the natural flux, a point to which I shall return later in the chapter. The challenge of change, the challenge of natural flux as prime mover, is the driving force behind the relentless selection pressures and behind the processes of evolution.

We have seen that the constant rhythmical movement or flux from a temporary order into disorder or natural chaos has formed the challenging background not only to the very origin of life itself, but also to the subsequent selection and evolution of life-forms. The challenge takes place in the three classes of environment affecting selection and evolution: the genetic, the physical and the biotic. Regarding the former, each molecule in living organisms interacts with numerous other molecules and membranes, not only within any one organism but within the entire gene pool of the local population in which it occurs, continuously exerting a changing selection pressure, a continuous selection for coadaptation and stability within the gene pool; while at the physical and biotic levels, all environments are changing continuously, which means, in terms of evolution, that the selection pressures vary continuously. And the changes in selection pressure affecting these environments include seasonal changes, secular fluctuations and cycles (including fluctuations of predators and available food supply), local and world-wide cataclysmic events and long-term trends of differing time intervals. Because they formed the background to the development and evolution of our species, it is important to examine some of these rhythms in greater detail. For their effect upon the ancestors of humankind must have been enormous, especially considering that they did not emerge from the sea with the early plants and invertebrates, but waited to serve an immensely long apprenticeship as vertebrate fish, subject to all the life-giving and inimical forces that are most apparent in the sea – and particularly in the shifting margins between land and water – before emerging from the waters at the end of the Devonian Period, some 360 million years ago. It was above all the ability to adapt, vulnerably and unpossessively, to these extraordinarily powerful forces that enabled our primordial ancestors to survive in a totally non-specialized way, eventually to evolve into *Homo sapiens* hunter-gatherer, artist and explorer.

Principal rhythms arise from continual changes in the power of the sun, whose energy also warms the Earth disproportionately, heating the tropics more than the poles: the temperature gradient thus created drives the climate, transporting heat from low to high latitudes. Other oscillations are due to the spin of the Earth on its axis, affecting the relationship of all living things to the sun. This results in varying degrees of light and darkness in each 24 hour period – the diurnal cycle – when one set of species of a community, the diurnal, is stimulated to activity by light, while the other set of species, the nocturnal, retreats from it, depending upon the particular evolutionary adaptation of each. Similar daily rhythms occur in the sea. Zooplankton, for instance, rise and fall in rhythmic movement, sinking by day and rising to the surface at night, where they feed upon the plant plankton.

Differing lengths of light or darkness in a day at different times of the year, rather than variations in temperature, may often be the principal agents of seasonal changes: they activate, for example, the physiology of many animals and plants in diverse ways. And not only do the rhythms of the seasons change from year to year, one May cycle of activity never being the same as the last; but the rhythms and the vital seasonal factors affecting physiology and behaviour – whether light, wetness, temperature, etc. – vary widely as between different parts of the world, and as between the two major ecosystems, the terrestrial and the aquatic. The Arctic, for example, experiences only three summer months of (continuous) daylight, which is followed by nine months of winter; while nearer the Equator, seasonal differences are more dependent upon amounts of rainfall. There are corresponding seasons in the oceans, dependent upon sunlight, water temperature gradients and the cyclic supply of food and minerals.

In addition to the effects of the revolution of the Earth in relation to the sun on all life, there is that of the moon. The cycle of intensity of moonlight during the month has been shown, for instance, to affect reproduction. The primary influence of the moon is, however, the combined gravitational pull it exerts with the sun on the seas of the world. The major effect of the tidal rhythms is found amongst life forms inhabiting the littoral regions, where rhythms are due more to the tides than to the daily cycles of sunlight and temperature. In fact, the effect of the moon and tidal rhythms upon the evolution of the life that has led to humankind cannot be overemphasized – a mass sea-memory that lies deep in the mind.

A variety of organisms seemingly respond to rhythms related to the sun, moon or tides, and in many instances their vital activities – such as navigation, feeding or reproduction – are regulated by what are known as 'biological clocks'. These may enable them to alter their way of life or behaviour in advance of any actual change.

All life is subject to a variety of rhythms and slow process of Earth change, both at the level of the microcosm and that of the macrocosm. For instance, concerning the amount of carbon dioxide in the atmosphere, there is what has been described as a seasonal 'heartbeat', when carbon is exchanged, by means of photosynthesis and respiration, between the atmosphere and vegetation in the land masses, which are mainly in the Northern Hemisphere.

Finally, there are rhythms which may cause world-wide catastrophe. Such is El Niño, a periodic reversal of currents and winds in the Pacific Ocean; when winds and ocean currents across the Pacific suddenly reverse every four or five years, for a period of up to a year. Such a reversal causes a great climatic upheaval, sometimes causing drought in southern Africa, Indonesia, eastern Australia and Brazil, hurricanes in the Pacific and heavy rainfall down the west coast of North America.

The alternations or oscillations within nature are fundamental to natural selection, and essential to the whole life process we know as evolution. Natural selection depends upon the fact that individuals of a population of living organisms vary genetically from each other in numerous ways. This genetic variability arises in part from changes or mutations that occur spontaneously in the DNA of the genes, and partly because genes occur in different combinations in different individuals. Such variations differ in the degree of biological advantage they confer, that is, in their survival value. In face of the changing and complex conditions of the environment, including the effect of pathogens such as bacteria and viruses on our genome, those individuals possessing the advantageous characteristics live to produce more offspring, thereby increasing the frequency of the advantageous characteristics. It is natural selection that ensures their differential survival in response to changes in the environment. The environment – or rather, the natural flux within the three classes of environment enumerated above – is the principal agent of natural selection; while natural selection is a governing process in evolution. Two other processes affect evolution. Even as environments shape organisms, organisms shape environments: the activities of all living things effect changes in their environments. Such activities, described as 'niche construction', are a significant factor in evolution. Another form of selection operating on species is sexual selection; when members of any one species act as the selective agents within that species. Evolution thus depends on the interaction of all these environmental and sexual agents: it involves the diversification and harmonious adaptation of living creatures as the result of a steady production of variation and of the selective effects of those agents on those variants, a process tending towards improvement, increased efficiency and stability of organisms. However, evolution is not primarily a genetic event; it is selection arising from the driving force of the natural flux that induces evolutionary change.

Although much change, as amongst communities of animals, is due to gradual environmental change, fundamental change is more often a rapid transition between stable states than a continuous transformation at slow and steady rates. An infinite number of infinitesimal changes do occur throughout the biosphere, but they tend to accumulate and suddenly announce themselves as critical states or fundamental changes. For instance, some systems are in a permanent state of disequilibrium, as exemplified in the complex patterns of currents, winds and weather caused by variations in the amounts of energy emitted by the sun shining continuously on the rotating Earth; while the continuous movement of tectonic plates builds up tensions in Earth's crust which are intermittently relieved in earthquakes. Global climate fluctuation and tectonic activity correlate with, though may not have caused, not only periods of speciation, when rapid evolution leads to the generation of new species, but also the major leaps in human evolution. However, stable states and structures are the norm, the whole governed by the natural flux, which, periodically, provides the challenge that elicits an appropriate response.

The natural flux implies a state of continual change, flow or movement within alternations, as well as a greater evolutionary movement resulting from such alternations. It is upon such a force in movement, the natural flux, that evolution and the whole 'balance of nature' depend.

The balance of nature is not a *status quo*. It is fluid, ever shifting, always adjusting itself. Nor is the balance of nature a single balance, but rather it comprises a multitude of balances. It is in effect a stability maintained in change: change rather than stability is the key to the understanding of life-forms and their evolution within the overall stability of an evolving Earth and its atmospheric environment. Despite – or rather, because of – variations in the output of heat from the sun, in the gaseous composition of the atmosphere, and in the vegetable, animal and mineral properties of the surface of Earth, the climate has changed very little, and Earth has remained extraordinarily stable in relation to its atmospheric environment, since life first appeared some 3,500 million years ago. It is hypothesized, however, that between 700 and 600 million years ago there were several periods when the whole globe was covered in ice, to be followed by hothouse conditions. These so-called 'cold and hot flushes' may have created conditions that encouraged new species to thrive: it is suggested that they may have triggered the Cambrian explosion of life. If true, it is further evidence of the key rôle of the natural flux in evolution.

Just as the original order of Earth emerged from the chaos of the Hadean Aeon, so the overall balance of nature is only such in flux between stability and instability, order and chaos. It is, I believe, the primacy of the challenge of the rhythms and cataclysms that make up the natural flux, together with the response of the biota to that challenge, which keeps the global environment generally stable. In other words, it is the stabilizing ability of the biota to maintain itself in the face of the primordial challenge of change that helps maintain the overall balance of nature. Living things – whether individual organisms, a species or the biota as a whole – are constantly adjusting in order to preserve their past and remain the same. This process, known as canalisation or developmental homeostasis, can occur only as long as the environment fluctuates within normal limits. Beyond that, challenges may force them to innovate.

This brings me to the other aspect of change to which I referred earlier, namely the ability of life-forms themselves to innovate, to develop a variety of methods of adaptation to meet the challenge of the natural flux – adaptive changes which are themselves expressive of the natural flux – and thus to survive change. In response to that challenge, life-forms change within themselves either through mutation, recombination or symbiosis,[3] or through behaviour such as mobility. These changes account for the evolution of all life-forms on Earth today.

First, governed by DNA, a living cell can replicate itself and maintain its identity by reproducing; yet, by also being susceptible to mutation, which randomly affects identity, a cell has the potential to survive change. A second evolutionary dynamic concerns the access of the world's bacteria to a single gene pool and thus to the adaptive mechanisms of the whole bacterial kingdom. Through recombination – the continual and rapid transfer of genetic material between individuals in response to environmental change – the bacterial microcosm supports the entire biota, making Earth both fertile and habitable for all other life-forms. Amongst the higher eukaryotic life-forms, however, recombination functions more slowly, through sexual reproduction and the crossing over of genes in subsequent generations. Such recombination is the most important source of genetic variation, and of the production of a great diversity of genotypes, as material for natural selection.* A third dynamic is symbiosis, the merging of organisms into new collectives; as when ancient bacteria began to take up residence within other micro-organisms, providing their hosts with oxygen-derived energy and waste disposal, receiving food and shelter in return. Such merged organisms eventually evolved into more complex oxygen-breathing life-forms.

Such a variety of evolutionary methods of change has arisen directly

---

*Genotype: the sum total of the genes in an individual, and the outcome of the interaction and recombination of genes comprising the gene pool of a local population. Natural selection may also be described as the differential perpetuation of genotypes.

as a result of adaptations to challenging changes in the environment, and to genetic changes. The latter can occur without environmental challenge; the genetic mutation itself may be the factor driving the change, allowing a previously inhospitable environment to be exploited. Both involve change: both are expressive of the natural flux. And amongst these methods of change

> It is no exaggeration to say that, as far as animals are concerned, behavior is the most important evolutionary determinant, particularly in the initiation of new evolutionary trends.[4]

This is most noticeable in the behavioural shifts undertaken by our ancestors. Each shift – from water to land, from forest to savannah, from vegetarian diet to increasing meat diet – initiated new selection pressures. Life-forms respond to the challenges presented to them. We are in fact genetically descended from animals which survived the Earth's most devastating extinctions. During the last 500 million years there have been five mass extinctions, including that at the end of the Permian Period, 245 million years ago, which destroyed some 95 percent of species living at the time; and one at the end of the Cretaceous, 65 million years ago, when some 75 percent of species, including the dinosaurs, were destroyed. As a result of some 99.99 percent of the species that have ever existed becoming extinct, the ancestors of our species inherited genetic riches from the mere 0.01 percent of the species that responded to and survived the challenges of geological and cosmic crises in the last three billion years. They won through because of their adaptability, their ability to change in obedience to the natural flux.

The balance of nature and evolution ultimately depend on the awful and majestic authority of the natural flux, that governs a mutable and not a static stable state of the Earth. The world is in dynamic equilibrium, a stable state in flux; and it is the primary challenge of the natural flux, combined with the secondary response of the biota, which so governs the Earth. Emigration, for instance, in obedience to the natural flux has been a cardinal rule of survival amongst plants, thereby creating colonies which may survive after life in the native territory has become untenable: many species of alpine plant only survived the last Ice Age because single plants had earlier migrated to warmer valleys or the plains, there to create colonies which kept the species from extinction.

The natural flux commands the ceaseless flow and change, the co-operative evolution, diversification and expansion of all life within the kingdom of nature, as seen in the natural succession of flora and fauna across the land that is essentially no animal's and no man's land. The evolution of wild nature may in fact be likened to the dramatic unfolding of an unbroken succession of symphonies by the same composer, each more complex and highly developed than the last. The natural flux is, as it were, the conductor of the orchestra playing those symphonies, providing the overall harmony, coherence and balance to the expanding movements of the symphonies of life of the kingdom of nature. The players – the succession of flora and fauna within nature – both co-operate and compete within the overall harmonious balance of nature. In this connection, it is important to understand that co-operation is a principal characteristic of evolutionary life on Earth. As pointed out by Margulis and Sagan, 'survival of the fittest' refers not to large muscles or predatory behaviour but to leaving more offspring. Fit in evolutionary terms means fecund. Life spread over the Earth by networking rather than by combat: life-forms multiplied and became increasingly complex more through co-operation with others than by killing them.

The players both co-operate and compete at the command of the natural flux, to produce the paradise of sight, of sound, of smell, of taste and of touch that is the essence of nature. Like music, wild nature consists of spontaneous re-creation, to produce many interpretations of the symphonies of life as they slowly unfold and develop. In nature, as in music, the whole orchestra co-operates under its conductor to produce the most perfect rendering of the composition.

The analogy with music may be taken even further. For if the origin of all life on Earth lies in the interaction in movement between certain chemicals and the forces of nature, that creative interaction or flux between order and chaos, combined with nature's propensity to spontaneous re-creation, may be described as the composer of life. Hence the natural flux is like a great composer-conductor of music. It may be described as the composer-conductor, lord, giver and perfecter of life in no man's land: the creative spirit of life that governs and pervades the stable state in flux of the paradisial kingdom of nature. It is the creative spirit which challenges the biota to respond and reveal itself in an ever increasing variety of forms. The biota itself may be said to respond to this challenge as the brain of the superorganism, Earth. For, as Margulis and Sagan argue,

> As tiny parts of a huge biosphere whose essence is basically bacterial, we – with other life forms – must add up to a sort of symbiotic brain which it is beyond our capacity to comprehend or truly represent.[5]

And that brain has so evolved as to respond to the demands of the natural flux. In short, the natural flux is pre-eminent. It is both omnipotent and omnipresent. In relation to the evolution of the self-regulating green envelope of life, upon the diversity of which all life depends, and in relation to the evolutionary succession of wildlife it inspires, the natural flux is the very spirit of wildlife. The natural flux cannot be seen: only its effects can be seen and felt. Invisible, like the wind, it resembles a spirit operating throughout space and time, activating – and destroying – life throughout the world. It is the creative spirit, which I also describe as the spirit of the Earth. In other words, Earth regarded as a self-regulating superorganism is governed by the natural flux. And though this seemingly metaphysical approach should be treated with due caution, it nonetheless serves as a description of what is a universal physical phenomenon. It was the obedience of one animal to the dictates of the natural flux, and its growing awareness of a creative spirit of the Earth as a guiding spirit in life, that enabled it to become fully human and to name that spirit, amongst other names, as the Great Spirit.

The ancestors of the early humans lived in the Pliocene Period, 5–2 million years ago; and while their ancestral line had already diverged from that of gibbons, gorillas and orang-utans, the lineage of the African chimpanzee diverged from ours only 6–8 million years ago. Hominids – apemen of the *Australopithecus* type and man-apes of the *Homo* type – appear in the fossil record of tropical Africa some 3 million years ago. Three prehistoric species have been identified as members of our genus, *Homo*. They are, in the order of their evolutionary appearance, *Homo habilis*, *Homo erectus* and the older subspecies of *Homo sapiens*. These man-apes spread from their apparent point of origin in Africa more than 2 million years ago. Modern humans originated about 200,000 years ago.

All primates today, except ourselves (and chimpanzees), are vegetarians or insectivores. They eat insects, fruit, nuts, berries and grasses; whereas our central nervous system and brain evolved as an adaptation not only to the eating of plants, but to the hunting and eating of plant-eating animals. However, it was during the Pleistocene Period, less than 100,000 years ago, that our ancestors began to flourish as hunter-gatherers as they met the challenges presented by the advance and retreat of ice during the last Ice Age.

The Ice Age began at least 1.5 million years ago as the global climate gradually cooled. Over the last 800,000 years the world has experienced some nine or more glacial episodes interspersed with much shorter warm intervals. The world's climate thus veered spectacularly between warm and cold. At their maximum extension ice spread over England past the river Thames, and in North America as far south as the present states of Illinois and Ohio. During the Pleistocene giant animals – such as the rhinoceros, mastodon and sabre-toothed tiger – gave way to new fauna – such as the woolly rhinoceros, woolly mammoth, aurochs and reindeer – which were better adapted to the cold. Our hunter-gatherer ancestors hunted these animals and flourished under the conditions of cold, ice and snow. So, while our heritage is tropical, we are children of the challenge the Ice Age represented, the challenging changes from warmth to cold, which forced our ancestors to respond or go to the wall.

For selection pressures are most acute at the mutable or shifting edges of habitats – at the edge of the sea, of the forest, of wetlands, or at the feet of mountains. Movement within and between shifting habitats and ecologically diverse zones at these edges is as important as climate change, genes and geographical barriers (that divide animal populations) in driving animal populations to diversify. Movement, for instance, between dense forest, peripheral stands of trees and open savannah enables animals to discover new sources of food and adapt to new niches, encouraging speciation. In the case of the evolution of *Homo sapiens*, major behavioural shifts occurred at these edges – in the movement from water to land, from forest to savannah, and in the movement accompanying the advance and retreat of ice during the Ice Age. It was the very fact of moving in a non-specialized and unpossessive manner in the midst of those natural oscillations at the command of the natural flux that enabled *Homo sapiens* to become intelligently and creatively human.

It was the mutability of nature that true men and women inherited, the source of their genius and of their humanity and understanding. I attach particular importance to this concept of the natural flux in relation to the evolution of *Homo sapiens* tested, as instanced above, by the advance and retreat of ice during the Ice Age. I do so because – and as will become apparent as the argument proceeds – a primitive agriculture and domestication originated at the end of the Ice Age some 12,000 years ago which, as it spread across the world, caused those who so adapted to lose many of their evolutionary characteristics. Valerius Geist has drawn attention to the extraordinary change in physique that occurred at this time. He points out that the phenotypic development of populations from Upper Paleolithic were notable.

> Ice Age people were remarkably well developed with large athletic bodies, robust bones free of disease, and brain sizes some 20 percent larger than our own... Confrontation hunting demanded superb strategic judgement, great bodily dexterity, and skills in using weapons,

great courage, and unflinching loyalty to the hunting companions, lest tragedy seal a hunt. Their physical development and robust health were achieved at the cost of great effort in mastering a multitude of diverse physical and intellectual skills... Their physical development contrasts sharply with populations from Europe during the Mesolithic, when small body size and brain size, diseased bones and teeth, and signs of homicide ... were the norm.[6]

This quotation will serve both to introduce the hunter-gatherer and to hint at what was lost in the transition to primitive farmer. In particular, unlike the hunter-gatherers who absorbed their past in flux into their present in unpossessive movement through the land treated essentially as no man's land, farming peoples, in becoming sedentary possessors of the land as someone's land, in effect denied their past in flux. They began not only to build against the operation of the natural flux but also to destroy the very ground of its operation and of their earlier evolution as true men and women: they began to destroy the wilderness, their erstwhile home. We are today the end product, not of the principal evolutionary process that I have been discussing in this chapter, but of a divorce from, a denial of and a direct opposition to that process. This is why it is essential to understand our past in flux as hunter-gatherers in order to understand the full measure of what was lost in the transition from hunter-gatherer to farmer, and how our primitive farmer forbears filled the consequent void. For it is that loss and consequent construction of physical and psychical artefacts to fill the void that have brought us to our present parlous predicament.

Chapter 2

The Hunter-Gatherers

Humans have evolved, not in isolation, but always in an intimate and co-operative relationship with all the innumerable other forms inhabiting the Earth with them. Springing from a common source, humankind and all the abounding life on Earth have grown up together. To pursue the line of growth amongst all these others is comparable to pursuing that of a single family within a nation. Until the end of the late Ice Age, some 15,000 years ago, the human family was still evolving in a primary organic unity within the greater family, the natural kingdom of flora and fauna united in obedience to the natural flux, succession and law. Humans evolved through various stages, including most recently as Neanderthal Man and finally as Cro-Magnon, or modern, Man. Modern humans seem to have spread from eastern Africa to Southeast Asia, and thence throughout Eurasia. They reached Australia around 60,000 BC and were in western Europe by 35,000 BC; they reached Siberia by about 14,000 BC. The occupation of Siberia and Alaska in turn led to the occupation of North and South America between 14,000 BC and 11,000 BC.

As Cro-Magnon Man, and from 30,000 BC to about 11,000 BC, all humans were hunter-gatherers. As such, each and every person – like the golden eagle, the tiger and the lion – was a king of natural food pyramids. In this context 'king' is an ecological term referring to the status of animals, whether male or female, residing as ultimate consumers at the summits of natural food pyramids. Both the male hunter and female gatherer, like the lion and lioness, are kings of natural food pyramids.

A food pyramid or chain is the process whereby energy from the sun becomes available to a community of animals in a form that each member is adapted to digest. Through the process of photosynthesis, much of the initial energy from the sun is converted into plant growth and reproduction. What remains may become a source of food to a whole community. Such plants are described as the producers. A gazelle, for instance, that feeds on the plants may be the first, or primary, consumer. A cheetah that preys on the gazelle may be described as a secondary consumer. When the cheetah dies, most of its energy is likely to be broken down by bacteria into food for plants, thus perpetuating the cycle.

Such food chains can be represented both as pyramids of energy and as pyramids of numbers. At the bottom of the pyramid of energy, plentiful energy is available to the producers: thereafter, as the result of animal activities, energy is so dispelled in its passage from link to link that it is stored only in the smallest amounts in the ultimate consumer at the top of the pyramid. Each level passes on to the next only that tenth of the sun's energy not used for its own sustenance. The energy absorbed from the sun by grass, for instance, is mostly dispersed in heat as the grass maintains itself. Only a tenth of the sun's energy that became grass is available to feed animals such as antelopes; while a human feeding on the antelope gains only a hundredth of the sun's energy that was initially absorbed by the grass. Between each level there is an approximate ten-to-one loss in bulk.

Seen in terms of a pyramid of numbers, masses of energy-producing plants (the primary producers) reside at the bottom, fed on by a smaller number of herbivores (the primary consumers), which in turn feed a yet smaller number of small carnivores (the secondary consumers), ending with an even smaller number of larger carnivores (the final consumers). The final or ultimate consumer – be it golden eagle, hawk, lion or human being – is the predator at the apex of the pyramid who is preyed upon by no other predator and who ends the entire chain. Ultimate consumers are kings, whose food consumption is unlikely to outrun supply because their numbers seldom increase as rapidly as those of their prey. According to the season or in times of dearth, the king may switch food pyramids (see figure 2.1).

It was the ability of the individual omnivorous hunter-gatherer to be the ultimate consumer or king of innumerable natural food chains. Each and every hunter-gatherer was the ultimate consumer at the pinnacle of a wealth and abundance of natural food pyramids. Each may thus be described as *Homo sapiens* king of natural food pyramids.

> ...by the Upper Pleistocene, humans had become the most widely distributed mammal worldwide. They had taken up residence at the top or close to the top of every regional food chain. In that position, they must have been important in restructuring these food chains. In other words, they had become a highly significant variable in

Part I: fig 2.1

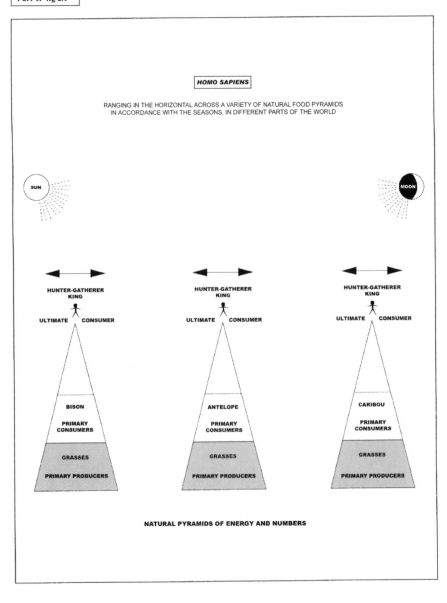

HOMO SAPIENS

RANGING IN THE HORIZONTAL ACROSS A VARIETY OF NATURAL FOOD PYRAMIDS
IN ACCORDANCE WITH THE SEASONS, IN DIFFERENT PARTS OF THE WORLD

SUN

MOON

HUNTER-GATHERER KING

ULTIMATE — CONSUMER

BISON
PRIMARY CONSUMERS
GRASSES
PRIMARY PRODUCERS

HUNTER-GATHERER KING

ULTIMATE — CONSUMER

ANTELOPE
PRIMARY CONSUMERS
GRASSES
PRIMARY PRODUCERS

HUNTER-GATHERER KING

ULTIMATE — CONSUMER

CARIBOU
PRIMARY CONSUMERS
GRASSES
PRIMARY PRODUCERS

NATURAL PYRAMIDS OF ENERGY AND NUMBERS

their own environment. Even where they were proximately reacting
to 'natural' variables, the humans themselves had become one of the
most important of these, because of their impact on the restructuring
of 'natural' variables.[1]

Because they were kings of innumerable natural food pyramids by
comparison with the more limited range of food pyramids available to
other species of animal kings, and because of their importance as a
'natural' variable world-wide, *Homo sapiens* was a king of kings. Even
the San (Bushman), though forced into the most inhospitable and
inaccessible parts of the Kalahari, lived until recently off a varied diet
comprising some 54 types of animal and 85 different plants.

There are several observations that may be made arising directly from
this, their royal status within the animal kingdom. Before doing so,
however, it is necessary to observe that any comparisons between Palaeolithic
hunter-gatherers and hunter-gatherer societies today should be viewed
with the greatest caution. This is particularly because hunter-gatherer
groups have been violently and adversely affected over the millennia by
farming and urban societies. Bushmen, for instance, were driven into
their last stronghold in the Kalahari by Bantu farmers, and then hunted
down by Boer farmers. Nevertheless, although it may be misleading to
use the characteristics and behaviour of contemporary hunter-gatherers
to reveal those of Ice Age hunter-gatherers, it is permissible to a certain
degree in the case of the Bushman. For, as argued by Herbert Read,

> There can be no doubt that we have in the art of the Bushman a
> survival of the art that flourished over a much wider area thousands
> of years ago – the art, in fact, of the pre-historical period.[2]

It is also reasonable to assume that certain other characteristics of the
Bushman bands that produced such art have similarly survived from that
earlier period.

There are in fact certain characteristics common to all recent hunter-
gatherer societies which were most likely shared by our hunter-gatherer
ancestors before the transition to agriculture. It is these common features
that I shall attempt to reveal. As the argument develops throughout the
book I shall reveal further characteristics of our hunter-gatherer ancestors,
contrasting them with those of farming peoples. In this way the argument
will remain firmly grounded in the evolutionary world of wild nature,
which is the foundation both of our humanity and of reality. It is from
this perspective that we can impartially observe the qualities inherent in

hunter-gatherer societies and compare them with our own, thereby avoiding the danger of romanticism. In the words of Hugh Brody,

> The qualities of hunter-gatherers are functional as much as moral: their ways of living are essential both for the economic success of the system and for harmonious interpersonal life. Egalitarianism, respect for the elderly, loving regard for children, diligent respect for the land, plants and animals on which people depend – these are the 'virtues', too often missing in the 'developed' world, that cause visitors to hunter-gatherer societies to experience deep admiration. To describe these things, and seek to understand them, is not romanticism but the most relevant kind of realism. [3]

Our hunter-gatherer ancestors formed 'the original affluent society'. A predominant feature is, and was, their royal status as kings of natural food pyramids. As hunter-gatherer kings, they were as absolutely free as it is possible for any animal to be. The freedom and individuality of each was based initially upon a total economic freedom as kings of innumerable natural food pyramids, which reduced disparities and competition amongst them to a minimum. Furthermore, the smallness and flexibility of their bands had important social and environmental consequences.

Most commonly hunter-gatherer bands number between twenty-five and fifty individuals. A band comprises a loose integration of a number of families, an integration achieved through notations of kinship – though the types of kinship patterns vary greatly – extended by marriage alliances, which also strengthen relationships and reciprocity with other bands. The economic division of labour within a band is by age and sex differentiations. Bands vary from time to time both in size and in composition: a process of fission and fusion that enables them to take advantage both of changing animal and plant resources and of seasonal social events. Hunter-gatherers spend approximately half the average hours of farming and industrial communities in gaining a livelihood, allowing them much time for other social and artistic activities, dancing and play. Band fission and fusion is a major element in conflict avoidance between individuals, allowing potential disputants to separate temporarily into different camps. Such smallness and flexibility of bands also militates against hierarchy and fosters co-operative equality. Above all, their activities, like those of other wild animals, enhance their environment. Their small bands are characterized by an absence of hierarchy – they have neither headman nor chiefs – and economic interdependence and equality of the sexes.

One of the features of most hunter-gatherer societies, in marked contrast to later agricultural and urban societies, is the lack of a rigid hierarchical structure. For example, the Kalahari Bushmen, the Hadza, the Mbuti Pygmies, the Eskimos, and the Australian Aborigines have no system of chieftainship. Leadership is usually determined by spontaneous mechanisms, based presumably on personality factors as well as on known skills or experience of individuals in different fields of endeavour. Thus leadership is often a transient phenomenon, depending on the nature of the subject under discussion or the activity of the moment – one individual emerging as leader of the hunt, another as leader of music-making and dancing, and another as leader in respect of spiritual matters.[4]

As Stephen Boyden[5] points out, males and females also have equal status. Such egalitarian individualism ensures that there is no institution of authority nor organization of power in mobile, flexible hunter-gatherer cultures. Each person is free to choose for him or herself when and where to hunt or gather and how to live their daily lives. Discipline is enforced, not by external means through codes or institutions, but from within by the culture and the environment, breeding a consciousness and setting bounds known and obeyed by all.

> The egalitarian individualism of hunter-gatherer societies, arguably their greatest achievement and their most compelling lesson for other peoples, relies on many kinds of respect.[6]

This is particularly the case in the relationship of men and women. Hugh Brody has pointed out that many hunter-gatherer languages make no distinctions according to gender and have grammars in which being male or female is irrelevant. However,

> Hunter-gatherers do establish well-defined rôles for men and women, but there is more mutual respect, a greater recognition of mutual dependency, than in any other kind of society.[7]

Brody argues that the well-being of hunter-gatherer societies depends on the economic activities of both men and women.

> Among hunter-gatherers, there is a widespread division of labour between men and women, with the men often devoting themselves to the pursuit of large animals across great distances. The men,

reading weather and tracks, depending on physical stamina, set out
to kill creatures sometimes larger and stronger than themselves...
Yet many studies of hunter-gatherer nutrition show that the hunting
of large animals by men produces less food than the hunting and
gathering done by women. In fact, both levels of harvest are important:
the men have a chance of making a kill that delivers a bonanza of
protein – but their rate of success is not high enough to be relied
on. The women harvest smaller sources of foodstuff, but do so with
great regularity and reliability... In the Plateau societies of the
northwestern United States and the interior mountains of British
Columbia, at least 30 per cent of nutrients comes from plants, most
of which are harvested and processed by women. The well-being of
these societies relies on the economic activities of both sexes. Each
is the complement – and is *acknowledged* to be the complement –
of the other. So division of labour does not result in either sex
achieving supremacy over, or independence of, the other.[8]

As regards the environmental consequences of the smallness and flexibility
of hunter-gatherer bands, such bands do not manipulate their habitat to
suit their society as do farming peoples: rather, they manipulate their
societies to conform to the availability of environmental resources. So
not only do fission and fusion of the band help regulate relationships
within the band, but they enable it to respond to changes in environmental
conditions by altering its size. In other words, the fission and fusion of
their bands in accordance with social and environmental needs means
they are in a constant state of flux, exemplifying their obedience to the
natural flux.

On the evidence, given that all men and women were kings of natural
food pyramids, they were subject to no man. They treated the land
unpossessively as no man's land, to the extent that they have generally
shared the land and its resources with all other wildlife, including their
own humankind. No-one owned the land: the land in general, and
everything on it, belonged to all and was for the use of all. The land,
unlike farmer-owned land, was never theirs to do with as they chose.
They might, like the Australian Aborigines, fire a section of forest to
drive animals, but always they have moved on, allowing a natural
regeneration to follow: essentially the land remained in the possession of
the natural flux, succession and law.

Hunter-gatherers did not demarcate the land with fences and walls,
though they appear under certain circumstances to have established
exclusive territories. Amongst the Mbuti pygmies of the Ituri Forest, for

instance, territory, represented by an area enclosed by recognizable boundaries – defined by reference to mountain ridges, ravines, rivers and streams – symbolizes the unity of the hunting band. Intermarriage between non-contiguous bands conveys rights each to the other's territory. It is the territory which has bounds, not the band, in that bands may disintegrate and integrate with one another in a continual state of flux, exchange visits and allow trespass with permission. Hence, far from occupying exclusive territories, for every individual pygmy 'there is an infinity of territories to which he may move if it pleases him.'[9]

The Bushmen, on the other hand, after being forced by Bantu and Boer farmers into their last stronghold, the Kalahari Desert, did establish specific territories.

> Although Bushmen are a roaming people ... each group of them has a very specific territory which that group alone may use, and they respect their boundaries rigidly.[10]

As regards demarcation of the land in North America, the observations of Heinmot Tooyalaket (Chief Joseph) of the Nez Percés are relevant:

> The earth was created by the assistance of the sun, and it should be left as it was ... The country was made without lines of demarcation, and it is no man's business to divide it ...[11]

Groups of Native Americans kept to familiar home ranges covering anything up to 2,500 square miles in area, parts of which they shared with other groups; while those of the Mbuti pygmies of the Ituri Forest and of the Bushmen of the Kalahari were several hundred square miles in area. The sense of freedom and space experienced by the hunter-gatherer is well conveyed by a Native American, Ten Bears of the Comanches, who said of himself:

> I was born upon the prairie, where the wind blew free and there was nothing to break the light of the sun. I was born where there were no enclosures and where everything drew a free breath. I want to die there and not within walls. I know every stream and every wood between the Rio Grande and the Arkansas. I have hunted and lived over that country. I lived like my fathers before me, and, like them, I lived happily.[12]

In some cases, territorial boundaries were likely to have been fluid, changing with the movement of the game herds, the size of the group and the time of the year. Certainly, in cases where a region might have been circumscribed, or where conditions so required, territorial behaviour acquired a greater significance, but demarcation was nonetheless a matter of agreed bounds conditional on shared resources rather than the establishment of boundaries conducive to the exclusion of others and the exclusive ownership of resources within. Fission and fusion of bands that permitted access to 'an infinity of territories', and ranging within fluid boundaries, are also more in keeping with the major climatic and geological changes that have taken place in the past, which have challenged hunter-gatherers not only to adapt aspects of their cultures but, more importantly, to migrate: they are entirely in keeping with their obedience to the natural flux.

A notable exception has been the Australian Aborigines, who are an exception precisely because they have been far removed from many of the changes, and associated challenges, that have affected the rest of humankind. For thousands of years the Aborigines have been prisoners in a huge sea-girt prison, where they were forced to develop alongside the marsupials, a sub-class of mammals.* The culture of the Aborigines has reflected the isolation and relative strangeness of the wildlife surrounding them. Isolated and strange, that is, only in relation to hunter-gatherers and wildlife in other parts of the world; for in relation to the settlers who invaded Australia in 1788 they were vastly superior in their adaptations to the land. The standard of nutrition of the Aborigines was probably higher than that of most Europeans at that time, whereas the first Australian settlers lived on the edge of starvation, alienated from the natural abundance of the land. The Aborigines evolved unusual techniques of survival, including the establishment and defence of tribal territories. Any warfare between them was usually an act of revenge in response to injury, resulting in little bloodshed: hostilities would normally cease at the death of a man. They appear not to have engaged in territorial conquest. Unlike Western societies, where individual ownership of land subsumes the possibility of total alienation, individual rights and responsibilities to lands are inalienable in Aborigine society.

In North America, bellicosity on such a scale was more likely to be found amongst more sedentary Native Americans. Where the principal

---

*Australia was cut off by sea from Eurasia some 60 million years ago, after it had been colonized by marsupials and probably by placentals as well. And while the latter wholly replaced the marsupials in Eurasia, it would appear that the marsupials were better adapted to conditions in Australia than the placental mammals, and were able to radiate into a number of branches, to occupy every available niche.

game was non-migratory, territorial boundaries were more important than they were in areas where principal game species were migratory. Bellicosity was of a correspondingly different character as well. Semi-nomadic or sedentary Native Americans were liable to be far more bellicose over trespassing incidents than Plains Indians who followed the migratory herds of buffalo. Such rivalry as did occur amongst Plains Indians had the aim of proving strength of character rather than killing rivals. It was the danger involved in face to face confrontations, the threat of death rather than killing, that provided the excitement and proved character. Such behaviour has, however, often been misinterpreted as exhibiting the intention to kill. This common misinterpretation of Native American behaviour reminds us that not only should comparisons between Palaeolithic hunter-gatherers and hunter-gatherer societies today be viewed with caution, but so too should recent studies of indigenous peoples. This is particularly important in the case of Native Americans. For when the first Europeans set foot in North America, only a few stable hunter-gatherer cultures remained in the continent, including those in the Subarctic and in what is known as the Great Basin of the North American West, extending across Utah and Nevada from the Rockies to the Sierra Nevada. By contrast, the Indians of the Great Plains, who are commonly regarded as typical Native American hunter-gatherers and became the image of all Native Americans, were not only feral hunter-gatherers, but had acquired feral horses and guns from the Spanish. The Plains Indians were feral hunters whose recent forbears had been, to a greater or lesser extent, farmers or influenced by farming cultures that had originated in Mexico and had spread up the eastern seaboard. And their horses, whose ancestors had once lived in North America but had died out there prior to or during the Mesolithic, were feral animals taken, or escaped, from the Spanish, who had introduced them to North America in the 16th century as domestic animals. These factors, combined with the European invasion that thrust tribe against tribe as they were forced to flee from east to west, corrupted the cultures and behaviour of the indigenous peoples of the whole continent.

However, human beings cannot be described as either innately aggressive or peaceful. When environmental conditions have threatened survival, competition for resources appears sometimes to have led to warfare amongst hunter-gatherers unwilling or unable to migrate to other regions, as in the Nile Valley some 18,000 years ago. As North Africa became increasingly arid during the Last Glacial Maximum, the people migrated to more hospitable areas, resulting in a concentration of peoples along the coasts and Nile Valley. This appears to have led to conflict along the Nile as they competed for limited resources, for there is evidence that some 40 per cent of people buried in a cemetery at Jebel Sahaba died violently. Nowhere else at this period does there appear to have been violence on this scale.

The evidence from past and from recent hunter-gatherer societies such as the Inuit, Saami and San suggests that while there are recorded instances of homicide and warfare, such societies have generally been peace-loving and very gentle people; and, like other mammalian species in their natural habitats, have not engaged in continual intraspecific warfare. It would appear that inter-tribal warfare only came into being after the transition to agriculture, when people acquired property – such as land, animals and stored grain – which could be coveted by others. Nevertheless, various scientists have argued that hunter-gatherers led violent lives, with war between villages common and murders avenged with more murders. The Yąnomamö people of the Amazon, for instance, who were closely studied (over 63 months between 1965 and 1995) by Napoleon Chagnon, have been portrayed as an example of people exhibiting such violent behaviour. They have also been cited as retaining our ancestral hunter-gatherer way of life and associated behaviour, which is quite untrue. The Yąnomamö are in fact, as Chagnon's study makes clear, primarily sedentary horticulturalists who also hunt, and as such exhibit the behaviour of settled farming and gardening cultures the world over, amongst whom war in pursuit of wealth and power is commonplace. True hunter-gatherers, such as the San and the Mbuti pygmies, have generally been nomadic, being without villages and possessions and peace-loving, a way of life from which we, and probably the Yąnomamö, have been alienated for thousands of years. Such alienation from our hunter-gatherer ancestry, rather than that ancestry itself, underlies our malign and violent behaviour.*

Present wisdom also treats hunter-gatherers as slaves of their environment, the more so the further back in time we go. However, as this book will show, far from throwing off the 'shackles of nature', the Neolithic revolution caused humankind to lose a majority of the characteristics that had enabled them to become and to remain truly human, and to lose the ground of that humanity, the wilderness. Those so-called 'shackles'

---

*A similar comparison has been made with chimpanzees. When Jane Goodall, in her book *Through a Window* (Phoenix Giant, 1998), revealed their often murderous intercommunity violence, it was assumed, because we share 98 per cent of our genes with chimpanzees, that they are our mirror, reflecting our own murderous intercommunity strife. In fact, the separation of the two evolutionary lines, some 6 million years ago, made for the development of a relatively peace-loving *Homo sapiens* hunter-gatherer. It was only with their transition to a sedentary agricultural way of life (or that of nomadic herdsman), and consequent alienation from their wild ancestral way of life, that they reverted to chimpanzee-like behaviour.

constituted the natural constraints or controls over their reproductive and other forms of behaviour, including in particular the inhibitions relating to the avoidance of intraspecific aggression.

All hunter-gatherers have been restrained by inhibitions – by disciplines imposed from within by the culture and the land – from behaviour detrimental either to their own well-being and survival as wild animals, or to the wild environment. And perhaps the most important basis of self-discipline and morality has been their awareness of, and obedience to, a creative spirit of the Earth or Great Spirit. As a microcosm of the macrocosmic wild world, *Homo sapiens* ranged widely in the horizontal – from horizon to horizon – all his senses integrated and attuned to what may be described as the call of the Great Spirit of wildlife, that is, the personification of the flux, forces and laws of nature to which I referred in the last chapter. To many Native Americans, for instance, every animal, every plant, every tree, every manifestation and force of nature – the sun, moon, wind, rain, thunder, lightning – had its own spirit.* The source and sum of the spiritual powers of wild nature, and of the peoples' spiritual powers, was seen by some Native Americans as Father Creator or Great Spirit (Plateau and Basin Indians) and by others as Manitou (Chippewa) or as Wakan-Tanka or the Great Spirit (Lakota). Depending upon their geographical location and language group, the Supreme Being, Creator or Great Spirit went under a variety of different names and often formed a special relationship with particular animals. These animals were also often regarded as having an 'owner' or 'master', portrayed by a great mythic animal of the species they most relied on for sustenance, and whose help and favour the hunter needed to win if he was to be successful in the hunt. A Master of the Caribou, represented by a mythic giant Caribou, might control the caribou herds, and a Master of the Buffalo the herds of buffalo. Amongst the San, a mythic giant Eland or a Hartebeest might control their respective favourite animal. In turn, the profusion of such animals was a principal manifestation of the beneficence of their guiding Spirit or mythic animal, a profusion and beneficence which are in fact governed by the natural flux – that is, by the Great Spirit. Life is given and governed by the Great Spirit. The Great Spirit is the composer-conductor, lord, giver and perfecter of life

---

* Spirit may be described as the essential character, nature or qualities of something. The spirit of a teacher may live on in the pupil; the spirit of a dog might be described as 'devotion' to its master; while 'The spirit of the hills is action, that of the lowlands repose' (Ruskin). The spirit of the hunter-gatherer relates each to all others in a cosmic unity within the biosphere, whose own essential character or spirit is stability in flux. All are thus spiritually united with the natural flux or Great Spirit. Hunter-gatherers comprehend the invisible spiritual essence of all and obey the Great Spirit.

in no man's land. It was the Great Spirit that gave life to *Homo sapiens*, and too the understanding to live in a state of balance, a state of grace, in sensitive movement within the university of wild nature.

I am aware that the concept of the Great Spirit may be a Victorian invention or interpretation of the beliefs of a seemingly amorphous mass of aboriginal peoples, but I shall use it particularly in order to differentiate between the Supreme Being or Creator of hunter-gatherer peoples – i.e. the Great Spirit that created, and governed the behaviour of, humans as hunter-gatherers at home in the wilderness, and intimately related to all other wildlife – and the Creator God of farming peoples – i.e. the God who ostensibly created, and has governed the behaviour of, humans as farmers alienated from the wilderness and antipathetic destroyers of the wilderness and wildlife. The Great Spirit is the antithesis of God – that is, the Creator God of Christian, Islamic or any other farming peoples. As the argument proceeds, the necessity to differentiate between these two Creators will, I hope, become increasingly apparent. For ultimately our understanding of ourselves as human beings depends upon our understanding of our origins and associated beliefs.*

The relationship between the hunter-gatherer, Great Spirit and hunted may be observed amongst the Naskapi hunting people of northeastern Canada. Their principal game is caribou, and their focal point of the act of hunting is a ritual meal at which caribou meat and bones are carefully prepared and consumed, without any waste. The function of the meal is to link hunter and hunted under the auspices of the Spirit of the Caribou. This ritual preparation for the hunt acknowledges an eternal agreement, namely that the game will come to the hunter as long as he continues to be worthy.

> The agreement is mythic in origin, made with an Owner of the Animals. In the Naskapi world this is the Animal Master of the caribou because the caribou is the mainstay of the Naskapi diet. The Animal Master is a single animal in a great mythic herd. He is both timeless and indestructible, an archetype of the species. It is he who 'gives' the hunter the animal to be killed and who has the power to keep the animals away from the hunter if he is unworthy... Game animals are holy. And the life of a hunting people is regarded as a sacred way of living because it grows out of this powerful, fundamental covenant.[13]

---

*I shall examine the fundamental and profound difference between the belief systems of the wilderness-loving hunter-gatherers and that of the wilderness-fearing farmers in the next chapter.

Hunter-gatherer bands obeyed, and placed implicit trust in, the quintessential spirit of the territory they occupied and of its inhabitants – whether that spirit was represented as the Supreme Being or Great Spirit, or manifested in a single mythic animal, or, as in the case of the Mbuti pygmies of the Ituri Forest, in the forest itself. For the latter, all men, women, animals and plants, even the air and wind, in the forest are endowed with spiritual power. They believe in the benevolence of that forest power which derives from a single source whose physical manifestation is the forest itself. To the Mbuti the godhead is the sum totality of the forest, 'down to the last grain of sand'.

> If you ask a pygmy why he has no chiefs, no law-givers, no councils, or no leaders, he will answer with misleading simplicity, 'Because we are the People of the Forest'. The forest, the great provider, is the one standard by which all deeds and thoughts are judged; it is the chief, the law-giver, the leader, and the final arbitrator.[14]

To the pygmies, 'the forest is everything' – Father law-giver, Mother provider, Lover and Friend. In practice, therefore, the social order and value system not only of the Mbuti but of all hunter-gatherers has depended upon a sacred covenant with the wild environment, that has required their loving obedience in flux to the spirits of particular inhabitants of their environment or to that of the whole environment itself.

Australian Aborigines have Creation myths that tell of legendary totemic beings, the Ancestors, who sang the world into existence in what is known as the Dreamtime. They created a labyrinth of invisible pathways throughout Australia, known to Europeans as 'Dreaming-tracks' or 'Songlines', but to the Aborigines also as the 'Footprints of the Ancestors' or the 'Way of the Law'. The Ancestors created themselves in their thousands from clay, one for each totemic species. Each Clan had its own totem, such as the Wallaby for the Wallaby Clan. Every Wallaby Man believed he was descended from a universal Wallaby Father, who was the ancestor of all other Wallaby Men and all living wallabies. As wallabies were his brothers, he was forbidden to kill them. Not only was every moment of life filled with the wonder and sacredness of the Dreamtime, but every aspect of the environment was directly related to the activities of the Ancestors: the wells the Aborigines used were where the Ancestors dug in the ground, and the trees grew where they put down their digging sticks. By so weaving a web of myths and stories around the landscape the Aborigines were enabled to remember an immense amount of natural and geographic information: they were

totally immersed in the meaningfulness and sacredness of the wild
landscape. Furthermore, the Ancestors were not only seen as creating the
environment but were also active in the present. All were guided and
governed by the spirit of Oneness, also known to the Aborigines as the
Great Spirit.

Every aspect of their lives reinforced the covenant with the Great Spirit,
thereby reinforcing their harmonious integration within the natural world
and guaranteeing their stability and well-being. This covenant was further
reinforced by the hunter-gatherer's psychical relationship with the Earth
which, in all its beauty and bountiful goodness – including particularly
its wealth and abundance of natural food pyramids – was regarded by
them as the Earthmother. To the hunter-gatherer, the Great Spirit and
Earthmother symbolized the sum total of the multiple animal, vegetable
and phenomenal spirits: they are the equivalent, in spiritual terms, of
the natural flux and the superorganism Earth. Just as the latter arguably
combine to form a unity that maintains a global environmental stability,
the Great Spirit and Earthmother may be said to have been combined
in the imaginations of hunter-gatherers as father and mother acting as
the ultimate sanction of all behaviour, forming a spiritual unity that
governed their behaviour and ensured their stability integrated in a loving
relationship with and within the wilderness.

As regal microcosms of the kingdom of nature, the physiology and
reproductive behaviour of the hunter-gatherers were likewise under natural
direction and control, enabling them to adapt to any and every natural
environment.

Hypothermic adaptation, for instance, provided the nearly naked
Australian Aborigine and the African Bushman with protection against
temperature changes. In cold conditions their skin protected them by
cooling down, so the body lost less heat and they fell into a torpor. The
Eskimo, on the other hand, hunted fully clothed. During prolonged
bursts of activity while hunting, he did not sweat under his clothes but
dissipated the heat through those parts of the face that were exposed to
the cold air. So instead of shutting down blood supply his body responded
with high heat production and blood flow to peripheral tissues. This
explains the Eskimo's warm handshake that so surprised early European
explorers.

The reproductive activity of hunter-gatherers is under similar natural
control, regulated, as in the case of other species in the wild environment,
by physiological and behavioural mechanisms in response to changes in
climate and the availability of food. An example of regulatory mechanisms
is provided by Laurens van der Post:

One night round the fire... Ben told us something which perhaps shows how deeply contained is the natural Bushman in the rhythms of the seasons, and how much he is a part of their grand plans. Ben told us that the little man's womenfolk would become sterile during periods of drought and, until the rains broke, would cease to conceive. He knew this from his own experience and from that of great hunters before him. That was one reason why the Bushman had such small families.[15]

Another reason was that the Bushman women breastfed their babies until they were three or four years old, thus preventing ovulation, menstruation and pregnancy. As a result they normally had babies every four years. Occasionally they would resort to infanticide if a baby came 'too early'. Thus a range of biological and cultural mechanisms such as birth spacing, depressed fertility (related both to climate and availability of food) and the use of contraceptive plants regulated population numbers. In effect, nature so channelled and directed *Homo sapiens'* aggressive creative life-forces and exploratory natures, and so controlled their physiology and reproductive behaviour, as to make for a world-loving stability in understanding of themselves and of their environment that was both holistic and profoundly ecological.

The successful evolution of the hunter-gatherers depended upon the integration of their brains with their sensory apparatus* in a freedom of unpossessive movement through the land, to provide a holistic ecological understanding of the world. That is to say, their understanding depended upon the optimum use and relative perfection of the whole sensory apparatus of the body, including the skin and entire nervous system as well as the special sense-organs. This is not the case with animals in general, which usually have a special sense with which they view the world. Dogs, for instance, tend to rely more on olfactory images than on their vision for their perception of the world around them; while dolphins and whales appear to rely more on acoustic images, making and hearing ultrasonic sounds, constructing acoustic representations of their world. Modern Western people on the other hand tend to rely to a great extent on visual images in building up their perception of the world. For us, seeing is believing; our truths are mainly in terms of visual clues. Hunter-gatherers, however, did not just rely on visual images in

---

* While the word 'sensorium' may be used to denote the brain and entire sensory apparatus, I refrain from using it because, as I shall argue later, when some hunter-gatherers adapted to a sedentary agriculture as a principal source of food, their brains and their sensory apparatus were dis-integrated from their original evolutionary integration and function as hunter-gatherers, and their sensory apparatus fell into desuetude.

forming their perceptions of the world. They received not only visual but olfactory, tactile and acoustic impressions of the wild environment, which built up into a visual + olfactory + tactile + tasting + acoustic image of the environment through which they travelled.

Eskimo hunter-gatherers have often had to travel in polar darkness and in whiteouts without the one thing needed by a Western navigator – an edge. The Aivilik, for instance, are able to find their way around a world often lacking either horizon or objects for reference.

> What the Aivilik perceive is relationships, clusters of information that include what type of snow is underfoot, the direction and sound (against a parka ruff) of wind, any smells in the air, the contour of the landscape, the movement of animals, and so on. By constantly processing this information, the Aivilik knows where he is and where he is going.[16]

All the parts, organs and tissues of the body, which are capable of receiving or transmitting impressions from without, received and transmitted such impressions to their brains, where they were transformed into an ecological understanding that was holistic just because it was greater than the sum of the impressions received. This made them profound observers both of the detail of their immediate surroundings and of the larger environment through which they travelled and explored.

The Bushmen of the Kalahari, for instance, display great ecological expertise.

> Each group knows its own territory very well; although it may be several hundred square miles in area, the people who live there know every bush and stone, every convolution of the ground, and have usually named every place in it where a certain kind of veld food may grow, even if that place is only a few yards in diameter...[17]

As an example of the close attention which hunter-gatherers paid to every object in their vicinity, however small, Elizabeth Marshall Thomas tells of the moment when a hunter surprised her and her companions by taking from his hunting bag twelve round nut-like tiny shells which they recognized as the cocoons or pupa cases of the poison grubs, the source of poison for the Bushman's deadly little arrows.

> It has always amazed me that the Bushmen ever discovered these beetles, which are only one species among thousands in South Africa,

and which the Bushmen say are poisonous only in their pupa stage...
Bushmen do eat certain beetles, certain ants, and certain caterpillars,
which, they say, are sweet as honey. But even if a Bushman were
to eat a poison beetle he would not die (unless he had a cracked
lip or an ulcer) because the poison works only in the bloodstream,
and even the black meat of an antelope taken from the site of the
arrow wound can be eaten with impunity.

Only people who pay the closest attention to every tiny object
and who investigate all its possibilities could ever have discovered a
thing like this.[18]

The Bushman's knowledge is the more comprehensible when we realize
that each and every hunter-gatherer was a scientist in the truest sense, a
systematic observer and explorer and a teacher of the knowledge thus
accumulated over millions of years of integrated communion with all the
flora, fauna and forces of nature. Each was a true scientist* in what may
be described as nature's natural laboratory, exploring, observing, generating
and testing hypotheses through experimentation, interpreting the evidence,
developing and using tools to solve particular problems, elaborately
classifying, understanding and imparting to future generations the secrets
of nature the better to survive in the wild environment. *Homo sapiens'*
complex system of knowledge and ecological understanding includes what
is sometimes called a 'cognitive map' of both the terrain and resources
of the environment, and is the key to the adaptive success of hunter-
gatherers throughout the world. The very act of perception of an observation
involved for them, just as it does for the scientist today, a process of
apprehending patterns, a capacity acquired both through *phylogenetic* and
ontogenetic learning,† including highly disciplined training. Apprenticed
to older hunter-gatherers, the young would have learned their way about
the existing maps of the real world, adding to, dissenting from or redrawing
those cognitive maps for future generations. They were profound observers,
not only of the detail of their immediate surroundings, but of the larger
environment through which they travelled and explored.

---

*Raymond A Dart, in a Foreword to *The Bushman*, writes of 'their scientific knowledge.'
Hans J Heinz, in the same book, writes, 'The Bushman is the original scientist.'[19]
One of the criteria of a natural science is its capacity for prediction, a capacity which *Homo sapiens*,
particularly through his understanding of the secret language of nature (see below this chapter),
possessed to the full.

† *Phylogenesis.* The evolution of the tribe or race, or of any organ or feature in the race.
  Ontogenesis. The origin and development of the individual living being. (Shorter OED)
See below this chapter for an examination of these characteristics.

Hunter-gatherers observed, interpreted, hunted and gathered by a co-ordinated use of their psyches, physiologies – including all the sensory apparatus – and behaviour, whose integrated whole in a freedom of unpossessive movement through the land was infinitely more than the sum of its parts. It is this that I describe as the holistic ecological understanding of the hunter-gatherer. It constituted the 'window to the world', or world view, of each individual. This understanding may also be described in terms of language, as speaking and understanding the secret language of nature.

Hunter-gatherers developed language, culture, artefacts, and arts as diverse as the landscape, flora, and fauna around them. Their languages, like their physiques, reflected that diversity. Though each band may have spoken a different language from every other, all spoke and understood the secret language of nature. That language speaks of the infinite number and variety of animal, plant, mineral, climatic, geographical and geodynamic forms, forces and phenomena to be met with, experienced and enjoyed as the individual hunter-gatherer ranges over the land. Infinite also because their senses are always experiencing an extraordinary, and extraordinarily variant, combination of sights, sounds, smells and so on. Infinite too because every natural biome* is itself ever subject to change in order to maintain an approximate equilibrium with its environment. Consequent upon the rhythm of the seasons and the greater periodic rhythms, together with the unceasing activities of the weather and of the innumerable fauna of the Earth, natural biomes tend to undergo a number of infinitesimal changes, whose aggregate may, for instance, warn the hunter-gatherer of an impending event.† Thus, a holistic ecological understanding of the infinite number of forces and forms experienced, and of the changes occurring within them, constitutes an understanding of the secret language of nature. Henry Beston captures the essence of this language and its understanding when he said of the animal kingdom to which *Homo sapiens* belonged:

> In a world older and more complete than ours they move finished and complete, gifted with extensions of the senses we have lost or never attained, living by voices we shall never hear...[20]

---

*A natural biome may be defined as a major regional land (or ocean) community which is distinguished by dominant types of plants – such as tropical grassland, coniferous forest or tundra – and animals, and which on land is controlled by climate, having its own pattern of rainfall, temperature variations and seasons.

†Although they were directly in the path of the 2004 Asian tsunami, the hunter-gatherers of the Andaman Islands apparently (according to Survival letter, April 2005) suffered no casualties and needed no help. As the waters fell, some instinct drove them inland moments before the killer wave struck.

Hunter-gatherers, who were equally complete, were pre-eminently so gifted. They too lived 'by voices we shall never hear'. As pointed out by Colin Turnbull:

> The forest is nearly always full of sound, and the Mbuti refer to this constant background by saying 'the forest is talking' (*ndura a lufu*). The Mbuti listen, and interpret, and make use of what they hear. If the forest stops 'talking', then it is a sign that something is very wrong and alerts the Mbuti to imminent danger.[21]

The following observation by Tatanga Mani, a Stoney Indian of North America, is relevant:

> Did you know that trees talk? Well they do. They talk to each other, and they'll talk to you if you listen. Trouble is, white people don't listen. They never learned to listen to the Indians so I don't suppose they'll listen to other voices in nature. But I have learned a lot from trees: sometimes about the weather, sometimes about animals, sometimes about the Great Spirit.[22]

Trees, sky, grass, water, snow, sand all had stimulating messages to be read and discussed. For the hunter-gatherers, seeing + scenting + feeling + tasting + hearing was believing, source of their consciousness, understanding and identity in the wilderness. Their self-concept consisted of self-vision + self-scent + self-feel + self-taste + self-sound. They could to all intents and purposes cross the species boundary that lay between them and the animal kingdom, conversing with animals and dramatizing the bond in their paintings, stories, dances and games. Such close identification was observed amongst the Native American Lakota people:

> Kinship with all creatures of the earth, sky and water was a real and active principle. For the animal and bird world there existed a brotherly feeling that kept the Lakota safe among them and so close did some of the Lakota come to their feathered and furred friends that in true brotherhood they spoke a common tongue.[23]

In addition, hunter-gatherers appear to have been capable of mental telepathy. Laurens van der Post[24] observed that when some Bushmen killed an eland some 50 miles from their sip-wells home, their womenfolk were immediately made aware of the fact, lighting fires and singing the Eland Song in welcome of the still far distant hunters. A recent study of the Baka pygmies of East Cameroon showed the Baka killing an antelope, and immediately the women at the camp started up a song celebrating the kill; they were too far away to have known of the kill, and can only have known of it telepathically. In Australia, Aborigine hunters appear regularly to have used mental telepathy to communicate. Marlo Morgan, writing about a group of hunter-gatherers, describes how, when the group stopped, listening

> Ooota turned to me and said the young scout who had left us earlier was sending in a message. He was asking permission to cut off the tail of a kangaroo he had killed.
>
> It finally dawned on me why it was quiet every day as we walked. These people used mental telepathy to communicate most of the time. I was witnessing it. There was absolutely no sound to be heard, but messages were being relayed between people twenty miles apart.[25]

The hunter-gatherers' co-ordinated use of their psyches, physiologies and behaviour as an integrated whole was infinitely more than the sum of its parts: it constituted the holistic ecological understanding of hunter-gatherers. Its quintessence was the spirit of the hunter-gatherer. Each observed, interpreted (through a combination of speech, mime, signs, painting, sculpture, technical products, music, song and dance) and used in hunting and gathering the infinite variety and succession of forces and forms seen, heard, smelt, tasted and felt; whose whole was also infinitely more than the sum of all the myriad parts of nature, and whose quintessence was the Great Spirit. In the communion through hunter-gathering of their spirits with the Great Spirit,* in their knowledge of the secret language of nature, lay the quintessence of their humanity and of their truly scientific understanding under the laws of nature. They did not distinguish between the world of people and the animals, plants and landscape around them: all were united in one spirit-saturated world. *Homo sapiens* and the Earth were of one body and of one mind; so too were all men and women, a condition conducive to harmonious co-existence.

In fact, the loving relationship of *Homo sapiens* with the wilderness provided the only possible ground for peaceful co-existence, for all men and women belonged to the land; all were equally kings of natural food

---

* See below this chapter for the phylogenetic basis of this communion of the spirit of the hunter-gatherer.

pyramids; and all lived in a primary organic unity within the greater family, the natural kingdom of flora and fauna united in obedience to the natural flux, succession and law. Their principal common bond was an unpossessive love and understanding of the wilderness, which surely provided the best possible background for a community of feeling uniting human to human.

Bearing in mind that they killed only for food and were themselves the regular prey of no animal, hunter-gatherers also lived in a state of harmonious co-existence with all beasts. In short, the meaning and measure of *Homo sapiens* as no man's man and of the land as no man's land were one and the same. In their independence in economic freedom and egalitarian individualism they were more absolutely free than any other animal king of natural food pyramids. Each was *primus inter pares*, a king of kings.*

The life of the hunter-gatherer was not, as we may like to think, 'incessantly dangerous', but rather it was a life vivifyingly attuned to the unexpected and the unknown. In the words of George Schaller, writing of his search for the gorilla:

> It is an exhilarating experience to wander alone through unknown forests when everything is still new and mysterious. The senses sharpen, bringing into quick focus all that is seen and heard. I knew that there were leopards on these slopes, and the trails of the black buffalo criss-crossed the area. Both animals have the reputation of being unpredictable, and I was watchful. Each creature has its own distance at which it will take flight from an intruder, and each will allow itself to be approached only so far before defending itself. It behoves man to learn the responses of each species; until he has done so, and is familiar with the sights, sounds, and smells around him, there is an element of danger. Even so, danger that is understood does not detract from but rather enhances the pleasure of tracking.[27]

It would seem there were few animals that were consistently dangerous to the hunter-gatherers, always provided they were moving in an awareness

---

*In the 17th century the English explorer William Dampier wrote that the Australian Aborigines were the 'most primitive, wretched people on the face of the earth'. Modern knowledge has shown the precise opposite. As Burnam Burnam, an Australian Aborigine of the Wurundjeri tribe, has pointed out:

> (The book) *Mutant Message* uplifts us into a higher plane of consciousness and makes us the regal and majestic people that we are.[26]

and understanding of their habits, which was of course their natural heritage and ability. In the same way, they moved in an awareness and understanding of the greater predators, the greater and lesser rhythms and cataclysms that demand change out of a present order, and that are only really dangerous to those animals that fail to adapt.

The evolutionary process which designed the biosphere is adaptive and directed towards stability. It is a stability that is maintained in a primarily horizontal movement and succession of life in obedience to the natural flux; a mutable state which I have described as the stable state in flux of nature. It is likewise the evolutionary purpose of animals to achieve a balanced and symbiotic relationship with their total environment, in obedience to the natural flux. An animal maintains its stability in the face of change by its structural, physiological and behavioural adaptations, reducing discontinuities – such as the greater predators of flood, drought, and epidemics – to a minimum. In the case of the hunter-gatherers, their stability was greatly dependent on the predominance of their learned behaviour.

It is most important to appreciate this physiological and behavioural relationship of the hunter-gatherers with the wilderness because, as I shall be arguing in the next chapter, of the tragic circumstances surrounding the adaptation of humankind to agriculture, when they were deprived of the very characteristics now under discussion. It appears that the hunter-gatherers were subject to two kinds of learning in their dealings with the wilderness. One was *phylogenetic* learning developed through the evolution of the human race, a collective innate knowledge that dealt with signals coming from the wilderness by constructing a model of it: in other words, they could know something of the wilderness innately, prior to their own experience of it, through the genes that determine the structure and function of the brain. Like their physiques, the generalities of their behaviour pattern in relation to the wilderness were thus formulated in terms of their genetic inheritance from the distant past.

Hunter-gatherers had long memories incorporated into their beings, phylogenetic memories going back to the sea-memory of our earliest ancestors. This collective unconscious spoke to the conscious mind through dreams and images: a further important avenue was intuition, which undergirded feeling and reason. As pointed out by Hugh Brody,[28] hunter-gatherers rely on a blend of the dreamer's intuition with a detailed environmental knowledge to guide them in their search for resources. Such entry into the collective unconscious connected the human spirit with the Great Spirit, bringing in its train an awareness and obedience leading to right action. It gave the hunter-gatherers their sense of belonging, of knowing and of being known most intimately within the wilderness.

The second kind of learning was *ontogenetic* learning – that is, learning during the process of individual development – including the lifelong acquisition of cultural, linguistic and scientific knowledge. Their phylogenetic and ontogenetic learning processes constituted the most important innovation that came with their evolution as human beings; namely, the capacity for innovation itself within the wild environment. These developments combined made for the self-regulating stability of the hunter-gatherers. They also made for the optimum life conditions conducive to the optimum health and well-being of humankind.

Stephen Boyden[29] has drawn up a list of optimum life conditions conducive to health in *Homo sapiens*, based on those that existed amongst hunter-gatherer societies. It comprises both the more tangible material life conditions and the more intangible psychosocial and behavioural ones. It includes clean air, clean water, balanced diet, sensory stimulation, opportunities for spontaneous and free inter-group movement, acceptable patterns of physical activity and rest, opportunities for the development of creative skills, variety in daily experience in a natural environment of high interest value, and a sense of belonging, of responsibility, of comradeship and love, of excitement, of enjoyment and of security.

In consequence, hunter-gatherers were generally free from deformity and 'without blemish', nor were they deprived of any sense. They were free from infectious diseases such as cholera, smallpox, typhus, typhoid, measles and influenza. In fact, all the literature indicates that the hunter-gatherer communities were in a remarkably good state of health. The studies of the late Dr Aleš Hrdlička,[30] for instance, who investigated the ills and medical practices of the Native Americans, particularly in the American Southwest, tended to confirm that the indigenous people were generally healthy compared with Europeans of the colonial period. As well as being, with a few exceptions, remarkably free from infectious diseases, he found that cancer was rare, and skin tumours, leprosy and precolumbian syphilis non-existent.* For many thousands of years the main causes of premature human deaths were accidents and wounds. Compare the optimum life conditions enumerated above with the often strife-torn, insecure, appalling life conditions and degraded environments suffered and endured by a majority of humankind today – whether in

---

* However, researchers in North America have found evidence of rheumatoid arthritis in the skeletons of six prehistoric Native Americans who lived during the Late Archaic cultural period, 3,000–5,000 years ago (*Science*, Vol. 241, p. 1498). The researchers speculate that the disease may have originated in the New World, and only spread to the Old World after the first European contact in 1492.

Europe, in Asia, in Africa or in the Americas, and note how very far removed they are from the optimum conditions, making people susceptible to debilitating diseases – infectious, occupational and nutritional.

Psychical, physical and behavioural adaptations, that make for the self-regulating stability and life conditions conducive to the health of *Homo sapiens*, are also the touchstone of the relative perfection of *Homo sapiens*.

The relative perfection of any wild animal lies in its ability to maintain, through psychical, physical and behavioural adaptations, a balanced and symbiotic relationship with its total (natural) environment. Perfection may exist only in relation to present environmental circumstances. It is not absolute nor independent, but is dependent precisely upon the ability of the animal to change in obedience to changes in the environment. In other words, as pointed out by Dr Harvey Croze, no natural mechanism is perfect: success is a quality that should be measured in terms of the probable rather than the absolute. Sometimes the mechanism will fail.

For instance, a red-chested cuckoo was late in depositing its egg in the nest of a robinchat. According to Croze, cuckoo eggs usually hatch first and the chick immediately begins ejecting the other eggs from the nest. Instead, in this case the cuckoo's egg hatched

> ... five days after the host bird's, by which time the larger robinchat was able to demand four times as many meals per day as the parasite. Thus the final infamy of the cuckoo was thwarted; try though it might ... it could not muster strength enough for its innate trick of heaving the host chick from the nest. Perhaps the energy it used in trying cost its life, for it died before the robinchat young was fully fledged.[31]

Similarly, each generation of our hunter-gatherer ancestors was made relatively perfect in flowing movement, in obedience to the Great Spirit, through a land transfigured and renewed by constant action of the natural flux, selection and succession. As today, hunter-gatherer mobility would have been high, both spatially and as between groups, fission and fusion of the bands being frequent. Flux was essential to their survival. This relationship with the natural flux cannot be stressed too strongly, for not only was the land shaped and renewed by the constant action of natural forces such as wind and water, but so too was each generation of hunter-gatherers, to perfect their adaptations to their present natural environment. It was precisely the loss of their relative perfection in flowing movement as hunter-gatherers in contact with all the forces of nature that led to their gross imperfection as farmers. Look at this process from the standpoint of a sculptor such as Henry Moore. Before asking himself what form he could best realize in the particular block of stone he had in front of him, Moore would first consider its structure, its degree of hardness and how it '...has reacted to natural forces like wind and water, for those in the course of time have revealed the inherent qualities of the stone.'[32] Similarly, human beings were so honed by natural forces over millennia as to reveal their inherent qualities, sharpen their faculties and perfect them as men and women, as works of art expressive of the action of the artist of all life, the natural flux or Great Spirit. Obedience to the natural flux has been vital, central to the evolutionary success of *Homo sapiens*. Such a world-loving passage in concert with the pageant of life of the kingdom of nature in turn inspired and promoted a natural altruism and righteousness. Their system of values and morality stemmed from the biological nature of humankind, as that nature was lovingly integrated within the kingdom of nature. *They obeyed the fundamental of environmental ethics, which is the basis of all ethics.*

A thing is right when it tends to preserve the integrity, stability and beauty of the biotic community. It is wrong when it tends otherwise.[33]

In short, they belonged to the land and universally obeyed its laws. Their moral principles, founded in social and economic equality, were based in universality, in their view of the wilderness as sacred and in their preservation of the stability of biotic communities world-wide.

Such a world-loving passage as that described above also made possible the realization of their natural creative potential in works of art. In South Africa's Drakensberg Mountains, for example, 'there are a hundred miles of Bushmen caves, among the greatest art galleries in the world'.[34]

In their obedience to the natural flux hunter-gatherers were not only relatively perfect players in the orchestra of life but pre-eminently ones who could appreciate to the full the paradise of sight, of sound, of smell, of taste and of touch that surrounded them (which all together constituted a continuous symphony of land, sky, water, weather and wildlife) and reproduced their appreciation in their arts. *Homo sapiens* was a highly imaginative toolmaker and artist. There is evidence that Palaeolithic people undertook much creative work with their hands, as indeed do recent hunter-gatherers, who spend a large part of their days making objects by hand. It was by creative endeavour that the small child in particular learnt to know his world. Concerning the hunter-gatherers' art, the significant feature was the representation of animals in rock paintings and engravings. Only occasionally did they paint human figures, and they were never portrayed with the same naturalism as were the lovingly observed animals. Majestic paintings of animals were already being executed in the Chauvet Cave in the Ardèche region of south-eastern France 32,000 years ago, a level of excellence also sustained in caves in south-western France and northern Spain until 12000 BC. At the height of the Magdalenian culture, some 16,000 years ago, the painters in the cave of Lascaux were creating beautiful, highly coloured, representational pictures of their world: images of deer, horses, bulls and other animals cover the walls of the cave. It has been suggested that these images represent the origins of Western art, but such is not the case. For during the Mesolithic, when the Magdalenian culture gave way to the Azilian, representational painting and engraving virtually disappeared, to be replaced by graffiti and repetitive patterns, including crude designs of lines and circles painted on pebbles. Techniques common to the Magdalenian artists, such as perspective and sense of movement, were not reinvented in Western art until the Renaissance.

The high quality of their painting shows them to have been people of high intellect, great artists comparable with the dominating figures of historical times.

More than that, the durability of that art, as shown by its 30,000 year existence, reveals the high quality of the experimental technological knowledge of chemistry behind its development. All together, their technology, artefacts and arts further enhanced the ecological understanding and hunter-gathering skills of *Homo sapiens*, securing them even greater stability within the kingdom of nature. Art, in that its practice sharpened their faculties, was a key to the survival of the hunter-gatherer.

The painting of animals, spontaneous music-making and dance gave people a heightened sense of identity and increased understanding as hunter-gatherers and artists of their own lives integrated within the greater work of art that was wild nature. Their works of art were a joyous outward expression of the harmonious integration of human nature within nature, of the human spirit attuned to the Great Spirit of wildlife.

Just as each species of wild animal is a masterpiece of evolution, exquisitely adapted through natural selection to its own particular environment, so too was *Homo sapiens*. In their relative physical and psychical perfection, they may be regarded as *models of what it is to be human*, and in their harmonious integration within the wilderness they were friends of the Earth. In fact, for three thousand generations or more, hunter-gatherers displayed such considerable self-regulating stability as to guarantee their species immortality; that is, everlasting life not to the individual but to the species for as long as the natural world, their home, should last. But suddenly, during the Mesolithic, 12,000 years ago, some of their kind were forcibly de-ranged – that is, prevented from ranging freely in the horizontal as hunter-gatherers as heretofore – both by environmental changes and by their adaptation to agriculture as a principal source of food. With the arrival of agriculture, the climax state of *Homo sapiens* gave way to crisis.

Chapter 3

The Watershed of the Mesolithic

The early days of agriculture were extremely hard. People did not take kindly to it. They were forced into it, as their population increased. The harshness of early arable farming is reflected in God's curse on Adam when he expels him from the Garden: only 'in the sweat of thy face shalt thou eat bread' (*Genesis*, chapter 3 verse 19). Pastoralism was no easier... (Colin Tudge)[1]

At the end of the Ice Age major cultural changes took place during the Mesolithic, which is the period between the last of the Upper Palaeolithic cultures of the Pleistocene and the adaptation to agriculture, which marks the beginning of the Neolithic. I believe that small groups of hunter-gatherers in different parts of the world – in the Middle East, in China, in Mesoamerica – were slowly *forced* to adapt to a primitive agriculture and domestication in order to survive; that in so doing, they inevitably lost many of their evolutionary characteristics as human beings; and that they then compounded their degeneration by destroying the wilderness and raising up permanent structures on its ruins. To show how, where and why this happened, it is necessary to examine the changes in climatic and environmental conditions prior to and following 8000 BC, 'the accepted Palaeolithic/Mesolithic and Pleistocene/Holocene boundary',[2]* before examining the cultural responses to such changes.

---

*NB The boundary in question refers to North Western Europe. The Mesolithic, the period between the Palaeolithic and Neolithic, which saw the transition from hunter-gathering to farming, occurred at different times in different places. It may be said to have begun in the Eastern Mediterranean and Near East circa 10000 BC, and was of very short duration as farming became quickly established in the Fertile Crescent. In North Western Europe, on the other hand the transition did not begin until 8000 BC and lasted for over 5,000 years as farming moved up through the Danube Basin around 8000 BC before becoming fully established in areas such as France and England circa 4000 BC and in Southern Scandinavia circa 3000 BC. All dates prior to 5000 BC are liable to modification in the light of new research.

The glacial-postglacial transition proceeded by stages rather than as one continuous process of deglaciation. The first phase followed a rapid climate change, beginning around 16000 BC, which caused about one third of the total volume of ice of the northern continents to melt. This phase was followed by a return to glacial conditions lasting until about 9000 BC, when the second phase began. This brought about the almost total disappearance of the European and American icecaps by 6000 BC. In North America ice withdrew at approximately 30km per century, sea-levels rose 10–15m per 1,000 years and wide shelves of land disappeared at the sea's edge at the rate of 5–10km per century. In addition, as the ice melted, inland regions of North America rose, tilting the continental crust so that the continental shelf sank by up to 100m. Global sea-levels rose by total amounts estimated at between 100 and 150m.

These changes, including rising temperatures, changes in precipitation, changes caused by the migration and expansion of vegetation, and changes in the composition of wildlife – some 75 percent of all large mammals, including mammoths and cave bears, became extinct* – must have been noticeable to generations of hunter-gatherers. Furthermore, considering that the remaining two-thirds of the ice volume of the northern continents were returned to the sea during the second phase of deglaciation, 9000–6000 BC, the environmental changes, if not as rapid, had, I believe, a far more profound effect upon the hunter-gatherer populations of the world. Not only did they face considerable environmental changes, but those changes led directly to their isolation in continents and islands, with the most profound effects upon their cultures (see figure 3.1).

America was cut off from Asia as the land mass referred to as Beringia was submerged, creating the Bering Strait. The islands of Britain and Japan came into being. Australia became a huge sea-girt prison, while New Guinea and Tasmania became much smaller prisons.

During the Last Glacial Maximum (c. 16000 BC) the sea level around Australia was 100–140 metres below its present level. The coastline around the Kimberley region (at the northern end of Western Australia) was as much as 250 miles (400km) further to the north-west, while the most northerly points of Australia were connected by land to New Guinea. The rising sea would have inundated the 250 mile wide strip of coastline around the Kimberley region and flooded the Gulf of Carpentaria. The

---

*There appear to be great variations in the timing of these extinctions – the megamarsupials of Australia appear to have mostly died out by 33000 BC, while the megafauna of North America hung on until about 10000 BC – and doubt over whether changes in the climate were alone responsible or whether *Homo sapiens* hunters played a part.

Part I: fig 3.1

KEY:

- ⌇ SHORELINE - 16000 BC

- ▨ ICE (INCLUDING SEA ICE) - 16000 BC

narrow channel that had separated Australia from Southeast Asia would have gone, as would the land (now the Arafura Sea) that formed the bridge to New Guinea. The effect upon the Aborigines must have been profound as their first campsites

> ... were drowned by the waters of the Timor Sea and the Gulf of Carpentaria, which rose so fast between 13000 and 16000 BC that the coast moved inland at a rate of three miles a year.[3]*

The submerging of the region known as 'Sundaland' which had been a sub-continent at the Last Glacial Maximum – comprising the Malay Peninsula, Sumatra, Java, Borneo and adjacent islands, with an area of more than 2 million sqare kilometres – could have been quite dramatic as the sea-level rose more than 100m. Where there had been a vast land mass there would now be a string of islands; rainfall would have increased, with resultant forests and new flora and fauna developing within them. All these changes must have had some very profound effects on the human cultures of the regions concerned. For instance, the development and expansion of agriculture began in regions to the north of Sundaland, while in the island remains of Sundaland there began a post-3000 BC population growth and rain forest exploitation which still goes on today.

In the Northern Hemisphere changes in climate brought about further major changes in the environment. Reconstructed patterns of climate reveal an abrupt change of climate as the Pleistocene Ice Age ended: glaciologists from the Greenland Icecore Project suggested that the ending of the last glaciation was followed by an abrupt warming as the temperature in Greenland rose about 7°C in approximately 50 years. However, though climate tends to change rapidly rather than gradually, the consequent response of the biota and adaptation of the environment was likely to have taken far longer.

One of the responses was the spread of forests: an invasion of waters was followed by an invasion of forests, particularly in northern Eurasia. Cultural changes then took place in response to these environmental changes. As steppe and tundra, which had been common during the Pleistocene Ice Age, were colonized by forests of coniferous and deciduous trees, wide-ranging hunter-gatherers who had lived largely on big game gave way to hunter-gatherer bands exploiting the new complex ecosystem containing a much richer mixture of plants and animals. One culture

---

* See below this chapter for the possible effects on the inhabitants of Arnhem Land in northern Australia.

that diversified into an economy based on hunting, fishing, fowling and food-gathering is known as the Maglemosian. Between 8000 and 6500 BC the Maglemosian culture extended from the Eastern Baltic region across northern Poland, Denmark, the then dry North Sea and eastern Britain. Animal remains recovered from Maglemosian sites reveal that aurochs (wild cattle), red deer and roe deer replaced the lost reindeer herds as the main sources of meat. These people also fished, hunted seals and small game, and gathered a wide variety of plants.

However, as the forests changed their composition and thickened, hunter-gatherer bands appear to have become restricted in their movements and become isolated, perhaps forcing them to make settlements near and around bodies of water. This appears to have occurred around the end of the seventh millennium BC.

> At the end of this time there was a massive invasion of hazel stretching from Ireland to Transylvania and from Estonia to the Pyrenees, where it was often five, twelve, and seventeen times more numerous than all other trees. Uncoppiced hazel is a formidable barrier to communications, and it is not surprising to find settlements now scattered along streams, round lakes, and on shorelines.[4]

Settlements around bodies of water, whether or not forced by an invasion of hazel, may account not only for the marked shift of hunter-gatherer economies from the resources of the land to those of water throughout the Eurasian forests, but also for some extraordinary changes in behaviour which now took place amongst these Eurasian foragers. For instance, the conditions of the hunter-gatherer life-style imposed an egalitarian social order world-wide, whereas socio-economic developments amongst the increasingly sedentary foragers of Eurasia permitted the accumulation of wealth, and the achievement of power and status. Before, however, elaborating further on the socio-economic adaptations of these Eurasian foraging peoples, it is important to examine both the degree to which these changes were the result of environmental and demographic stress, and to recall the traditional modes of responses to the challenge of environmental change and stress.

Various studies have pointed to the part played by risk and stress as determining factors in promoting hunter-gatherer social and economic strategies and in generating culture change. They would appear to have been crucial factors in the development of post-glacial hunter-gatherer social and economic strategies in the temperate zone, which favoured procurement strategies and social adaptations which minimized both seasonal and regional inconsistency of resources. For when faced with the necessity of finding a constant supply of food from resources which were unevenly distributed both seasonally and regionally, people could either range through the land in search of food, or develop social, economic and technological strategies for survival, including storing food when there was abundance.

So, in the Mesolithic, some hunter-gatherers remained mobile in their search for food and resources, using essentially the same general strategies for survival as their Palaeolithic forbears, moving in obedience to the natural flux. Other hunter-gatherers, however, particularly those in the temperate zone, began to develop ever more complex technological, economic and social strategies for survival, including resource storage systems, becoming increasingly sedentary in the process. This meant that they were abandoning a principal mode of adaptation to environmental change and stress, that of unpossessive mobility as hunter-gatherers.*

The two main sedentary strategies arising in the Mesolithic in response to stress occurred amongst permanently settled hunter-gatherers and those who underwent the Neolithic revolution and became sedentary farmers. Each type of sedentary community experienced a decrease in flexibility, increased population size and risk of local resource over-exploitation or decline. Such communities would thereafter be profoundly affected not only by climate change and stress but also by stress arising within and between their societies.

Sedentary and more specialized hunter-gatherers, such as the Eurasian foragers referred to earlier, occupied higher latitude environments along the Atlantic and North European coasts and included those who relied to a large extent on aquatic resources. They developed storage facilities, including the introduction of pottery as an aid in storing food, which greatly contributed to the sedentary nature of these Mesolithic populations. Such groups have been described not only as 'affluent', in the sense that their adaptations provided material security and wealth, but also as 'complex', referring to the degree of development of their socio-economic organization and technology based on the large-scale storage of food. Fundamental features of such groups also included increased population density, socio-economic differentiation – as observed

---

*Archaeological evidence from Moravia in Central Europe indicates that certain groups of hunter-gatherers, in the face of extreme climatic conditions 24,000 years ago during the Ice Age, established settlements numbering 100 people or more. They moved between up to five different settlements in separate hunting grounds. The men hunted mammoth, while the women hunted smaller animals with nets, and foraged.

in their cemeteries – social division of labour, commodity trade and warfare.*

Most of the ethnographic examples of complex foragers come from the coastal regions of the temperate zone. Other complex Mesolithic/Epipalaeolithic† settlements have been found along the Bug and Dniester rivers and further south in the Balkans and Carpathian basin, notably at Lepenski Vir and other sites in the Iron Gates region of the Danube. The Lepenski Vir culture, dated to c.6000 BC, consisted of large villages stretching along large river valleys and exploiting a variety of resources, riverine ones being amongst the most important. This practice of intensive fishing, as also amongst Mesolithic communities in the southern Urals, played an important rôle in facilitating a settled way of life.

The second main sedentary strategy arising in the Mesolithic in response to environmental change and stress was farming, whose origin introduced the Neolithic. I have already referred to the possible effects of environmental changes in East and Southeast Asia, the most important being the development and spread of agriculture in regions to the north of Sundaland. During the tenth to eighth millennium BC, in Southwestern Asia, in the Near and Middle East, an agro-pastoral system grew out of the domestication of cereals, pulses and ungulates. The origin of farming was almost certainly in response to the challenge of a world-wide desiccation which coincided with the world-wide rise in temperature and in sea-levels, together with population pressures and related food crises.

---

* In this connection, note the importance of commodity trade (developed systems of exchange) as, when and where it developed.

> Commodity trade generates the intensification of production and a consequent tendency towards specialization, and these conflict with the relatively equal participation in production, distribution and consumption that characterizes egalitarian arrangements. Thus increasing trade and specialization militate against the reproduction of egalitarian social relations, and, with sedentarization, eventually lead to their transformation. The well-known rank societies of California and the Northwest Coast of North America exemplify the nature of this transformation.[5]

In fact, of all the relatively sedentary hunter-gatherer societies in North America, only those on the Northwest Coast were strictly hierarchical. Those in northern California shared many of the same values as those of the Northwest Coast, while those in central and southern California remained relatively egalitarian hunter-gatherers. For at the end of the Ice Age, in common with much of North America, big game hunting gave way to a life based on the hunting of smaller animals, fishing and gathering wild plants. As farming spread north from Mexico to the Southwest and Southeast of North America, the West coast peoples further refined their hunter-gathering economy by harvesting and storing acorns which in due course they might turn into bread. This, together with their other hunting and gathering activities, enabled them to subsist within relatively small defined territories in settlements of a hundred or so people under village headmen.

† Epipalaeolithic: term applied to the continuation of the late Palaeolithic hunter-gatherer system in the postglacial period.

It has been suggested that the world-wide rise in temperature c.10000–8000 BC increased the aridity of the steppe and other semi-arid zones of the Near and Middle East and elsewhere in Eurasia, generating the need for increased cereal collection and production within the more restricted habitats of suitable wild grasses. For instance, one of the world's earliest 'villages', dating back to c.10000 BC, has been discovered by archaeologists at Tell Afar in northern Iraq. The inhabitants appear still to have been hunter-gatherers, gathering wild cereals, both wheat and barley, but not growing them. The site lay between mountains and semi-desert: coping with both rising sea levels and with sudden and substantial increases in aridity must have been much easier in the foothills, where changes in altitude offered a range of alternative habitats. Major cultural changes throughout southwestern and Central Asia have been shown to coincide with four major periods of increased aridity, detected from the fluctuations in the level of the Caspian Sea. In the Holocene the level fell, or regressed, four times.

> During the first of the Caspian Holocene regressions, the Begdash, dated to the ninth millennium bc, plant cultivation and animal husbandry appeared in the Near East and in the south Caspian region, while further to north the groups inhabiting the Central-Asian plains and southern Urals adopted more intensive forms of food procurement, with the development of fishing and the use of the bow and arrow... During the second regression, the Magyshlak, in the late seventh and early sixth millennia bc, domestication occurred in the steppe and forest-steppe of the southern Urals, presumably as a response to the shortages in food supply provided by hunting and fishing. However, foraging remained the principal means of subsistence, while stockbreeding probably played no more than a subordinate rôle. In South-Central Asia, on the other hand, we can observe a marked shift to food production, which included not only stockbreeding but also intensive arable cultivation (the Djeitun culture). During the period of increased aridity, marked by the third regression, the Jilaldin (late sixth to early fifth millennium bc), cultural changes took place in Central Asia that were associated with the Eneolithic... During the last major regression, the Makhachkalinsk (late fourth to early second millennium bc), Bronze Age cultures came into existence in the arid regions of Central Asia.[6]

One other important adaptation occurred following the periods of desiccation in Eurasia. The domestic horse appeared in the southern Urals c.6000 BC, while a group of sites in the area of the River Tobol in western Siberia reveal faunal assemblages dominated by bones of the horse, suggesting the further development of a food-producing economy specializing in horse breeding. Increased reliance on horse breeding appears in turn to have led sedentary populations around the eastern Urals in the third millennium BC to adopt a more nomadic existence. With their development as increasingly specialized nomadic pastoralists, these steppe peoples of Eurasia had, by the second millennium BC, finally established themselves as specialized cattle and horse nomads. They had completely adapted to a food-producing economy, though in the process the horse nomads had re-acquired a mobility which, by comparison with that of non-specialized hunter-gatherers, can only be described as parasitical upon the horse. (I shall return to the question of parasitism in Chapter 5.)

The challenge of desiccation, combined with population pressures and consequent food crises, in forcing sedentary hunter-gatherers to adopt and intensify food production is also notable in the Levant* where, in the late Pleistocene (13000–8000 BC), in a climate that was cooler and wetter than today, and in a countryside that was well-wooded, people hunted in small bands and occupied small seasonal campsites. They hunted deer, horse, boar, aurochs, gazelle and hartebeest. Then, in what has been described as the Natufian period, the climate became warmer and drier, grassland replaced woodland, and permanently settled Natufian 'villages' began to appear, whose inhabitants gathered wild cereals, harvested acorns, hunted large mammals such as gazelles, as well as small ones such as hares, and fished. A similar development occurred, c.11000 BC, at a site called Abu Hureyra near the Euphrates River in Syria. The favourable climate enabled settled hunter-gatherer populations at these sites, and at others throughout what is known as the Fertile Crescent, to flourish. But their very settled state made them vulnerable to sudden climate change. A prolonged and severe drought forced people, as in Abu Hureyra, to turn to cereal cultivation. By 9000 BC agriculture was spreading throughout the Fertile Crescent and beyond. People now lived in walled villages and were sowing and harvesting domesticated wheat and barley. They now possessed domesticated dogs, sheep and goats, while still hunting deer, aurochs and boar.

Agriculture was now also beginning in India and in China (c.6000–3000 BC), and in the New World, in Mexico (c.7000–1000 BC) and in Peru (c.4000–1000 BC). I have already noted the extraordinary changes that

---

*Countries bordering the Eastern Mediterranean.

occurred with the submersion of the sub-continent of Sundaland, and consequent loss of perhaps one million square kilometres of land. A further million square kilometres were lost to the present Yellow and East China Seas. Such a severe reduction of available land space for hunter-gatherers in China and Southeast Asia and concomitant high population densities may have contributed to the economic shift to rice production in China (c.5000 BC) and Southeast Asia generally. Parallel developments in the domestication of wild animals were also taking place in these areas. For example, the wild humped cow in India (distinct from the aurochs of Europe and the Near East, from which are descended the European cow) was domesticated, to become the zebu cattle of today; while, in Southeast Asia, buffalo, and perhaps pig, were probably independently domesticated. Parallel developments also took place in Middle and South America, where a camelid (the guanaco) and the guinea-pig were domesticated. Interestingly, the peoples of the Old World domesticated many animals and comparatively few plants, whereas in the New World the opposite was the case.

Both plant cultivation and the domestication of animals, in the Old World and the New, arose from the need of settled people to guarantee food supplies at a time of intense and widespread drought. With the onset of further drought conditions threatening starvation, farmers in Mesopotamia, in Egypt, and later on in the Americas, began building cities (such as Ur in Mesopotamia) the better to control water supplies and produce more food. But such cities, that were established as defences against small climate changes, often proved vulnerable to larger ones, and collapsed.[7]

In Europe farming may have begun indigenously in some areas, but it appears that the essence of the farming economy was introduced from Southwest Asia, while undergoing a substantial degree of local development as it expanded across Europe and elsewhere. This can be deduced from the breed of animals and the types of cereals which were, without exception, the same animals and cereals domesticated earlier in Southwest Asia. (In the New World, farming spread from Mexico up the eastern seaboard of North America, while undergoing a similar degree of local development: the cultivation of maize, squash and beans had, by 500 AD, spread as far north as the Great Lakes.) In general, the advance of agriculture through Europe, though an erratic and relatively slow transition, was nonetheless as inexorable and overwhelming as the earlier waves of advance of waters, of forests and of aridification. Many of these advancing farmers were refugees from the catastrophic flooding of the Black Sea.

The Black Sea was a large fresh-water lake c.8000 BC, whose water level was perhaps 40 metres below that of the Mediterranean. As the general sea-level rose world-wide, evidence suggests that a salt-water river eventually opened up through the Bosphorus from the Mediterranean, and started seeping into the Black Sea. Soon, around 5500 BC, a trickle became a deluge. It is estimated that the waters of the Black Sea rose some 160 metres, causing the shore-line to retreat at the rate of one kilometre a day for perhaps 100 days, engulfing more than 100,000 square kilometres of land and driving people before it into the hills. It was around 5500 BC that members of the Linear Pottery Culture (the Linearbandkeramik complex) began moving north and west from their origins in the Black Sea area and Carpathian Mountains, taking with them a way of life based on cultivation. By 4500 BC they had reached the Paris Basin. John M. Howell argues that

> The uniformity of the Linear Pottery villages is one sign that agriculture was introduced into Europe by immigrants and not merely by the spread of new ideas... By the beginning of the middle Neolithic in about 3500 BC even more profound developments were under way, as is shown by changes in the type, location and distribution of sites. Unlike Linear Pottery villages, middle Neolithic sites can be found outside the ecological niche of the valley bottom. Along with the change in location came a sharp increase in the proportion of sites defended by ditches and heavy palisades built of tree trunks. Apparently society had entered a phase of warfare. It had also become more dependent on cattle, which in the middle Neolithic account for more than 50 percent of animal remains, much more than in the earlier period.[8]

Howell deduces that

> ...resource pressure – in particular demographic pressure on arable land – was one of the driving forces of social and cultural change during much of the Neolithic period in northwestern Europe. Population pressure appears to have been one of the key factors in causing the remarkable centralization and fortification of settlements that appeared during the mid-Neolithic.[9]

As well as all the pressures I have mentioned making for the consolidation and intensification of farming were the rapid development of metallurgy, growing trade and increased tensions resulting in warfare. These in turn accelerated social stratification and the rise of military élites, merchants and craftsmen, all groups not directly concerned with food production who nevertheless needed to be fed, accelerating the spread and intensification of farming.

From the foregoing it will be apparent that the transition to farming, that is, the replacement of hunter-gatherer adaptations by farming as a way of life, was, generally speaking, the outcome of extraordinary instability on the part of the relatively more numerous and powerful farmers by comparison with the inherently stable, though relatively small and weak, hunter-gatherer bands, and the consequent 'competition between two mutually incompatible ways of life.'[10] Furthermore, it is difficult to escape the conclusion that the adaptations to farming and domestication were, in general, *forced* upon people. For profound cultural change is a costly response to perturbation, and it is least costly, and ultimately more adaptive, to change as little as possible, particularly when, as in the case of the hunter-gatherers, their evolutionary adaptations had already proved enormously successful over tens of thousands of years. If the main reason for domesticating animals was to guarantee reliable supplies of meat, there was no obvious motive for doing so when plenty was to be had by hunting. It follows that the farmers who did domesticate animals and plants had every reason for pursuing this course. All the indications are that they were escaping the threat of dearth and starvation, brought about not only by environmental stress and loss of animals to hunt but also by a combination of pressures, particularly climate and demographic pressures, arising directly from their adaptation to the sedentary farming way of life. Thereafter, once the adaptation to the farming way of life was set in train, an increasingly important factor was the inevitable erosion of their hunting abilities and therefore the loss of many of their evolutionary characteristics. For it will be appreciated that, however fast or slow the transition from hunter-gatherer to farmer, once the reliance on wild animals as a principal source of meat had passed a certain point (say 60 per cent) and given way to domestic animals as the principal source, early Neolithic peoples would have been living increasingly as sedentary farmers and no longer as hunters, leading to the increasing decline in hunting skills of the majority of their people. In this connection, Stephen Boyden argues that the change

> ... provides an early example of a biohistorical principle of great importance – *the principle of technoaddiction.*[11]

When new techniques have been introduced into a society, they have not necessarily been essential for the survival and well-being of all; rather, they may have been of benefit to a few individuals only. However, in time, societies tend to reorganize themselves around the new techniques and to become increasingly dependent on them. Such was the case with the populations of Çatal Hüyük (Anatolia) and Abu Hureyra (Levant), who by 7000 BC had become entirely dependent on farming for their survival, though some of their food still came from hunting.

So, whether or not the initial change from hunter-gathering to farming took place as a direct result of environmental pressures combined with population pressures, what is certain is that those peoples who so adapted underwent an extraordinary change in their physiques, in their techniques and in their behaviour, resulting from, and resulting in, the loss of their hunter-gatherer abilities and concomitant loss of many of their evolutionary characteristics as human beings. I drew attention in Chapter 1 to the degenerative change that occurred as between Ice Age hunter-gatherers and populations from Europe during the Mesolithic. Hunter-gatherers were as relatively perfect as any other wild animal in their physical and psychical adaptations as they were in their hunting and gathering techniques. They were in fact masters of the natural environment. It is unlikely, therefore, that they *chose* to adapt out of a highly developed hunter-gatherer way of life – one that was absolutely conducive to their health, happiness, general stability and well-being – to a primitive agriculture and protected village environment. After all, who would choose to change from a highly developed, free-moving paradisial state to an extraordinarily primitive, poverty-stricken, protected prison-like static one? Who would choose to exchange a relatively healthy carefree life of movement for a relatively unhealthy sedentary one that tied them to the soil and compelled them to work – a sentence to hard labour – eventually forcing them to intensify production as their numbers grew and became concentrated? On the contrary, evidence of hunter-gatherers resisting such an adaptation abounds, namely in the last two centuries in North America and Australia, and amongst the San. When asked, so the story goes, why they did not take up farming the !Kung San of the Kalahari Desert replied somewhat quizzically, 'Why should we plant when there are so many mongongo nuts in the world?' Noel Mostert, in his book *Frontiers* has argued that

> In a period of severe drought affecting their Kalahari habitat and near-by Botswana, the !Kung were scarcely affected and in excellent health while Bantu-speaking farmers in neighbouring territories had to be saved from starvation through United Nations food relief. For hunter-gatherers in Africa farming therefore represented a harder,

less rewarding and even dangerous option, as it must have done in many other parts of the world.[12]

Katherine Wright, after studying grinding stones and other tools for processing cereals from prehistoric sites in the southern Levant, has averred

> ...that the processing of wild cereals to make them edible is such hard work that no one would do it unless they were desperate.[13]

Even the foods themselves would have been utilized out of necessity rather than from choice. Grasses are generally not foods that most people prefer; people world-wide tend to eat meat and fruits when they can, and only eat cereals when they must. In addition, people are poorly adapted to digesting cereals, because allergies to the different varieties are widespread, and they are conducive to rickets.

All the evidence suggests that it is unlikely that people chose to adapt to a degraded existence as primitive farmers. Rather, a more likely scenario is a slow shift from big-game hunting and gathering, through more sedentary hunter-gatherer cultures – including the hunting of smaller game, fishing and the gathering of wild food plants – to agriculture and domestication by people, both in the Old World and in the New, who found environmental changes, particularly aridification, population growth and consequent food crisis, threatening their survival. Subsistence stress – including reduced hunter-gatherer mobility and the subsequent increase in the size of the human population, and reduction in the reliability of suitable prey – helped transform hunter-gatherers into primitive farmers. Instead of migrating and/or refining aspects of their hunter-gatherer cultures and technology as had been the norm of evolutionary behaviour for tens of thousands of years, some groups adapted by degrees, via incipient agriculture, to farming and domestication as a principal source of food, to the virtual exclusion of hunting. Whether they were forced so to adapt by environmental pressures or chose to adapt to the more sedentary agricultural way of life is less important than the fact that, in so adapting, their adoption of a primitive agriculture as a principal means of providing food would so adversely have affected their physical and psychical development and health as to cause a degeneration in their physiques, judgement, dexterity and skills, eventually making the hunter-gatherer way of life impossible to them. Loss of hunter-gathering ability and of health, would so have interacted with each other as to degrade them from a state of relative perfection as hunter-gatherers to one of increasing imperfection. And this was particularly the case because farming as a principal means of providing food was not only a response to, but a cause of, an increase in population, primarily because farmers lost the natural constraints which had governed their reproductive behaviour as hunter-gatherers. They were, in effect, made sedentary or forcibly de-ranged, possibly by extreme changes in the environment, certainly by their adaptation to farming and consequent loss of evolutionary perfection. *They were forcibly de-ranged degenerate human beings.** In that condition they were no longer superb masters of the wild environment: they 'had crossed a threshold of environmental vulnerability'[14] and were now at the mercy not only of the wild environment which they had continually to subdue in order to survive, but also of the natural flux, and in particular catastrophic changes of climate.

Their adaptation to agriculture certainly produced the most profound physical, psychical, cultural and behavioural changes which can only be described as degenerative. It is important to note that domestication first occurred, amongst both people and animals, in those areas less affected by the advance and withdrawal of ice during the Ice Age, and, in the case of animals, amongst the most primitive and small brained of the species concerned.

> The environment in the Near East and South Asia ... remained much more uniform during this whole period. Populations living there did not have to adapt so much to changed conditions as those further north and were in addition relatively isolated from their northern relatives by the geographical barriers of the Black Sea, the Caucasus Mountains, the Caspian Sea, and Soviet Central Asian deserts and the high mountains of Inner Asia. So the forms in the near East were able to remain evolutionarily conservative while constant evolutionary change was taking place in the north. So, after the Ice Age, a large reservoir of comparatively unprogressive large mammals had collected in the Near Eastern region – a reservoir for important domestication.[15]†

---

*A similar degeneration has taken place throughout history whenever and wherever hunter-gatherers – e.g. Native Americans and Aborigines – have been forcibly made sedentary. Once farming peoples began invading territories outside their places of origin, they in turn have usually forced the indigenous hunter-gatherer population to move out when its territory was required by farmers or to submit to domestication. This has been the case throughout history, particularly in more recent times in North America and Australia. Thus forcibly de-ranged, once proud Native Americans and Aborigine peoples have become the poorest and most dislocated minorities in the USA and Australia respectively. They are plagued by severe unemployment, alcoholism, disease and suicide.

† See Appendix i for an amplification of this argument.

Applying this argument to humankind, whereas selection pressures of cold may have enhanced the evolution of those hunter-gatherers exposed to ice and snow, degeneration following adaptation to a primitive farming way of life and domestication occurred in the Near East amongst both people and animals who would appear already to have been amongst the less progressive of their kind.

Increased sedentariness, population growth, and reliance on farming, in both the Old World and the New, brought declines in health and an increase in diseases. There were three kinds of new diseases – nutritional, occupational, and infectious – interacting with one another.

A noteworthy change occurred in the diet as farming expanded. In time, the proportion of food taken by hunting dropped as a percentage of the total quantity of meat consumed, implying increasing reliance on a few species of domesticated animal. An even greater change occurred in the plant diet as farming expanded. Hunter-gatherers had relied on some 150 species of food plant; this diverse diet was reduced by farmers to only some 8 species of plant, based on grasses. This, together with their reliance on increasingly fewer species of animal, represented an extraordinary narrowing and deterioration in diet amongst farmers. This shift from a perfectly balanced diet as pre-Neolithic hunter-gatherers to one that caused a chronic energy deficiency amongst primitive farmers would in turn have exacerbated the physical, psychical and behavioural degeneration that occurred with the loss of the hunter-gatherer way of life.

The archaeological record reveals that people were under considerable nutritional stress following the transition to agriculture. A comparison of skeletal indices from burials in the Middle East prior to the transition with those of farming peoples a few thousand years later reveals that the latter were, on average, about 4 inches shorter and 15 lb lighter, and were liable to skeletal diseases such as osteoporosis. Skeletons from the Near Eastern regions of Greece and Turkey are even more revealing of a dramatic change in height. At the end of the Ice Age the average height of hunter-gatherer men in that region was 5 feet 10 inches, and of women 5 feet 6 inches. Following the adaptation to farming, height declined rapidly, until by 4000 BC it was only 5 feet 3 inches for men and 5 feet 1 inch for women. Since then heights in the region have slowly risen again, but not yet to the heights of the earlier hunter-gatherers. A recent study of the skeletons of Native Americans in Ohio has shown a similar degeneration amongst hunter-gatherers when they began to cultivate corn. Tall, healthy hunter-gatherers were reduced to stunted, sickly farmers who suffered from a range of diseases including tuberculosis, yaws and osteoarthritis.

As well as the degenerative effects on the anatomies of primitive farmers of nutritional stress, there was the effect of the grind of everyday life. Studies of the bones of 162 individuals from Abu Hureyra, from about 9500 BC–5500 BC, have revealed considerable spinal damage, damaged hips and knees, and severe osteoarthritis in toes, particularly amongst the skeletons of women forced to kneel to roll stones to crush corn. Hence nutritional stress was compounded with repetitive stress injuries from work.

In addition, their increasingly crowded, malnourished and sedentary conditions encouraged the spread of diseases such as tuberculosis, typhus, leprosy, and cholera. Accumulating refuse and polluted water made breeding grounds for rats, lice, mosquitoes and other disease-carrying organisms, while their close proximity to their newly domesticated animals introduced a mixture of pathogens from which potent new diseases evolved. Smallpox probably evolved from cowpox, measles from rinderpest or canine distemper, and influenza from swine diseases. Such crowd epidemics could neither arise nor persist amongst small bands of mobile hunter-gatherers.

Furthermore, because of their dependence on one or a few crops, farmers ran a greater risk of starvation than did hunter-gatherers if one food crop failed. For hunter-gatherers had a wide choice of wild foods, that allowed both for failure of certain sources and for seasonal non-availability. Such wild plants and animals were, by virtue of natural selection, also able to survive climatic extremes in their environment. Farmers, on the other hand, replaced this variety of hardy wildlife with a few alien species – or even only a single crop – whose periodic failure placed them in danger of starvation. As recently as the mid-nineteenth century in Ireland a blight attacked the potato, the staple food of Irish farmers, causing some one and a half million to die of starvation and of diseases brought on by hunger. Many of the surviving population emigrated, principally to the USA. So a major crop failure in one small part of the world caused not only immediate famine but far reaching political effects which are still with us today.

Another degenerative effect of farming concerns reproduction. Following the recent enforced settlement of the San, for instance, women who had lost their birth-spacing characteristics, began to wean their babies at an earlier age, and the population began to explode. (Increased frequency of menstruation came to be seen as a 'curse' amongst women settled on farmland and in cities.) Such was surely the case amongst primitive subsistence farmers, whose reproductive behaviour was not only no longer under biological and cultural control, but also responsive to the farmer's need for children to help work the land. Thereafter exploding populations began to interact with food shortages, with devastating consequences.

From a cultural standpoint, many of the painting techniques that had been applied in Lascaux, such as perspective and a sense of movement, were lost.

> Even more disconcerting than the cessation of large-scale art is the disappearance about the same time, of small-scale artist's and craftsman's work. Compared with the delicate engraved and carved Magdalenian spear-throwers and 'bâtons', the Mesolithic fish-spears, leister prongs, and so on, are almost without exception monotonous utilitarian objects. The inferiority of red-deer, compared with reindeer, antler and mammoth ivory does not explain the loss but supports a belief in the essential unity of drawing and engraving on small objects and on large surfaces as a single artistic tradition. Disruption of the one entailed the decay of the other.[16]

And not only their art but the subject matter of their art now changed in a radical and most revealing way; when they invented the bow and the boat and domesticated the dog, caricature appeared in their drawings *and so for the first time did the representation of war.* A study of the behaviour of Ice Age hunter-gatherer societies, as also reflected in the behaviour of present day hunter-gatherer societies such as those of the Inuit, pygmy and San – whose ways of life, until recently, may be said to have most closely resembled those of their Ice Age forbears – reveals no evidence of the regular wholesale slaughter of their fellow hunter-gatherers. In fact the San would do everything in their power to avoid killing one of their own kind. The very title of Elizabeth Marshall Thomas's book, *The Harmless People,* shows the extraordinary difference in behaviour between peaceable hunter-gatherer peoples such as the San she describes and the belligerent, harmful and destructive Bantu and European farmers who decimated the bands of San and drove them into their last stronghold, the Kalahari Desert. The art of the Palaeolithic hunter-gatherers shows no evidence of intraspecific warfare, whereas there are 'signs of warfare between different bands'[17] in Mesolithic art (8000–2000 BC), and particularly in the art of the Spanish Levant.*

Intraspecific warfare amongst hunting peoples prior to 8000 BC appears to have been the exception rather than the rule. During the following millennia, however, we learn of war amongst hunter-gatherers. For instance, conflict appears to have arisen in Australia around 8000 BC, as exemplified in paintings of that period in Arnhem Land, amongst the most ancient depictions of conflict known. As the polar ice melted and the seas rose, parts of Arnhem Land were engulfed and Australia became a prison. It is probable that one territorially-orientated group would have been inexorably forced back by the rising waters on another, giving rise to conflict as the Aborigines were forced to share less land and food.

Elsewhere there are records of war amongst hunter-gatherers, and between them and farmers and between farmers themselves. In Mesolithic cemeteries excavated in Europe and North Africa, there is evidence of warfare amongst hunter-gatherers. Such conflict may often have been triggered by pressure from advancing farmers, just as the Native Americans came into conflict with one another as they were driven across the country by invading European farmers. And although many farming peoples are known to have been at peace with their neighbours over long periods of time, it is nonetheless most noticeable that violent hostilities became increasingly widespread with the spread of farmers across the world. There is, throughout history, documented evidence of the genocide of hunter-gatherers by the more powerful farming peoples. There is evidence too of a sharp rise in the middle Neolithic in the proportion of sites protected by ditches and heavy palisades; in the building of, and assaults on, fortified settlements by early farming people in the south of England around 3000 BC, and thereafter in the rapid evolution of fortified towns and cities, and concomitant growth of armies, throughout the civilized world.

---

* East coast of Spain, including sites such as Valltorta, Morella, Dos Aguas and Cogul. There appears to be a gap of several thousand years, an abrupt discontinuity, between the Franco-Cantabrian pictures of 12000 BC and those of the Spanish Levant or 'Second Hunter' style circa 6000–2000 BC. Furthermore, human figures in motion – often combined with animals in scenes of hunting and other activities – are portrayed in these rock pictures, in contrast to the rare occurrence of human figures amongst the innumerable pictures of animals in the Franco-Cantabrian style.

After a similar discontinuity or gap of several thousand years, art began to appear in the farming communities. However, amongst the deeply introverted farmers – who were introverted because they were imprisoned in enclaves and prevented by their loss of hunter-gatherer techniques from ranging freely through the wilderness, which eventually became a hostile environment to them – animal-centredness, a main characteristic of the extrovert hunter-gatherer's mental and emotional make-up, was replaced by human (or self-) centredness or communal narcissism, which persists to this day. Carved figures or statuettes of humans were the typical art-form of the farmers of the Neolithic and early Bronze Ages.

These farmers were no longer members of a climax social system integrated within other climax ecosystems. They were dis-integrated from the world-wide hunter-gatherer society and deprived of an extended family and cohesive community – that is, the natural kingdom of flora and fauna. And, as Elizabeth Marshall Thomas[18] has pointed out, the fine skills required to live in the wilderness may be forgotten within the space of a single generation, and without which these people would die there. With the disappearance of these skills went the loss of their evolutionary identities and stability. In short, they degenerated physically, psychically, culturally and in their behaviour. Their fundamental structures as human beings were destroyed.

The extent of that degeneration – that is, 'the fall away from ancestral excellence' – may be assessed as follows. Prevented, for whatever reason, from ranging freely as hunter-gatherers, de-ranged people lost their hunter-gathering skills and so their economic freedom and independence. Not only were their highly efficient structural, physiological and behavioural adaptations, evolved over hundreds of millennia, no longer relevant, but it followed that their life processes were no longer self-regulating. As well as losing their superb physical and psychical development and health, they lost their ability to adapt hypothermically, which meant that both heat and cold now became enemies to be conquered by cultural and technical means. They lost too the natural constraints or controls over their reproductive and other forms of behaviour: in particular, they lost the inhibitions relating to the avoidance of intraspecific aggression. They lost their efficiency, traditions, and experience, the quality and continuity of the teaching as hunter-gatherers, and the remarkable atmosphere of co-operation. They lost their traditional structure of relationships – both as between themselves and between themselves and nature – that was oriented primarily to a freedom of movement in an equality of all human beings, obedient to the Great Spirit. No longer living within the wilderness, their brains and sensory apparatus were dis-integrated from their original evolutionary setting and function as hunter-gatherers, and their sensory apparatus fell into desuetude.* They lost their speech forms, mime, signs, painting, sculpture, technology, music, song and dance as these had developed and were inseparably related to one another and to hunter-gathering. They suffered a marked deterioration in diet. With all these losses, they lost the evolutionary basis, the foundations, of their entire

---

*Other wild animals, as Helmut Hemmer[19] has shown, likewise suffer not only a decline in brain size such as that referred to by Valerius Geist in Chapter 1 but also a loss of environmental sensitivity on being domesticated.

See Appendix i for an amplification of this argument.

value system and inherent morality. They lost too their ecological understanding, which meant that they lost their loving world view and ability to speak the secret language of nature. They lost their cognitive maps of the real world, together with their abilities to classify and to categorize phenomena, to read a wide variety of animal tracks and signs, to know causes and to identify regularities and use these to forecast the future course of events. (Thereafter, it would be many thousands of years before causal relationships and theories about the natural world would grow beyond the level of superstition, magic and myth.) They were no longer environmental scientists in nature's natural laboratory. They lost too their primary memories of their past as hunter-gatherers – as strikingly shown, for instance, by the disbelief attending the discovery, in the 19th century, of the hunter-gatherers' cave art – and so they lost their true identities which they replaced with manufactured identities, as in the Middle Eastern myths of Creation.*

In short, they lost the life conditions conducive to health, the optimum life conditions specified earlier, because their highly developed psyches and physiques, together with their systems of knowledge, their arts, their beliefs and their moral behaviour, collapsed. They were disastrously deprived and desensitized, both in relation to the wild environment and to other people: their loss of solidarity with the rest of humanity and with the wilderness placed them in a position of isolation. They were alienated or estranged from their own true natures as hunter-gatherers and from their original parents and home – the natural flux and law (the authoritative Great Spirit or Great Father of humankind) and the providential succession of natural food pyramids and enchanting wild land (the Earthmother of humankind): thereby they lost not only many of the evolutionary characteristics which made for their humanity and relative perfection as human beings, but they lost, too, the wild grounds of their humanity and perfection. They were people who were alienated from the legitimate natural authority that had properly governed the evolution of their species for millions of years. In consequence, they lost the grounds of their status, stability and security as human beings. These forcibly de-ranged, degenerate humans were rendered powerless in, as it were, a powerful land. Their protected environments constituted prisons in the wild world, and they themselves prisoners in conflict with that world. This is the essence of their primary fall, which the myths of a Fall distort and conceal.

---

* See Appendix ii for further evidence of the slow loss of a primary memory, the implications of the loss and the subsequent acquisition of a collective mythical memory as de-ranged peoples.

No longer able to range freely as hunter-gatherers through the wilderness, de-ranged people slowly became alienated from it. For though the primitive farmers were necessarily aware of the rhythms of the biosphere and of their dependence on 'Mother Earth',* nonetheless divorce proceedings had begun. The process of separation from nature both proceeded from, and resulted in, the further loss of many of their evolutionary characteristics. Slowly their well-beloved homeland became an unknown, frightening foreign place to them, when an emptiness within de-ranged people faced a nothingness without. It was these people – physically, mentally and emotionally crippled – who had to eliminate and replace the forests with their protected environments in order to survive, who now spread their prison walls out over the face of Europe and elsewhere, forcing the relatively perfect and highly developed hunter-gatherers in their path to adapt to farming or go to the wall.

In many territories, a degree of cultural comparability, together with their own experience, allowed the more sedentary foraging societies to enter into dialogue with the equally sedentary but more powerful primitive farmers, initiating a process of acculturation that enabled the former to 'exert a significant influence over the cultural diversity of the greater part of Neolithic Europe.'[20] But in general, given the incompatibility of the two ways of life and, too, the noted reluctance of hunter-gatherers to adopt farming, the eviction, marginalization or violent end to the hunter-gatherer way of life was the more likely outcome of the competition between them. However, whether the transformation from Upper Palaeolithic, through Mesolithic to Neolithic or Bronze Age took a few or many thousands of years, or whether the hunter-gatherer protagonists were marginalized or met a violent end, or whether they were forced to change their way of life or they chose so to adapt – that is, 'chose' to become acculturated to the more powerful farming cultures – is less important than the fact that such a transformation occurred, and that the effect on those involved was far-reaching and profound. It saw the beginning of a process, which is now virtually complete, that involved the replacement of the pure hunter-gatherer type by the pure farmer. Furthermore, it opened the way to the emergence of the stratified society.

This meant in effect the replacement of the true human by the degenerate human, by one who had fallen away from ancestral excellence and high estate and lost many of the evolutionary qualities proper to humankind. This may be described as *a primary degeneration*, for all

---

*The concept of 'Mother Earth' has in fact entirely different connotations for hunter-gatherer and farmer, as I will show in Chapter 7.

subsequent developments by farming peoples have arisen out of this primary degeneration and have therefore in themselves been degenerative, constituting what may be described as *a secondary historical degeneration*, which is itself directly associated with what constitutes the second major aspect of the fall. Before, however, discussing these further, it is necessary to examine the most profound effect of the primary stage of degeneration on its victims, which was that of *humiliation*.

Throughout the book I use the word 'humiliation' in its most profound sense of mortification, of destroying vitality, of threatening individual or national identity, security and survival, as indicated in the following extracts from the *Shorter Oxford English Dictionary*:

Humiliate: i. To make low or humble in position, condition or feeling; to humble.
            ii. To subject to humiliation; to mortify.

Mortify: To cause to feel humiliated; to cause (a person) mortification.
            To deprive of life; to kill. Also, to make as if dead; to render insensible.
            To lose vitality.
            To kill (in transf. and fig. senses); to destroy the vitality, vigour, or activity of; to neutralize; to deaden.

The primary humiliation to which every generation of farming peoples is condemned is the mortification or destruction of the individual's evolutionary sovereign status, identity and security as an independent hunter-gatherer and a true human being. It was primarily the hunter – the male of the species – who suffered the most profound humiliation. It would thereafter be the male who, in a drive for status and power, would generally come to dominate de-ranged societies throughout the world, to humiliate in his turn both women and the wilderness, often regarding both with fear and hatred. As the argument proceeds, it will become apparent that humiliation and the threat of humiliation underlie the whole process known as 'The Ascent of Man'.

As their hunter-gatherer antecedents and abilities receded into the mists of the Mesolithic, humiliating ignorance and fear of the wilderness and forces of nature slowly replaced an earlier ecological understanding and love. Ignorance breeds fear, which in turn breeds hatred because fear humiliates. These farming peoples were humiliated by their primary degeneration, that is, by their ignorance and consequent fear, and therefore hatred, of the wilderness as an environment hostile to them – a humiliation and a hatred which, as will be argued in the next chapter, revealed itself both in their myths and in their behaviour towards the wilderness.

Ignorance, fear and consequent humiliation in the face of the wilderness and inexplicable natural phenomena constituted the basis of the relationship of sedentary farmers with the wilderness around them, making for an implacable hatred of it. But there was a further source of profound humiliation, which arose from ignorance and fear of their own natures, as those natures were divorced from their evolutionary setting and perverted to the growth of stratified societies. The humiliating loss of many *Homo sapiens* characteristics and inhibitions, that were common to hunter-gatherers who did not commit rapine and murder, gave rise to self-hatred that would express itself particularly in the farmers' destruction of the hunter-gatherers down the millennia – that is, in the unwitting destruction of their own true natures.*

Hatred of the wilderness, combined with self-hatred, formed what may be described as a dark veil between farmers and their hunter-gatherer past and wild home. Because their fall involved a loss of the grounds of their status, stability and security as human beings, that loss and related humiliation and powerlessness initiated a search for status, stability and security through the exercise of power over their fellows and over nature, a power which in turn so humiliated people that it created a cycle of humiliation which has been the principal driving force behind the growth and spread of stratified societies down the millennia.† This introduces the second major aspect of their fall and associated secondary historical degeneration.

From being world-loving creatures whose creative abilities, ecological understanding and controlled behaviour were directly related to their expanded horizons ranging as hunter-gatherers from horizon to horizon, these farmers, imprisoned as they were by their primary fall, suffered a frightening contraction of horizons that forced them slowly to open up physical and psychical horizons of escape and control in the vertical. To that end a few began to cultivate themselves, to climb as it were, on the backs of their cultivator fellows – to create stratified societies. Not only were people now humiliated in each generation as forcibly de-ranged

---

*At the same time, with the perversion of that nature to the growth of stratified societies, there grew up a self-love, or narcissism, on the part of many of those at the summits of stratified societies, as evinced in their titles and myths of self-glorification, and in their self-centred art.

† See next chapter, and Part III, Chapter 2, for an amplification of this argument.

hunter-gatherers, but further degraded as domesticated animals to the lowly condition of peasant cultivators for a few elevated or cultivated as Chiefs and Kings of stratified societies: they suffered from both primary and secondary historical humiliation and powerlessness. Their situation in relation to élites of stratified societies may be highlighted by a precise understanding of what is implied by the word 'domesticate':

Domesticate	v. 1.	To cause to be at home; to naturalize.
	3.	To tame or bring under control; to civilize.
Tame	v. 1.	a. To bring (a wild animal) under the control or into the service of man; to reclaim from the wild state; to domesticate.
		b. To bring (a wild plant) under or into cultivation; to reclaim or improve (land) by cultivation.
	2.	To overcome the wildness or fierceness of (a man, animal, or thing); to subdue, subjugate, curb.
Subdue	v. 1.	To conquer (an army, an enemy, a country or its inhabitants) in fight and bring them into subjection.
	2.	To bring (a person) into mental, moral, or spiritual subjection; to render (a person or animal) submissive.
	3.	To bring (land) under cultivation.
Subjugate	v. 1.	To bring under the yoke or into subjection; to reduce to the condition of a subject country or people.
	2.	To bring into bondage or under complete control; to make subservient or submissive.

(*Shorter OED*)

All wild animals, including *Homo sapiens* hunter-gatherers, were already 'at home', 'naturalized' and free in the wilderness, the evolutionary home of all. All domesticated animals, on the other hand, are, generally speaking, tamed, subdued, subjugated within artificial homelands alienated from their earlier wild home. Each generation of domesticated people is likewise brought into bondage, first by their loss of freedom and ecological sensitivity ranging through their wild home, secondly by the suppression from childhood of evolved true characteristics, and lastly by their physical, mental, moral and spiritual subjection to the requirements of élites of stratified societies. Domestication is a cultural as well as a biological process. Domestication, the physical exploitation of people and of animals, complements the psychological control of nature, represented by the categorization both of humans into various divisions of labour and of the animal kingdom, by élites of stratified societies. Furthermore, women, to the extent that they personified a now incomprehensible and frightening wild nature in the perfervid imaginations of many now dominant males, were often subdued like domestic animals as chattels, domestic slaves to be bought and sold like any other piece of property.

From an evolutionary standpoint, the words 'domesticate', 'tame', 'subdue' and 'subjugate' are virtually synonymous. Domestication is a euphemism for bondage. The very land itself has been conquered, as an enemy, and brought into subjection. To domesticate is most profoundly to humiliate, both in the degradation of men and women from their evolutionary status as hunter-gatherers, in their degradation as primary producers at the bottom of stratified societies, and in the degradation of the subjugated and exploited wild animals and land.

Domestication involves physical and psychological mutilation. All domesticated children are put through an unacknowledged, though nonetheless real, systematic process of dehumanization, leaving them with disordered personalities; and they become so dehumanized and deprived even from birth within their stratified societies.

> The existence of a critical period of susceptibility of a part of the young brain to deprivation or abnormal experience is quite general in the animal kingdom...
> ...it seems that the critical period is the time in life when a particular neuronal subsystem matures, and proper use of the system during that time is essential for its normal development...
> Children so deprived (of normal experiences) might be unable to unfold their genetically determined developmental program properly since ... phylogenetic learning may include the anticipation of particular patterns of postnatal sensory input.[21]

The proper evolutionary use and maturation of the neuronal subsystem of the human being was of course as hunter-gatherer infant and adult, in what constituted normal experience within the wild environment. With the loss of the cultural conditions and environment conducive to normal experience, those conditions were replaced with the abnormal artificial conditions of the early stratified society. So what persons knew of the world innately, prior to and independent of their own experience, was no longer relevant. Phylogenetic learning and the associated models dealing with signals coming from the real, or wild, world, and designed for survival in that world, were nullified.* Thus deprived at birth of their evolutionary inheritance, they had only a primitive ontogenetic learning – the lifelong acquisition of a rudimentary cultural, linguistic, religious and technical knowledge as primitive farmers – to ensure their survival alienated from, and at war with, the real world. In other words, not only did their phylogenetic and ontogenetic learning processes no longer complement one another but they were now in direct opposition to one another, potentially tearing the individual apart. In addition, it should be noted that their development may have been further stunted by the chronic energy deficiency suffered by early farming communities over thousands of years.

Malnutrition and starvation, persisting over many generations, may permanently damage the intellectual part of the brain. But nourishment is also necessary for the emotions and interests of the child and adult. With their adaptation to a primitive subsistence farming way of life, they would have suffered a lifelong deprivation of mental and emotional stimulation that had been the *sine qua non* of hunter-gatherer bands interacting with the sights, sounds and smells of the wilderness. Such malnutrition and deprivation at many levels would surely have had a profoundly deleterious effect on their brains.

A radical change that did occur was the appearance of Type A blood amongst sedentary farming peoples. The major change in diet brought about by their adaptation to agriculture and animal domestication, and the onset of crowd diseases, resulted in an adaptation in the digestive tracts and immune systems of the Neolithic peoples and an associated mutation from Type O blood to Type A. This enabled the cultivators to survive the multitude of infections brought about by deleterious dietary changes, increased population and the close proximity of domestic animals. Type B blood appeared later amongst the specialized cattle and horse nomads of the steppes of Eurasia.

With the intensification of agriculture, the emergence of stratified societies and the subsequent development of the early urban phase in human history, the divorce between farming societies and wild nature became nearly complete. In the terms employed by Stephen Boyden, these farming societies had undergone near total evodeviation – they had

---

* See Appendix iii for the effects of this nullification on the minds of de-ranged farming peoples as they erected cognitive barriers between themselves and the wilderness.

lost or deviated from most of the life conditions conducive to health in *Homo sapiens*:

> ... natural selection produces animal populations in which the majority of individuals are well suited in their genetic characteristics to the set of conditions prevailing in the ecological niche in which the evolutionary forces are acting. These forces are selecting for optimum performance in the given environment. It follows, therefore, that if the conditions of life suddenly deviate from those of the natural habitat (to which the species has become adapted through natural selection), then it is likely that the individual animals will be less well suited, in either physiological or behavioural characteristics, to the changed conditions. Consequently some signs of maladjustment, physiological or behavioural, may be evident. In this book this fundamental concept is referred to as the *principle of evodeviation*, and the adjective *evodeviant* is used to describe life conditions which are different from those which prevail in the natural habitat of a species. Disturbances in physiology or behaviour which result from evodeviations are referred to as examples of *phylogenetic maladjustment*, because they are essentially responses typical of the species and are due to the fact that the phylogenetic characteristics of the species are not suited to the new conditions.[22]

To the extent that farming societies had not only lost many of their evolutionary characteristics but had also become divorced from wild nature, they had suffered near total phylogenetic maladjustment.

Thereafter these farming peoples remained like orphaned, rejected and deprived children in relation to the wilderness around them. First, because they were people deprived of the 'good authority', beneficence and love of their Great Father and Earthmother, and of their honoured position as hunter-gatherers within the greater family of animals and wilderness. Secondly, because they had lost many of their evolutionary characteristics and were no longer able to evolve as hunter-gatherers, they were not only forced to remain in a state of retarded or arrested development, but their subsequent development as domesticated people was perverted to serve the growth of stratified societies. It is this perverted redirection of the combined physical and psychical energy, or life-force, of the individual out of a freedom of movement through the wilderness into a sedentary building up of physical and psychical structures of ascent, in a wilderness exploited to that end, that constitutes both the secondary historical degeneration and the second major aspect of the fall. In short, it constitutes what is now described as 'The Ascent of Man', a process initiated by humiliation and powerlessness in situations of geographical isolation.

They formed geographically isolated islands of primitive farmers split off from, and increasingly isolated from, their ancestral hunter-gatherer stock and wilderness home, a situation conducive to the transmutation of the species *Homo sapiens*. I shall explore the evolutionary effects of such geographical isolation in Part II.

These imprisoned, deprived farmers began to seek *lebensraum* and power in expansion and conquest of the ever threatening wilderness. In effect, they became doubly deprived as they vented their fear and hatred on the wilderness and its inhabitants.

It has been shown that multiple deprivation such as farming people suffered following the Neolithic period so humiliates that it may lead to what has been described as 'double deprivation', when those thus rejected or deprived tend to revenge themselves and further deprive themselves through delinquent or criminal behaviour which reflects their inward experience of what has happened to them. For these primitive farmers were like unloved, rejected children – and the greatest terror a child can have is that he is not loved, and rejection is the hell he fears. With humiliating rejection and deprivation comes anger and hate, when he turns his past terror into power and/or commits some kind of crime in revenge for the rejection. One child may steal so that the money he acquires will make him loved; another will tell and believe lies against the hated object; a third may set out to conquer the world. The myth of the expulsion of humans from the Garden of Eden, and the subsequent efforts to conquer the world to recover a lost Paradise, are attempts to explain and to avenge the humiliating rejection and consequent guilt. These primitive farmers were, in effect, imprisoned, impoverished, ignorant and vengeful children who would commit all the crimes in the book against one another and against the wilderness as they began to build up their stratified societies. In becoming sedentary possessors of the land they effectively denied their past in flux and began not only to build against the operation of the natural flux but also to destroy the very ground of its operation and of their earlier evolution as true human beings: they began to destroy the wilderness and its inhabitants, which had only yesterday been their beloved home and family, thus further depriving themselves. The following quotation from an Earthlife pamphlet, *Paradise Lost*, says as much about the width and depth of the knowledge of the wilderness possessed by people living within that world as it does about the farming-based peoples of the world who not only lost that knowledge but have ever since systematically destroyed the ground of that knowledge, thereby destroying the ground of their own humanity and understanding.

> As we fell the forests we are burning a vast library of irreplaceable knowledge – before we have done more than dip into a few of its volumes.
> The destruction of the custodians of that library, the forest peoples, is the most shortsighted act of all. For they alone know where the medicines, foods and wealth of the forests are to be found. In north-western Amazonia alone the Indians use over 1,300 plant species as medicines.[23]

This destruction also in great part occurred because, as multiply deprived people, they were translated from an activity and landscape charged with meaning in the utmost possible degree to one that was utterly meaningless, frighteningly void. They were no longer under the 'good authority' of the Great Spirit and were no longer able to communicate with the wilderness. Absence of real authority and inability or failure to communicate leads to misunderstanding and conflict, particularly when the overriding intellectual and emotional characteristics involved are humiliating ignorance and fear arising from their experience of socio-economic disintegration and deculturation.

Their subsequent ascent in stratified societies originated in, and found its most profound expression in, conflict arising out of the humiliating suppression of their own wild natures and concomitant conflict with the wilderness, from which all other conflicts stem. The whole of history, following the crisis of the Mesolithic, has in fact been one of crisis and conflict, of 'one emergency following upon another as wave follows upon wave...'[24]

Chapter 4

Prisoners in Conflict

Unlike hunter-gatherer humankind that evolved in an intimate and co-operative relationship with all other life, farmers have grown up in isolation from the wilderness. Their protected environments constituted prisons in the wilderness, and they themselves prisoners in conflict with that world. They were now forced to develop their own abnormal structures and behaviour established apart from, and in opposition to, the wild environment and law. In relation to the world-wide evolutionary hunter-gatherer culture and laws of nature, they formed anti-evolutionary and unlawful sub-cultures of degenerate people, who were forced to meet the basic aims of survival and stability in ways totally different from those of their hunter-gatherer forbears. The controlled behaviour of *Homo sapiens*, oriented primarily to a freedom of movement in the horizontal, gave way to that of sedentary people competing to escape captivity and dearth by climbing rudimentary social ladders raised up by the exploitation of their weaker fellows, escaping as it were in the vertical, eventually to create stratified structures. But the fundamental expression of captivity and conflict related to their adaptation to agriculture, their usurpation of the land to that end and their need to conquer and destroy the wilderness to survive. No matter what our fleeting achievements, throughout the whole of history we have remained and behaved like delinquent adolescents, while yet often having the appearance of responsible adulthood. That appearance of adulthood is perhaps the most dangerous of all the delusions under which we labour. For everything we have done or achieved has ultimately been at the expense of the parents and the home which nurtured us to a true maturity as hunter-gatherers over tens of thousands of years. In other words, because our cultural ancestors were forcibly de-ranged, because their principal drives as hunters were frustrated and dammed up, their responses were not only redirected in the vertical but also against one another and against the wilderness.

76

Before examining the basic aims of survival and the responses of these farmers in greater detail, it is necessary to appreciate the extent to which their responses were the result of what may be termed 'conflict behaviour', of redirected responses arising from ignorance and fear of the unknown wilderness.

The term 'conflict behaviour' is used by students of animal behaviour to denote the behaviour of wild animals which are strongly stimulated in several ways at once, when the requisite behaviour patterns are frustrated and conflict with one another. An animal threatened by another may in the same instant be stimulated to attack and to flee – it is aggressive at the same time as being afraid. This is particularly the case when animals confront one another at the boundaries of their territories. The combination of the thwarted fighting urge and thwarted flight tends to find an outlet in what has been described as displacement activity, which is conflict expressed in an irrelevant manner, as when a herring-gull indulges in grass-pulling; or in redirected response, when the frustrated animal aims its feelings at a substitute object, as when a gorilla or chimpanzee pounds or beats something to make an intimidating noise. These displacement activities and redirected responses tend in time to become ritualized.

By ritualisation the movement becomes more and more different from its original. This means that the underlying central nervous structure changes. In other words, the ritualised displacement-activity becomes more independent than it originally was, and it becomes increasingly difficult to decide to which drive it belongs: to the instinct from which it is 'borrowed' or to the instinct by which it is used. With progressing ritualisation, the displacement-activity loses its displacement character and becomes incorporated into the pattern of its 'new boss'.[1]

Such expressions of inner conflict may also be observed amongst domesticated humans, as when an angry man, unable to express his feelings directly, scratches his head in frustration (displacement activity), or vents his feelings on a substitute target, as when he bangs a desk with his fist (redirected response). However, I shall use the term 'conflict behaviour' in a much deeper sense, to denote the collective behaviour of farmers whose requisite behaviour patterns in relation to the wilderness were humiliatingly frustrated, eventually to give rise to stratified societies which represented the ritualization, through institutionalization, of their collective redirected responses in relation to the wilderness.

As their commitment to farming increasingly deprived people of their independent movement and understanding as hunter-gatherers, that loss forced them more and more to rely on agriculture for survival. Devoid of many of their wild characteristics they could now neither freely advance nor retreat. As primitive subsistence farmers they were collectively threatened by the ever-present, ever-advancing wilderness. They were confronting wild nature not only at the boundaries of their territories, in the shape of encroaching forests and marauding wild animals, but within their territories as well, as they contended with heat, drought, snow, flood, disease, crop failure and the growth of pernicious weeds. Their overriding intellectual and emotional characteristics must have been humiliating ignorance and fear of the wilderness outside their enclaves, as evinced in the defensive walls and palisades they erected against that world and in their myths. Caught between fight and flight, they were in a situation of stalemate. Their controlled behaviour as hunter-gatherers, oriented primarily to a freedom of movement in the horizontal, gave way to what I describe as conflict behaviour oriented primarily in the vertical.

The three basic aims of any wild animal are to find food, to reproduce and, if it has any, to seek protection from its enemies. All these requirements had been met naturally by hunter-gatherers, obedient to the control mechanisms, flux and laws of nature. As the new sub-cultures of primitive farmers replaced the hunter-gatherer cultures, so these responses to the three basic aims as wild animals were replaced by their responses as domesticated animals – that is, by adaptation to a primitive agriculture, over-reproduction and the building up of self-protective walls of mud and stone. Two further responses may be noted: the raising up of rudimentary social pyramids of men competing to escape captivity and dearth, and the development of a primitive religion that provided a spiritual dimension to their conflict behaviour and created a psychical wall between them and the wilderness. All these were the responses of animals that had lost their natural control mechanisms as hunter-gatherers; all are expressions of conflict behaviour, of redirected responses on the part of farmers in their efforts to survive and to achieve a steady state in the midst of what had become, for them, an unknown and hostile environment. Redirected because, prior to the Mesolithic, survival and stability had depended upon cultural adaptation and adaptation in movement in the horizontal as hunter-gatherers in obedience to the natural flux; survival and stability now depended to an increasing extent on the settled activities of building, the domestication of animals, sowing, reaping and the raising up of stratified societies and their protection within walls, and digging down for the purposes of mining and burying the dead, which may be described as primarily sedentary, vertically-oriented, activities. These in turn required the suppression of the primarily horizontally-oriented natural succession of wild forms.

The first basic aim, that of finding food, was met by destroying an existing and highly complex environment of natural food pyramids and exploiting the land to serve the simple requirements of the early farmers. One effect of early farming on the biosphere was the series of changes wrought in the distribution of many different animals and plants, at first locally and then world-wide. Domestication of animals led to the local concentration of such as sheep, pigs, cattle and goats, to the exclusion of other unwanted species of animal; while the raising of food crops necessitated the clearing away of unwanted species of plants and their replacement with as pure stands as possible – or monocultures – of desired food plants such as cereal crops. Thus the early farmers greatly reduced the diversity ratio, that is, the ratio between the number of species and number of individual organisms, within their newly created specialized ecosystems. So from the very beginning the requirements of the farming economy have not only been in conflict with the hunting-gathering mode of subsistence, but also with the processes of natural selection. For as the faunal records show, agriculture and stockbreeding rather than the distribution of wild resources increasingly determined the location of settlements. With the intensification and spread of agriculture across Eurasia, Africa and America, the conflict between farmers and the hunter-gatherer way of life and the processes of natural selection also intensified and spread. No matter how balanced, how much in harmony with nature, such farming communities may appear to be, all are engaged in a war against their own true natures and against the wilderness out of which their agricultural holdings were hewn. All must prevent the return of their domesticated natures, children, animals and land to their true wild state; all must suppress, in however small a degree, the normal processes of ecological succession of wild flora and fauna to prevent development towards climax communities, holding the community at an early stage of succession where gross productivity to the farmer is maximized. This conflict between farmer and wilderness – that is, the war against unwanted plants and animals, including the hunter-gatherers – constituted *a declaration of war on their own true natures and on nature itself,* and is fundamental to all other conflicts.

However, the farmers were not alone in their conflict with nature. Pastoralists and nomads, as highly specialized as farmers, were parasitical upon their herds of semi-domesticated animals and their activities have been almost as destructive of the wild environment as those of the farmer. Although global climate changes have been in part responsible for the desertification that can be seen, for instance, south of the Sahara in the Sahel and northern Kenya, such a process has been exacerbated by habitat destruction resulting from indiscriminate burning, deforestation, over-cultivation and consequent soil exhaustion by farmers; the herding of goats and other domestic animals by pastoralists and nomads has further exacerbated the degradation of the land.

The second basic aim of any living creature, after finding food, is to reproduce its own kind. The extraordinary fecundity latent in many plants and animals is little evident in the life of a balanced community. However, as hunter-gathering gave way to agriculture as the predominant economic activity, so their stabilizing and control mechanisms that were dependent upon their adaptations as hunter-gatherers were lost. The human population of the world, which had reached a figure of perhaps 10 million by 10000 BC, appears suddenly to have leapt, during the following 5,000 years, to a figure of around 86 million and has continued to increase ever since.

M.N. Cohen[2] has argued that human population has been growing throughout its history, and that such growth is the cause, rather than simply the result, of much technological change, particularly in the sphere of subsistence. He argued that by c.10000 BC hunter-gatherers had, through population increase and concomitant territorial expansion, entirely occupied those areas of the world which could easily support them, and that the development of agriculture was an adaptation forced on them in response to their own increasing numbers. His argument, however, does not take account of the fact that, after some 60,000 years occupation, there were still only some 300–800,000 Aborigines in Australia before the arrival of Europeans. The Aborigines had, like any other wild animal, achieved a relatively stable population density within their diverse environments. The 10 million other hunter-gatherers had probably achieved a similar balance world-wide which was only destroyed c.10000 BC when a few sedentary hunter-gatherer groups in different parts of the world began to lose the characteristics that regulated their physiques, psyches and behaviour as they adapted to farming.

As well as being a response to the loss of stability and self-control as hunters, over-reproduction became a compensatory activity and a requirement of the primitive agricultural way of life. People began to over-reproduce themselves to compensate for the debasement, and combat the relative shortness, of their lives – and to create more hands to protect and work the land. Food and children – nutrition and nurture – became principal obsessions and tokens of the beneficence of these farming communities, later summed up in the term 'Providence'. Population density and gregarious greenhouse-like conditions further aggravated this process. Sex, from playing a relatively minor rôle in a balanced constellation of natural rôles of the unprolific hunter-gatherer, now assumed a place of dominance and importance. Following subsequent catastrophes, such as earthquake and war, farming communities would tend again to indulge in phrenetic procreation. For example, an earthquake in Armenia in 1988, which killed 25,000 people, a third of whom were children, and rendered thousands homeless, gave rise to a demographic response on the part of the survivors. As Agnieszka Piotrowska said:

> I still remembered despairing people I had met in February (1989) telling me: 'A nation without children is a dying nation.'
> 'All healthy women are trying to get pregnant now', Vladimir Tonikyan, chief doctor of Leninakan's maternity hospital had told me, 'so that our nation will not perish.'[3]

As for the demographic effects of war, in 1759 the British under Wolfe defeated the French on the Plains of Abraham outside Quebec. To the French it was a disaster. Abandoned by France to an enemy that despised their culture and religion, the will to survive amongst these French Canadians took over: in the next ten years they developed one of the highest birthrates ever recorded of a European people.

The third basic aim of any living wild creature is protection from its enemies. I intimated earlier that the world-loving hunter-gatherers, as masters of their environment and the regular prey of no animal, were virtually without enemies and had little to fear, so long as they obeyed the Great Spirit, an obedience that ensured effective adaptation and development. With the change to a primitive farming that situation was radically altered; whereas the hunter-gatherers had built – and the San still built in the 1960s – temporary shelters whose structures were often so delicately made as to be almost invisible, these farmers now built structures intended as permanent refuges against the weather, wild beasts and wilderness. Thereafter the new fixed investment, the planted land, together with the growing material possessions that their settled condition permitted, became the object of territorial defence. As well as the defensive ditches and palisades in mid-Neolithic Europe already referred to, massive defences, comprising a rock-cut ditch with stone walls and bastion-like towers, were erected around the original Natufian encampment at Tel-es-Sultan, Jericho. In Mesopotamia, cities and city-states began to appear. These were defensive responses both to climate change and consequent aridity that had triggered agriculture, and to subsequent conflicts over water supplies and territorial boundaries; conflicts which were in turn exacerbated by increasing aridity and the incursion of nomadic peoples. Mesopotamia, in ancient times, consisted of 20,000 to 25,000 square kilometres of fertile gardens. Fernand Braudel has drawn attention to

> ...the vulnerability of the gardens – whether in the plains or the oases – in that they had constantly to be recreated and protected against their tireless enemies: in the case of Mesopotamia, the sand, the silting up of the canals, the bursting of dykes, as well as the near-primitive nomads from the neighbouring steppe, from whom, as if from locusts, the gardens had to be defended. Even at the end of the nineteenth century, there was not a village in Mesopotamia without its watchtowers and sentinels to give warning of invasion by the shepherds.[4]

As well, therefore, as the continual wars waged between cities and by farmers against the incursions by wild nature there arose the perennial conflict between nomadic herdsmen and farmers. The nomadic herding way of life grew out of the domestication of cattle, horses, camels, sheep and goats. The subsequent habit of grazing the land and then moving on to new, ungrazed land, has both threatened and brought them into conflict with farmers. This tense rivalry over land-use has persisted down the millennia until nearer our time, when, for example, conflict arose between farmers and cattle herders in Southern Africa.

Given all the hostile forces confronting farmers, the actual and psychological importance of the wall, palisade or frontier cannot be too greatly emphasized. The Great Wall of China was built for protection against marauding nomads. Hadrian's Wall in England was a defensive barrier against the northern tribes. A bitter almond hedge was planted in 1660 by Jan van Riebeeck, leader of the first Dutch settlement at the Cape of Good Hope, to keep the settlers in and to keep out the Khoikhoi cattle herders. Every wall, palisade or frontier is descended from the first walls built against the wilderness; every one has established, emphasized and perpetuated an insider/outsider, us/them relationship, to become institutionalized in a thousand laws to protect against the potentially threatening outsider.*

It is not, as Edward O. Wilson contends, that human beings 'are strongly predisposed to respond with unreasoning hatred to external

---

*The most recent and sophisticated concept of a wall, in military terms, is that being developed by the USA, a Missile Defence Shield to keep the threatening barbarians at bay.

threats',[5] because all the evidence shows that hunter-gatherers have generally been open and welcoming to strangers, and will do everything in their power to avoid conflict. It is people devoid of a natural inheritance, and either migratory as guardians of herds of semi-domesticated animals or more especially those ensconced behind high walls, who 'tend to fear deeply the actions of strangers and to solve conflict by aggression'.[6] In other words, their conflict behaviour and aggression in relation to the laws of nature has led inexorably to intraspecific conflict, precisely because the theft of the land from the control of wild nature – theft, that is, from the standpoint of the laws of nature, and as instanced in the theft of the Australian continent by farmers from its true Aborigine inhabitants – and its enclosure has led to world-wide conflict over land use. As the direct outcome of the two-fold fall of humankind, history is witness to a falling out, as it were, amongst farming and nomadic gangs of thieves.

In effect, farming peoples were imprisoned by the circumstances of their adaptation to agriculture. All domesticated animals are bred in captivity, and that includes all domesticated human beings. Their domesticated environments may be variously described as prisons or zoos. They, and we, their more civilized descendants, have always lived under zoo-like conditions – that is, in various degrees of captivity and unfreedom – which encourage varying degrees of aberrant behaviour, or behaviour deviating from the thousands of years evolutionary norm of behaviour as hunter-gatherers.

> ...man, during most of his history, has lived in a zoo and not 'in the wild' – i.e., under the condition of liberty conducive to human growth and well-being. Indeed, most data about man's 'nature' are basically of the same order as Zuckerman's original data on the Monkey Hill baboons in the London Zoo.[7]*

Only in the cramped quarters of zoo cages, or in prisons, do we find anything resembling the sedentary human condition, including dominance/subordinate relationships, status struggles, acts of violence, and deliberate cruelty to subordinates and outsiders. Such aberrant behaviour correlates with the further most important response on the part of farming communities, that of the raising up of rudimentary social pyramids of people competing to escape captivity and dearth on the backs of their weaker fellows, thereby providing leaders and rudimentary

---

*See Appendix iv for a summary of that data and for the humiliating effects of imprisonment. See also Appendix v for an examination of the humiliating effects of the deprivation of love, rejection and illegitimation to which I referred in Chapter 3 above.

institutions to consolidate their status and the three basic aims of finding food, reproduction and self-protection. Such leaders and their institutions became additional agents of imprisonment.

As bands of hunter-gatherers gave way to tribes of sedentary farming peoples, the strongest males, as amongst the captive baboons in the London Zoo, would have prevailed over the weaker, and over the females. Male leaders appeared and became dominant. As populations grew more dense, chiefdoms appeared, and with them grew up rank distinctions according to family membership, the consolidation of leadership on a hereditary basis, the growth of trade and associated redistribution of wealth under the control of the ruling élite, and a more sharply defined division of labour. As cities and states grew out of chiefdoms, kings, emperors and nobles acquired hereditary status as élites of stratified societies; while below them bureaucratic and craft specialization formed the basis for the stratification of people into classes and castes. With the progressive stratification of societies, women in particular experienced in general a profound regression from that of equality amongst hunter-gatherer peoples to being increasingly constrained by custom and law until they had regressed in many societies to the status of chattel, to be traded and sold at will.

The ascent of élites of men at the expense of their weaker fellows, and at the expense of women and of wild nature, is one of the most profound results of the redirection of responses following the Mesolithic. Ruling élites had taken over from the wilderness as the principal jailers: it was they and their artefacts that would now become the principal causes of humiliation and conflict. Altogether their stratified societies, with their physical and psychical systems of attack and defence, are collective expressions both of conflict behaviour and of direct conflict. Their forts and castles, their law-courts, ziggurats and temple towers, their defensive walls and armed men, all have had overtones of aggression superimposed upon them, particularly in relation to the wilderness. These (intentionally) intimidating artefacts have not only threatened, but invited, direct conflict, precisely because they have humiliated and oppressed members of stratified societies themselves, and because they have appeared as humiliating threats to the survival of other and similar stratified societies, nomads and hunter-gatherers.

The redirection of the responses of farming peoples during and following the Neolithic thus became ritualized and institutionalized within stratified structures. Most importantly, stratified societies, that were originally organized around humiliating fears of the wilderness, institutionalized fear, making fear – that is, the fear of humiliation and humiliating fear

– *the* fundamental psychological feature of their societies.* As in the case of individual wild animals whose underlying central nervous structure changed as a direct outcome of the ritualization of their conflict behaviour, so I believe the underlying central nervous systems of farming peoples changed as their redirected responses became incorporated into the pattern of their 'new boss', to use Tinbergen's terminology – the stratified society itself. The individual nervous system and brain were now attuned to the collective requirements of the stratified society, itself expressive of a ritualized conflict behaviour arising initially in relation to the wild environment and thereafter also in relation to other similar societies looming out of the wilderness. Their stratified societies could only be maintained by continual conflict that is, by outright aggression against the wilderness and by intraspecific aggression.

The occasional intraspecific strife between individuals and bands of hunter-gatherers was now overshadowed by conflict between tribes of landowning farmers, and between them and nomads and hunter-gatherers. Such aggression was, in the main, a collective aggression directed against other peoples, viewed and treated as though they were different and inferior species. As revealed particularly by history, archaeology and art, and as I argued in the last chapter, an environment of conflict and war now prevailed.

It will be appreciated that all these changes both caused and reveal a profound change of consciousness on the part of these primitive farmers, both in relation to the wilderness and to their fellow human beings; a fundamental change in the intellectual and emotional response of people to the wilderness and so to the world, from one of understanding and love as pure hunter-gatherer to one of ignorance and fear as pure farmer. I shall examine this change in some depth, because it led to the development of organized religion, which added a spiritual dimension to their conflict behaviour as farmers: it not only persuaded them to view natural phenomena in a supernatural light, but in many cases sanctioned and sanctified conflict with the natural world.

A system can only function properly in an environment resembling that to which it has been adapted by its evolution. In this connection, the flow and organization of information in relation to the environment is particularly important. This information reaches animals through their sense organs, through each animal's 'window to the world'. Information is then organized by the system for the purpose of providing a model of that system's relationship with its environment, in order to mediate

---

* See Part III, Chapter 2, for an amplification of this argument.

and control adaptive behaviour and maintain stability. If changes get out of hand, and the environment no longer resembles that to which it has been adapted by its evolution, the system can no longer function as before. It is then out of control. This is what happened to the primitive farmers. Only in their case, as a result of changing the basis of their relationship with the natural environment, they changed the environment to one that no longer resembled that to which they had been adapted by their evolution. Everyone needs to belong and farmers no longer belonged to the natural world. They were disconnected from the traditional structures of that world and forced to create new artificial structures and homelands that gave them a sense of belonging set apart from, and in opposition to, the natural world. At the same time, the ecocentric world view of the hunter-gatherer, which ascribed a fundamental equality between the sexes and between human and non-human life, was replaced by the narcissistic anthropocentric view of the farmer societies, which ascribed intrinsic value only to certain humans while valuing nature only to the extent that it might be exploited. They in turn underwent a profound change in consciousness, from one of world-loving insiders to one of world-fearing outsiders.

The consciousness of the hunter-gatherers was based upon their understanding and love of the wild environment. With their enforced de-rangement, their brains and sensory apparatus were severed from their proper evolutionary function, and were in their turn dis-integrated and their ecological understanding of the environment destroyed. The whole sensory apparatus of the body, including the skin and entire nervous system as well as the special sense organs – all the parts, organs and tissues of the body which are capable of receiving or transmitting impressions from without – became desensitised. The primitive farmers now had no means of organizing and interpreting the ceaseless flow of information that bombarded them. The land that was essentially meaningful to the hunter-gatherers had become frighteningly meaningless and void to the farmers. A great darkness of ignorance – a spiritual, mental and authoritative void – settled upon them. In their voided condition their overriding passion in relation to the wilderness was one of fear. Everywhere, except their tiny agricultural enclaves, was wilderness. Colin M. Turnbull, in his book *The Forest People*, neatly points this profound difference between hunter-gatherer and farmer.

> The world of the forest is a closed, possessive world, hostile to all those who do not understand it. At first sight you might think it was hostile to all human beings, because in every village you find

the same suspicion and fear of the forest, that blank, impenetrable wall ... these villages are set among plantations in great clearings cut from the heart of the world around them. It is from the plantations that the food comes, not from the forest, and for the villagers life is a constant battle to prevent their plantations from being overgrown. They speak of the world beyond the plantations as being a fearful place, full of malevolent spirits and not fit for anyone to live in except animals and BaMbuti, which is what they call the pygmies. The villagers, some Bantu and some Sudanic, keep to their plantations and seldom go into the forest unless it is absolutely necessary. For them it is a place of evil. They are outsiders. But the BaMbuti are the real people of the forest... It is their world, and in return for their affection and trust it supplies them with all their needs... They know the secret language that is denied all outsiders and which makes life in the forest, for them, an impossibility.[8]

Turnbull's description of villages surrounded by threatening forest could as easily exemplify the situation of the original primitive farmers surrounded by a 'tide of obliterating forest'[9] during the early Neolithic, and their consequent battle to prevent their settlements from being invaded by wild nature. Furthermore, Turnbull reveals very clearly what has been lost in the transition from hunter-gatherer to farmer. The truly scientific knowledge of the pygmies is similar to that of the San. Such knowledge and understanding were the possession of each and every hunter-gatherer.

All spoke and understood the same secret language of nature, and celebrated their present understanding and that of their evolutionary past in stories, art, song and dance. The songs and stories of Australian Aborigines, for instance, provided them with a geographical, natural and racial history of the continent over the past 60,000 years or more. Their arts and sciences combined to contribute directly to the stability and well-being of each. Colin Turnbull has attested to this well-being in the case of the pygmies: the BaMbuti

...roam the forest at will, in small, isolated bands, or hunting groups. They have no fear, because for them there is no danger. For them there is little hardship, so they have no need for belief in evil spirits. For them it is a good world.[10]

Turnbull dedicated his book to a pygmy, Kenge, 'for whom the forest

was Mother and Father, Lover and Friend; and who showed me something of the love that all his people share in a world that is still kind
and good ... and without evil.'

In contradistinction to this apparently harmonious and loving relationship
with wild nature on the part of hunter-gatherers, some authors cite the
Native American inhabitants of the Northwest Coast of North America
as evidence that our hunter-gatherer ancestors lived in constant fear of
the unknown. However, unlike the latter, the Northwest Coast Indians
were prisoners of their artificial environment. In their villages they
were trapped between forbidding forests and high mountains on one
side and a potentially chaotic ocean on the other. They lived their
lives on the narrow ribbon of shoreline and on the coastal waters.
They developed an exclusively maritime culture and almost total
dependence on salmon. This meant that, even though they developed
storage facilities like farmers, in the event of persistent failure of salmon
runs they were in danger of starvation. Unable, like nomadic hunter-
gatherers, to follow their main source of food or to adapt to a variety
of other food sources, they initiated rites and propitiatory ceremonies to
ensure the return of the salmon and the safety of their villages, while
their stories harped on the terrors of the unknown, of fearful monsters
lurking in the dark forest and in the hidden depths of the sea. So,
possessed of a profoundly fragile human identity in relation to the awesome
wilderness surrounding them, powerless in relation to the all-powerful
world of nature, they aspired to enhancing their identities by acquiring
power over their fellows. In their sedentary state they pursued status and
wealth, creating stratified societies whose bases rested on slaves captured
in battle or purchased in trade. In every way, therefore, their behaviour
has been more akin to that of farming peoples than that of hunter-
gatherers.

This comparison between farmer enclaves founded in fear of and
embattled against the natural world, and hunter-gatherers living in joyful
fulfilment within that world, not only conveys the extraordinary intellectual
and emotional loss sustained in the transition from hunter-gatherer to
farmer – the loss of the scientific knowledge and love of the wilderness
– but also the fundamental and equally extraordinary change in their
view of the wilderness, which became for the farmer the home of
malevolent spirits. As world-fearing outsiders the primitive farmers
underwent a profound change of consciousness. So when they eventually
acquired the collective strength and technology to advance through the
wilderness, they did so as outsiders imbued with a consciousness of it as
a place of evil. It was particularly in this connection, in their awareness

that the wilderness was an environment hostile to them – which of course it was, given their degeneration or fall – that the worship of the Goddess, the practice of magic, and then of organized religion, came into being. It should be understood, however, that the transition from pure hunter-gatherer to pure farmer in many parts of the world involved an intermediate stage – when many of those who had adapted to farming still hunted – which may have lasted for many millennia. But the most important aspect of that transition, whether or not it involved an intermediate stage, was that their religious rites developed in order that farming societies might control and regulate the hostile world around them. That such control and regulation were required implies that they had lost the natural processes of control and regulation that had governed their evolution so successfully over thousands of years as hunter-gatherers; but more than that, it implies that they had sustained a period of disorientation and crisis, of however long or short duration, between losing their physical and psychical identities as hunter-gatherers and replacing them with artificial identities as sedentary farmers.

Religious movements and cults can often be found to have their origins in periods of crisis.[11]* Periods of rapid social and demographic change, or of foreign domination, leading to a breakdown of the traditional way of life and loss of faith in traditional values, particularly amongst the poor and dispossessed, cause a crisis of mass disorientation and chronic insecurity. Under the circumstances, religious dissent provides such groups with compensatory fantasies.

The first major crisis of disorientation and chronic insecurity was that which accompanied the breakdown of the traditional way of life and traditional values amongst those hunter-gatherers degraded as poor, primitive farmers. The Mesolithic was a period of crisis – of environmental crisis, of population pressures, of food crisis. It was, however, more than a period of crisis: it ushered in a period of mass disorientation, when those whose psyches had been oriented for tens of thousands of years to a freedom of movement as hunter-gatherers lost their traditional, evolutionary, orientation to one another and to the natural world that such movement had entailed. The first religious dissenters were those self-same farmers who rejected the world-wide call of the Great Spirit and established religious rites and then their own exclusive religions more suited to their sedentary agricultural modes of existence and to their humiliating status

---

*Historically nonconformist movements have appealed to the poor, the downtrodden and those without hope: such, for instance, was the case with the teaching of John Wesley and Methodism in the mid-18th century.

as dispossessed outsiders imprisoned in, and dominated by, a foreign and a frightening wilderness. Furthermore, when a social group has adopted a particular religion, the reasons have often been social rather than religious.[12] The underlying motive has been to re-establish the identity of the group in the face of profound disorientation, powerlessness and humiliation by establishing a new system of values and identity distinct from the dominant socio-economic group or from the mainstream society where they no longer belong.

These descriptions of people attempting to re-establish an identity in the crisis of mass disorientation in periods of rapid social and demographic change, or in the face of foreign domination and humiliation, also fit the situation of people forcibly de-ranged in the midst of an alien wilderness, and who were themselves alienated from the mainstream society of hunter-gatherers. No mass disorientation nor breakdown of a traditional way of life can have been more profound than that now affecting these primitive farmers.

If their adaptation to agriculture, the necessity to congregate as doubly deprived people and their need to destroy the wilderness to survive were the foundations of their conflict behaviour; that conflict behaviour was now heightened, or given a spiritual dimension, with the widespread development of the worship of the Goddess, and the development of tribal magic.

The concept of the Goddess may be said to have derived from the hunter-gatherer's veneration of the Earthmother, the Mother provider of the wild fruits of nature. She was occasionally represented in Venus-like sculptures at the entrances to, and inside, caves in Europe. She, together with the Great Spirit, symbolized the sum total of the hunter-gatherer's pantheon of animal, vegetable and phenomenal spirits. With the transition to farming the Great Spirit faded in memory and the Earthmother of the hunter-gatherer became transformed into the Great Goddess, representative of Mother Earth – that is, of the Earth regarded as land to be possessed, cleared of wildlife and sown with seed which, with the aid of the Great Goddess, would produce a bountiful harvest.*

The destruction of the wild fruits of nature and their replacement with the fruits of the farmers' labour constituted the rape and enslavement of the Earthmother and initiated her replacement by the artificial Goddess. This devastating change in the relationship between people and the Earthmother would have equally devastating effects upon the 'Collective Unconscious' of humankind, profoundly affecting the relationship between

---

*See Part I, Chapter 7, for an amplification of this argument in terms of Providence.

men, women and wild nature, making for what has come to be known as the 'dark' side of human nature. The subsequent treatment of women by men has been an ambivalent equality at best, but more often enslavement and sometimes cruel death, as, for instance, the enforced self-immolation of widows (India) and the burning of witches (Europe).*

Deities personifying the Great Goddess were venerated in India, throughout the Fertile Crescent and around the Mediterranean basin. In other areas, particularly in the more heavily forested parts of Europe which were difficult to clear for farming and where there was greater danger to livestock from wild animals, tribal magic emerged. Both the worship of the Goddess and the development of tribal magic may be said to have occupied an intermediate stage in the transformation of the psyche, which corresponds to the intermediate stage between pure hunter-gatherer and pure farmer, a period lasting from 1,000 to 5,000 years following the introduction of farming in 10000 BC. Both the Goddess and tribal magic would, in later millennia in Europe, give way to sky gods and goddesses.

This intermediate stage has existed in two main forms. There was that found, for instance, amongst the Algonquians of the Northeast coast of North America. They still regarded the wilderness as sacred and remained an integral part of that world despite their adoption of cultivation. Following the spread of farming from Mexico up the East coast to the Great Lakes, many Algonquian hunter-gatherer communities added farming to their range of survival strategies: in the main their women-folk undertook the sowing and harvesting while the men hunted. They possessed no large domestic animals. They neither demarcated nor enclosed land as exclusive property: rather they possessed rights to hunt, fish and grow crops in defined areas, cultivating the same area for no more than a few years before moving on to allow regeneration. And although cultivation allowed their populations to expand, and although they entertained some of the less attractive customs and characteristics peculiar to farming communities everywhere, including the growth of tribes and of tribal leaders and tribal conflict (which was, however, generally limited to inflicting minimal damage to achieve maximum benefit), they nevertheless maintained a condition of relative harmony with the wild environment. The other main form is that which would eventually lead many of its protagonists into full-time farming and separation from the wilderness. Many sedentary peoples in England and Europe remained at this intermediate stage in the millennia before the arrival of Christianity: they mixed

---

*In this connection see Appendix iii.

farming with a degree of hunting, thereby retaining a measure of their ecological understanding of the wild environment. (Such an intermediate stage is still to be found amongst indigenous peoples throughout the world today.) In England, for instance, there were a few hundred thousand people living in small tribal societies numbering a few hundred to a few thousand persons: they comprised chieftains, medicine-men, shamans, warriors, farmers and hunters. Settled on moorland and in forest clearings, they lived under the threat of starvation during hard winters and of attacks by other tribes and wild animals. As well as warriors and walls to provide a measure of physical protection, there was the need for psychical security. This was provided by the shaman who acquired and disseminated prophetic knowledge as magical power over future events, over the destiny of the tribe.

Shamanism has generally comprised a set of spiritual beliefs and practices in which the shaman attempts to influence the spirits governing the good and evil of life. To that end the shaman might, in a state of trance, leave his body and enter the spirit world to engage the life forces of the universe. It may well be the case that certain hunter-gatherer peoples resorted to the use of shamans and magic long before the advent of farming. Their aims, however, would have been as profoundly different as the differences between far ranging hunter and sedentary farmer. Shamans and magic would have helped the hunter-gatherers survive and prosper in the sacred wild world which they loved and to which they belonged; whereas they have helped farming and gardening peoples survive and prosper in enclaves of Sacred domesticated land which belonged to them, while providing an imaginative escape route from the ravages of the wilderness, which they feared, towards the heavens above.

Regulating the weather and the provision of healing incantations were other important functions of the shaman of farming peoples, as was maintaining contact with the strange, the Unexplainable or Wyrd (weird), which, as the force which underlay all life, was the Sacred. Symbolic elements, such as stone circles or trees, and associated ceremonies, rituals and sacrifices were manifestations of the Sacred: they formed ladders to other worlds which farming societies would eventually people with gods and goddesses demanding veneration, leading later to organized religion.

James Frazer, in his book *The Golden Bough*, drew attention to the importance of the tree-worship of the earliest Aryans throughout the oakwoods of Gaul, Prussia and Scandinavia. In these immense primaeval forests people were living in scattered clearings which were like islands, or enclaves, in an ocean of green. Guardians of the sacred trees around which each sedentary community cohered were often regarded as priest-gods and priest-kings who lived and died as an incarnation of the supreme Aryan god whose life was in the mistletoe, or Golden Bough, growing on the sacred oaks. In Italy Diana, as a goddess of fertility, was worshipped in a sacred grove at Nemi, where she was attended by a succession of priests known as Kings of the Wood, who personified the oak god Jupiter. They were kings, not of the city, but of nature. The Italians associated the oak with their highest god, Jupiter, and the Greeks with Zeus: they were divinities of the sky, the thunder, the rain and the oak. Further north, amongst the Celts of Gaul, sacred groves of oak were scenes of the worship of Zeus.

Knowledge of these pre-Christian tribes has come to us from two main sources. Firstly, from collections of Scandinavian poems which elaborated belief systems common to tribes throughout western and northern Europe. In particular they refer to the archetypal journey into shamanic knowledge undertaken by the great god Woden-Odin, whose journey on the Cosmic or World Tree echoes the apparently universal experience of shamans in tribal cultures. It was Odin who, with the help of two other gods, Hoenir and Lodur, breathed life into two trees and thereby created the first mortals. Thereafter the cult of Odin was joined with that of Thor, the god of thunder, making these the chief gods of the oak and of the ancient Teutons.

Secondly, such knowledge has come to us through the writings of the earliest Church leaders, who urged their priests to drive out necromancy, divination and healing incantations in sacred tree circles.* The conflict of the earliest Churchmen with the indigenous pre-Christian tribal societies reflects the fearful attitude of the pure farmer societies to the wilderness and their need for dominion over nature. They thus removed the Sacred from trees and from the shamanic ascent of trees and instead installed it within the four walls of temples, whose priests still sought physical and psychical salvation in ascent to worlds above.

The temple and church replaced the tree as the take-off point to Other Worlds in space in pursuance of what came to be seen as our highest aspirations. Science and spacecraft have now provided civilized men with the vehicles with which to realize their aspirations.

So whereas the hunters' physical and psychical life-force had been

---

*Corrupt versions of the Old Religion of the early Neolithic – the horned god, fertility rites and sacred tree circles – were combined with Eastern magic and parodies of contemporary religions to form the stock-in-trade of witches in later millennia. Witches and witchcraft would be savagely persecuted in the Christian era.

oriented primarily to movement in the horizontal in search of game, while the whole natural environment had been sacred to them, the life-force of these sedentary farming-cum-hunting tribes was now reoriented in the vertical, while the Sacred was centred upon that part of the natural world – and in particular a certain tree or grove of trees – which the shaman invoked as the source of the collective spiritual power or Life-Force of the community. The primarily sedentary, vertically oriented activities of settlements were now organized around a focus, an axis, a vertical co-ordinate to which the surrounding countryside was related. With the growth of chiefdoms and kingdoms – and their associated villages, towns and cities – and the concomitant replacement of the pure hunter-gatherer and intermediate farming-cum-hunting societies with pure farming communities, organized religion began to develop, thereby reinforcing the vertical re-orientation of the psyches of these sedentary people.

Firstly, ignorance and fear of the wilderness and forces of nature replaced an earlier understanding and love. It was out of such ignorance, fear and loss of love that religions grew up. Knowing neither true authoritative Great Spirit, nor true Mother, nor true home, they were forced to invent them. For instance,

> The ancient peoples of Middle America saw themselves as insignificant beings at the mercy of a capricious universe. Attempts to reduce the mysteries of nature to understandable and predictable terms led them to create elaborate religious systems in which gods were numerous and often could assume more than one identity and function in the supernatural hierarchy.[13]

Because farming peoples were imprisoned by natural forces that threatened to destroy them, what they invented was the antithesis of what they had lost. They invented a new stabilizing authority and psychical setting for themselves. But it was a static vertically oriented stabilizing authority – whether Farmer Gods or Goddesses – and a world-fearing psychical setting that were illusory and the antithesis of their earlier horizontally oriented stabilizing authority in flux and world-loving psychical setting. Religion fulfilled the now pressing need for security, to be loved; it was, too, the sacred binding together of society in fear of the awful and seemingly malevolent powers ranged against them and bent on destroying them; powers which they transformed into gods and devils. Like the physical wall, religion was primarily a psychical wall, a defence mechanism of the psyche, erected in response to the shaming emptiness within and fearful void without. It was also an imaginative escape mechanism oriented in the vertical, in emulation of the shamanic ascent of the oak tree and of the social tree of the stratified society, a ladder to the heavens that would eventually appear to offer a new paradisial home to replace that lost here below. Thereafter religion became the belief in a superhuman being or beings controlling the universe and entitled to worship and obedience; and the practices resulting from such belief, as built into a system of faith, doctrine and worship. Religion both justified the challenge of these farming cultures to the traditional hunter-gatherer way of life and legitimized them as a substitute for the prescriptive authority of the Great Spirit. In short, organized religion was born, providing primarily a new stabilizing authority which sanctified and made legitimate cultures which, from an evolutionary standpoint, were fundamentally unlawful.*

Secondly, religion also supplied a supernatural explanation of human and cultural origins and events in the form of myth, providing a description and explanation of the nature of the social universe, and a means – ritual – for manipulating it. Myth is a sacred narrative told by people in order to make sense of their existence. It provides a collective social memory, recounting original events leading to the present condition of existence. While integrating past and present, myth indicates the direction of the future, providing a sense of continuity and perspective. It would be strange indeed if the de-rangement, destruction, cultural disintegration, and virtual incarceration of many of humankind 10–5000 BC by floodwater – particularly the flooding of the Black Sea – forest and aridification and their adaptation to agriculture, combined with the loss of many of their evolutionary characteristics, were not main contributory factors in the making of the most fundamental of all the myths: those of a Flood, Fall and new Creation based upon agriculture and pastoralism.

It is important to note that the essential difference between the myths of hunter-gatherers and those of sedentary farming communities is that the former have generally voiced reverence for the Earth, revealing the sacredness of all wildlife and helping integrate them meaningfully within the wilderness; whereas the myths of the latter, in their de-rangement and disintegration from the wilderness, have tended to ascribe sacredness to Farmer Gods and Goddesses and the associated structures and domesticated ground of their veneration and worship, while anathematizing the wilderness. Zevedei Barbu rightly argued

---

* See Appendix vi for an amplification of this argument.

... that the conflict between man and his external environment, which must have been terrifying in the early stages of human civilization, had something to do with all the narrative tales about the origin and the meaning of the universe.[14]

The frightening conflict between farmers and their environment had much to do with the origin and use of myth to regulate and transcend the conflict; a reconstruction of the world in terms of the emotional conditions it created. Given the world-wide distribution and depth of the conflict that did occur, such a redirected response on the part of farming peoples is all the more comprehensible. Denied access to the real world of a body, mind and imagination integrated in movement through the wilderness, these people began to dream up and to create new worlds, both physical and psychical, oriented in the vertical – mythical worlds that were consistent with their growing stratified societies. Most importantly, the Near and Middle Eastern myths are obsessively devoted to controlling and destroying the chaos-dragon, representative of the wild forces of nature.

> Mythologically, there is a clear connection between dragon-slaying heroes and the cataclysm of the deluge... Since the world had been created by the division of the primeval waters, it was feared that they might still close in to engulf and destroy life. The waters must still be kept at bay, and the responsibility for maintaining order was handed down by the Creator to the dragon-slayer – by whatever name he was called.[15]

The widespread myths of a Flood and of a Paradise lost, together with their obsessive devotion to the destruction of the chaos-dragon before the acts of Creation could take place, are surely evidence of prehistoric conflict of frightening proportions – and also of the imaginative attempts of farming peoples to impose their wills upon events.

> ... the first urban societies in Mesopotamia were 'the first societies to abandon a religious attitude of oneness with nature and to adopt one of separation'. In Mesopotamian mythology nature was depicted as being in a state of chaos, and the task of human beings and their gods was to overcome this chaos and to establish order.[16]

For chaos is intolerable; some kind of sense has to be made of it. Some kind of pattern has to be perceived, or at least created, so that suffering and pain are explicable and made acceptable. To that end, farming peoples began to live through the compensatory power of fantasy founded in the supernatural.

However, it was not only nature that was seen to be in a state of chaos, but also the nature of humankind. The trustworthy model of what it was and meant to be human – the aeons old model as hunter-gatherer – had gone. Farming societies had to create, out of nothing, not only a new model of what it meant to be human within a stratified structure, but also one that would explain how they had arrived at their seemingly dehumanized condition. In this connection, most important because of its potential long term effects, was the sense of being punished for some past crime or sin, and the search for a scapegoat. The Middle Eastern myths of a Fall and Flood, for instance, blamed the disaster on original ancestral sin, while the myth-making itself shows how questions asked by people without the necessary information to answer such questions tend to evoke answers in terms of myth, thereby concealing the true cause and effect of the disaster – as at the time of the Black Death (1347–1350), which was followed in England by post-plague accusations of irreligion and depravity. A search for the 'why' went on amongst the survivors, and a search for scapegoats ensued. In Germany, the Black Death gave rise to the appalling Jewish pogroms. It fostered, too, the weird spectacle of the Flagellants, who frantically whipped themselves through the streets in the hope of appeasing God's all too evident anger. Similarly, early urban societies began to invest the memory of their antediluvian ancestors with evil doings, and decided that it was the increasing lawlessness and violence of human beings which had finally decided the Farmer God to destroy the race.

... to the Hebrew writer the myth of the Flood, fixed in the traditions of his people, as various poetic and prophetic references show, had become an awful portent, the final catastrophe brought about by man's rebellion against God. It has become an episode in the 'salvation-history', because a remnant was spared to carry on the divine purpose of ultimate restoration. This is the reason why further mythical material is introduced as a prelude to the Flood myth, in order to show how completely corrupt mankind had become. In (Genesis) 6:1–4 we have a fragment of mythical material, originally unconnected with the myth of the Flood, but used by the Yahwist (i.e. the priestly writer) to explain the increasing

lawlessness and violence of mankind which finally decided Yahweh
(the Hebrew God) to destroy the race.[17]*

In South America, in the regions of what are now Chile and Peru, a
widespread dessication had a similar effect. People turned to fishing and
a primitive agriculture, raised up stratified societies and made myths
which explained that the aridification of a fertile Eden was the result of
the evil doings of their ancestors, whom the Gods turned into beasts,
creating a better, civilized, humanity in their place.

Bearing in mind that the psychological effects of the Middle Eastern
Flood and the South American dessication were similar, my subsequent
argument, while being principally concerned with developments in the
Middle East and Europe, reflects parallel developments in South America
and elsewhere.†

The Middle Eastern myths mask and falsify a real condition of
humankind that existed before the Flood. For though the myths do refer
to an original Paradise on Earth, they imply that everything between the
time when people moved in that Paradise and the period immediately
preceding the Flood was evil. As the first guides to history and to an
understanding of the past, the myths therefore drew a falsely condemnatory
veil over the past that effectively concealed the true paradisial past of all
humans as hunter-gatherers, concealed too the transition from hunter-
gathering to a primitive agriculture, prevented an understanding of cause
and effect in the present, and ensured a romanticized view of the paradise
that was lost. Probably entirely unaware of the co-operative way of life,
kingly estate and holistic ecological understanding of their hunter-gatherer
forbears, the Sumerians and their descendants learnt, through the myths
of a Fall and Flood, to impute their banishment from Paradise to beastly,
irreligious and corrupt ancestors, whose sinful behaviour had angered the
gods, so learning to despise them and any remotely resembling them.
Indeed, because their mythical acts of Creation explicitly equate the act
of divine creation with their farming communities and civilization,
everything prior to or lying outside their acts of Creation – including
particularly the hunter-gatherers – was equated with the chaos of the
waters and so with the chaos-dragon that must be destroyed before the
act of Creation can take place. The wilderness – which had become for
farming societies the home of dragons, a place of danger, darkness and
chaos – was in effect equated with the chaos-dragon. In the old maps

---

* See Appendix vii for a fuller discussion on the mythical Fall of Man and its implications.

† The study of the world-wide convergence of behaviour is a principal concern of Part II.

the unknown beyond the bounds of the civilized world was often marked with the legend: 'Here be dragons'.

In the East, however, and particularly in China, the view of the dragon has been more ambivalent. In China the dragon was regarded as a creature of good omen, a portent of good fortune each new year. The Emperor occupied the Dragon-throne; chaos – *luan* – was anything threatening the survival of the Emperor and people. The dragon came to represent the male principle of fertility, while still associated with water and with its apparent effect on germination and generation. The dragon was envisaged – as revealed on the bowls, dishes and vases made at the Imperial command of the Dragon-throne – inhabiting clouds, rising from the waves or twisting between the mists and spume of both. The Gobi Desert has been known as 'the sand-dragon'. A less benign view of the dragon obtained in north China at the beginning of the 20th century. A terrible drought and famine in north China, 1897–1902, combined with the presence of many foreign missions, convinced many ordinary people

> ...that the construction of so many arrogant foreign missions, churches and cathedrals has disrupted the *fengshui* or geomantic balance of nature, thus awakening the Earth Dragon and causing floods and drought.[18]

Whether the dragon has been related positively to fertility and farming, as in China, or negatively to the wilderness, as in the West, the result has been the same: a psychical reorientation which erected a spiritual barrier that not only affected a present relationship of farming peoples with wild nature (and so with the world in general), but seriously distorted their relationship with their past as hunter-gatherers, as revealed, for instance, in their changed relationship with cave-art.

> The caves were not abandoned all at once. There are Carbon 14 dates around 10000 at La Vache; Lascaux was visited as late as c.6000 BC, and there are other signs that in the Neolithic and even in the Bronze Age, men still occasionally frequented the same caves. When the tide of obliterating forest cut them off from the old easy intercourse of the hunting life, when the sacred places were no longer visited, the image of the caves may not have died, but have [*sic*] remained, no less obsessive for being no longer understood. As well as the physical barrier there arose a spiritual barrier, and the real journey to the cave sanctuary becomes the journey to Hades,

the Land of No Return, the 'descent' of mystery religions, Annwn in Britain, and the Underworld journey of shamanic ecstasy.[19]

Here is further evidence of a redirection of response amongst people trapped in enclaves and threatened with a 'tide of obliterating forest'. Unable to travel as hunter-gatherers, they were forced to redirect not only their physical but also their psychical responses into the 'ascent' and 'descent' of mystery religions. These drew on ideas of fertility in agriculture – what is 'underground' is the source of 'wealth', for when the grain is cut it dies but yields seed and grows again – to symbolize the journey of the soul. An illusory journey replaced the real journey to the caves.

The hunter's god is one who comes, the farmer's one who rises.[20]

The hunter-gatherers' god – the Great Spirit – is one who comes and calls them to move freely through a land treated as no man's land; the farmer's god is one who rises and sanctions people raised up by the exploitation of others on land treated as belonging to someone. While the essence of the Great Spirit is change, the nature of the Farmer God – particularly of the later Judaeo-Christian God – is unchanging. Even as the sedentary farmer is the antithesis of the mobile hunter-gatherer, the Farmer God is the antithesis of the Great Spirit. From an evolutionary standpoint, spirituality bound hunter-gatherers together in bands as world-loving insiders united with the wilderness in obedience to the Great Spirit, whereas religion bound farmers together in societies as world-fearing outsiders united in opposition to, and escape from, the wilderness in obedience to their Farmer Gods. The thrust of the spiritual life of farming peoples in the West has been upward, away from the daily round and the natural, relegating the world, the flesh and the devil to the lowest levels. The otherworldliness of the Gospels – as in St John 8:23 – has helped consolidate the farmer's attitude which devalues and exploits the wilderness.

In effect, farming peoples erected psychical as well as physical walls against the wilderness, denigrating it as the home of monsters and dragons, while blackening and blotting out their own true heritage and home with myths of Hades, the Land of No Return. They created a new past for themselves in myths of Creation, which also served to sanction and sanctify their stratified societies in the present. For thousands of years, farming communities have built on fictitious pasts, strengthened by genealogies of mythical Kings and Emperors. Their true past would remain hidden until revealed in the late 19th century with the discovery of the hunter-gatherer's art in caves like those at Lascaux and Altamira.

From this it will be understood that a primary evolutionary memory of people integrated within nature was now lost. It is well known that at the individual level, the effects of memory loss are devastating. For the way we solve problems and how we view the future depends to a great degree on our memories of past experience. Loss of memory leads to the loss of the ability to make sense of anything seen or heard. Our memories are our identities. Without memory, posited Descartes, humans cease to exist.* Such was the condition of farming societies that lost all memory of their previous, and proper, existence as hunter-gatherers, and so of the wilderness as their true home. They could no longer make sense of anything seen or heard within the wild environment. They lost their true personalities, and their powers to communicate and to think within the wilderness. They thus ceased to exist as real people.

This surely is the core of the conflict of farming societies with the wilderness. As the primary evolutionary memories of people were replaced by a collective mythical memory, itself pretending to go back to the beginning of time, a world that was earlier remembered by hunter-gatherers as a beloved and harmonious home came to be seen and mythologized by farmers as the home of the much feared chaos-dragon. A love and understanding of the wilderness that could no longer reach out and touch it in love became confused, and slowly turned, through incomprehension and fear, to hatred of the wilderness.

> One of the great conditions of anger and hatred is, that you must tell and believe lies against the hated object, in order ... to be consistent.[21]

Arising out of this perversion of the psyches of farming peoples, myths served as the foundation charters of their societies, describing the creation of the world and of people, explaining to them their cultures and religious beliefs. They formed an important part of a society's history, and have been used in the education of children. Myth has in fact played a central rôle in religion, helping to ensure the stability of the traditional agricultural society by consecrating or sanctifying both the society's social structure

---

*See Appendix ii for the implications of the loss of a primary memory.

in relation to its mythical past and the generalities of its behaviour patterns.

In every region of the ancient agricultural world religion and myth were inseparable from peoples' ordinary lives. All stratified societies comprised both gods and people, whose relationship was expressed literally as a human relationship. Where a god was seen as father and the people as his children, the implication was that they were literally of his stock, forming a single natural family with reciprocal family duties. Where a god was seen as king and the people as his servants, the implication was that the guidance of the society was in his hands, requiring the people to pay him homage and to consult his will. Social behaviour, then, encompassed both religion and daily life; there was no stratified society emerging from what has been described as 'prehistoric darkness' whose religion did not conform to the general type described above. This remarkable uniformity was brought about by farming peoples' common degeneration and loss of a world-loving understanding and its replacement with world-fearing myth, which provided a supernatural explanation of cultural origins and events, sacredly binding the people to the stratified society the better to survive in a hostile world.

The myths provided the *raison d'être* of the stratified society, replacing a lost natural identity of socio-economic equality with a superlative manufactured identity of a god-like few and concomitant diminished identity of the many born to serve the few and of a wild environment likewise exploited to that end. Ignorance – in their case, ignorance of the wilderness and laws of nature – was the progenitor both of arrogance and of the arrogation and exploitation of no man's land as someone's land. Myth not only blotted out the past, not only supplied a false foundation charter and a false basis to the histories of these early agricultural societies, but falsified their relationship with the real world of wild nature. Myths distorted reality. A main function of societal myth was to make 'normal', 'natural', and thus 'inevitable', stratified structures which in reality were grossly abnormal, unnatural, criminal societies which had abnegated the world-wide laws of nature and replaced them with their own regional laws. What had been normal and natural from an evolutionary standpoint – that is, their past evolutionary identities as hunter-gatherers – would come to be seen as abnormal, unnatural, lawless. It was as if a veil was drawn across their evolutionary past as hunter-gatherers, diffracting and darkening memories of that past. This psychical veil of myth is expressive of the dark veil formed by hatred of the wilderness combined with self-hatred. With the aid of myth the catastrophe of a deluge, from being a natural phenomenon, was falsely raised in status to being a supernatural one, and was thereafter regarded by farming peoples as the Flood: the outward expression of the wrath of their Farmer God, himself a figment of the displaced imagination. In this connection, their myths supplied them with a new model – a world-fearing model – of their relationship with the wild environment which was entirely at variance with the world-loving model of hunter-gatherers. The information conveyed by such a model was to the effect that unless they obeyed the injunctions of their Farmer Gods they would be visited, if not by a world-wide Flood, then by fire and brimstone, earthquake or other equally unpleasant phenomena. The fall of Jericho (c.1250 BC), the destruction of Sodom and Gomorrah (c.2000 BC) and similar biblical events were probably caused by recurring earthquakes along the Dead Sea Rift. At the time these events were regarded as evidence of the power and vengeful wrath of their Farmer God for the sins of the people, and mythologized accordingly.

Traditionally societies have used the metaphors of religion and art to give meaning to events. Sacred texts, such as the Old Testament, and religious dramas present cataclysm as a divine instrument which can be propitiated but not controlled. A transcendent interpretation of cataclysm is still apparent in the daily lives of settled peoples throughout the world. When a large earthquake devastated a 10,000 square mile area of southern Italy in 1980, leaving 4,800 dead and tens of thousands homeless, the Bishop of Naples declared it to be the Lord's judgement on a people who had voted for abortion. In Japan, from June to August 1994, severe drought, particularly in Japan's fourth largest island, Shikoku, was met by Shinto priests, dressed in 8th century-style costumes, chanting prayers – 'Rain Gods, we need water. Deliver us rain' – while farmers cloaked in sheaves of rice performed an ancient rain dance. Similar rain dances are performed under similar circumstances of drought all over Africa.

The myths of stratified societies represented an imaginative attempt to impose some control over events, an activity now undertaken by science. However, if science now appears generally to have replaced a world in which people have been governed by supernatural beings, bewitching myths, legends and sorcery, and to have opened our minds to the meaning and measure of the natural world and of the universe, it is essential to understand that we are still the direct descendants of the myth-makers and that our own meaning and measure as doubly deprived degenerate people still remain hidden behind the belief that we are true human beings – a fraud that this book sets out to expose. Given that they are the products of similarly degenerate people – priests and scientists – the effects of myth and of applied science are essentially the same. Both deny the human reality, perpetuate stratified societies and destroy the reality of the world.*

This introduces the last of the three major functions of religion. It is the one which, in its concern with, and effect on, the natural world, may be considered the most important of all. Religion, in its combined authoritative stabilizing rôle and its interpretative rôle as myth, constituted a new collective world view to replace the individual world view of an ecological understanding lost. Authoritative experts filtered and controlled the flow and organization of information in relation to the wild environment and universe, imposed an artificial measure and meaning on otherwise frighteningly meaningless events and a frighteningly meaningless land, and, in many farming communities, they tended to demonize other 'outgroups', in particular hunter-gatherer bands and other wildlife.

I have already discussed some of the natural events that stratified societies have tended to mythologize, as in the case of earthquakes in the Old Testament. To a degree almost unimaginable today, early stratified societies feared annihilation by natural catastrophe. Warding off the threat of extinction was, for instance, one of the most important functions of the priest-scientists of the Mesoamerican and Egyptian civilizations. Both the Mayans and the Aztecs studied the movement of the Pleiades to see if the world was coming to an end. If the Pleiades successfully reached and passed the zenith, they knew that the danger had passed and that the world would continue for a further 52 years. In the Toltec and Aztec civilizations enormous numbers of victims were sacrificed to assuage the fear that the sun might set forever on the nation. Only by being fed with the most precious of liquids, human blood – or human hearts, as on the altars of Tenochtitlán, the Aztec capital – would it consent to rise again, and the nation survive and prosper. The priest-scientists who possessed the knowledge and techniques to release such energy and power were performing the same rôle on the national stage as the priest-scientists of Egypt, who ostensibly raised the Pharaoh to the sun in order that he might follow and monitor its movements and ensure it rose again on the morrow.

The defence against insecurity and anxiety was one of the principal elements that bound settled peoples together. Surrounded and dominated as they were by the now frightening and unknown natural world, their anxiety was assuaged with promises of supernatural assistance and protection by the authoritative experts – medicine-men, magicians, astrologers and priest-scientists – cultivated at the summits of their increasingly stratified

---

* See Appendix viii for the relationship between myth and science.

societies. Looking away from the now meaningless and hostile wilderness, astronomers and astrologers searched the heavens for, and found, meaning – albeit illusory – amongst the stars. They invented, with the aid of myth, the new world view of the farming communities. They controlled the flow and organization of information which imposed and imparted an artificial measure and meaning of the natural world that were the antithesis of, and antipathetic to, its true measure and meaning as understood by hunter-gatherers. They performed sacrificial rites as a further guarantee of the stability and well-being of their stratified societies.

With the arrival of the Greek civilization men still feared the wilderness. Though they saw beauty in nature, Greek art was the expression of people looking at the external world from the safety of the civilized setting – an idealization of nature. Their fears found expression in their god Pan, regarded as the personification of Nature. The Ancient Greeks dreaded encountering Pan as they passed through the mountainous regions and forests. The word 'panic' derives from the fears of travellers alarmed by strange sights and sounds in the wilderness which they attributed to Pan. At the same time, however, men like Thales of Miletus (c.624– c.545 BC) began to lay the foundations of natural philosophy, studying natural objects and phenomena, but always of course from the settled standpoint. They sought, as outsiders – outside the wild environment, looking in, as it were – to explain natural phenomena in terms of natural causes, eventually enabling them to develop theories and technology to master and exploit the wilderness. Elsewhere in the civilized world belief in the hostility of the natural world and in the necessity of divine intervention and in supernatural causes remained deeply entrenched. Nowhere was this more apparent than in the relationship of civilized people to the microcosm.

Plagues and sundry diseases that have beset farming communities down the millennia caused them to regard the bacterial microcosm as hostile. Those who suffered from leprosy or mental disease were often seen as unclean or possessed respectively, necessitating divine intervention to cleanse and cast out devils. Medicine came to be seen as a battleground, with bacteria regarded as germs to be destroyed. Yet people's first relationship with the microcosm was as hunter-gatherers, and it was friendly to them, and, together with the macrocosm, was regarded with respect, awe and understanding. Hunter-gatherer information systems were like those of bacteria – i.e. 'trading bits of information like a computer network with a memory accumulated over billions of years of continuous operation'[22] – before such systems and associated memory bank were lost to farming societies. Modern human information systems are perversions of the earlier ones, employed to exploit and control nature rather than to experience and enjoy it in its wild state. An optimum measure of health was a principal mark of hunter-gatherer societies, just as, and just because, an understanding of natural phenomena in terms of natural causes – including a profound knowledge of drugs and cures – was inherent within the psyches of hunter-gatherers as true scientists. As insiders, it could hardly have been otherwise. Whereas the early Greek philosophers and modern scientists have been divorced from that oneness: they have been, and remain, outsiders, still seeking cures for diseases which exist and persist only because of the evodeviation of sedentary peoples. Today scientific experts experiment on and sacrifice millions of animals yearly to the same ends as the early priestly-scientific experts, namely, to improve the health, safety and well-being of their stratified societies, to whom the microcosm has been as hostile as the macrocosm.

In further pursuit of well-being and stability, many farming communities have regarded the wilderness not just as hostile, but as the home of evil spirits, and have in consequence sanctioned and sanctified the destruction of the wilderness and of wildlife regarded as malevolent.

For the Israelites, the wilderness was the home of the scapegoat, the home of the goats released into the wilderness bearing the sins of the people. In a similarly pejorative vein, we speak today of politicians who have lost office and power as enduring 'their wilderness years'. As for the inhabitants of the wilderness, what we do not understand tends to become exaggerated in importance in our minds. There has been, for instance, a general tendency amongst settled people everywhere to exaggerate the size of mystery animals: they would learn the misleading myth rather than experience the reality for themselves. The persistent view of the gorilla, for example, until George Schaller exploded the myth, has been

> ...as a ferocious and bloodthirsty beast with an amazing array of human and superhuman traits, all basically treacherous.[23]

More than that, however, animals previously understood and admired by generations of hunter-gatherers would become 'wild beasts' and dangerous to generations of farmers, to be destroyed on sight. They projected their combined fears and hatred onto those wild animals, including hunter-gatherers, that were perceived most to threaten their societies – in particular the wolf.

According to B.H. Lopez,[24] 'keeping the wolf from the door', both figuratively and literally, has been a principal preoccupation of farming populations since time immemorial. It represents both the frightening darkness of encircling forests and starvation in environmental hells. As the idea grew that farming and domestic animals were God-given and innately good – they represented, after all, a new found (Providential) prosperity and security – so the idea grew that wolves were evil, 'the Devil's hounds'. Throughout the Middle Ages in Europe the wolf was regarded as the Devil in disguise, a threat both to the spiritual world of peasant farmers and to their physical world – a hungry wolf would dig up and eat the bodies in consecrated graveyards, and he preyed upon their stock which represented both sustenance and wealth. Indeed, as pointed out by B.H. Lopez, anything that threatened the precarious existence of the peasant was 'the wolf', including famine and a greedy landlord. The wolf lived in the wilderness, seen as a place without God, as the home of the chaos-dragon and Devil. So farming peoples concentrated their fear and hatred of the wilderness into fear and loathing of the most often encountered denizen of the wilderness. The wolf in its wilderness home then represented the chaos-dragon, and wolf-hunters represented the dragon-slayers of old.

Similar paranoid fears have pursued farming societies down the millennia, surfacing particularly in periods of humiliating insecurity, evoking atavistic fears originating with the two-fold fall. Because the existing order has ostensibly been established by their Farmer God, anyone and anything allegedly posing a threat to the religio-socio-economic order may be seen as a denial and inversion of that order, and sacrificed accordingly. Just as opposing the wolf was to affirm order, and to pursue and kill wolves was to further the divine purposes, so too, for instance, was the pursuit and killing of women as witches (seen as servants of the Devil) in the 15th and 16th centuries in Europe and in the 17th century in North America.* Societies governed by a similarly fanatical Communist ideology have likewise been affected by the virus of paranoid insecurity, torturing and killing alleged enemies of the State in their millions. All such human and animal sacrifices are a reflection of the humiliating insecurities inherent in their relationship of conflict with the wilderness and with their own true natures. The fundamental difference lies between the beliefs of hunter-gatherers *who belonged to the land* and the religions of farmers *to whom the land belonged.*

Whereas, before the Mesolithic, the wilderness was home to human beings, a place of freedom, equality and relative safety, following the Mesolithic and Neolithic the world increasingly became a place of imprisonment, oppression, gross inequality, conflict and danger. For while

---

*In this connection, see Appendix iii.

each stratified society constituted a new home, ostensibly a place of safety in the now meaningless and dangerous wilderness, these stratified societies may also be described as pyramids of power to ascent and collective security, within which all their forms of conflict behaviour became ritualized and institutionalized. In other words, they were structures of gross inequality and oppression which actually intensified the effects of imprisonment, conflict and danger.

Chapter 5

The Stratified Society, a Pyramid of Power

Nowhere in the world (that is not an exaggeration) do we see agriculture specifically designed to feed people. Its prime task, everywhere, is to make profit, or to prop up some ancient system of fealty, or quantify the importance of some chief in heads of cattle. (Colin Tudge)[1]

Having defined the main adaptive radiations of farming peoples in terms of conflict behaviour, it will be helpful to examine those same radiations in the light of their contribution both to a physical energy (food production, reproduction and self-protection) and to a psychical energy (religion and science) for the ascent and collective security of the community. Together these made for the growth of the stratified society, which is the expression of their collective conflict behaviour, ritualized and institutionalized.

The earliest settled communities, like the pure hunter-gatherer societies before them, would seem to have been egalitarian in their organization. Such would appear to have been the case with the farming peoples who began to colonize the southern and eastern parts of Britain about 4000 BC. They came from the coasts of Europe across the Channel and North Sea in skin boats, bringing with them their wheat and small numbers of cattle, sheep, pigs and goats. After the first settlement these early Neolithic farmers probably grew in numbers fairly quickly, with a correspondingly profound effect on the environment. As they spread throughout the land, they deliberately cleared the forests and also caused their degeneration to thickets of scrub by the prolonged grazing of their animals. By late Neolithic times, c.3000 BC, much of the country had been transformed into the sparsely-wooded open grassland that exists today.

It was about this time, around 3100 BC, that the first henges – circular ceremonial structures of wooden or stone uprights – began to be built in Britain. Then, around 2500 BC, a series of huge henges was built, as at Durrington Walls.

Durrington Walls, like Stonehenge, gives us an idea of the amount of labour devoted by the Late-Neolithic people of the area to 'public works'. To build the earthwork would require nearly a million man-hours, or 100 men working six days a week for four years. It cannot have been easy, either, to fell, transport and erect the large oak tree-trunks used in the timber buildings here and at Woodhenge. The largest of these were over 1m (3.3ft) in diameter and could have been up to 11m (36ft) in length. An unseasoned oak trunk of this size weighs nearly 11 tonnes.[2]

R.J.C. Atkinson, who excavated the large earth mound, Silbury Hill, found evidence to suggest that it was constructed a little earlier than Durrington Walls, over a period of two years, and estimated that it required 18 million hours of labour. A sustained operation of such magnitude suggests it was conducted by a central authority, a rudimentary pyramid of power with a chief at its summit. If that was the case, not only was the egalitarianism of the hunter-gatherer and early Neolithic communities now well and truly dead, but the physical condition of many members of these farming communities was lamentable. Archaeologists have found evidence of this in the twisted spines, damaged bones, diseases, short lives and violent deaths of the men and women who undertook these immense projects.

New groups of immigrants, the Beaker people from Holland and the Rhineland, crossed the North Sea and settled in southern and eastern Britain circa 2500 BC. They appear to have introduced the working and use of the first metals – copper, tin and gold – and to have opened up trade routes to Wessex and other parts of Britain, thereby laying the foundations of a British bronze industry which lasted nearly two thousand years. The Beaker people also introduced burial of the dead singly under a round mound or barrow, which became the widespread practice for people of note.

This was the case around Stonehenge, which was probably erected about 2000 BC on the authority of the ruling families of the Early Bronze Age in Wessex, who most likely acquired their wealth through farming, cattle-ranching and control over the metal trade with Europe. Stonehenge was a communal and ritual centre, and a monument that emphasized the eminence of the chief, who may have been buried in one of the surrounding barrows. It also demonstrated not only the importance of the ruling families within their own community, but that of their community in relation to others in southern Britain.

Here then is evidence of one of the first stratified societies to rise up in Britain. Colin Renfrew has described Stonehenge as the

...climax of a long, local building tradition within the context of the quite complex social organisation of prehistoric Britain.[3]

But it represents too the climax of a stratified society comprising

Homo sapiens sapiens   consumers,

Homo sapiens non sapiens   producers,

the climax of chief and aristocracy risen up on the bent backs – the twisted and damaged spines – of the common working people, who were not buried in barrows and whose only memorial was Stonehenge itself.

To arrive at their imprisoned condition, each person had undergone a primary and a secondary historical degeneration. I describe such degenerate people as *Homo degener.* Hereinafter, I differentiate between *Homo sapiens,* meaning true human being evolved as hunter-gatherer; and *Homo degener,* meaning degenerate human being imprisoned within an agricultural/industrial social pyramid, consisting of *Homo sapiens sapiens* (cultivated, knowledgeable, of high grade intellectual or landowning status), and *Homo sapiens non sapiens* (cultivator or labourer without knowledge, of low grade manual work status), (see figure 5.1).

The first ever human food pyramids of social élites supported by peasant producers and surrounded by threatening wilderness may have arisen under circumstances similar to those described above; that is, through the internal pressure of population growth and the need to organize their feeding and their employment on 'public works', combined with the need for physical and psychical protection against the external threat of wild nature, leading to the erection of ceremonial centres such as Stonehenge. Or perhaps the rise of an aristocracy during the Late Neolithic, either in Britain or elsewhere, occurred primarily as a self-protective device, the result of external pressures from raiders from some hostile tribe, pressures similar to those which gave rise to a European

Part I: fig 5.1

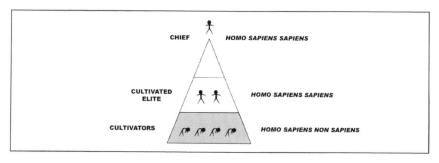

aristocracy a few millennia later, forcing many cultivators to become dependent upon a few cultivated to protect them. Kings, as I shall show, probably originated under similar circumstances of external threat. There is, however, a most important corollary. As argued earlier, these were people, or descendants of people, imprisoned in colonies. At first their loss of hunter-gathering abilities and the external threat of the wilderness were the agents of their incarceration. Thereafter that rôle was increasingly taken by the inmates themselves as the stronger acquired power over their weaker fellows. This is not only a recognized form of animal conflict behaviour, as amongst baboons forcibly incarcerated in small enclosures, but also amongst people incarcerated in prison colonies, concentration camps and prisons. Therefore, while stratified societies are essentially states of relative imprisonment, particularly for those subordinate to the power of others above them, it is likely that such societies generally arose through a combination of internal and external pressures. What is undoubted, however, is that their monumental artefacts were raised up by the exploitation of the common working people, thereby reinforcing not only the eminence of the chief and the authority of the ruling dynasty but also the debasement of the common labourer.

The rise of social élites, and the associated birth of inequality, began to turn some of these world-fearing outsiders, who now resided behind high walls, into world-fearing 'insiders'; the common person, together with other peoples and the true world-loving insiders (the hunter-gatherers), came to be regarded as 'outsiders', 'beyond the pale'. As an illustration, in Roman Britain,

> The most demonstrative of all the Roman urban developments, and the one which came to symbolise the town for the next one and a half millennia, was the wall which contained it. Roman towns did not begin with a wall, as one assumes with the hillforts that preceded them or the Anglo-Saxon *burhs* that followed. The wall was added to enclose most, or part, or sometimes only a small part of a pre-existing and presumably flourishing Roman settlement. The psychological effect of such a barrier can be imagined. It created, out of a familiar amenity, a defensible enclave where space was at a premium, and ensured that from now on there would be two conditions of men – those on the inside and those without. Although one of the motives for building a wall may have been protective in the military sense, there were other protective aspects, for example commerce and class, that prompted this particular expression of civic pride.[4]

Part I: fig 5.2

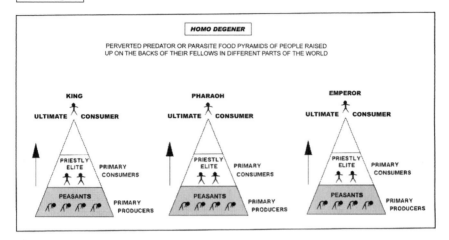

From now on, generally speaking, those on the inside would decide the fate of those on the outside.

Stratified societies of primary consumers, based upon the cultivating activities of the primary producers, began to grow up in Britain and elsewhere, leading eventually to the elevation of one man as the Chief, King, Pharaoh or Emperor, the ultimate consumer at the summit of each (see figure 5.2).

Comparison of Part I fig 5.2 with Part I fig 2.1 reveals the extraordinary and tragic change that had occurred in the destiny of humankind. People whose ancestors had been kings (ultimate consumers) of natural food pyramids were now not only humiliated as forcibly de-ranged hunter-gatherers, but further degraded as domesticated animals to the lowly condition of peasant cultivators (primary producers) for a few elevated or cultivated Kings (ultimate consumers) of stratified societies.

The generality of domesticated humankind – whether peasants, labourers, workers, servants, serfs or slaves – had become, as it were, the grasses at the bases of the new food pyramids. (We speak of 'the grass roots' of the party, and of 'the feeling on the ground', when referring to the common person.) These food pyramids may be described as artificial, as opposed to natural. More accurately, because of the parasitical or predatory relationship that has existed throughout history between social élites and peasant producers – particularly where the latter have been conquered or enslaved – these artificial food pyramids may also be described as parasite or perverted predator food pyramids (see figure 5.3).

Viewed as a parasite chain, multitudes of inferior plant-like producers

Part I: fig 5.3

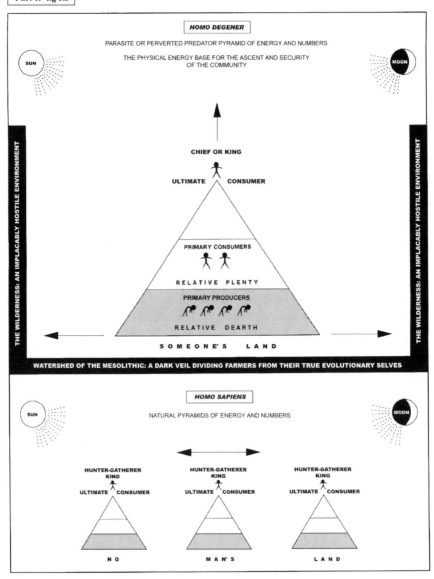

KEY: THE CULTIVATOR AT THE BASE OF THE PARASITE FOOD PYRAMID IS THE EQUIVALENT OF THE GREEN PLANT AT THE BASE OF THE NATURAL FOOD PYRAMID

have been parasitized by a few superior consumers who have exploited the physical energy of the producers and also, by means of taxes and so on, robbed them of their energy store. Here again, the English experience in the development from fortified village to town is relevant. Though the initial choice of site often appears to have been strategic, it has been argued that it was also to protect a pre-existing assembly point for cattle or grain paid as taxation or toll. For millennia much of England's agricultural produce was ultimately destined for payment to a lord, a bishop or a king. By the end of the 8th century compulsory tithes – that is, one-tenth of the annual produce of the land – were being given to the Church for the support of the priesthood and religious establishments.

Although most biologists use the terms 'parasite' and 'parasitic' to describe interactions between, not within, species, they may be used in describing the relationship between *Homo sapiens sapiens* consumers and *Homo sapiens non sapiens* producers, and between them and their domestic animals. Though both partners – *Homo sapiens sapiens* and *Homo sapiens non sapiens* – obtain some benefit from the association, such as collective security against depredations, it is nonetheless an association whose ultimate beneficiaries have been *Homo sapiens sapiens* élites, whom *Homo sapiens non sapiens* labourers have worked for, slaved for, served and fed down the millennia. Parasitism is a one-sided, exploitative relationship in which the parasite harms its host, an intensity of effect ranging from the slightest local injury to total destruction. This has certainly been the case amongst sedentary peoples: the whole of history bears witness to the enslavement, the reduced potential, the shortened lives and outright destruction of untold millions down the millennia at the whim of tyrannical élites, who themselves developed a relatively healthy life-style in contrast to that of the disease-ridden masses. The relationship established between domesticated people and the domestic animals they live upon is likewise one of parasitism. It too is a one-sided, exploitative relationship which destroys the animals' true potential as wild animals. In short, whereas the hunter-gatherers had established a co-operative relationship in equality with their fellows, and a true predator/prey relationship with wildlife, maximizing their own potential and that of their prey in the process, *Homo sapiens sapiens* élites have established a parasitical relationship with *Homo sapiens non sapiens* and with certain animals such as cattle and sheep, creating parasite food pyramids which have steadily eroded and replaced the earlier natural food pyramids and their kings.

Viewed as a perverted predator food chain, within any one pyramid the plant-eating primary producers have generally comprised a domestic plant-to-human food chain that has in turn supported a meat-eating élite comprising a domestic plant-animal-human food chain: meat-eating consumer élites and kings have been raised up and supported by the plant-eating plant-like many, acquiring thereby a protein diet like that of their hunter-gatherer forbears. However, unlike those forbears who were true predators within the animal kingdom, meat-eating élites have been perverted predators within man-made Kingdoms. As well as domestic animals, their diet, unlike that of the peasant producers, has been supplemented by the hunting of wild animals. Hunting was an essential function of royalty, and its elaborate ritual was a mark of noble status. Hunting was also regarded as a training for war.

At this point it is important to note that kingship originated, in all probability, in the need of farming communities to select short-term war leaders in order to meet sporadic external threats, as for example in Mesopotamia, as their myths give us to understand. War leaders continued to lead the people in times of peace. Although some of these leaders may have come up from priestly origins, all led the people in both offensive and defensive warfare against other city states. Kingship, rooted in war, imprinted a pattern of rivalry and predatoriness in pursuit and defence of power. Kings indulged not only in predatory expansionism over the territories of rival powers, but also across the no man's land of wilderness.

The perverted predatory nature of consumer élites and kings is further exemplified by the Mogul Empire, whose brilliant courts were centres of such conspicuous consumption that they could be paid for only by the creation of a tax system whose agents preyed without mercy both on merchants and peasants, no matter whether trade or harvest were good or bad. In the absence of any kind of checks on such systematic plundering, taxation was known as 'eating'.[5]

The remarks of Thomas Jefferson on Europeans are relevant here.

> Jefferson saw the wolves pretending to guard the sheep. 'It seems to be the law of our general nature,' he observed in Paris in 1787, 'in spite of individual exceptions; and experience declares that man is the only animal which devours his own kind; for I can apply no milder term to the governments of Europe, and to the general prey of the rich on the poor.'[6]*

Artificial food pyramids of humans began to grow up – in Britain, in

---

*Although, in the light of modern knowledge, this observation that 'man is the only animal which devours his own kind' is not strictly true, it is nonetheless revelatory of the predatory and inhuman behaviour of *Homo degener*.

Europe, in Asia Minor, in India, in China and elsewhere – leading from primary producers to primary, secondary and ultimate consumers. In other words, their adaptive radiations around agriculture formed the physical energy bases for the ascent and collective security of settled communities comprising consumer élites dominating a mass of producers. Seen in terms of a transference of energy out of the horizontal into the vertical, multitudes of energy-producing plants at the bottom of natural food pyramids formed the energy base for the evolution of the hunter-gatherers as ultimate consumers, ranging freely through the wilderness. Multitudes of energy-producing plant-like cultivators at the bottom of artificial food pyramids now formed the energy base for the ascent of *Homo sapiens sapiens* élites; a *Homo sapiens sapiens* cultivated few 'ranged' above the *Homo sapiens non sapiens* cultivating many exploited as someone's people, on land exploited as someone's land, leading eventually to one King as dominant ultimate consumer over all: a division of labour to form what is known as a social hierarchy, social pyramid or stratified society (see figure 5.4).

I stated at the beginning of this chapter that as well as examining the main adaptive radiations of farming people in the light of their contribution to a physical energy for ascent and security, I also wished to examine those same radiations in the light of their contribution to a psychical energy (religion and science) to the same ends. At the same time as artificial food pyramids of people began to grow, artificial trees of a mythical-cum-mathematical knowledge of the world began to grow out of organized religion, to form the mental energy bases for the ascent and security of farming communities.

Unlike mobile hunter-gatherers, sedentary farming communities suffered severely from events such as epidemics and the failure of the rains which, with the aid of shamans and priests, they attempted to combat by invoking friendly powers and propitiating those hostile to them. To that end, they resorted to self-abasement, solemn ceremonial and human sacrifice. Skeletons dug up from Danish bogs in the 1940s were probably youthful victims of a fertility cult that developed amongst farming peoples in Northern Europe c.3500 BC; while in Britain, at Avebury – where, c.2000 BC, the largest of Britain's pre-historic stone circles was built – people are believed to have met on summer days and winter nights, dancing with painted faces, 'circling the sarsens, drums beating, torches burning' as they participated in fertility rites and other rituals to protect them from the inexplicable perils of their daily lives.

In time, with the growth of urban centres, religions became more complex. Religion, it is important to recall, provided a new stabilizing

Part I: fig 5.4

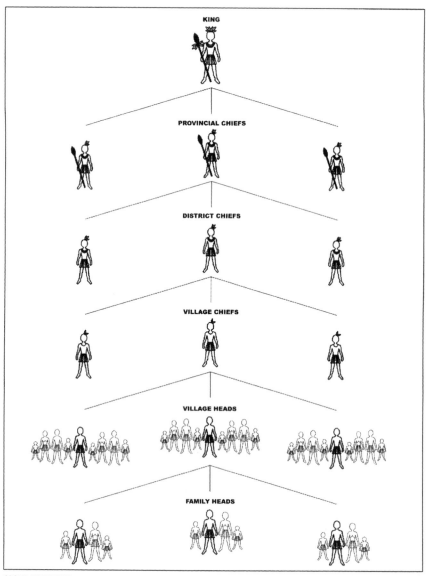

SOCIAL HIERARCHY   (AFTER T. BARNES ET AL)[7]

authority and psychical setting for their protected environments, a new collective world-fearing world view, and a supernatural explanation of cultural origins and events in the form of myth. In particular, the myths of Creation provided these people with new birth-certificates, as it were, to replace those lost as hunter-gatherers: they provided a core of certainty in the midst of the uncertainty surrounding their fallen condition in an alien world. Priest-scientists created Farmer Gods and Goddesses to personify friendly phenomena such as the sun, the moon and rain that ensured human and crop fertility, and chaos-dragons and devils to personify those seemingly meaningless and cruel forces, such as diseases, wolves and natural disasters, that assailed them. In short, they consecrated all those forces relating to the stability and prosperity of their artificial food pyramids, and execrated those relating to illness, instability, dearth and death, in myths of supernatural Powers, or Gods of Creation and Destruction respectively.

From knowledge of these myths, rites and rituals would grow the great trees of knowledge of each stratified society, leading from ignorant primary producers to knowledgeable secondary and ultimate consumers, who, with the aid of a primitive astronomical and mathematical knowledge, proceeded to erect ceremonial centres wherein the community might be ritually imbued with this knowledge (see figure 5.5).

It is noteworthy that their trees of knowledge had their roots in similar – if more profound – needs, hopes and fears as those of tribes, in pre-Christian western Europe and elsewhere, who resided under sacred trees of shamanic knowledge. In other words, The Cosmic or World Tree of magical shamanic knowledge to regulate and control the world has been transformed, down the millennia, into the priestly and scientific trees of mythical-cum-mathematical knowledge to the same ends – to regulate and control the natural world from which they were divorced.

In Mesopotamia the inhabitants of the Tigris-Euphrates valley were confronted with a plethora of natural phenomena to be explained. There were the mysterious experiences of childbirth, life and death, the need for back-breaking labour, and the onset of pain, disease and natural disasters. Knowledge about these conditions was therefore all-important, in order to control or propitiate the powers behind them. Such knowledge was imparted through the myths and associated rituals. The rituals were accompanied by a recital of the myths, which had the same supernatural power as the rituals. The myths eventually provided a supernatural explanation of cultural origins: they also formed what may be described as the trunk of the tree of knowledge out of which the various branches, such as those of astronomy and mathematics, would grow. They were

Part I: fig 5.5

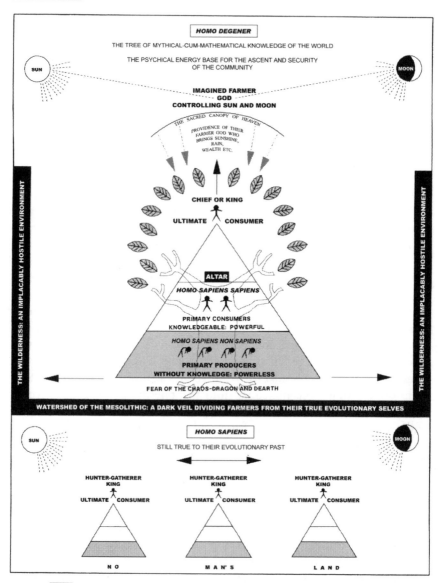

KEY: **ALTAR**   ALTAR OF SACRIFICE. CONCRETE EXPRESSION OR PETRIFACTION OF THEIR FEARS OF THE CHAOS-DRAGON AND DEARTH AND OF THEIR HOPES OF SALVATION

bi-polar constructs of disintegrated, de-ranged and vertically displaced minds and imaginations – from the negative myths of a chaos-dragon and Fall up to the positive myths of a Farmer Sun God and Creation. As well as viewing their situation in terms of friendly and hostile forces and related myths, we may interpret it in terms of light and darkness.

Seen in terms of light and darkness, the light of ecological understanding had gone out of the lives of the *Homo degener* peoples and they were plunged into a profound darkness of ignorance, incomprehension, uncertainty and fear, and consequent powerlessness and insecurity. Nature and their own natures, which had hitherto been suffused with light, were now cast into the deepest darkness, a profound void. Ever since priest-scientists, scientists and explorers have been trying to dispel that darkness and the accompanying uncertainty and fear. As François Jacob put it,

> What man seeks, to the point of anguish, in his gods, in his art, in his science, is meaning. He cannot bear the void.[8]

Human nature abhors a vacuum – or more precisely, as one philosopher said, 'A vacuum, or space in which there is absolutely no body, is repugnant to reason.' With the aid, first of magic, then religion (myth) and then science (astronomy and mathematics), *Homo degener* peoples began to fill the void; they began to create, as it were, pools of light or cores of certainty in the midst of the surrounding darkness in order to give them control over their environment, health and assurance of their destiny. For thousands of years it was a light cast only by magic and myth. Pre-eminently the mythical Farmer God came to represent Light, the Creator creating a Sacred Canopy or Umbrella of Light over the people, providing a mythical meaning and security to their stratified structure.* The call of the religious through the ages has been 'Lighten our darkness, we beseech thee, O Lord'. Light became a supreme symbol of civilization: the Light is within and above, the Darkness without and below; the Light is ahead, the Darkness behind. In addition, the creation of the constellations (numbers of fixed stars grouped within the outlines of imaginary figures), as well as satisfying a human need to bring order to

---

*The fantasy of security provided by the Umbrella of Light of the Farmer God had its modern counterpart in the science fiction fantasies surrounding the Strategic Defence Initiative or 'Star Wars' system. This was a laser system intended to prevent a Soviet first missile strike from wiping out all American missiles, but believed by many, including President Reagan of the USA, to offer the promise of an impermeable umbrella over America. This was yet another possible actualization of ancient fantasies concerning the security of stratified societies. SDI is to be replaced with a scaled down version called the National Missile Defence (NMD) System. This has also been described as a Shield, a wall against the barbarians. In this connection see Appendix viii.

the apparent random disorder of the heavens, was the wish to humanize the frightening blackness of night; they made the hostile night sky friendly.*

Abstracted and isolated as outsiders from contact with the real world, priest-scientists and philosophers slowly began to develop the capacity to abstract and isolate, to classify and categorize phenomena. At first explanations of the external world were based on scholastic theology and the authorities of Plato and Aristotle. The Greek philosophers believed that they lived in an orderly and purposive universe accessible to rational explanation. Their concepts constituted a trend away from superstition, magic and mythology. Their teleological (i.e. goal-directed) conception of the universe was that things could be explained in terms of the ultimate purposes that they were presumed to serve, and in particular the service of humankind. For Aristotle, plants existed for the sake of animals, and animals for the sake of humans. He ranked all living things on a natural scale according to their degree of rationality. He justified slavery by claiming that humans were not created equal, making it natural for some to be born masters and others slaves. He posited a similar subhuman status for women, maintaining that the male is, by nature, superior and the female inferior: he extended this principle of dominance/subservience to all humankind. The Old Testament reinforced the Greek view of the human relationship to the non-human world, as in Genesis which calls on men to 'subdue' the Earth and to 'have dominion over' all living things. Science and scientific experimental method as we know them only arose in the 16th and 17th centuries, at the time of Copernicus, Galileo, Kepler, Bacon and Newton. Bacon saw the acquisition of knowledge as power to enlarge 'the bounds of human empire, to the effecting of all things possible'; while Descartes – regarded as 'the father of modern philosophy' – saw non-human animals merely as complex machines, believing that the new science would make us masters of nature. The active search to obtain knowledge as power to acquire mastery over nature in order to enlarge 'the bounds of human empire' has, until recently, represented the dominant world view of Western scientists, a world view founded in Greece and actively reinforced since the Renaissance. Yet when Voltaire wrote, 'Before Kepler, all men were blind. Kepler had one eye, Newton had two...', he was writing – and they were working – without any knowledge of the prior existence of true humans filled

---

*The ancient Chinese astronomers divided the night sky into many more constellations than did the Greeks. They viewed the heavens as a macrocosm of China, representing almost every aspect of life, including the Emperor, Keeper of the Law, Celestial Prison, Row of Shops, Celestial Granary, etc.

with the light of thousands of years of insider observation, experiment and ecological understanding, or of the subsequent degeneration into total darkness of our cultural ancestors. This darkness, or dark veil, is exemplified in the recent autobiographical writings of François Jacob who neatly points his aim as a scientist, which is 'to understand the world that is veiled' and to rebuild the world in the light of that understanding.

Jacob first asks what drives people so passionately to explore and interrogate the world. The response from those who love science is that it is curiosity, the desire to appropriate nature and to improve the human condition; those who do not love science declare it to be ambition, greed, the will to power, the love of glory. There are, however, Jacob suggests, deeper reasons.

> There is the attempt, the temptation to understand the world that is veiled. The revolt against solitude. Against a reality that escapes you, is unaware of you, and without which there is no life. A metaphysical need for coherence and unity in a universe one seeks to possess but does not even manage to grasp. Nature is not mute. It eternally repeats the same notes which reach us from afar, muffled, with neither harmony nor melody. But we cannot do without melody. We have desperately sought it on the earth and in the sky before perceiving that no-one will ever come to play for us the longed-for music. That it is up to us to strike the chords, to write the score, to bring forth the symphony, to give the sounds a form that, without us, they do not have. Such was, to my eyes, the function of science. Science meant for me the most elevating form of revolt against the incoherence of the universe. Man's most powerful means of competing with God; of tirelessly rebuilding the world while taking account of reality.[9]*

These words reveal as much of what it meant to be a hunter-gatherer artist-cum-scientist – and so of what humankind has lost – as they do of the modern scientist. For the former there was no veil, no solitude, while there was coherence and unity, and the music was already playing for them. They formed an integral part of the symphony of life of the kingdom of nature conducted by the Great Spirit. Their technology and art gave rise to an extraordinary efflorescence of painting 30,000 years ago that has not since been surpassed, and whose durability – and therefore

---

* See Appendix ix for examples of similar desperate searches by individuals for meaning, for the music that always eludes the seeker.

the quality of the knowledge of chemistry behind its development – has already been proved by its 30,000 year survival. The world had to wait until the Renaissance before the technology of *Homo degener* began to develop pigments and brushes that enabled artists to achieve anything like the quality of painting of 13–30,000 years ago, and whose durability has yet to be proved. (The Greeks, we are told, were excellent painters, but little has survived.) The science, technology and art of *Homo sapiens* developed through their intimate understanding of the secret language of nature, whereas modern science has developed mainly through astronomy and the arcane language of mathematics, the latter as abstract as its sedentary *Homo degener* practitioners are abstracted from the real, or wild, world they seek to understand.* Modern scientists attempt to discover the meaning of the universe, but hunter-gatherer scientists were already living that meaning, were an integral part of that meaning. 'Incoherence of the universe', the necessity to rebuild the world, the desire to improve the human condition arose only as a result of the fall of humankind into thousands of years of sedentariness in darkness. The basic problem for modern science, like architecture, is that it is a product of that two-fold fall. Scientists, like architects, are shaped by a complex of aesthetic, technical, social, cultural and historical forces originating in the Mesolithic, whose sum sustains the hierarchical order of each stratified society: scientists' world view and view of the natural world are similarly so shaped. Unlike the hunter-gatherers who knew the world intimately from the inside, and in their wisdom treated it over tens of thousands of years with respect, *Homo degener* scientists take natural formations apart and reassemble them to suit the needs of their stratified societies, an explorative and exploitative activity that has accelerated the destruction of the wilderness in a mere 300 years. Even if scientists disclaim responsibility for the technology and its use that has made such despoliation possible, and claim instead that science is a body of ideas – explanations of how the universe works – and that the real justification for science is that such explanation is a proper end in itself, they still perceive, and make sense of, the natural world and universe through a set of cultural spectacles which, because of their unrecognized re-evolutionary origins as *Homo degener*, merely serve to darken the original veil through which they peer. No matter how much knowledge they acquire and accumulate as outsiders, the dark veil not only remains intact but darkens, further concealing the reality of themselves, so perverting all their discoveries and ideas.

---

* See Appendix viii, where I show that the language of mathematics has been developed by *Homo degener* élites to help unlock the secrets of nature, many of which were already inherently known to hunter-gatherers through their intimate understanding of the secret language of nature.

Scientific knowledge, like its purveyors, is fatally flawed. *Homo degener* tends to pervert almost every discovery, every idea, no matter how pure in intention initially, to other and baneful ends. This is precisely because we are unaware of our own dehumanization as *Homo degener* – our very dehumanization is the cause of our blindness. Our search for meaning and our discoveries have been distorted because our accumulating observations have failed to reveal our two-fold fall, and have therefore increasingly distorted our view of our origins. For instance, science has replaced the myths of Creation with a biological theory of evolution the better to throw light on our origins. Indeed the theory throws light on the origins and evolution of all true life, including *Homo sapiens* moving at the pinnacle of evolution. But, like the myths of Creation, the theory distorts and conceals our own origins and descent as doubly deprived peoples. So if the early agricultural enclaves, and the trees of knowledge growing within them, stood as centres of order, certainty and light against the surrounding chaos, uncertainty and darkness, it was a light of knowledge cast by men alienated and become outsiders looking into the now frightening darkness of nature, and therefore blind to their real evolutionary situation from that day to this.

According to the testimony of Hugh Brody, Colin Turnbull and other anthropologists, modern hunter-gatherers have regarded their wild environments as meaningful, friendly and sacred. It seems likely that this was also the case with their hunter-gatherer forbears. To sedentary farming peoples, however, only the domesticated land, people and produce of that land lying under its own Farmer Gods and tree of knowledge were meaningful, friendly and sacred, and were celebrated as such in ceremonial centres. All else was regarded as meaningless and hostile. Each tree of knowledge, together with its branches and seats of learned authority – amongst the earliest of which were those of the priestly-scientific astronomers, mathematicians, architects and engineers concerned with the building of religious monuments – provided an intellectual and imaginative platform that enabled *Homo sapiens sapiens* élites to consolidate their elevated positions of escape from debasement, and of environmental control, at the summits of artificial food pyramids. Ostensibly propitiating and holding the awful powers without at bay, and agents of the fertility of domesticated animals, plants and plant-like people, the priestly-scientific ministers of their Gods were now in complete control of all sources of information and communication. Together, therefore, artificial food pyramid and artificial tree of mythical-cum-mathematical knowledge represent the physical and psychical foundations – the physical energy bases and the mental energy bases – of a new power to ascent and security. Together they formed the grounds – the fields of land and fields of knowledge – upon and by which began to grow the separate stratified societies (see figure 5.6).

The natural pyramids of energy and numbers so conducive to the evolutionary well-being of all humankind as hunter-gatherers have been replaced by artificial pyramids of energy and numbers, or pyramids of power. Energy, the vital energy or life-force that had been properly directed to the evolution of *Homo sapiens* ranging as self-reliant socio-economic equals – each a person of combined physical and psychical power over their own destiny – was now perverted to the growth of artificial pyramids of gross inequality and dependence; people's energies were converted into the manual energy of the *Homo sapiens non sapiens* cultivators and the cerebral energy of *Homo sapiens sapiens* cultivated at the summit of the stratified society, who thereafter began to wield immense physical and psychical power over the destinies of the *Homo sapiens non sapiens* many. These individual energies (or life-forces) to ascent were thus combined into what may be described as the Life-Force to the ascent and security of the stratified society.

The plant-like cultivator bent to the ground, and miner underground, had in fact joined the green plant as primary producers and source of energy for the growth of a pyramid of energy and numbers, leading up to the *Homo sapiens sapiens* head and brains of the community, who grew off their labour and 'lawfully' robbed them of their energy store. While, as in a natural pyramid of energy, there would appear to be a ten-to-one loss in bulk in a parasite pyramid of energy, there is also, approximately, a ten-to-one gain – the conversion rate, as it were, of manual into cerebral energy, that is reflected in the grading of rewards. Expressed in modern terminology, for every £1 (or equivalent) per annum acquired at the bottom of the pyramid, £1,000 (or equivalent) per annum is acquired at the top, a structural inequality that has now spread across the world. Such a pyramid of energy and numbers was also a pyramid of power of an élite over the mass of people, which made inevitable a structural inequality in every sphere of activity. It also gave rise to the twin tyrants of ambition and avarice that have ensured torture and hell for the mass of humankind and the natural world. Power and privilege guaranteed not only a concentration of knowledge and possessions at the summit, but also the best food (see figure 5.7).

As all the physical and psychical energies, all the hopes and fears to the ascent and security of settled communities combined to concentrate villages into chiefdoms, and chiefdoms into kingdoms, or states in which a king ruled over a number of chiefdoms, a king arrived at the apex of

Part I: fig 5.6

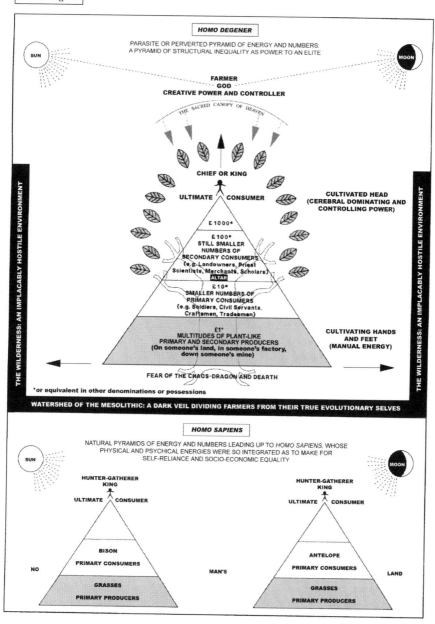

Part I: fig 5.7

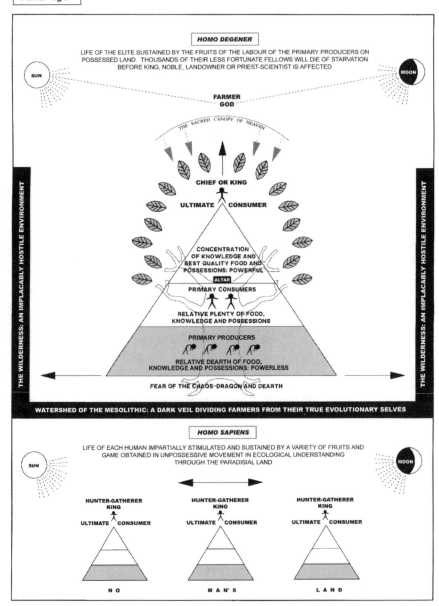

a pyramid of power. In many communities sacred kings developed out of magicians: in early societies the king was often a magician as well as a priest. As a means of controlling nature, magic was often an essential function of kingship, and through their ostensible possession of a powerful spirit such kings sometimes came to be regarded as gods in their lifetime. Above them might reside a High God, or a pantheon of Farmer Gods and Goddesses organized in the same hierarchical fashion. Together they formed the governing head of the stratified society. More than that, their High God was the apotheosis of the Life-Force of the stratified society. The tree of religious and scientific knowledge provided the principles and tools of government, which was primarily concerned with order and chaos. The implication is that government was also concerned with good and evil, to the extent that the friendly forces making for the security of the stratified society were good, and the hostile forces making for chaos, for the destruction of the stratified society, were evil. This identification provided the moral basis of power within the community.

An example of the identification of goodness with those in power at the summit of the social pyramid is provided by the seemingly providential rise of the aristocracy out of the anarchy of the early Middle Ages in Europe, when anyone who could bring order, no matter how harsh, to the life of the people was good by definition – Heaven-sent, as can be seen from the use of titles such as 'Lord' for both the Deity and the local resident of the manor house. Likewise, those who brought order to the early settlements out of the chaos of the surrounding wilderness, to become the governing heads of communities, would have been good by definition – and of power almost divine to those who benefited from it – while those posing a threat to their survival would have been regarded as evil. As their pyramids of power grew, inevitably their scales of value, together with their hopes and fears, were polarized in similar fashion, to form the moral backbone of the entire pyramid of power (see figure 5.8).

Within this moral ambience the King and élite now had at their disposal the means not only to govern but to perpetuate their pyramids of power. This was achieved by means of what may be described as a fivefold concentration of power for the self-aggrandizement and prosperity of élites, and for the security of the community. For although the sources of power are now many and various, I shall examine these five facets because they may be considered fundamental to the rise and security of the early stratified societies, drawing on modern examples where necessary because these traditional sources of power are still very much alive, forming a major part of the Life-Force of the stratified society. This fivefold concentration of power comprised:

Part I: fig 5.8

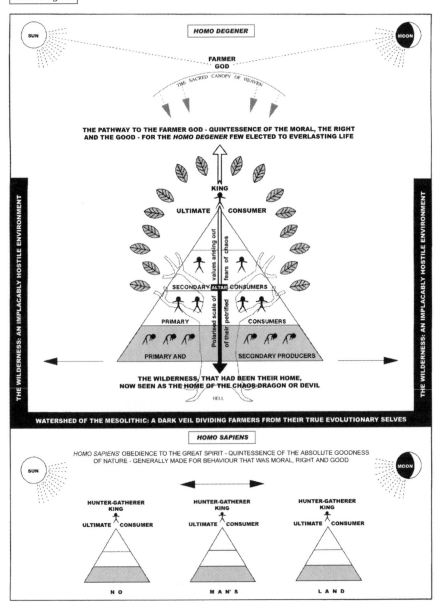

1) Exclusive royal, state or private ownership of the land, of the means of production, of the producers and the produce of the land, and of the tax and trade (as slaves) of those people and of their produce.
2) Armed control.
3) A priestly-scientific moral control.
4) A priestly-scientific linguistic, and mathematical measuring, control.
5) The Farmer God and King, quintessence of divine and secular law, order and power, including the secret power over life and death, even in a life hereafter (see figure 5.9).

First, concerning the ownership of property and of the means of production, I suggested at the beginning of this chapter that the earliest settled communities were egalitarian in their organization. With the creation of food surpluses, trade and related growth of different classes went the invention of metallurgy; iron, copper and bronze weapons and tools enabled the emerging classes to consolidate their position through the ownership of property and control of the means of production, which further opened the way to the exploitation of people. For, whatever its form of government, the actual power in a country has always resided in those who owned property. (Under Socialism, that power devolves upon those administering the national property.) The development of property, together with the ownership and control of the means of production, of the producers and the produce of the land – as in the exploitation of people and land for the purposes of mining – constituted further agents of power – first of kings to whom the people and the produce of the land belonged; then, more recently, of mine and factory owners controlling armies of workers and slaves.

As regards tax and trade of the produce of the land as a source of wealth and power, I have already referred to the dominance of the Wessex people of the Early Bronze Age in Britain, whose wealth was probably due not only to their success as farmers and cattle-ranchers, but to their controlling position on one of the trade routes between Ireland and the nearer parts of Europe. A similar process took place during the late Iron Age in central Africa about a thousand years ago, when there was a marked increase in the size of cattle herds, a move to easily defended hills and the opening of long-distance trade routes to the Arab world and India. These developments led to the creation of the early central African states of Mapungubwe (on the Limpopo), Great Zimbabwe, Mutapa and Rozvi. These were involved in exporting raw materials, ivory and gold, and some manufactures, and importing consumer goods such

Part I: fig 5.9

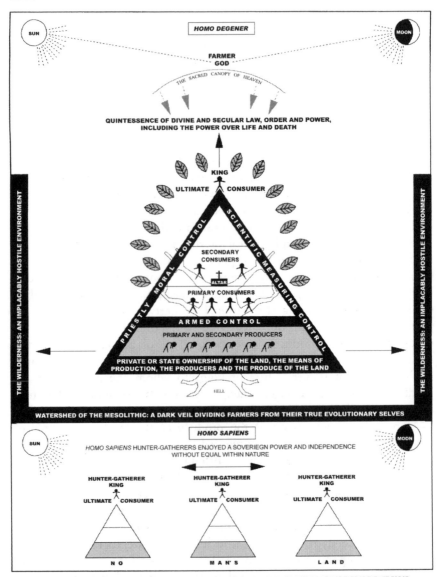

HOMO DEGENER

FARMER
GOD

THE SACRED CANOPY OF HEAVEN

QUINTESSENCE OF DIVINE AND SECULAR LAW, ORDER AND POWER,
INCLUDING THE POWER OVER LIFE AND DEATH

KING
ULTIMATE CONSUMER

THE WILDERNESS: AN IMPLACABLY HOSTILE ENVIRONMENT

PRIESTLY MORAL CONTROL

SCIENTIFIC MEASURING CONTROL

SECONDARY CONSUMERS

ALTAR

PRIMARY CONSUMERS

ARMED CONTROL

PRIMARY AND SECONDARY PRODUCERS

PRIVATE OR STATE OWNERSHIP OF THE LAND, THE MEANS OF
PRODUCTION, THE PRODUCERS AND THE PRODUCE OF THE LAND

HELL

WATERSHED OF THE MESOLITHIC: A DARK VEIL DIVIDING FARMERS FROM THEIR TRUE EVOLUTIONARY SELVES

HOMO SAPIENS

HOMO SAPIENS HUNTER-GATHERERS ENJOYED A SOVERIEGN POWER AND INDEPENDENCE
WITHOUT EQUAL WITHIN NATURE

HUNTER-GATHERER
KING
ULTIMATE CONSUMER

HUNTER-GATHERER
KING
ULTIMATE CONSUMER

HUNTER-GATHERER
KING
ULTIMATE CONSUMER

N O 　 M A N' S 　 L A N D

KEY: ✝ ALTAR 　 HIGH ALTAR: MEETING PLACE OF THE FIVEFOLD CONCENTRATION OF POWER FORMING A MAJOR PART OF THE LIFE-FORCE
OF THE COMMUNITY, MEDIATED BY THE PRIEST-SCIENTISTS TO THE PEOPLE THROUGH THE SACRED WORD AND THE SACRED
FOOD CONSUMED AT THE ALTAR

as cloth and glass beads, symbols of wealth and status in the communities. Gold mining, being extremely profitable, was controlled by the rulers and ivory hunting was heavily taxed by them. Through payment of 'taxes' or tribute, it was made clear to the people that the king and his line were the most important, demonstrating their control of power within the state. In thus taking some or all of the surplus goods from the producers, the ruling few were further exploiting the main bulk of the people to their own ends.

The illustrations in figure 5.10 will assist understanding of the interrelationships and distribution of power within these central African states, and in other early states.

Secondly, there was the power of the armed men, the physical guarantors of the existing pyramid of power. For example, the individual acquisition of wealth and possessions has in turn often necessitated the use of military (or police) power to protect it, and to protect the rich from the more numerous poor. The army and police have usually been under the control of the ruling few. Pyramids of power themselves attempt to enhance and protect their wealth and power in relation to others. For instance, as recent studies have shown, the Great Powers down the centuries have striven to enhance their wealth and their military power, to become (and to remain) both rich and strong. For 'wealth is usually needed to underpin military power, and military power is usually needed to acquire and protect wealth.'[11] Since earliest times, technological advances, such as the development of copper and bronze weapons, have greatly enhanced that power. The military also spearheaded territorial expansion, becoming arbiters of life and death on the altar of the battlefield. Successful commanders were often ennobled and/or rewarded with grants of land.

Thirdly, with regard to the moral control pertaining within any one stratified society, I have already pointed out that the chiefs and kings of stratified societies have generally resided under the moral ambience of order and goodness, whose principal guardians have been religion and law.* Providing, as they have, the moral backbones of the earliest stratified societies, they ensured that successive generations were brought up to accept the values, beliefs and laws handed down to them – and, in particular, to accept the parasite pyramidal structure under which they resided as being of divine origin and under divine protection. In other words, the ruling class used religion and law to support its privileged

---

*In Britain today we are constantly reminded that the Establishment comprises 'the Great and the Good'.

Part I: fig 5.10

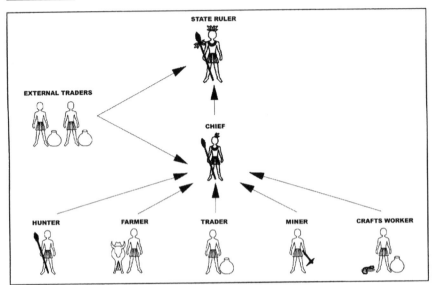

MOVEMENT OF GOODS WITHIN THE SOCIETY

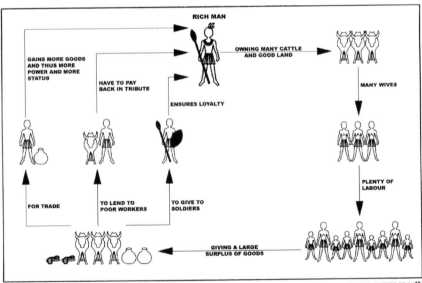

CYCLE OF WEALTH WITHIN THE SOCIETY   (AFTER T. BARNES ET AL)[10]

position, while making exploitation acceptable to the mass of people. To that end, societies not only looked back to cultural ancestors to justify their values and beliefs in the present, but also established and invoked covenants with Farmer Gods. So, whereas earlier the spirit of the hunter-gatherer was united in a covenant with the Great Spirit, symbolized in a ritual meal, with their adaptation to farming a new covenant was generally established within artificial pyramids with a Farmer God, often symbolized in a ritual sacrifice and meal, such as Holy Communion at the High Altar. The new covenants sanctified their pyramids of power, together with farming and the collection and redistribution of food by king and administration. Furthermore, Farmer God and king provided a fourth-dimensional link, as it were, with an immemorial past: the genealogies of both Kings and Gods were regarded as stretching back into the mists of time, sanctifying their past and also their power structure in the present in the light of that past.

In thus sanctifying the past, religion assumed immense power over the present and the future. Major decisions taken by a ruler – such as whether or not to go to war, or in times of famine due to drought – were usually taken after consultation with the spiritual representatives of the land. This shows the direct link between the political system and religion. Today such consultation for solutions to problems lies increasingly with rulers and their scientific advisers. However, in the early stratified societies the alliance of political authority and religion had the added bonus of convincing the mass of ordinary people that the political organization of the state was correct or legitimate: the political power structure was reinforced with every religious festival.

Given the moral ambience of sacredness, legitimacy, rightness and goodness under which ruling élites and their cultures resided, it was inevitable that any challenge to their authority would be regarded as unlawful, evil or wrong. This gave rise to measures to combat not only potential hostility between ruling élites and people but between the various in-groups and out-groups constituting stratified societies. As well as the use of armed force to suppress conflict between rich and poor – or between the 'insiders' and 'outsiders' to whom I referred earlier – societies introduced regulations to protect their members from one another, and the institutionalization of punishments for disobeying them.

In Mesopotamia, for example, urban specialization and stratification resulted in a society of insiders and outsiders, making the distinction between 'us' and 'them' an important feature of the life conditions of the majority of people. The close proximity of competing out-groups posed a constant threat of hostilities breaking out between them, which had to be controlled before the situation could threaten the peace of the state. In the absence of natural mechanisms of social control that had governed the behaviour of *Homo sapiens, Homo degener* had to develop new measures of control. In this they were greatly assisted by the introduction of writing. Laws were introduced, as were punishments for disobeying them. Both laws and punishments were already being codified and given divine sanction within the city states of Sumeria by 2400 BC. These early codes were subsequently revised and eventually embodied in regulations like the Code of Hammurabi around 1750 BC.

As hunter-gatherers no-one made the law, nor was any person subject to such law: all equally obeyed the universal laws of nature, the natural mechanisms controlling social behaviour. With their loss, pyramids of power developed laws specific to their own societies. Those who had made the laws, based on the legitimation of their usurpation of the land and subjugation of the peoples and the land, now wielded the ultimate instrument of power, the power to pardon and condemn, including the ultimate sanction of death as a punishment. However, as in the case of the Mosaic Law, human law in most communities has been made subject to Divine Law, itself the apotheosis of man-made law, with its power to reward good behaviour with eternal life and to punish bad behaviour with eternal damnation. The law most often punishes those who are already punished by being doubly deprived, repressed and imprisoned by socio-economic circumstances at the bottom of each social heap. In short, the identification by the governing head of the society of friendly (good) and hostile (evil) forces, which, as I argued above, provided the moral basis of power within the community, was now legally reinforced with rewards and punishments.

Fourthly, regarding the linguistic, and mathematical measuring, control of the people and of the land, *Homo degener* peoples no longer spoke the secret language of nature and were no longer of one body and one mind with the Earth.* Rather the meaning and measure of a person and of the Earth came more and more to depend upon the knowledge acquired and imparted by the priestly-scientific experts and King. By means of specialist mythopoeic and mathematical languages of domination and control, they established the meaning and measure of a person as subservient to the Gods ranged above, and so subservient to those appointed by the Gods as priestly-scientific mediators between Heaven and Earth. Language

---

*See Appendix viii concerning the loss of a universal language of nature and its replacement with a prototype Indo-European language in S.W. Asia. For while the hunter-gatherers certainly spoke different tongues, they shared a knowledge of the secret and universal language of nature, which enabled them to move through, and adapt to, virtually any environment in the world.

– both spoken and written* – has come to represent a statement of power of élites over the masses, and over wild nature, reinforcing and perpetuating the hierarchical order and division of labour.

Homo degener's search for (hierarchical) order, in a world which to *Homo sapiens* had been ordered and timeless, led to the development of the calendar. Depending as it did on elaborate mathematics, the calendar was the product of élites of stratified societies. In Egypt, for instance, only the priests and certain members of the nobility understood the intricacies of calendrical computation. In Rome the calendar was essential to the domination of the subjects of the empire: it regulated their days and established the rhythm of their lives, just as it does those of the majority of *Homo degener* peoples today.

As well as naming and numbering the days and months of the year, those in authority named, numbered and registered the people for tax, as revealed in both the Old and New Testaments of the Bible, and they named and measured the land. They established the meaning and measure of the land as some Farmer God's land, and so as *someone*'s land, as measured for instance in units relating to the length of a King's arm, or a whole day's ploughing. In England the acre was originally a long narrow strip of land fixed by Edward I in 1305 and based on the amount of land a man with two oxen could plough in a day. Later it was limited by statute to the equivalent of 4,840 square yards. All were measured and held thus in a *status quo* by the Farmer God, as God's children and God's Earth. As people and land became hierarchically ordered as someone's people and land, the wilderness remained essentially void, a mythical No Man's Land between measured and known lands – a meaningless, measureless and unknown wasteland.

Thereafter, as their trees of mythical-cum-mathematical knowledge bore fruit in their manifold artefacts and arts, the moral, linguistic and mathematical-measuring control of the people were met together most obviously in step pyramids, ziggurats and temple towers built to study, and ostensibly control, the movements of the sun, the moon and the stars, and to reinforce the eminence and authority of the astronomers and King. For architecture is

> . . . the most potent of the arts because it is at once the most immediately expressive and the least avoidable. It is no surprise that absolute monarchs of the past, and dictators in our own century,

---

*Agriculture involved the physical cultivation of the land by *Homo sapiens non sapiens* peasants, while writing and literature involved the cultivation of the minds of *Homo sapiens sapiens* élites, themselves cultivated on the backs of *Homo sapiens non sapiens*.

have turned first to their architects and builders to provide them
with the substance of their authority.[12]

As Alan Bullock wrote of Hitler:

> Architecture appealed strongly to him – especially Baroque – and
> he had grandiose plans for the rebuilding of Berlin, Munich, and
> Nuremberg and the other big German cities. The qualities which
> attracted him were the monumental and the massive as in the new
> Reich Chancellery: the architecture of the Third Reich, like the
> Pyramids, was to reflect the power of its rulers...[13]

Height is important too to the ordinary citizen, for it equates with status:
the Victorians, for instance, built imposing houses on hills not just to
escape a satanic industrial environment but also to reinforce the social
pecking order.
Above all,

> Architecture ... is always creation *against* nature; its history is the
> story of the subjection of nature to the constructive activity of the
> ruling classes.[14]

The history of architecture is also the story of the subjection of *Homo
sapiens non sapiens* as slaves to that constructive activity. The building of
many great monuments of the ancient world depended largely upon the
toil of slaves, while the development of architecture, and in particular
classical architecture, throughout Europe in the 18th century is acknowledged
as being the direct result of revenues from slavery.

The architecture of the pyramid of power itself both reflects and
reinforces the subjection of nature and human nature in the interests of
the ruling classes. In particular, the temples of yesterday and Courts of
Justice today have provided the principal centres of state sanctification
and enforcement of the dominant social censures of each stratified society.
Within their temples, as within their Courts of Justice, priests and
scientists have provided proof of innocence or guilt; when those deemed
to have transgressed the established laws have been punished accordingly.
In addition to these principal centres of Law and Order, of moral,
linguistic and measuring control, architects provided stages on which the
priestly-scientific actors or experts re-enacted, year in and year out, the
drama of *Homo degener*'s relationship with the friendly (orderly, good)
and hostile (chaotic, evil) powers before audiences comprising the mass

of the people. For instance, the size and central position of the Greek and Roman theatres in their respective towns is out of all proportion to their entertainment value. Social control through entertainment was their primary object. They formed a communication point between ruler and people. The Greek tragedies were interpreted by the priest and the oracle. In many places, such as Delphi, the theatre and the oracle were next door to one another. Artistic, social and scientific experts on television, relayed to vast audiences via communication satellites, are their direct descendants – as are the Courts of Justice – and, with the aid of oracle-like computers, perform similar dramatic rôles today.

A dominant *Homo sapiens sapiens* few play distinguished on-stage rôles, as principal actors on the national stage. Other sub-dominant *Homo sapiens sapiens* play minor supporting and behind-the-scenes rôles; while a *Homo sapiens non sapiens* majority remains totally obscure in the darkness of the national auditorium – that is, unless events force some into playing poorly learned parts in the theatre of war. Television has greatly accentuated this state of affairs, turning all the world into a theatre. In the USA, for instance, the television debates relating to the selection of candidates to run for President – the Primaries – have been described as 'auditions for the rôle of "chief actor" of the USA'.* All such acting rôles are attended by uncertainty and acute and intense insecurity. Meanwhile, though Britain has lost an empire, she has nonetheless been governed ever since by an empire of the mind, the deeply ingrained desire amongst British Ministers that they should still perform as Great Players on the World Stage.

Perhaps the greatest theatres of all were the temples of sacrifice. In order to placate the powers that seemed all too ready to overwhelm them and to ensure the health and well-being of society, ancient peoples, as pointed out earlier, often resorted to animal and human sacrifice; a defeated enemy might supply a reservoir of human victims. More recently, scientists and surgeons have performed a similar rôle in their laboratories and operating theatres, using a variety of animals and, in the case of Germany and Japan during the Second World War, Jews and prisoners of war respectively – since when they have also drawn on a reservoir of baboons and other primates for experimentation and sacrifice for spare parts for degenerate human beings.† Here again, the passive audience of

---

*When President Franklin D. Roosevelt met the actor Orson Welles, he said, 'Orson, you and I are the two best actors in America'.

† In Part II, Chapter 6, I shall examine in greater detail the relationship between those wielding power and the victims of power.

millions watching televised organ transplants is as essential an aspect of the architecture of power as were such audiences in the days of the Aztecs and Toltecs. Their presence both enhances and protects that power, making the whole process appear morally acceptable while concealing the cruelly exploitative and grossly immoral means that made possible the accretion of knowledge that led to such achievements.

Fifthly and finally, the Farmer God, as the divine embodiment of the overall ideology of Law and Order pertaining within a particular pyramid of power, was the apotheosis of secular power within that stratified society. Their God was not only the most perfect embodiment of the four major sources of power enumerated above – as well as being Possessor of the Lands and Providential Provider of all good things, he was also represented as the God of Battles, the Law-Giver and the Great Architect – but he thereby legitimized them and guaranteed their perpetuation; the King, even as late as medieval kingship in Europe, was the sacred embodiment and representative of the powers that govern the cosmos, an incarnation of the divine intention and moral law, guaranteeing the order and rightness of the world. His ministers – whether nobles, government ministers, priest-scientists or judges – have wielded in the name of their God the ultimate instrument of legitimate power, the power of life and death over the community, both in this life and in a life hereafter, precisely in order to preserve the existing sources and panoply of power.

The ostensible existence of a Farmer God – as the ultimate source of power sanctifying that of Princes and Kings – has also been psychically invaluable to those at the bottom of the pyramid of power, whom those at the summit have exploited to their own ends and who have therefore most often lived lives of powerlessness and despair. They have habitually called on such a God to relieve them of their burdens in this life, if only by the promise of rewards in a life to come.

As Creator and Defender of the Providential Order – the giver of all good things – and Destroyer of its enemies, the Farmer God ostensibly protected the static State from internal subversion and invasion, particularly by wild nature. This brings me back to the moral backbone of the entire pyramid of power referred to earlier (see figure 5.8). For the whole essence of the survival and prosperity of the *Homo degener* community lay in the preservation of the existing power structure (the ultimate good) against chaos, and particularly against wild nature. It was indeed this profound relationship of conflict with wild nature which, perhaps more than any other, threw up the tyrannical theocratic governments of the past. Thereafter the preservation of order and the prevention of threatening change were paramount: change was inimical to the pyramid of power, the core of which has lain with those who secretly manipulate the power to destroy those agents – whether human or natural – that would initiate such change. In their secret knowledge and manipulation of the will of their God to those ends lay the immense power of the King and ruling élite. It was part of the Divine Right of Kings. The divine embodiment of sacred and secular power, and in particular the secret power to reward (or give life) and to punish (or destroy life), not only in the immediate present but in a life hereafter, reached a zenith in the Pharaoh, Son of the Sun God, apotheosis of the pyramid of power as he daily traversed the skies in the Chariot of the Sun or lay entombed within the secret chambers of a pyramid. From him emanated, it was believed, the spiritual energy to illumine or put out the sun, and so to illumine or destroy Egypt and the Egyptian social pyramid.

Today the Divine Right of Kings is the prerogative of Governments and their scientific advisers. Heads of Government, however, with the aid of their secret police, often act alone. Stalin, for instance, ostensibly carrying out the wishes of the embalmed Lenin, showed people he had absolute power and control over them. Life and death depended on his whim. He could have them tortured, have them rescued, have them rewarded and then have them killed. He had the power of God over life and death throughout the USSR. Elsewhere national secret services, such as MI5 in Britain and the CIA in the USA, are shrouded in secrecy and have the licence to kill. More generally, the power to energize and protect the stratified society has lain increasingly with the scientist, who, under God (or an ideology such as Marxism), has become, like the priest-scientist of old, the guardian of society and giver of all good things. American presidents, for example, have turned increasingly to scientists to advise them, particularly in matters of security. At the height of the American Civil War Lincoln established the National Academy of Sciences, and in 1916 the National Research Council was set up, while the National Science Foundation was a product of the Cold War. The thinking of presidents, combined with science policy since the Second World War, has been greatly concerned with the importance of nuclear weapons. In addition to the protection of society, the scientists' domain now covers every aspect of food production and redistribution, health – including the increasing power to prolong life indefinitely in this world, even as Gods and priest-scientists promised everlasting life in a world here-after – and the supply of energy; and secret information is their special concern.

Much basic research, the development and licensing of drugs, the development, operation and deployment of nuclear weapons and the offensive-defensive products of molecular biologists are closely guarded secrets. Governments and their scientific advisers decide whether certain knowledge should remain shrouded, as in Britain, by such as Official Secrets Acts, or shared with the general public. For to share knowledge is seen as a sign of weakness, a sharing or dissipation of power and a threat to security. So it is that the core of power – the secret information as power to create and to destroy human life, which now lies within the domain of the scientist rather than the priest – will and must remain secret and potentially dangerous to all those not a party to its secrets.

This fivefold concentration of power for the self-aggrandizement and prosperity of élites and for the security of their stratified structures is expressive of, or represents, a ritualization and institutionalization of their conflict behaviour, that arose initially in relation to a now unknown, chaotic and frightening wilderness. It has grown up within an overall moral ambience of rightness and goodness, an ambience generated and sustained by its God or Mandate of Heaven. It is important at this point to note the true moral implications of this bestowal of a sacred status upon their pyramids of power that both negated and replaced the original sacred status of the wilderness. For, as I argued earlier, the dichotomy between farmers and hunter-gatherers and wilderness created a dualism between friendly and hostile, good and evil in the minds of *Homo degener* peoples. This dualism was then reinforced following the division of labour between *Homo sapiens sapiens* and *Homo sapiens non sapiens*, between those cultivated with knowledge and the cultivators without knowledge, a polarization between psyche and physique, when those so elevated came to regard themselves as sacred, orderly and good, while further demonizing those regarded as potential threats.

With the polarization of the few cultivated as cerebral dominating controllers of the stratified structure and the majority as 'feeling' vegetable-like cultivators, there slowly arose a dualism between mind and matter, between intelligence and feeling, between the rationality of the thinking male at the summit of the stratified society and the potential chaos of the feeling masses, of women and of wild nature. Mind, intelligence and rationality became associated with (male) divinity, order and good; body/matter, feeling, women and wild nature were liable to be equated with disorder, chaos and evil (see figure 5.11).*

These later dualisms further intensified the division between *Homo degener* and wild nature. Whereas hunter-gatherer scientists saw themselves as one of a diversity of animals harmoniously integrated within the

---

* See Appendix iii for the origin of these dualisms.

Part I: fig 5.11

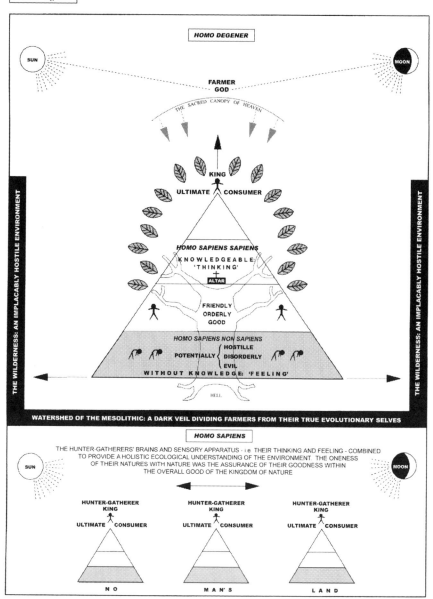

wilderness, dualisms as between human/animal, culture/nature now became firmly entrenched, particularly in Western science.

Ever since the early Neolithic, knowledge has been increasingly acquired and concentrated under the ambience of such dichotomy and dualism, enabling and encouraging the spread and enrichment of pyramids of power at the cost of the wilderness. This extraordinary change in the possession and use of knowledge – from its possession and use by all hunter-gatherer bands, enabling them to live in, and to share equally, the wealth of the wilderness, to its possession and use by *Homo sapiens sapiens* élites of pyramids of power, enabling them to exploit that natural wealth to enrich their stratified structures – is revealed in the following comments on the battle for the forests of Sarawak. For Mohamed Idris, then president of Friends of the Earth in Malaysia, the battle was

'...a clash of different systems, of different civilizations – on one side a powerful modern system motivated by greed; on the other a traditional system that is oriented towards fulfilling human needs. Despite the so-called greatness of knowledge of modern science and technology, the modern man is far less knowledgeable, in fact far more stupid, than the indigenous, native man who lives close to nature.'...

One Western scientist who knows the Sarawak forests better than most is Robin Hanbury-Tenison. He spent more than a year with the Penan in the 1970s, while head of an international science expedition to the Gunung Mulu area in highland Sarawak... His scientific expedition had contained some of the best biologists in the world, yet, he says, 'it was universally acknowledged by those scientists that the Penan were their forest professors. It is with the Penan that the real wealth of the rainforest lies.'[15]

Homo degener peoples everywhere have destroyed the real knowledge and real wealth of the world for the sake of the wealth of élites of pyramids of power. Like architecture, the architecture of the pyramid of power is always creation *against* nature. The history of both is the story of the subjugation of nature, and of human nature, to the constructive activities of the ruling classes.

It will be appreciated that an almost incredible change had occurred in just a few thousand years in the fortunes of humankind, which may once again be expressed in terms of energy. With the loss of their relative perfection and power, *Homo degener* peoples began to redirect their energies into *the vertically oriented structure-building behaviour of the de-ranged community*. With the aid of a Farmer God and farming, a natural solar energy and primary habitat – conducive to the evolution of *Homo sapiens* – were transformed into a supernatural Solar Energy and secondary 'safe' domesticated habitat, conducive to the cultivation in the vertical of wealthy and powerful *Homo sapiens sapiens* élites on the backs of poor and powerless *Homo sapiens non sapiens* cultivators. Thus it was that, as members of pyramids of power, the command of each person over his or her own destiny as hunter-gatherer king was replaced by the command of a King and his advisers over the destinies of all his subjects. Throughout the remainder of the book I differentiate between the real sun energizing the growth of natural food pyramids, and man-made Suns – e.g. Farmer God or Marxism – energizing the growth of parasite food pyramids.

The dominant rôle of élites implies that people are by nature unequal. But such is not the case. People have been made unequal by their grossly unnatural, degenerate captive condition within stratified societies.

> An analysis of historical society, with five or six thousand years of exploitation of the majority by a ruling minority, shows very clearly that the dominance-submission psychology is an adaptation to the social order, and not its cause.[16]

Concepts and promises of liberty, equality and fraternity for members of stratified societies are, and must ever remain, fictions, illusions entertained by *Homo degener* people which swiftly turn to disillusionment and despair just because they can only truly exist in hunter-gatherer societies, the real estate of humankind.

In the absence of any understanding of their real condition, all *Homo degener* members of stratified societies – whether the ruling few insiders or the uncomprehending masses – are, of course, in relation to wild nature, uncomprehending outsiders. The ruling few at the summits of stratified societies, their brains and sensory apparatus dis-integrated and divorced from the wilderness, manufacture or receive and mediate down to their subordinate fellows information regarding themselves, other societies and the wild environment that is, was, and always will be, the fabrication of people divorced from the real world and therefore fundamentally false. In destroying the real world that was a wilderness, *Homo degener* peoples have destroyed not only the ground of their wholeness and relative perfection, not only the ground of a true universal humanity and potential unity in equality, but also the very ground of reality itself. Not only have *Homo degener* peoples lost touch with reality, but for that very reason they destroy the reality of the world.

Chapter 6

A Collective Primary Schizophrenia

'When memory dies a people die.'
'But what if we make up false memories?'
'That's worse, that's murder.'

(A. Sivanandan)[1]

Prior to the Mesolithic, the Earth and *Homo sapiens* were of one body and one mind. Now the bodies and minds of certain isolated groups of *Homo sapiens* were alienated from the wild environment and Great Spirit. De-ranged people were forced out of a safe, familiar and well-beloved home into a world that was unfamiliar and extremely unsafe, in which everything was strange and unreal, just because their five senses and brains no longer functioned in an integrated fashion in loving movement through the wilderness. The foundations of their common sense reality of themselves and of the world were thus destroyed. They withdrew behind high walls into their own artificial worlds, opening up world-fearing 'windows' of myth to the outside world. The myths, and in particular the myths of a Fall, are a function of that earlier fall. The Fall myths reveal humanity's awareness of suffering from something like a universal neurosis — a universal inhibition or imprisonment of people in an inhuman life pattern — that overlays a combined physical and psychical disturbance at a deeper level, a level that is not so readily observable nor responsive to historical diagnosis. That disturbance was a form of schizophrenia involving disintegration of the personality and alienation from the reality of a cosmic unity within the kingdom of nature — that is to say, the two-fold fall of *Homo degener* is of the nature of a psychosis rather than a neurosis.

Neurotics retain sufficient of a hold on the real world that they can be brought to recognize that their behaviour is irrational; psychotics lack that insight. Psychotics are oblivious to the truth that they are ill. In

146

schizophrenic psychoses we find a disorganization of behaviour patterns which involve primarily the formation of contact with reality. Schizophrenia is a total personality disorder in which the victim has become alienated from the outside world and has withdrawn into his own world. As Franz Alexander points out,

> ... the psychotic has, in a sense, no respect for reality. It is easier for him to relinquish his contact with reality than to control his own emotions, and as a result he solves his inner conflicts by changing the picture of reality to suit his subjective demands.[2]

These farming communities displayed symptoms of a total personality disorder when a majority had, to all intents and purposes, severed contact with the wilderness beyond their enclaves. They not only withdrew behind high walls into their own artificial worlds, but they changed the picture of reality in their myths of Creation to suit their subjective demands. Indeed a schizoid condition! These farming communities in fact underwent changes in personality and behaviour that can best be understood in the light of similar changes that take place in victims of schizophrenia.

Schizophrenia is probably not one illness but an umbrella term covering a number of different diseases, each having its own cause, but sharing the same psychiatric symptoms. It is commonly accepted that there is a genetic vulnerability to schizophrenia. It is a common condition that affects one person in every hundred of the general population of the world.

> There is indisputable evidence that schizophrenia is a genetically inherited disease... The exact genetic picture is not yet clear. One, two or more genes or genetic factors may be involved. These genetic faults are mediated through the body's chemistry.[3]

Genetic predisposition does not, however, mean that a person will necessarily develop the illness; in certain instances environment – including intolerable childhood or adulthood experiences – may play an important rôle as the trigger to schizophrenia. Whatever the cause, biochemical mediation of genetic faults initiates a change in personality.

> Very gradually the behaviour, thought and emotions of the patient are almost totally changed... If previously he had been a conservative before becoming ill he may now become an ardent socialist or vice versa. If once he was a respecter of the law and a conformist he

may now commit criminal acts, sometimes small and sometimes horrifyingly large. He may become violent whereas he was previously a very gentle shy person.

Thus the change in personality may be huge and the ill personality, which has so insidiously developed, may overlay the true personality like a blanket or a cloud... His knowledge and self-awareness of his condition may be almost nil.[4]

Gwynneth Hemmings argues that the symptoms by which schizophrenia is usually defined are hallucinations (most often auditory), delusions (which may be paranoid, grandiose or religious) and thought disorder. Anger, violence and criminality are also common symptoms.

It is these symptoms that I shall now examine in greater detail in order to reveal more fully the pathology of *Homo degener* peoples, who underwent personality changes which likewise overlaid their true personalities like a cloud.

In a study of schizophrenia, Gwen Howe examined one case, that of Steven, who changed from being an outgoing, popular student and games-player at school to becoming increasingly distant, unapproachable and rejecting of both his family and his friends. He began to become a stranger to them. He had in fact undergone a dramatic personality change. He had entered a private nightmare world, beset with paranoid ideas that provoked hostility towards those around him, paranoid ideas that had no basis in reality. Everyone and everything seemed to pose a threat to the terrified lad. He felt he had committed an appalling crime. The overall effect was to turn his family 'in on itself' in self-protection.

The strange and frightening ideas that Steven experienced are typical of a classic cluster of symptoms which we call acute schizophrenia. It is interesting that most of these bizarre symptoms have been described in exactly similar terms by sufferers from different cultures all over the world... There are three main strands to this type of schizophrenic illness and these are *altered perception, thought disorder* and *delusional ideas*, the last perhaps best described as fixations which are patently false and impervious to reasoned argument ... these are probably provoked by, and certainly aided and abetted by, *altered perception...* Any or all of the five senses may become distorted or actually relay faulty messages, as happens when the individual is hallucinating.[5]

Gwen Howe argues that not only do the two most important senses of hearing and vision become distorted, manifesting the patient's fears in relation to the confusing and nightmare environment, but so do the senses of touch, taste and smell. In short,

> ...all five senses are likely to fail sufferers in their attempts to make sense of their surroundings. This can be a gradual, destructive process that tends to nullify everything they have previously understood about the world around them... It seems reasonable to assume that human life as we understand it depends on the brain *making sense* of all the messages reaching it. If delusional thinking is the natural result of the brain trying to create order out of an escalating chaos, then this would explain the remarkable constancy of content in schizophrenic delusions, with so many sufferers finding such similar explanations for what is happening to them. For those who are tormented by distorted feelings of guilt for being 'evil' (a word frequently used by such individuals in connection with themselves), it is a short step to feelings that they should and will be persecuted in some way... In other words, as the perceived threat of danger escalates, paranoid sufferers may believe that the worst horrors appropriate to their particular culture are about to descend upon them.[6]

Similarly, all five senses may be said to have failed *Homo degener* peoples in their attempts to make sense of their wild surroundings. It too would have been a gradual, destructive process tending to nullify everything they had previously understood as hunter-gatherers about the wilderness around them. Just as Steven changed from being a friendly, outgoing lad to one who became distant, rejecting both his parents and friends, so *Homo degener* peoples changed from being world-loving hunter-gatherers to being introverted world-fearing farmers who rejected their *Homo sapiens* family – including the Great Spirit and Earthmother – and animal friends. Like schizophrenics they suffered from altered perception, thought disorder and delusional ideas. Just as most of the bizarre symptoms affecting schizophrenics – whose five senses have failed them in their attempts to make sense of their social environment – have been described in exactly similar terms by sufferers from different cultures all over the world, so societies of farmers around the world – whose five senses and brains no longer functioned in an integrated fashion within the wilderness – reveal a remarkable constancy of content in their delusions in myth. These arose from the collective brains of their stratified societies trying to create order out of an escalating chaos that affected their relationships not only within their social environments but with the wilderness as well. Their inability to communicate with, or understand, the wilderness made nonsense of the stimuli they now received from that world, making it *appear* threatening. Their situation may be compared with that of one man who remarked to Gwen Howe that the bombardment of stimuli during several acute breakdowns '... is like a radio receiving half-a-dozen stations at once'.

'What a frightening and isolating experience this must be![7'] commented Gwen Howe, as indeed it must have been for the early farming communities. Likewise, as revealed for instance in the Middle Eastern myths of a Fall, they were collectively tormented with distorted feelings of guilt, of being born in sin. They, too, suffered from a sense of persecution.

As with many schizophrenics, reality for many farming cultures became a nightmare world of distorted images, of fantasy. They likewise suffered from paranoid symptoms which are typically associated with those closest and dearest to them – in their case, the perception of the greater family of wild nature as presenting a threat of danger, causing them to react defensively and violently. Their symptoms may in fact be compared with what Gwen Howe describes as

> ... the 'negative' symptoms of schizophrenia, so named because they *take something away* from the individual's original personality... Where the illness has damaged the personality, the loss is as real as it is for the athlete who loses a limb or the pianist who loses a hand. They have all lost a part of themselves and a part that has contributed to their lifestyle and their aspirations. The loss may be far more profound for those damaged permanently by schizophrenia as they have lost more than this; their experience of *themselves* may have changed. They have in effect lost the person they knew most intimately.[8]

This was indeed the case with *Homo degener* peoples who lost the greater part of their hunter-gatherer characteristics and true potential as human beings. In consequence, their ego structures were quite broken down; just as more recently the ego structures of Aboriginal, Native American and Eskimo hunter-gatherers have broken down following their enforced settlement. As in the case of Steven quoted above, they underwent a dramatic personality change, but as well as losing 'the person they knew most intimately' they also lost the ground of that knowledge, the wilderness.

Like a family with a schizophrenic member in its midst, whose tendency is to turn 'in on itself', these primitive farming communities turned in on themselves, building walls against the society of wild animals –

including the world-wide society of hunter-gatherers – and wilderness. Like schizophrenics, they underwent a destructive process that not only tended to nullify everything they had previously understood about themselves and about the world around them but turned the reality of the wilderness as the true home of humankind into an appearance of being the home of demons and devils. They believed that the wilderness was a threatening place, and that they were being persecuted by spirits residing therein. In fact, they were suffering from a collective paranoia in relation to the wilderness. Such delusional thinking is at the core of schizophrenia, just as it is at the core of the thinking of sedentary farming peoples world-wide.

A most important corollary is the extent to which all agricultural peoples may likewise have undergone an actual change in brain organization. Because the cultural environment in which people grow up differs from millennium to millennium, their brains may be said to be wired differently and to be different in their chemistry, and are therefore different in the way they operate. They are different because what is perceived and learned differs so considerably that the brain probably has to make new synaptic connections to store long-term memories relative to the totally different environments in question. Dramatic evidence that learning can cause 'rewiring' in mammals has come from an experiment by Michael Merzenich of the University of California at San Francisco.

> Merzenich encouraged a monkey to touch a rotating disc repeatedly with only the three middle fingers of its hand. As a result, the part of the animal's cortex devoted to processing messages from these fingers expanded at the expense of that devoted to the other fingers.[9]

Both the monkey and the farmer underwent a change in behaviour from the normal to the abnormal.

If the above hypotheses are correct, almost certainly the most significant change in cultural environment, and therefore in what was perceived and learned and hence in the wiring and chemistry of the brain, took place following the adaptation to farming and the development of settlements or maximum security prisons against the wilderness – just as a structural alteration to the brain is liable to take place amongst schizophrenics. Furthermore, just as each and every breakdown of a schizophrenic person brings with it a danger of irreversible damage, damage to the point that there can be no resumption of a normal life-style, such damage that some need hospitalization or similar institutional care for the rest of their lives, so de-ranged people reached a point when they could no longer resume the normal hunter-gatherer life-style, having been so damaged that they became imprisoned in hierarchically ordered institutions in order to survive.

As a prison sub-culture creates its own reality, these sub-cultures of farmers proceeded to change the picture of reality, particularly in their myths, to suit their subjective demands for security and compensation.

Before examining these symptomatic demands in greater detail, it is necessary to establish what they are symptomatic of. Such a perversion of reality has taken place in two stages. First, to the pygmies, for example, the forest was 'Mother and Father, Lover and Friend', whereas to *Homo degener* the wilderness had become the feared and hated Land of No Return. Their fear and hatred of the wilderness unwittingly incorporated a fear and hatred of the evolutionary Mother and Father of humankind. Furthermore, following the disintegration of their *Homo sapiens* personalities and the building of stratified societies, a major part of their human identities and their evolutionary spiritual parents now lay outside their protected domesticated environments. Parts of the *Homo degener* personality and emotions were thus split off, to be further repudiated and destroyed every time they loomed in the shape of the hunter-gatherers and wilderness, when they fostered anxiety, fear, hatred and guilt. As Melanie Klein argues,

> The violent splitting off and destroying of one part of the personality under the pressure of anxiety and guilt is in my experience an important schizoid mechanism.[10]

The ongoing destruction of *Homo sapiens* and of their erstwhile spiritual parents and home constituted a near total loss of the grounds of *Homo degener's* evolutionary reality. At the same time, however, *Homo degener* was replacing a repudiated reality with artificial realities, which is the second stage in their perversion of reality.

Their creation of stratified societies and Gods and Goddesses filled a desperate need for security and love at the same time as they expressed a desperate fear of intimacy with the wilderness in their delusions of it as a place of evil. As Gwen Howe says of schizophrenics in their fears of chaos and isolation,

> Small wonder that we note again and again in sufferers the phenomenon of a clinging, dependent relationship with one other human being, usually the mother. This pathological relationship is a hallmark of an acute schizophrenic illness, and is a visible demonstration of a 'drowning' human being using another as a lifeline.[11]

As I argued in Part I, Chapter 4, many primitive agricultural societies entered into a relationship with an artificial mother figure, the Great Goddess, a relationship which may be described as a clinging, dependent one to save them from 'drowning' under a multiplicity of pressures; a relationship which would later become a characteristic of those relegated to the bottom of the social heap following the rise of patriarchal Gods of rudimentary stratified societies. For example, Mary, the mother of Jesus, was elevated c.800 AD to the mythical Mother of God. Venerated as the Queen of Heaven, Virgin Mother of God, she became the centre of devotion of the largely illiterate peoples of Western Europe. In times of adversity the long-suffering poor would call upon her to intercede for them.[12]

Henceforth farming societies regarded their domestic environments under the protection of their artificial Farmer Gods as holy and good, and their former home – the wilderness – as unregenerate, disorderly and evil. This is still a prevailing view in the USA and Russia, where wilderness still exists as a potential threat to farming communities.

Homo sapiens sapiens
Homo sapiens non sapiens

stratified societies thus changed reality to suit their own failed and fallen state. They blackened what to their hunter-gatherer ancestors had been, as it were, white – the wilderness – and whitewashed what was, from an evolutionary point of view, black. This has not only constituted a collective falsehood but, in diagnostic terms, the essence of a collective madness. Bearing in mind, therefore, that their God-sanctioned, or whitewashed, stratified societies were, from an evolutionary standpoint, black, *Homo degener*'s collective psyche was now itself black, a 'heart of darkness', suggesting a collective schizoid personality disorder. These de-ranged people were thus the victims of a primary derangement of the brain and of the senses, of what may be described as a *collective primary schizophrenia*.

Amongst the symptoms of a collective madness, arising from the changes in behaviour and beliefs of de-ranged people, was the development of the wall of demarcation, palisade or frontier, the outer skin between themselves and the wilderness. This was a concrete expression or petrifaction of their fears of chaos, and an outward expression of their alienation from wild nature. It formed the outer skin of a collective primary schizophrenia, whose internal manifestations included the traumatic deprivation in children of their evolutionary inheritance as hunter-gatherers; communal activities of self-stupefaction, namely the raising of plants apparently for the sole purpose of self-intoxication; communal activities of self-delusion, such as religious ceremonial and worship; and violent, destructive and psychopathic behaviour.

With regard to the trauma sustained by each generation of *Homo degener* children, each is born and brought up in an environmental setting that is entirely alien to its evolved – that is, normal – genetic and behavioural potential as hunter-gatherer. Children thus deprived of normal evolutionary experience at the outset of their lives might not be able properly to develop their genetic potential because phylogenetic learning may depend on their experiencing certain post-natal sensory patterns. Just as the victims of schizophrenia may have suffered from an inherited predisposition, I suggest the victims of a collective primary schizophrenia suffer a traumatic deprivation (of normal hunter-gatherer experience) and thereafter are unable to unfold their genetically determined developmental programme properly.

A second manifestation was the communal activity of self-stupefaction. It has been said that grain was grown for intoxication before it was cultivated for food, so great has been people's need to escape from reality. On the evidence this is only true of *Homo degener* peoples who suffered social and cultural disintegration and loss of meaning in their lives. Surely it was to compensate themselves for the loss of reality through the loss of an evolutionary identity, stimulation and security as hunter-gatherers, together with the subsequent monotony and drudgery of the peasant life, that they turned to intoxicants and drugs. More recently the Native Americans turned to peyote and the Eskimos and Aborigines to liquor after they too had been robbed of their hereditary freedom in movement, sovereign identity and self-respect as hunter-gatherers. During the latter part of the 19th century, the Native Americans died of diseases hitherto unknown to them, turned to drug-taking and alcohol, committed suicide or died, like Chief Joseph of the Nez Percés, of 'a broken heart'.

Another principal manifestation, and a communal activity of self-delusion, was their adoption of a primitive religion. Concentrated in tightly enclosed environments fearful of the wild outer world, *Homo degener* peoples also sought to escape the pressures of life through religion, which has been described as an opiate of the people. Religion, like alcohol and drugs, was a way of escaping from the dominance of an imprisoning environment, transforming the world around them. Their psyches became re-oriented in the vertical into primitive fertility religions. They reached up like plants towards mythical Gods and Goddesses whom they hoped would help them escape and control their parlous situation, and provide them with new identities and security. Each enclave formed the nucleus of a new reality that blinded and drugged them to the reality of their situation and of the world. It was a new reality that was entirely artificial, unreal. For the more true events and memories faded amongst those now alienated from their evolutionary past as hunter-gatherers, the more they fabricated for themselves a convenient reality, constructed a convenient truth. As Primo Levi pointed out of concentration camp inmates, the unreal prevailed over the real.

> Everyone dreamed past and future dreams, of slavery and redemption, of improbable paradises, of equally mythical and improbable enemies; cosmic enemies, perverse and subtle, who pervade everything like the air.[13]

Likewise these farming peoples dreamt new realities into existence commensurate with the exigencies of their double deprivation and incarceration. These new realities found their spiritual expression and justification in the Farmer God creators and chaos-dragon (or Underworld Devil) destroyers peculiar to each society; they found their concrete expression in solid structures devoted to the variety of activities which constituted the cultural backgrounds to their sedentary lives. Their fantasies were thus made actual in solid structures, to form for them, together with farming, the ground of reality. Priest-scientists, with the aid of myths and altars of sacrifice, mediated between God and people, sanctifying their parochial worlds and at the same time promising the people they would eventually be transported to other and better worlds in the heavens above, while holding the real world of their hunter-gatherer forbears at bay. Their religions, temples and trappings thus formed psychical walls against the world without, while opening up and sanctifying new pathways of pyramidal escape in ascent to the heavens above.

To these *Homo degener* peoples from whom we are culturally descended, reality and real life were now discovered and lived in apparent safety within their protected environments, under the guidance and protection of Gods and Goddesses. Everything outside and beyond the protected environment remained darkly veiled. Their myths refracted the true light of nature, bending it so that it would appear quite other than it really was, as unregenerate and dark. Furthermore, their own true natures underwent a similar 'blackening' transformation. As Gwen Howe has noted, it is common for sufferers of schizophrenia to be '...overwhelmed with feelings of distorted guilt and worthlessness...'[14]

In the case of *Homo degener*, this is again most apparent in the myths of a Fall. The doctrine of the Fall is that the first parents of the race, Adam and Eve, were created without sin, but that they voluntarily disobeyed God's law, fell from the state of innocence and were ejected from the Garden of Eden. In consequence, all their descendants have become guilty through inheriting the stain of that 'original sin' and related unworthiness, and were thereafter amenable to divine condemnation and punishment. Here, in myth, is evidence of the humiliation and self-hatred which, combined with humiliation and hatred of the wilderness, have characterized the attitudes and behaviour of *Homo degener* peoples ever since their two-fold fall, to form the dark veil, or darkening window, between them and their hunter-gatherer past and wild home.

In addition, the myths of Creation actually speak of cities of the Gods as pre-existing humans, who are portrayed as being created to serve the Gods. Both the Sumerian and Babylonian myths of Creation agree in the object for which man was created, namely, 'for the service of the gods, to till the ground and free the gods from having to work for their living.'[15] The Sumerian myth goes on to describe a further act of creation by Enki, the god of wisdom.

> He creates a human being who is feeble in mind and body, and then asks Ninmah (the goddess of birth) to do something to improve the condition of the miserable creature, but she is unable to do anything and curses Enki for making such a creature. One of the Hebrew words for man is *enosh*, a root one meaning of which is 'weak' or 'sick'. This aspect of humanity is often emphasized in Hebrew poetry, and this curious element in the Sumerian myth may possibly underlie the Hebrew representation of man as failing to measure up to the place in the universe which the divine purpose had intended for him.[16]

This is an early instance of an awareness of the failed or fallen condition of humans, and of their destiny as toilers of the earth. The representatives of the Gods, of course, were those who created them in the first place – the priest-scientists, chiefs and kings of the various stratified societies. It was in their service that the toilers of the earth would till the ground and free them from having to work for their living. For thousands of years thereafter, civilizations grew up with an hierarchical view of those at the summit as righteous (as whitened by the Sun of their Farmer God), of their antediluvian ancestors as unrighteous (as blackened by sin) and of the wilderness as a hostile environment and alien void (as evil, disorderly and dark). Thus, if only by implication, they blackened their original home and truly providential condition as hunter-gatherers, which had been wholly innocent and good – that is, white – and dubbed it unregenerate and evil, turning the *Homo sapiens* inhabitants of the wilderness into the dark menace of the myths. In addition, they unwittingly blackened the Great Spirit, Earthmother and true sun that had energized and illumined the original evolutionary path of humankind. For in obliterating the meaning of the sun for humankind by exploiting its energy to raise up and sustain pyramids of power, while negating its evolutionary rôle by anathematizing in myth, and destroying, the wilderness, they have in effect blackened the sun.* In other words, the sun, the source of the energy of the original paradisial life of the wilderness, now shone down on an increasingly dangerous and despoiled world in which the sun itself now constitutes a danger to life following the thinning of the ozone layer, caused by the polluting activities of *Homo degener* nations, each energized by its own Sun to grow faster and faster towards the sun. *Homo degener* set the reality of each stratified society as home against their own evolved reality and that of nature, their true home (see figure 6.1).

The veils of illusion – or rather, the delusional ideas expressed in the myths of a Fall, Flood, Paradise Lost and Creation, amongst others – formed, in effect, a skin separating *Homo degener* peoples from their past, while at the same time falsifying the past and the present. Not only did they act like a skin of ice separating people from the deep dark waters of chaos, but joined with those waters (and forests) to form a double skin of ice separating them from their original evolutionary path.†

The destruction of their wilderness home, together with violent and psychopathic behaviour against their fellows, is the final manifestation of collective madness to which I referred earlier.

What we also see is the emergence of violence and terror as the main bases for political organization. If you doubt this, take the time to read through Genesis, or any of the equivalent early accounts of world history. It is irrelevant whether each individual story is literally true. What matters is the overall impression given by the accounts – accounts which must have reflected what was happening on the political ground. What comes through repeatedly is that the political leaders were psychopathic killers who used religion to justify their political control, art to glorify their political success and murder to quell all opposition. The leaders in all fields, both the good and the bad, were those same sorts of people who are over-represented in the families of schizophrenic and bipolar people.[17]

---

* It may be of interest at this point to refer to Appendix xix.

† See Appendix ix for a further discussion on this subject.

Part I: fig 6.1

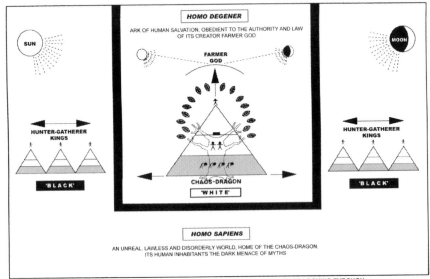

a) SITUATION IN THE EARLY NEOLITHIC INTERPRETED AND EXPERIENCED BY *HOMO DEGENER* LOOKING THROUGH
WORLD-FEARING 'WINDOWS TO THE WORLD'

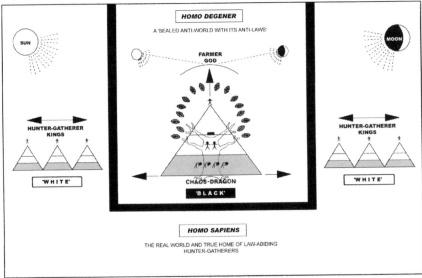

b) SITUATION IN THE EARLY NEOLITHIC FROM AN EVOLUTIONARY, OR REAL, STANDPOINT

Part I: fig 6.2

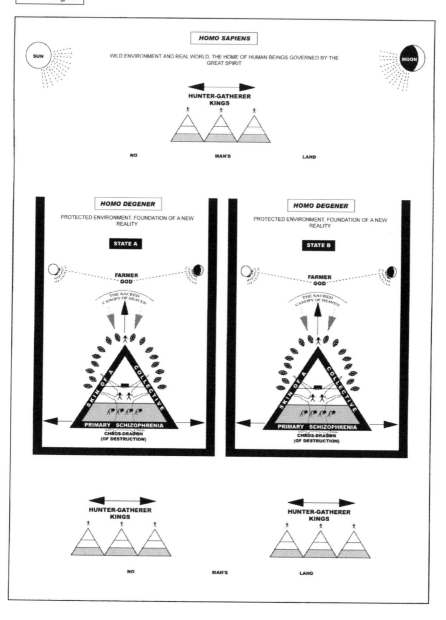

Altogether, and in the light of these manifestations of collective madness, the new reality to be found in *Homo degener*'s protected environments was both anti-evolutionary and anti-reality (see figure 6.2).

In blackening the whole of their past existence as true men evolving under the sun in the sacred wild environment, and in whitening as sacred their anti-evolutionary pyramids of power, *they and their pyramids were in reality black, each energized and illumined by a black Sun.* Memory, truth and reality were now perverted to serve the sacred certainties surrounding their pyramids of power.

As their memories of themselves as hunter-gatherers who belonged to the land died, they began to make up false memories – idealized images – as

<u>cultivated person,</u>

cultivator

whose way of life and exploitation of the people and the land as someone's people and someone's land respectively were mythologized as sacred under their Gods in heaven. They desecrated and waged war on their erstwhile home and on its inhabitants in the name of their Gods. In their case, false memory issued in murder on a grand scale.

Truth, it is said, is the first casualty of war. This was certainly the case in the war between *Homo degener* peoples and nature. Their myths about themselves and nature distorted and hid the truth, replacing it with an elaborate and consistent un-truth – consistent also because, as pointed out earlier in Chapter 4, a condition of hatred, such as *Homo degener* felt for the wilderness, is the necessity to lie against the hated object for the sake of consistency. The collective urge to live by such elaborate and consistent anti-realities and un-truths, and the inability to tear aside the mask, has remained with *Homo degener* down to this day.

These de-ranged people were thrice drugged against reality by the new (artificial) realities created, exhibited and expressed by each world-fearing community. *So to be de-ranged is to be deranged, to be out of one's normal senses.* The individual's being was cleft first of all in the horizontal, as it were, when the true self and ground of the true fulfilment of the psyche, senses and physique was left outside the domesticated environment. Secondly, it was cleft in the vertical, as the activities of priestly and scientific élites became primarily intellectual to the exclusion of feeling, while those of the masses have been primarily emotional to the exclusion of thought. This separation of thinking and feeling has profoundly affected both reason and sanity. As Erich Fromm once observed:

Reason flows from the blending of rational thought and feeling. If the two functions are torn apart, thinking deteriorates into schizoid intellectual activity and feeling deteriorates into neurotic life-damaging passions.*

Human reason initially stemmed from a blending of rational thought and feeling within the wild environment. These two functions were now not only divorced from their integrated evolution within the wild environment, but were further divorced from one another in the domestic setting at both the social and individual levels. *Homo degener* peoples had destroyed completely the links between cause and effect and established, by means of schizoid intellectual activity and false memories, illusory links in their place. They thus suffered from a primary derangement of the self and of the senses – a collective dementia, a turning inwards away from a world-loving hunter-gatherer self and reality of the world and into world-fearing collective selves – which I have described as a collective primary schizophrenia which would thereafter characterize all their states and behaviour.

This primary stage of schizophrenia, which has perpetuated an unnatural and inhuman condition of *Homo degener* peoples subjugated by and subjected to political, military, religious, social, economic and natural pressures, whether separately or combined, has made possible the second stage of schizophrenia. A secondary schizophrenia is the last bastion, when deranged people genetically predisposed to schizophrenia and consequently affected by biochemical changes in the brain, triggered perhaps by disease, drugs, malnutrition or manifold stresses within the social environment, retreat right into themselves, into an internal world, the almost inaccessible and unassailable stronghold of the secondary schizophrenic. If this second generation schizophrenia can be described as one of the most important mental diseases in children, adolescents and adults – there are some 500,000 people in Britain who suffer from schizophrenia – how much more important is it to observe and to recognize the existence and symptoms of a collective primary schizophrenia.

Furthermore, these world-fearing stratified societies, whose members suffer multi-faceted divisions between mind, emotions and behaviour, would continually suffer collective delusions of grandeur and of persecution and threats to their collective survival, a psychotic condition which I describe as a *collective primary paranoia*.† As sufferers from a collective

---

*As I argued above in Chapter 5, a further dualism arose within the brains of the dominant members of stratified societies which profoundly affected their relationship with women and with wild nature. For an amplification of this argument, see Appendix iii.

†I shall examine this condition in greater detail in Part II, Chapter 3.

primary psychosis, *Homo degener* peoples are oblivious to the truth that they are ill.

As they spread across the land, *Homo degener* peoples moved as deranged primary schizophrenics, carrying with them, as it were, their segregating and imprisoning walls, their distorted perception of reality, their anxieties and fears and paranoid ideas and behaviour. They cut down the forests and cleared the land for their settlements, thereby committing acts of violence against nature in violation of the laws of nature. Deranged people had not only left their original evolutionary path, but had taken over the processes of selection from those of nature. They had undergone a primary re-evolution.

Chapter 7

A Primary Re-evolution

With the revolution of cow and plow came the social divisions that characterize Eurasian cultures, as between rich and poor, lords and serfs, and men and women. War became commonplace, and warriors set themselves up as kings. (Nigel Calder)[1]

I argued earlier that *Homo degener* peoples had undergone, not a revolution, but a re-evolution. At the most elementary level they had undergone a re-evolutionary change from being hunter-gatherers to being sedentary farming peoples. They had undergone a primary re-evolution out of freedom into captivity – the imprisonment both of *Homo sapiens* and of wildlife. This was accompanied by a ritual redirection of the energies of *Homo sapiens* out of an evolutionary hunter-gathering movement in the horizontal into the vertically oriented structure-building behaviour of the Neolithic peoples, to form rudimentary pyramids of power. These provided permanent vertical escape routes and means of dominating and controlling the environment. What we like to think of as the great leap forward – from hunting and food gathering to the peasant village with its domesticated animals and domesticated crops – was in reality a great leap backwards and downwards for all concerned, and then a slow climb backwards and upwards out of the abyss by the ruling few on the backs of their fellows. For all, it was a degeneration into an imprisoning life-style. This beautiful world was no longer their home; it was their prison (see figure 7.1).

The first stage of that imprisoning re-evolution may be seen in a comparative study of the pygmies, who have lived in the forest for thousands of years, and the Bantu farmers who arrived much later and who clear the forest for their villages and garden plots.[4] They exhibit not only the extraordinary difference in cultural behaviour as between mobile hunter-gatherer and sedentary farmer, but the consequent exploitation by the re-evolutionary farmer of the evolutionary hunter-gatherers and

163

Part I: fig 7.1

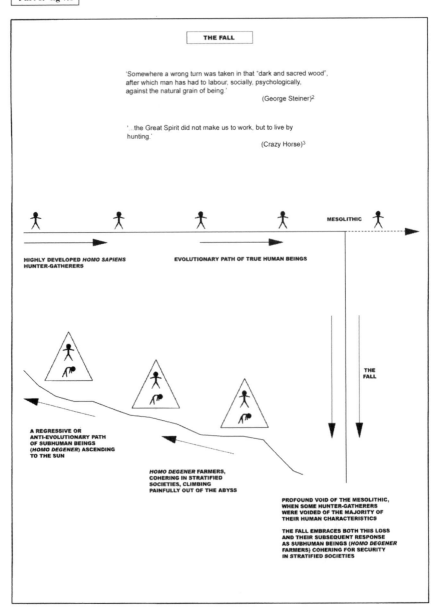

THE FALL

'Somewhere a wrong turn was taken in that "dark and sacred wood",
after which man has had to labour, socially, psychologically,
against the natural grain of being.'

(George Steiner)[2]

'...the Great Spirit did not make us to work, but to live by
hunting.'

(Crazy Horse)[3]

MESOLITHIC

HIGHLY DEVELOPED *HOMO SAPIENS*
HUNTER-GATHERERS

EVOLUTIONARY PATH OF TRUE HUMAN BEINGS

THE
FALL

A REGRESSIVE OR
ANTI-EVOLUTIONARY PATH
OF SUBHUMAN BEINGS
(*HOMO DEGENER*) ASCENDING
TO THE SUN

HOMO DEGENER FARMERS,
COHERING IN STRATIFIED
SOCIETIES, CLIMBING
PAINFULLY OUT OF THE ABYSS

PROFOUND VOID OF THE MESOLITHIC,
WHEN SOME HUNTER-GATHERERS
WERE VOIDED OF THE MAJORITY OF
THEIR HUMAN CHARACTERISTICS

THE FALL EMBRACES BOTH THIS LOSS
AND THEIR SUBSEQUENT RESPONSE
AS SUBHUMAN BEINGS (*HOMO DEGENER*
FARMERS) COHERING FOR SECURITY
IN STRATIFIED SOCIETIES

their habitats. The pygmies can set up camp in a few hours. They range freely through the forest without fear or danger, living on its bounty – hunting, fishing and collecting plants and honey. The Bantu, on the other hand, are at war with the forest they are afraid of. They spend months building villages; felling trees and clearing the land for their garden plots involves backbreaking labour. Their settlements are dusty and hot and open to attack from disease-carrying insects. The Bantu, who are more numerous and powerful than the pygmies, regard them as their slaves and, in their fear of the forest, exploit them to collect honey and other forest products for their settlements. The pygmies help foster this fear and are willing to forage for the Bantu because it keeps them out of the forest.

The second stage, that of the raising up and exploitation of different levels of people to form the stratified society, is found by looking at a typical gold mine, carved out of the wild veld of the Orange Free State in South Africa.[5] Though isolated, a mining community provided a strong sense of security. Its social hierarchy – ranging from General Manager down through mining engineers and mine doctor, all living in company houses, down to black mine workers living in dormitories and working underground – provided a sense of order and demanded unquestioning conformity. The mine property catered for all life's needs, providing work, sport, entertainment and medical attention from the cradle to the grave. Sheltered by the company plantations of blue gums, surrounded by high, dog-patrolled fences, the inmates were unaware of the threatening void of the veld without. Once eland, springbok, hartebeest and San hunter-gatherers had roamed there, but there were none who could remember.

Although this particular stratified society is the outcome of several agricultural and industrial revolutions on the original re-evolution, and therefore vastly more comfortable, it nonetheless exemplifies a similar hierarchy – from General Manager (Chief), through mine doctor (witch-doctor) down to mine workers – a similar foundation on protected property, a similar isolation, a similar introversion, a similar unquestioning conformity and a similar imprisoning effect of the wilderness with its threatening emptiness, just because it was a frontier society similar to the original stratified societies of the early farmers. All these started life in the same relationship with wild nature, as stratified structures in a hostile environment – *terra terrifica et incognita*.

The primary re-evolution was an (unwitting) act of infidelity, declaration of independence of the providence, steady state in flux and laws of nature and denial of the world-wide hunter-gatherer culture and potential unity in equality of all human beings. It was a betrayal of the Great Spirit and Earthmother. It set a seal upon the atomization and division of the human family – both within itself and from the greater family of the kingdom of nature – that was initially achieved with the adaptation to a primitive agriculture during the early Neolithic (see figure 7.2).

The primary re-evolution was however also much more than this. For as a direct result of their alienation from the natural order and natural food chains, and consequent imprisonment within, and fear of, the wilderness, these farming peoples were isolated from most natural selective pressures. They began to operate their own processes of selection, both in relation to their own domesticated human kind and in relation to the kingdom of animals: they selected many of the former to serve as labourers, serfs and slaves, and some of the latter as domesticated animals, whilst expelling or exterminating all wild species which stood in their way. They manufactured Father Gods and Mother Goddesses to make their domesticated worlds meaningful, prosperous and safe, to make themselves legitimate and loved, and to legitimize their exploitative and destructive behaviour as doubly deprived delinquents. Their stratified societies – artificial worlds all – thus provided them with an artificial physical and psychical Providence, stability and laws that were in direct conflict with those of nature and of their own true natures, being both profoundly corruptive of their natural counterparts and also delusive.

I shall examine first and compare the domestication of *Homo degener* with that of domestic animals; for the situation of the generality of domesticated humankind may, in all essentials, be described as analogous to that of domesticated animals such as sheep, goats, pigs and cattle. I shall then examine the conflict between an artificial and a natural providence, then that between an artificial and a natural stability, their relationship to the laws of nature, and finally the relationship of these artificial processes of selection to those of a natural selection.

The generality of domesticated humankind – whether as peasants, labourers, workers, servants, serfs or slaves – has been protected and encouraged to breed to the advantage of élites of stratified societies. They, like domestic animals, have satisfied the basic needs of élites for food, clothing, warmth, supply of raw materials for many other different products, performed work and so on. To those ends, domesticated humans have undergone psychical, physical and behavioural changes from the wild hunter-gatherer state as profound as those undergone by the transition of other wild animals to the domestic stage. In particular, the environmental sensitivity – described by Helmut Hemmer as 'environmental appreciation' – of domesticated humans, like that of domestic animals in relation to their wild forbears, is innately reduced by comparison with that of their

Part I: fig 7.2

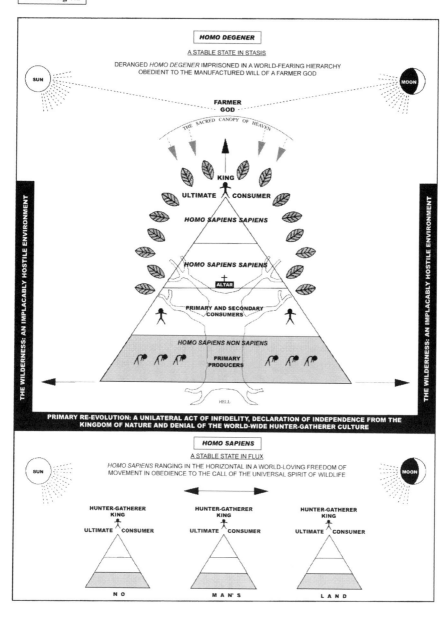

HOMO DEGENER

A STABLE STATE IN STASIS

DERANGED *HOMO DEGENER* IMPRISONED IN A WORLD-FEARING HIERARCHY
OBEDIENT TO THE MANUFACTURED WILL OF A FARMER GOD

SUN

MOON

FARMER
GOD

THE SACRED CANOPY OF HEAVEN

KING
ULTIMATE CONSUMER

HOMO SAPIENS SAPIENS

HOMO SAPIENS SAPIENS

ALTAR

PRIMARY AND SECONDARY
CONSUMERS

HOMO SAPIENS NON SAPIENS

PRIMARY
PRODUCERS

THE WILDERNESS: AN IMPLACABLY HOSTILE ENVIRONMENT

THE WILDERNESS: AN IMPLACABLY HOSTILE ENVIRONMENT

HELL

PRIMARY RE-EVOLUTION: A UNILATERAL ACT OF INFIDELITY, DECLARATION OF INDEPENDENCE FROM THE
KINGDOM OF NATURE AND DENIAL OF THE WORLD-WIDE HUNTER-GATHERER CULTURE

HOMO SAPIENS

A STABLE STATE IN FLUX

HOMO SAPIENS RANGING IN THE HORIZONTAL IN A WORLD-LOVING FREEDOM OF
MOVEMENT IN OBEDIENCE TO THE CALL OF THE UNIVERSAL SPIRIT OF WILDLIFE

SUN

MOON

HUNTER-GATHERER
KING
ULTIMATE CONSUMER

HUNTER-GATHERER
KING
ULTIMATE CONSUMER

HUNTER-GATHERER
KING
ULTIMATE CONSUMER

N O

M A N'S

L A N D

wild hunter-gatherer ancestors. And this has far-reaching evolutionary implications.

> Normally the course of mammalian evolution is progressive, which is mainly attributable to the complexity of the brain and the sensory performance. The parallel, higher development of the brain is a phenomenon that can be observed independently in all groups of mammals. On the other hand, regressive evolution involving a reduction of a level of sensory capability, once reached without the decreasing performance of one sensory organ being compensated for by increasing performance in another and with a reduction of the central nervous system, is known from the development of sessile and parasitic forms in various lines of invertebrates. Since, however, the decline in environmental appreciation in the course of domestication involves just such a reduction, domestication may indeed be regarded as a special kind of regressive evolution. At least for the brain, it must be taken into account that domestication, where it began with species that were geographically widespread and in various stages of progression, was initiated with the least progressive populations in each case...[6]*

The same argument is, I suggest, applicable to those people who became domesticated. The primary re-evolution they have undergone is a regressive evolution which has long been concealed beneath the veneer of an ostensibly Providential progression of humankind, which in turn has worked against the true providence of nature.

The world-wide providence of nature, whose beneficent care of humankind depended absolutely upon their integration within nature and understanding as hunter-gatherers of the demands of the Great Spirit and Earthmother, was slowly replaced by a notion of Providence based upon the fertility and productivity of domesticated animals, plants and plant-like producers in homelands seen as being under the special care or Providence of the Great Goddess. Thousands of years before the appearance of cities *Homo degener* peoples worshipped a female 'spirit of the earth' as the mother of all living things, as represented in Great Goddess effigies found in Natufian Jericho. She was worshipped in shrines in Çatal Hüyük. She was venerated too by generations of Neolithic farmers from the Mediterranean to the coasts of western Europe and thence to Siberia. Following their final transition to pure farmer the Great Goddess gave

---

*See Appendix i.

way to Gods and Goddesses as the source of the Providence of the ascending pyramids of power.

The mother, as the reproductive centre of the family, became the instrument of this new kind of Providence. The husband sowed the seed and reaped the harvest both of his possessed woman and his possessed land. To ensure the legitimacy of his children and to secure the entailment to them of his land, both his wife (or wives) and land became property to be closely guarded. The function of religion in this process was to foster the fertility of the plant-like producers and to preserve intact the family organization – and so too the land on which it stood – by surrounding it with supernatural sanctions and taboos designed to prevent relationships that might threaten the economic and psychological foundations and harmony of the stratified society. It was a notion of Providence that contained in effect a powerful element concerned with the supernatural origins of kingship and of related élites, and the keeping at bay and destruction of the wilderness. The implications are profound. For not only did they thereby curse and destroy the ground of the earlier providence of humankind, that imposed a natural restraint on their numbers and behaviour, but the elaborate regulations safeguarding marriage and marriage to the cultivated land, to the absolute exclusion of any natural or wild strain of plant, animal or human, in effect annulled the marriage between the Great Spirit and Earthmother. Humankind's archetypal, evolutionary Mother and Father were thus torn asunder; they and their marriage were annulled both in myth and in the actual practices of farming and mining communities everywhere. It was as though they had never existed. For an understanding of the Great Spirit died with the destruction of the hunter-gatherer and wilderness, while their Gods sanctified the rape and enslavement of the Earthmother by the farmer, fostering her subsequent fertility – together with that of the *Homo degener* peoples and their domestic animals – as subjugated Mother Nature or Mother Earth. Mysterious forces associated with the fertility of the mother and of Mother Earth would later be personified in seasonal sacred dramas of regeneration ascribed to Gods and Goddesses – such as the Greek goddess Gaea, or Pacha Mama, the all-providing earth-mother of Andean Peruvian and Bolivian peasants – or other symbols such as the snake.* These they

---

* As *Homo degener* became increasingly preoccupied with the fertility of the soil, a completely new kind of symbolism developed in art: it was the snake, symbol of the soil. Snake motifs, with their phallic associations, appeared in art in Mesopotamia, India, China and Mesoamerica. Given the association of the female with the fecundity and fertility of the soil, the snake was also a symbol of female sexual energy and power. The rise of civilizations and the ritual destruction of the serpent or chaos-dragon by male heroes and Gods coincided with the diminution of the power of the Great Goddess, and of female power generally, throughout the ancient world.

invoked to promote sedentary human, animal and plant fertility as being
necessary to their survival and prosperity, as against the true drama of a
natural regeneration in a successional movement in obedience to the
natural flux.

It was this fundamental relationship between Farmer God, farmer and
the Earthmother prostituted as Mother Nature that formed the foundation
of what has come to be known as Divine Providence, as met for instance
in Christian harvest festivals of thanksgiving. How profound is this change
in attitude and behaviour towards the Earthmother may be judged from
the following comment by a Native American, Somhalla, on being invited
by a white man to take up ploughing:

> You ask me to plough the ground. Shall I take a knife and tear my
> own mother's bosom? You ask me to cut the grass and make hay
> to sell, and be rich like the white man, but how dare I cut my
> mother's hair?[7]

No such scruples as those of Somhalla bothered the white man, who did
so dare out of blind ignorance and contempt of the laws of nature. The
Providence of *Homo degener*, by comparison with the world-loving
providence of *Homo sapiens*, was a world-fearing, world-enclosing, world-
dominating, world-subjugating and world-exploiting Providence. It was
one that would eventually favour a few cultivated (or selected) at the
summits of their stratified societies at the expense of those parasitized
and destined to an eternity of hardship and want at the bottom – and
of course at the expense of the Great Spirit and Earthmother of humankind.
Just as their vertically oriented Providence based on parasitism or a
perverted predation was no true providence, but a cruel delusion, their
vertically oriented stability was fundamentally unstable, and equally
delusional.

The (unconscious) aim of sedentary people in all their adaptations
was, like any other animal, to establish and maintain a steady state. For
thousands of years the stability of human groups lay in unpossessive
mobility: mobility in obedience to the natural flux has been at the core
of the evolution of humankind and was the most feasible solution to
social and economic problems, and the wild environment itself was the
ever-present storehouse and home. With the loss of their status as hunter-
gatherers went the loss of their storehouse, steady-state and home. The
only place of safety and the starting-point for the discovery and establishment
of a new stable identity and resource-security was the nuclear family and
home of the primitive farmer imprisoned within a nuclear enclave.

Increasing economic intensification and social complexity, the development of resource-storage systems and associated ideology in support of possessions and hoarding, and the burial of successive generations in cemeteries inhibited movement. Such sedentariness was in turn a passport to instability. For increasing complexity amongst sedentary peoples as a solution to problems inevitably entailed a decrease in flexibility, increased population size and risk of local resource over-exploitation and decline, all making for instability. In their search for wealth and security Neolithic and later societies became locked into pursuing techo-economic intensification and social and organizational complexity, raising up élites, and so too their stratified structures, ever higher in the process, while ostensibly guaranteeing their security with the aid of Gods whose natures – as in the case of the Judaeo-Christian God – have tended to be unchanging. Sedentariness, with all its potential for inequality, oppression and instability, was now sanctified.

A true self-governing freedom and stability of *Homo sapiens* obedient to the Great Spirit commanding change in mobility was replaced by the necessity for *Homo sapiens sapiens* King and ministers so to govern and exploit the *Homo sapiens non sapiens* labourers as to perpetuate their stratified structures and communal identities of

<u>dominant, powerful,</u>

subordinate, powerless

in obedience to their Farmer Gods commanding an unchanging *status quo*. The maintenance of order and stability in sedentariness *in situ* still remains one of the prime tasks of the government of any stratified society. Each structure was a Stable State in stasis oriented primarily in the vertical on land treated as an exclusive possession: each constituted a blockage in the bloodstream of the kingdom of nature, particularly because all agricultural communities are engaged in a war against wild nature, preventing the natural tendency of flora and fauna to change towards the steady state in flux of the ecological climax.

In addition to all the risks inherent in sedentariness to which I have already drawn attention, possessive sedentariness that leads to the growth of élites of stratified societies, and so to social inequality, constitutes a grave danger to *Homo degener* peoples in the event of sudden stress such as major climatic change. If under stressful circumstances an élite loses its power, the social order is liable to collapse and anarchy ensue. Such would appear to have been the case with the Mayan civilization between 800 and 1000 AD. The structured immobility of stratified societies constitutes not only a blockage in the bloodstream of the kingdom of nature, but, in consequence, a growing danger to their very own existence.

Their vertically oriented structure-building behaviour is in fact inherently inharmonious and unstable, both internally and in the inescapable event of profound environmental change.*

Hence, on one side of the Mesolithic, we find all humans evolving as hunter-gatherers, flowing as it were with the evolutionary tide of nature; while on the other side we find a completely new breed of human beings, stratified societies of

Homo sapiens sapiens

Homo sapiens non sapiens

farmers divorced from the universal providence and operating their own re-evolutionary Farmer God or Providential processes of selection, stability and laws, the whole standing in direct opposition to, and in contempt of, the natural processes. In short, *Homo degener* peoples replaced a steady state in flux with man-made steady states in stasis, a natural harmony with a man-made disharmony, a stability in the freedom of all creation with a stability maintained through tyranny over all creation.

At the most fundamental level, therefore, the relationship of each stratified society to nature was *contra natura*: their pyramids of power formed the physical and psychical energy bases for the redirection and perversion of the true energy flow of humankind, exploiting a variety of energy sources to that end. Billions and billions of tons of animal, vegetable and mineral materials world-wide have been transformed down the millennia to service *Homo degener*'s vertically oriented structure-building behaviour and associated ascent to the stars. This changed relationship with nature may be said to be the essence of the primary re-evolution amongst people, and the foundation of all future development of *Homo degener*. Each stratified structure, in its delusive condition and passive and active behaviour against nature, was not only 'anti-reality' but a 'sealed anti-world with its anti-laws' (see figure 7.3).

It is as though we were studying the properties of free-flowing running water (*Homo sapiens*) at one instant, and of that same water suddenly dammed up by an avalanche and displaced to form a deep lake of static, and in time polluted, water. A few climbed on the backs of their fellows to raise their heads above water, to become *Homo sapiens sapiens*. Thereafter, those at the surface, with the aid of their Gods and Goddesses, bent and diffracted the light of the sun filtering down to the gloomy depths below, to *Homo sapiens non sapiens*. Eventually those dammed up and

---

*Hugh Casson, President of the Royal Academy of Arts (1976–1984), pointed out that one of the basic rules of a harmonious environment is horizontality. Verticality and hierarchy make for disharmony – the more so when the fundamental disharmony is glossed over with an appearance of harmony.

Part I: fig 7.3

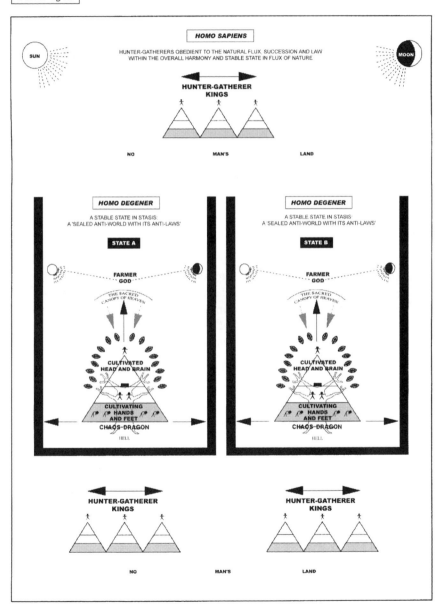

polluted waters would find an outlet. As the original dams began to crack, the now polluted water began to flow along new channels, at first as a trickle, then as a deluge, polluting and destroying the wild environment in its path.

They began to make roads through, and inroads into, the wilderness. What has been described as one of Britain's oldest roads – the Neolithic Track on Shapwick Heath – was built 6,000 years ago, using an estimated 200 tonnes of wood. A more recent example of this re-evolutionary change in behaviour can be seen in the following extract of an account of the Mato Grosso based on the Royal Society and Royal Geographical Society expedition to central Brazil 1967–69, just in advance of rapacious hordes of Brazilian farmers. The expedition began by investigating all the land around the completed sections of the north/south highway (the Xavantina road). Whereas the Indians hunted and gathered fruits along invisible pathways without transforming the land, this road, by providing access, would eventually lead to the transformation of tens of thousands of square miles of forest.

> Like a hairline crack in the dam it will surely lead to a particular kind of deluge, the kind that modern man has been making so inexorably almost everywhere else... The unexplored territory ... formed a fantastic dividend from the past. The road was carving through it, a surgical incision of the twentieth century certain to spread its kind of infection in every direction.[8]

That 'hairline crack in the dam' and 'particular kind of deluge' to which Anthony Smith refers began when *Homo degener* peoples first spread outwards in waves from S.W. Asia. They carried with them, as physical and psychical baggage (their 'kind of infection'), their original re-evolutionary conflict behaviour, possessions and prison walls as the dark glass through which they would automatically view and treat the wilderness as a hostile environment. Thereafter it would be the failures of every society – the exiles, the outsiders, the misfits both in relation to the wilderness and to their own societies – who would tend to be to the forefront of the advance of farming cultures through the wilderness. The first European settlers in South Africa were

> ... social and economic dropouts who ... had failed to make it in the competitive society of seventeenth-century Holland.[9]

And as Robert Hughes wrote of the Australian experience:

To succeed on the frontier, a man needed the kind of violent, grabbing drive that only failure or mediocrity in his former life could fuel.[10]

It is the misfits and failures who have been the pioneers at the forefront of the advance of farming cultures. Their principal obsession was survival, at any cost. To survive they have had to bargain with, or slaughter, the aboriginal hunter-gatherers whose lands they encroached on, and they have had to tame the wilderness. They have progressed, *not by absorbing their past to their present* as had their hunter-gatherer ancestors, *but by destroying their past*, by destroying the very ground of their earlier being as true people (see figure 7.4).

Soon we see them crowding into towns and cities. Here again, whereas the hunter-gatherers had moved freely and happily along invisible pathways, the roads that now led into and linked city with city were, for many, roads into varying degrees of despotism and tyranny, of forced labour and slavery, as, for example, in the Near East.

In Egypt, Herodotus considered the great road which carried the stones of the pyramids to be scarcely inferior to the pyramids themselves. But that road was a road for slaves, not for free men. Long before the era of Herodotus, the Near Eastern roads of tyranny had been brought to their best by the Assyrians, whose provincial governors remained in day-to-day touch with their lords through professional messengers. These travelled along post roads by horse or mule, exchanging steeds at specific places – thus originating a system of imperial control which lasted till the nineteenth century AD.[11]

As for the bulk of the populations along these roads (and canals), they were in the main treated as forced labour (particularly in China), serfs or slaves.

Every major project of agriculture in the Near East and Mediterranean in antiquity depended upon slaves. So did both those industrial undertakings which depended on agricultural products, and those mines whose products were then concerned to improve agriculture as well as to furnish weapons for war. On the other hand, slaves were not so much employed in those projects in agriculture which depended on irrigation. There ... the population would be more likely to be subject to various forms of forced labour.[12]

Part I: fig 7.4

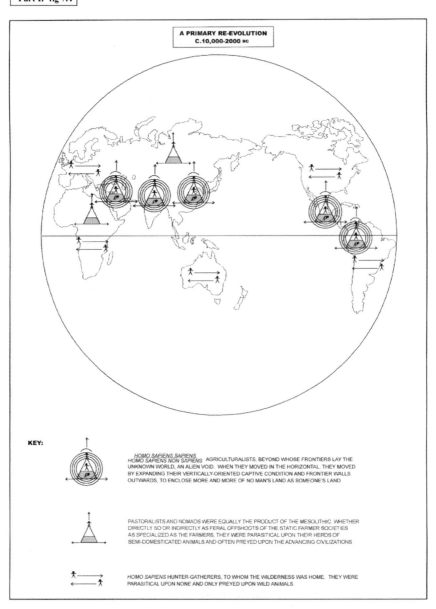

A PRIMARY RE-EVOLUTION
C.10,000-2000 BC

KEY:

HOMO SAPIENS SAPIENS
HOMO SAPIENS NON SAPIENS AGRICULTURALISTS, BEYOND WHOSE FRONTIERS LAY THE UNKNOWN WORLD, AN ALIEN VOID. WHEN THEY MOVED IN THE HORIZONTAL, THEY MOVED BY EXPANDING THEIR VERTICALLY-ORIENTED CAPTIVE CONDITION AND FRONTIER WALLS OUTWARDS, TO ENCLOSE MORE AND MORE OF NO MAN'S LAND AS SOMEONE'S LAND

PASTORALISTS AND NOMADS WERE EQUALLY THE PRODUCT OF THE MESOLITHIC, WHETHER DIRECTLY SO OR INDIRECTLY AS FERAL OFFSHOOTS OF THE STATIC FARMER SOCIETIES AS SPECIALIZED AS THE FARMERS, THEY WERE PARASITICAL UPON THEIR HERDS OF SEMI-DOMESTICATED ANIMALS AND OFTEN PREYED UPON THE ADVANCING CIVILIZATIONS

HOMO SAPIENS HUNTER-GATHERERS, TO WHOM THE WILDERNESS WAS HOME. THEY WERE PARASITICAL UPON NONE AND ONLY PREYED UPON WILD ANIMALS

According to Kevin Bales,[13] conditions may have greatly improved in Mesopotamia and Egypt, but many of the farmers in India who are still enslaved as bonded farm labourers might be the direct descendants of labourers so bonded over 300 generations.

Hence, the roads that led out of the Mesolithic into the Neolithic and beyond have been, generally speaking, highways out of the illimitable freedom of all people as hunter-gatherers into the enslavement of many as *Homo sapiens non sapiens* members of stratified societies. The freedom of *Homo sapiens* hunter-gatherers was as near absolute as is possible to any wild animal. Such freedom was the condition for the fullest development of humankind, for their optimum physical and psychical health and well-being. Freedom does not imply lack of constraint, for growth occurs only within a structure, and structures require constraints. The constraint in the case of the hunter-gatherer was self-regulating, autonomous – that is, it arose from the necessities of growth inherent in the structure of the person, integrated and perfected within the structure of wild nature, whereas our 'freedom' takes place within the structure of a stratified society itself divorced from the structure of nature, and which functions primarily for the sake of élites and institutions, which possess exceptional power to coerce the majority. Freedom is only relative, or non-existent, for *Homo degener*. The majority of *Homo degener* peoples are mere wage slaves of society, which makes it all the more likely that many of the poorest and most vulnerable will be made destitute and forced into slavery during periods of rapid population growth and socio-economic change. Slavery is already on the increase world-wide.

Given the inherent desire for freedom, nations and classes throughout history have fought their oppressors.

> The history of mankind is, indeed, a history of the fight for freedom, a history of revolutions, from the war of liberation of the Hebrews against the Egyptians, the national uprisings against the Roman Empire, the German peasant rebellions in the sixteenth century, to the American, French, German, Russian, Chinese, Algerian, and Vietnamese revolutions. Leaders have all too frequently used the slogan that they are leading their people in a battle for freedom, when in reality their aim has been to enslave them. That no promise appeals more powerfully to the heart of man is evidenced by the phenomenon that even those leaders who want to suppress freedom find it necessary to promise it.[14]

Just as exploding populations, destruction of wilderness and wildlife, despotism, forced labour, serfdom, slavery and revolution became the norm, war between stratified societies became another type of normality.

> The importance of war in early history is shown by the fact that the epics of almost every country deal with a conflict of one sort or another... The Bible, the Homeric poems, Herodotus, and almost every work giving useful historical evidence, are all full of terrible wars to the death, heroes being almost always successful warriors, successful nations being almost always those successful in battle. Death in action was considered the noblest way to die throughout most of history.[15]

In short,

> The most persistent sound which reverberates through men's history is the beating of war drums.[16]

War provided an important mode of maintaining a (delusive) steady state and stimulus to *Homo degener* – to architecture, art, religion, science and technology – a steady state and stimulus that had previously been provided to *Homo sapiens* by the hunting of animals. Diseased in their minds as well as in their bodies, these deranged peoples, from being hunters of animals had become hunters of people; a change in behaviour in turn celebrated and assisted by their religions, arts, sciences and technology. In order to maintain a steady state, *Homo degener* peoples began to select against each other and against the wild environment; in particular, they began to wage a cruel war of attrition against *Homo sapiens* and against the wilderness, which continues to this day. They were primarily the agents not of order but of anarchy.

Homo degener societies and their governments grew up and have remained in a state of criminal behaviour outside, and in contempt of, the laws of nature. A modern analogy of their criminal behaviour, and their consequent ruination of the wilderness, is that of modern organized crime and its disruption of modern society. Cause and effect in both cases are similar: both stemmed from socio-economic disintegration and deculturation, and both have spread instability, ruination and fear.

> For several decades, scholars and social reformers have stressed the cause-and-effect relation between poverty and social disintegration on one hand, and criminal and deviant behaviour on the other.
> The framework within which industrialization and urbanization

have taken place over the last two centuries in the countries of the West, and the forms that so-called 'modernization' is presently taking in certain large Asian and Latin American nations – a 'modernization' that entails growing social injustice, poverty and violence – indeed leave little doubt that socio-cultural disorganization plays an important rôle as a seedbed for the growth of crime.

A certain level of social disintegration is an essential precondition of organized crime, whose power is based to a considerable extent on the ability to use terror and physical violence unsparingly against competitors and enemies...

...one of the most important new features of the last few years has been the tendency for this classical relationship, in which crime depends upon socio-economic disintegration, to be *turned on its head.*

The most powerful criminal groups have shown (and are showing) that they can influence society and economic processes to a greater extent than they are determined by them. They are more and more capable of *creating* marginalized and ruinous enclaves, even in environments previously free of them.[17]

Likewise, stratified societies that arose out of enclaves of extreme socio-economic disintegration and deculturation, in which criminal groups acquired their power by exploiting the delinquency and aggression consequent upon the profound processes of deculturation, subsequently reproduced the social soil in which they originally grew. They created, with the aid of their armed men, using 'terror and violence unsparingly against competitors and enemies', new enclaves of socio-economic disintegration and deculturation throughout the world, including in particular 'marginalized and ruinous enclaves' of hunter-gatherers and wildlife. Like today's terrorists, such as al-Qaeda, they effected a paradigm shift that transformed the world. This is not to say that the primitive farmers knew their behaviour was criminal. Far from it, for what was criminal from the evolutionary standpoint of *Homo sapiens* and the laws of nature soon became respectable and the norm under man-made laws. A remorseless process of criminal behaviour – the theft and clearance of land, homicide and genocide – was set in train by farming communities forced to make war on the wilderness and each other for *lebensraum* and survival. They and their governments, no matter how constituted, were and are antithetic and antipathetic to the true governing processes, law and order of the world. Each and every one governs a structure that is 'anti-reality', and fundamentally anarchical. In reality, law and order within

Homo degener societies are lawlessness and chaos dressed up as law and order. This change may be expressed diagramatically as diametrically opposed pendulums swinging between order and chaos, as follows:

Part I: fig 7.5

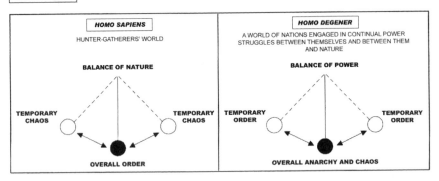

Anarchy and chaos, not order, have been predominant features of history.* This accords with the earlier argument, that collectively members of stratified societies, who were in origin doubly deprived, have behaved ever since like criminal adolescents, causing giant pendulums of terror, desolation and destruction to swing relentlessly back and forth down the ages and throughout the world. These orphaned and illegitimate people had thus become the agents of what may be described as *a perverted psycho-social or cultural selection.*†

Instigated by the élite of each stratified society, a perverted cultural selection replaced the processes of natural selection, selecting in favour of powerful *Homo sapiens sapiens* élites parasitizing *Homo sapiens non sapiens* workers within each, and in favour of the strongest stratified societies over the weaker and over the wilderness and its inhabitants. Forced themselves to adapt to agriculture 12,000 years ago, *Homo degener* peoples have in their turn forced other hunter-gatherers – in the Americas, in Africa, in Australia – so to adapt, or be exterminated like vermin. 'Survival of the fittest' in evolutionary terms began to be replaced by 'survival of the fittest' in re-evolutionary, or anti-evolutionary, terms.

An example of a perverted cultural selection may be seen in the way a privileged few have been able to ape the behaviour of their hunter-

---

*In Part II, Chapter 7, I discuss the anarchical effects of the rise and fall of empires and the anarchical condition of the international system.

†See Part II, Chapter 1 *et seq*, where I argue that this perverted cultural selection is in essence a perverted memetic selection.

gatherer ancestors, while a majority have suffered degrees of relative deprivation.

> ... the liberty, the excitement and, above all, the unexpectedness of the hunting life had gone; communities were fixed in one place or within a small range and every man, woman, and child had to undertake those chores that must be repeated day after day as far as the mind can see. The human male has never forgotten the hunting life which was the habit of mankind for a period a hundred times longer than his history as a farmer and citizen. Even now to be able to hunt, shoot, and fish is the highest privilege of social standing or financial success. Good, fresh meat and furs, too, are among the privileges of the rich. It is one of the ironies of history that having achieved all he has, man now struggles to enjoy so many of the things which his ... ancestors took for granted ten thousand years ago.[18]

In other words, the very similar life conditions conducive to health experienced by all humankind as hunter-gatherers gave way to stratified societies characterized by vast disparities in life conditions between different occupational and socio-economic groups – differences in material wealth, size of dwellings, diet, learning experience, leisure, health and behaviour – within any one stratified society, and as between stratified societies. Such societies have ensured the survival of the fittest in anti-evolutionary terms at the cost of the survival of the fittest in evolutionary terms, including of *Homo sapiens*. The suffering of the latter, dispossessed of, and imprisoned or exterminated in, their ancestral lands – in North America, in South Africa, in Australia, in Tasmania – has to be taken into account in order to present the human condition in a true perspective.

A natural selection of true forms was slowly replaced by a perverted cultural selection by, and of, degenerate forms – a selection conducive to the survival, growth and spread of stratified societies of degenerate people, and a degeneration of the environment throughout the world. In consequence, a natural flux and selection making for world-wide harmony and order began to be overlaid by a man-made flux and perverted cultural selection making for world-wide disharmony and disorder. Such a man-made flux and forces of terror, desolation and destruction have combined with the natural flux and forces – to which their sedentary state had made them profoundly vulnerable – to devastate civilizations.

Evil thus entered the otherwise good land following the two-fold fall, *an evil compounded by the apotheosis of that fall, the worship of agricultural deities, leading to the profoundest of all evils, the perversion of the processes, and destruction of the products, of evolution.* The Mesolithic was indeed a watershed in the affairs of humankind.

As argued earlier, wild animals change to remain the same. They undergo minor mutations, such as a change in skin colour that camouflages them against a predator newly arrived in their territory, rather than undergoing a major evolutionary adaptation such as changing their mode of locomotion. *Homo sapiens* underwent minor cultural changes to the same ends. *Homo degener* on the other hand has changed out of all recognition. *Homo degener* farmers were *the original alien invaders of Earth: they were subhuman aliens who would thereafter regard and treat their hunter-gatherer forbears as though they were subhuman.* By subhuman I mean less than human, a condition arising from the loss of the majority of their original evolved hunter-gatherer characteristics and subsequent domestication. Their domestication is a special kind of regressive evolution: domesticated people are those who are genetically programmed to behave and evolve as hunter-gatherers, yet are forced to remain in a state of retarded development. All their subsequent anti-evolutionary characteristics and behaviour stem directly from that humiliating retardation and the perversion of their development to serve the ascent of parasite pyramids of power. Throughout the book I shall also describe these subhuman aliens (*Homo degener*) as subhuman beings or subhumans.

Physically and psychically alienated as farmers from the true hunter-gatherer self, further alienation has followed with every revolution on the original re-evolution. As well as exterminating their own and other species of wild animal, *Homo degener* peoples have introduced alien species of flora and fauna into a variety of environments across the world, threatening biodiversity. So whereas evolution, energized by the sun, enabled the development of *Homo sapiens* as hunter-gatherer kings of natural food pyramids, a primary re-evolution, and subsequent revolutions under the black Suns of their Gods (or ideologies), have energized the ascent of *Homo degener* Kings, Presidents, Dictators and élites of parasite (food) pyramids of power who, through their collective powers of a perverted cultural selection by conquest and subjugation, have almost entirely overwhelmed their evolutionary counterparts, thus nullifying the evolutionary energies of the real sun and natural selection. It is this lunatic process which is fundamental to, and the essence of, history.

Chapter 8

A Story of Escalating Madness

Conquest has been the greatest lever of change in human history. We may pray it is not still so today – but of the past, there can be no question. Large groups absorb the smaller tribes in the area and a paramount chief is in a fair way to establish a kingdom. The conquered tribes keep a subsidiary existence, possibly as vassals and the kingdom is likely to go through a feudal phase. Loyalty to the tribe is transformed into loyalty to the leader or the dynasty. The language of the conquerors is imposed or there arises from conqueror and conquered together a new common tongue. The area of cohesion is thus enlarged and for long periods of history, the dominant political form is the dynastic state or the dynastic empire. (Barbara Ward)[1]

Before the arrival of the farmer there were no human conquerors. The arrival of farming heralded the arrival of the first conquerors; and their first conquests were the subjugation of large tracts of wilderness.* Because the conquest of wilderness was subsequently legitimized and then made the subject of tribal and national inheritance under divine laws, the conquest and development of wilderness was, and remains, the foundation of power and source of conflict, and a principal lever of change.

History is essentially the story of the struggle of *Homo degener* peoples to acquire status, power and security following the loss of many of their human characteristics as hunter-gatherers (which had given individuals status and power over their own destinies in the wilderness) and their consequent powerlessness and insecurity in face of a now frighteningly meaningless wilderness. They who had been supreme masters of their

---

*Conquest is still the greatest lever of change in history; if not of other peoples, then of the remaining tracts of wilderness, of the weather and of space. However, the principal driving force behind this lever of change is humiliation and the threat of humiliation. See Part III, Chapter 2, for an amplification of this argument.

environment as hunter-gatherers regressed both from the standpoint of ecotypic adaptation (that is, the effects of selection of the local wild environment in producing their most conspicuous characters) and of phyletic evolution: as *Homo degener* populations they were at the mercy of the wild environment, powerless in a powerful land. History is thus the story of the rising up of fallen humans, primarily through the conquest and subjugation of wild nature to their needs, and their development in progressive revolutions on the original re-evolution. In terms of economics, the story is not however one of steady progress, but a cycle of successes and humiliating failures, a rise and fall of stratified structures, in which the structures and the stakes have been continually rising. History is therefore also the story of the forcible transference of energy – both human and natural – away from its original and true flow in a primarily horizontal movement and succession of forms into the vertical: the exploitation, concentration and contraction of more and more of the land space and resources of the world to the ascent of pyramids of power towards the sun.

Prehistoric agricultural societies, as in Britain, oscillated between two different sources of possessiveness and power, both concerned with the raising up and maintenance of social élites to enable the new communities to acquire some measure of control over their own destinies.

> In certain groups, power is expressed through the control of prestigious possessions and their distribution, and through the ability to build spectacular monuments. In other phases, however, we find a change towards the political control of land and other productive resources, marked, above all, by a process of enclosure.[2]

All these, in various combinations and in varying degrees, are expressive of a pyramidal possessiveness and power to ascent and collective security. All represent a compensatory power-craving consequent upon their loss of individual power as hunter-gatherers, seeking status and power that would restore their human dignity, particularly through the enclosure and subjugation of wild nature, thereby simultaneously ridding themselves of their humiliating inadequacy and insecurity in the wilderness.

Once started, therefore, agriculture began to turn the weak and deprived into the collectively strong, the deranged few into the deranged many, as farmers spread outwards in waves from their places of origin across Europe, Africa, Asia and America. With the gradual development and improvement of farming techniques over the years there was an immense proliferation of hamlet, village and town all over the ancient world. Between 3500 BC and 2000 BC there were deranged societies developed half-way between the early farming phase and the beginnings of civilized life who built the great megalithic monuments of north-western Europe, such as the stone avenues of Carnac in Brittany, and the stone circles of Avebury and Stonehenge in Britain. As the increasing exploitation of increasing numbers of primary producers over greater areas of cleared land enabled social élites to be raised up ever higher as conspicuous consumers, it is not surprising to learn that the ascent and maintenance of social élites repeatedly led to widespread environmental degradation and eventual failure and collapse of social structures.

Increasingly archaeologists are discovering that prehistoric peoples destroyed their own environment. In Palestine there are signs that deforestation caused the collapse of communities in the southern Levant (the area of present-day Israel, Jordan, and southern Syria) around 6000 BC; in the highlands of central Mexico soil erosion has often been so severe since people began to cultivate maize extensively c.1500 BC that communities have been forced to abandon their settlements. Similarly, as I pointed out in Chapter 4 above, migrating pastoralists and their domestic animals, and farmers, spread south and east through Africa, helping create the arid wastes found today south of the Sahara.

Increasing population density, environmental degradation and climate change have been principal driving forces underlying social and cultural change amongst primitive farmers and pastoralists. The desiccation in North Africa was replicated in other areas such as Arabia and south-western Asia. This desiccation and drought, following so closely upon the flooding of the Mediterranean and Black Sea littorals – particularly as the deluge affected the Mediterranean area, which thereafter became tectonically active with its frequent earthquakes and volcanic eruptions, together with the land rising out of and disappearing into the sea – would have had a profound effect on people in these areas. Driven by floodwaters out of the fertile Mediterranean and Black Sea littorals, out of the fertile plains of the Persian Gulf and into the hills, these primitive farmers and pastoralists were, on the evidence, now forced by a combination of increasing population density and desiccation towards more permanent sources of water. They moved into the fertile areas of the Nile Valley and the plains of the Tigris and Euphrates rivers, there to build the systems of irrigation upon which the Egyptian and Sumerian civilizations respectively would grow.* The Sumerians,

---

* In a report in the *New Scientist* (Vol. 162, No. 2187, 22 May 1999, pp. 38–41), anthropologists argue that around 3800 BC the El Niñö/Southern Oscillation cycle had profound effects on farmers and herdsmen world-wide – particularly in Europe and the Middle East, where it brought desiccation in its wake – causing them to innovate in the direction of greater cultural complexity in order to survive.

for instance, appear to have come into the delta from the mountainous region to the north-east of Mesopotamia: the earliest of their myths of Creation shows that they had lived amongst fir trees, which were not to be found in the delta.

The first civilized societies in the world began to grow up in Sumeria, in Egypt, in the Indus Valley and in China. The first cities came into being, probably in Mesopotamia, in the valleys of the Tigris and Euphrates rivers c.3500 BC. Much later, cities began to appear in Egypt. Cities also appeared in the Harappan civilization following its development in the valley of the Indus River around 2500 BC, and following the development of civilization in the Yellow River valley c.2000 BC. In the New World, the Olmec civilization had come into being near Vera Cruz in Mexico by 1200 BC, and cities began to appear in Peru c.600 AD. The rise of cities constituted the second great revolution in human culture following the Mesolithic, a revolution on the primary re-evolution into agriculture. All the physical, psychical and behavioural adaptations which led to the growth of stratified societies now became intensified and more fully institutionalized. There, on the banks of Tigris-Euphrates, the Nile and other river systems in India and in China, people began to create a centralized agriculture – encouraging an increased density of population – irrigation systems, literate urban communities, specialized craft and ritual centres, and military establishments devoted to organized war. Their cities were their original physical and psychical walls of self-defence writ large against the incomprehensible and frightening wild environment, and in particular against deleterious climate change; they were also offensive-defensive enclaves established against other cities and invading barbarians. All, however, whether in the Old World or in the New, constituted lesser or greater pyramids of power of ascent to the sun.

The effects on human history of the early urban phase were to accelerate the growth of stratified societies. It will be useful to examine, with particular reference to Mesopotamia, four of what may be considered to be the most important of these effects. First, the near-total physical and psychical divorce of a great many people from the intimate interactions with the natural environment which are associated with the primeval and early farming phase of human history. For with the building of cities, there occurred a rapid increase in population density. Most of the inhabitants were not farmers, and thus relied on the activities of others to supply them with food.* In

---

*This behaviour, while being unique amongst vertebrates, is common amongst social insects such as bees, in whose colonies the queen and drones do not help collect food. It is precisely because the phenomenon of human kings, queens and drones, or non-manual workers, came into being in stratified societies that they have come increasingly to resemble societies of social insects. I explore this phenomenon further in Part II, Chapter 5.

other words, a great part of the population of cities was now no longer involved even in the quest for food in the domesticated farming environment, let alone in the wild environment. At the same time the inhabitants of the cities of Mesopotamia moved away from a spiritual integration with nature to religions based on separation from nature; nature itself was represented in myth as being in a state of chaos, which the people and their gods had to overcome to establish order. The primary, secondary and ultimate consumers in cities were now entirely separated from their hunter-gatherer past. They were therefore divorced from the natural controls and laws that had governed their ancestors. Just as they had been forced to re-channel their ranging habits and imaginations as hunter-gatherers during the early farming phase of human history, they began now to re-channel and harness (i.e. to domesticate or subjugate) the waters of the great river valleys to feed their growing populations. The distribution of food and other essential commodities, together with the organization of massive collective labour to build and maintain canals and dams, led to centralized states powerful enough to organize this work. Therefore they needed specialized bureaucracies and engineers, who provided civilizations with yet more power to dominate nature and the natures of the mass of their inhabitants.

This introduces the second main effect on human history of the early urban phase, the growth of stratified societies through the institutionalization of the five-fold concentration of power to the self-aggrandizement and prosperity of élites and to the collective security of their stratified structures. The development of intensive agriculture with the aid of huge irrigation projects, and the profits of commercial enterprise, permitted the rise of non-manual élites – kings, nobles, priest-scientists, administrators, artists, lawyers, merchants, musicians, scribes – who were supported out of the economic surplus. Below the non-manual élites were potters, weavers, stone-masons, shop-keepers, soldiers and so on. For the past 5,000 years, every civilized community has included both manual (primary and secondary producer) and non-manual (primary and secondary consumer) workers in varying proportions: the hands and feet supplying and supporting the head and brain of the community. The priestly-scientific (secondary consumer) professionals or 'experts' of Sumeria and Egypt, forerunners of all Western moral, arts and technical experts, began to fill the space between zero – their starting point following the fall – and infinity in the vertical with abstractions of numbers, words and ideas. From their preoccupation with measurement, mathematics began; from their preoccupation with the stars, the science of the universe grew. They mined metals and made them their most efficient tool. Medicine too began. In time the knowledge thus acquired grew into authoritative disciplines or branches of abstract moral and technical knowledge as controlling power – e.g. astrology, astronomy, architecture, law, theology, philosophy, mathematics, medicine and military science – and temples, ziggurats and pyramids of earth and stone that were the visible signs of such dominant knowledge binding each community together in a vertical order against the threat of the hostile world without.*

The main temple was, perhaps, the most important component of the early cities. In Ur, for instance, the temple complex was built above the level of the rest of the city. At one end of the complex stood the Ziggurat, a staged tower some 68 feet high, at the top of which was the shrine of the Moon God. At a slightly lower level was the palace of the King, the earthly representative of the Moon God. Lower still, beside the Ziggurat, lay offices and store-rooms to which the tenant-farmers of the Moon God's lands brought sacrifice and rents. So, in Ur, we see the forerunner of a psychological tool employed down the ages in cities: the use of large buildings, often aligned to take advantage of astronomical phenomena and often set on top of a hill, to generate awe and respect towards the establishment.† That sense of awe and respect was deepened by the rituals and accompanying myths which were performed within, or associated with, these places, providing a further bond and protection against the unknown and feared forces, both of nature and of other cities.

Most of the texts from which our knowledge of the rituals and myths of Mesopotamia and Egypt comes have been discovered in temple archives. Ritual activities were carried out by large staffs of priests in the temples at regular times. The rituals, consisting of the part which was done, were accompanied by the myths, the spoken part which told the story of what was being enacted. This story was not told to entertain: it was a word of power which, together with the ritual, was intended to ensure the well-being of the community by controlling the incalculable forces which beset it.

Inevitably those responsible for such powerful words and deeds acquired enormous power over their fellows. So it was that the power of élites was impressed on the masses by a combination of the structures, institutions and activities which dominated their lives.

---

* Modern Universities, with their Chancellors and Vice-Chancellors, their regalia and ritual initiation ceremonies that turn outsiders into intellectual insiders, are the direct descendants of the early temples.

† As well as citing the Ziggurat in Ur as one such psychological device, Steven Boyden, in his book *Western Civilization in Biological Perspective* (Oxford University Press, 1989) p. 142, gives several more recent examples, including the Kremlin in Moscow and the Capitol in Washington DC. Great mosques and cathedrals may be said to have played a similar rôle throughout the world.

From ancient Babylonia to China, Mexico and Peru, and from empire and city-state to the tribe, astronomical information was gathered, recorded and used by those whose interests lay as much in the spheres of status enforcement and political ideology as in predicting rainy seasons or planning agricultural schedules. By the trick of rendering natural phenomena appear liable to social manipulation, in the form of cosmological myth, cleverly aligned architecture and appropriately timed religious ritual, the predictive value of astronomical knowledge served as an impressive display and justification of élite power and prestige.[3]

As the *Homo sapiens sapiens* heads and brains of these communities were raised imaginatively up to the skies and became infinitely superior, the *Homo sapiens non sapiens* hands and feet remained primitive, ignorant and profoundly inferior, forced to toil incessantly on and below the ground. In addition, not only did the quantity and quality of possessions become symbols of status, but clothes began to be used to signify status, position and rôle in society. The priests wore vestments of a quality and appearance quite different from those of the common labourer, while the mandarins of China, in addition to wearing costly robes, left their finger-nails uncut to show that they did not need to use their hands. Today we can immediately identify the occupation and standing of the soldier, policeman or priest from his clothing. Such identification has helped reinforce the hierarchical structure of society. What is more, generations of people could now be born dominant or subservient. A person could be born dominant, to become a king or member of the nobility, or born lower class or even a slave, completely subservient to the will of others.

> Apart from their rôle as 'Lords of the Fertilizing Waters', the first Dictators called themselves 'Shepherds of the People'. Indeed, all over the world, the words for 'slave' and 'domesticated animal' are the same. The masses are to be corralled, milked, penned in (to save them from the human 'wolves' outside), and, if need be, lined up for slaughter.
> The City is thus a sheepfold superimposed over a Garden.[4]

In effect, a majority of people had also become like monkeys in a zoo: expert hands fed food to their captive minds and imaginations, hands that a majority dare not bite.* Indeed, far from wishing to bite them,

---

* See Appendix iv.

they were generally as spiritually corrupt as their masters, with the wage-slave's characteristic acceptance of the yoke. Their passivity, quite as much as the aggressive predatory behaviour of those above them, was a main corrupting factor. That a deranged human being can get used to anything – e.g. learn to live with the degradations of civilization – is one of the most frightening aspects of their existence. More than that, as Herbert Marcuse has pointed out: 'The working class, preconditioned to slavery, can be counted among the fiercest defenders of the existing order.' In short, the majority had become servants of self-exalted élites and their Gods, and were represented as such in the Middle Eastern myths, core of their institutionalized religions. The two main effects of the early urban phase on human history which I have discussed were in fact greatly enhanced by the presentation of their past in myth in such a way as to justify and reinforce their present, and thereby secure their future.

It was the majority in each stratified society whom the Middle Eastern myths described as 'feeble in mind and body' who were now governed and guided by the god-like priestly-scientific few who created those myths. It was they, after all, who benefited most from the civilized state and from its continuation down to today. Unlike the optimum life conditions experienced by hunter-gatherers world-wide, there now existed big differences in the life conditions of different groups of people living within the same stratified society. They experienced different patterns of health and disease: inevitably those at the bottom of the social heap suffered the worst health and shortest lives. New cultural developments could also benefit one group of people in a community but adversely affect another. At the same time, the Middle Eastern myths of a Fall, Flood and Creation denigrated their immediate ancestors, whose sins had apparently brought them to their present captive condition, and thus, if only by implication, anathematized the wilderness as the home of such beasts. In other words, the optimum life conditions of *Homo sapiens* and their wilderness setting were set at naught by those who benefited most from the civilized state of humankind.

The myths of Creation surrounding the birth of civilizations thus unwittingly deprived people of an honourable past as hunter-gatherers, a chilling and total eradication of all record and trace of *Homo sapiens*. For *Homo degener* peoples, until the 19th century AD, ordered human existence, history and time began with, and in, their myths of Creation. The shock and disbelief attending the discovery of the hunter-gatherer art in caves in France and Spain towards the end of the 19th century shows how far they had deviated from their original evolutionary path and ecological understanding. The experts of the time simply refused to believe that the 'primitive' Ice Age people could have had the intelligence, skill or aesthetic sensitivity to paint such beautiful pictures.

Such an understanding of the past and present, as evaluated and presented by the priestly-scientific professionals and experts, was further reinforced by the development of writing. In Mesopotamia writing originated around 3500 BC to facilitate the collection of taxes. It also enabled people to put laws and agreements on record. (In Babylon, Hammurabi composed a written code of law in cuneiform around 1750 BC. It heralded the arrival of a privileged literate élite who could use written laws further to impress their power on the people, thereby reinforcing the hierarchical society.*) The commandments of the king could be spread far and wide and recorded for posterity. Written records made possible a continuous historical consciousness. Writing and laws enabled rulers to spread their rule over 'lesser breeds without the law'. They enabled the city states to grow into empires, as did organized war.

It will be appreciated that the rise of cities not only deepened the outsider relationship between *Homo degener* and the wilderness, but now too between *Homo degener* communities themselves and between them and the nomadic herdsmen. This introduces the third main effect on human history of the early urban phase, that of the acceleration of the growth of stratified societies through climate change (to which they were increasingly vulnerable), organized war and conquest, and their transformation into super-powers and empires of ascent to the sun. In the early days of Sumerian civilization, for example, there was no regular army. When required the men of the city would muster a fighting force, usually against invading bands of barbarians. But with the growth of city-states, each under its own Farmer God, land and water became increasingly scarce, making border disputes between neighbouring states increasingly likely. As warfare developed between them, standing armies began to make their appearance around 3000 BC. A Sumerian text, entitled 'Gilgamesh and Agga' in *The Ancient Near Eastern Texts*, reflects the struggles for domination between the early Sumerian city-states.

---

*As reported in the *New Scientist* (Vol. 176, No. 2373, 14th December 2002, p. 21): 'The first written language in the New World was developed in south-eastern Mexico by a civilization known as the Olmecs. That dates the emergence of early American writing to 650 BC...' Unlike the Old World, writing in the New World was used to pledge allegiance to a superior authority.

The anthropologist Claude Lévi-Strauss has observed that 'the only phenomenon which, always and in all parts of the world, seems to be linked with the appearance of writing ... is the establishment of hierarchical societies, consisting of masters and slaves, and where one part of the population is made to work for the other part.'

He argued that writing was connected first and foremost with power, with 'the power exercised by some men over other men and over worldly possessions.'[5]

Here were the beginnings of organized war, a disciplined struggle between the God, king and priest-scientists of one Sumerian city and those of another. Sometimes one city would establish an ascendancy over others, and exact tribute from their populations. Most important of all was the carrying off of the city Farmer God, to become a subordinate in the city temple of its conqueror. The taking of the God Head of the city added to the stature of one community while diminishing that of another. (This was one very good reason why the Jews would have nothing to do with graven images: their peculiar Farmer God could not then be stolen from them. He was not tied to one locality: he was everywhere. To annihilate their Farmer God of Battles it would first be necessary to annihilate the people that believed in him.)

It is important to note that whereas obedience to what I have described as the Great Spirit of the hunter-gatherers was a principal safeguard against lethal violence, with the two-fold fall and total divorce of civilized communities from the wild ground of their evolutionary past the opposite was the case: organized war in the name of the Farmer God of the community became the norm, while warrior heroes arose amongst the people. It was the patron Farmer God of each stratified society that gave the ultimate seal of approval to war, not only between *Homo degener* and wild nature, but now also between *Homo degener* communities and between them and the nomads. In other words, myth was again used to sanction and perpetuate the prevailing conditions, justifying the superiority of the civilized over those regarded as less civilized; justifying too the conflict that arose between cities bent on expansion. In Sumerian myths, as well as in those of Akkad and Babylon, is found what is known as 'the tablet of destinies', or *me*, the possession of which was one of the attributes of deity: like the aura surrounding the possessor of the atomic secrets of a nation (as for instance that surrounding the late Robert Oppenheimer of the USA). Like atomic secrets and their possessors, the tablets were stolen or taken by force on several occasions. For the God who possessed the tablets of destiny had the power of controlling the order of the universe, to his own ends. In the myth dealing with the organization of the universe, the goddess Inanna wishes to confer the blessings of civilization upon her city, Uruk. She journeys to the city of Eridu, where Enki, the god of wisdom, lives, in order to acquire the *me*, or divine decrees, which are 'the basis of the culture pattern of Sumerian civilization'.[6] The myth contains a list of over 100 items which constitute the elements of Sumerian civilization. Having taken the *me*, the goddess brings to Uruk the blessings of civilization – that is, the visible expressions of the landed, moral and technological superiority of the elect over the masses and over other cities.

Similar myths reflect the rivalry which existed between the various city states of Sumer. Professor Hooke points out that the first items on the list of the *me* which Inanna obtained from Enki are those referring to lordship. The crown, throne and sceptre are mentioned, 'from which we may infer that the struggle for the hegemony of Sumer is one of the motives underlying these myths of the organization of the universe'.[7] An initial outcome of that struggle may be observed in a very ancient inscription at Nippur that records the 'empire' of the Sumerian city of Uruk. Just as India clothed England and was the jewel in England's Crown, and her Queen was Empress of India, Uruk acquired a panoply of possessions that elevated her Farmer God and King above all others. (See figure 8.1)

The collective structural, physiological and behavioural adaptations that had taken place in Mesopotamia led to the growth of the power of the landowning, knowledgeable, soldierly cultivated élite over the powerless, landless slave, a stratified structure of extraordinary inequality. As city began to overwhelm city, the structural inequality of one became superimposed, as it were, on the structural inequality of the other, and city-state grew to become an empire. A pyramid of power had become a super-power, the first of many and increasingly larger pyramids of ascent to the sun. But with the growth and spread of empires came the growth and spread of disease.

The fourth main effect on human history of the early urban phase was the spread of environmental degradation and the growth of diseases, which played as great a rôle as climate change and war in the rise and fall of empires. The three kinds of new (interacting) diseases – nutritional, occupational and infectious – were enhanced by urban life. Work, for instance, brought with it many occupational diseases, which Stephen Boyden has described as 'examples of phylogenetic maladjustment resulting from the evodeviant life conditions experienced by workers in different occupations that came into existence as a consequence of urbanisation'.[8] Boyden quoted a few – including chimney-sweep's cancer, baker's asthma and flour-worker's dermatitis – from a list of some 130 occupational diseases. The evodeviant conditions of urban life also enhanced the main kinds of infectious disease transmission – airborne, waterborne, direct contact and by insects or other vectors. Once cities could accommodate several thousand people, they were able to support crowd diseases, though the population threshold of infectious diseases such as measles and influenza is some 300,000 people. By the Bronze Age there were cities larger than 10,000 people in Mesopotamia, Egypt, India and China, while intensive agriculture enabled large cities to arise later in Peru and in Mesoamerica.

Part I: fig 8.1

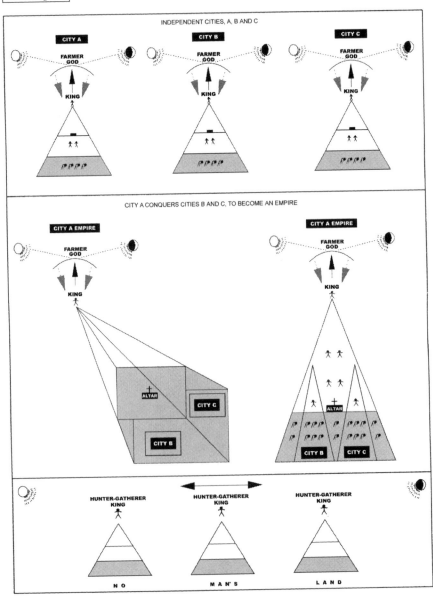

Amongst the most important of the infectious diseases throughout the early urban phase in Eurasia were tuberculosis, enteric fever, typhoid, typhus, bubonic plague, smallpox and cholera. Fragmentary accounts of urban epidemics are to be found in the ancient writings of the Sumerians, Babylonians, Hebrews, Egyptians, Indians and Chinese. India and China both suffered pandemics at the end of the first millennium BC which considerably reduced their populations.

Travel, trade and war helped spread more and more epidemics across the world. During the first centuries AD, for instance, the conquering Huns swept across Asia into Europe and North Africa, driving waves of displaced peoples before them, bringing wars and epidemics to the Roman world.[9] When Roman troops returned home from operations in Syria in 166 AD, they carried with them an infection which was probably smallpox. It ravaged the empire for fourteen years, killing some 4–7 million people. In 252 AD an even worse epidemic, arising probably in Ethiopia, spread throughout Europe. It lasted for sixteen years, killing, at its peak, more than 5,000 people a day in Rome. The disease recurred in Europe for a further three centuries.

For some 10,000 years epidemic disease has been the biggest cause of deaths; it has played a major rôle in invasions and wars. For example, the European invasion of the New World had as profound an effect upon its inhabitants as the invasion of the West by the Huns. The Spanish carried smallpox to the New World in the 16th century – it played a key rôle in their conquest of the Aztecs of Mexico and the Incas of Peru. The invasion of North America by French and English settlers had a similar effect on the Native American inhabitants. Over four centuries the original New World population of perhaps 50 million was reduced to about 10 million by epidemics.

If the effects on human history of the early urban phase were to accelerate the growth and ascent to the sun of stratified societies – an evodeviant cultural growth that was both greatly facilitated by, and undermined by, climate change, war and disease – that growth, which has also driven the evolution of microbes, had its origins in *Homo degener*'s war on, and exploitation of, the wilderness and its inhabitants.

Meanwhile, in Ancient Egypt agriculture evolved around the Nile, which provided a regular supply of water and fertile soils. From the fifth millennium BC, as a result of the need to control the floodwaters of the Nile and to enhance the pursuit of trade, farming communities along the Nile gradually began a process of cultural, political and economic integration. It led to the emergence of a single kingdom and the establishment of the First Dynasty when, it is related, King Menes united the delta region (Lower Egypt) and the river valley (Upper Egypt) in 3100 BC, founding a capital at Memphis. Administrative centres were established and the hieroglyphic script was developed, a source of great power to the literate priestly-scientific élite. The succeeding period of the Old Kingdom (2686–2181 BC) saw the building of the great pyramids as royal tombs.

It was in Egypt that the second revolution on a primary re-evolution achieved an initial climax, as the Pharaohs vied with one another to build the greatest pyramid of self-aggrandizement to the sun. Eventually the people were bound together, like one great machine, to raise the apex of the Egyptian pyramid of power even as high as the sun: one man became Pharaoh, omniscient, omnipotent and omnipresent *Homo sapiens super sapiens*, Son of the Sun God and whiter than white Light, Life-giving Possessor and Controller of all the people and the lands in a single Theocratic Stable State in stasis.

The supreme expression of the divine power and stability in stasis of the Egyptian rulers lay in their pyramids and temples. These were aligned in relation to the seasonal location of heavenly bodies and built in accordance with the relevant and precise mathematical prescriptions in order to secure the well-being of the dead in a life hereafter.*

The Egyptians created and used an energy surplus to build up and feed a 'megamachine' of thousands of workers to build the pyramids to house their Pharaohs for all eternity. Many of the workers who dragged and laid the 2.5 tonne granite blocks that formed the pyramids were seemingly worked to death. As compared with the nobles, who lived between 50 and 60 years, the average age at death of the workers was 30–35. As in the case of the workers who built the henges in England, their physical condition was lamentable. Their skeletons reveal broken limbs, deformed bones and damaged spines.† Archaeologists have estimated that it took some 4,000 workers perhaps 20 years to build Khufu's monument, the Great Pyramid of Gizeh.‡ In effect, the workers constituted a machine, or megamachine, for the ascent of élites to the sun.

The machine, far from being, as is generally believed, a modern invention, has been shown by Lewis Mumford[10] to have originated in

---

*The building of the pyramids required a specialist knowledge of geometry and trigonometry.

†Slaves working in the gold and copper mines of Nubia, the Sudan and Sinai, were, according to the Greeks, in even worse condition: water was rationed and men died by scores in the heat.

‡Many were peasants who only worked on the construction of the pyramids during the three months when the Nile flooded their fields and left them without work or food. They were housed and fed in barracks at the site.

the use of a large number of men by one ruler, together with a bureaucracy, to build ceremonial centres like Stonehenge, walled cities, irrigation works and pyramids. The human megamachine – whether achieved by slavery, forced labour, suppression of the peasantry or labourers forced off the land into factories and down mines – comprised, like the modern machine, many working parts, specialized to the highest degree of precision. Each of the hundreds, or thousands, or hundreds of thousands of men was the equivalent of a cog or bolt in the machine, human components that have been translated today into their mechanical equivalents in machines under similarly centralized control. The original megamachine was based on human components controlled by priest-scientists through their exact scientific knowledge in astronomy, while today it is based on machines developed and controlled by scientists and engineers, and to the same ends: the ascent, wealth, status and security of élites of pyramids of power.

Egypt itself was a Temple to the sun, and the Pharaoh immured within a pyramid an Altar to the sun. Pharaoh and pyramid formed the core of ideological certainty and Life-Force of the community – in this world and the next. As the earthly embodiment of the primitive notion of Providence, the Pharaoh was the Bread and Water of Life; as the Sacred Number and Sacred Word he was the first Word made Flesh. He was the Master Mason and Builder, beneath whom all others were as Apprentices. He was also the Sacred Verb, to become, the Gateway to Heaven and Lord of the Dead. (In Egypt, preparations for life in the next world took precedence over life in this.) The Pharaoh was in truth the epitome and apotheosis of hierarchical order, of a Providential (Theocratic) Stable State unto Eternity, that was most Providential to an élite of nobles and priests.

The Pharaoh was the apotheosis of the pyramid of power that was Egypt. As such, he was also the apotheosis of a unilateral act of infidelity, declaration of independence of nature and denial of the world-wide hunter-gatherer cultures of equality. The pyramids that the Pharaohs built as tombs and memorials to themselves – whose shapes represented the rays of the sun slanting down to Earth, and too the rays of Light emanating from the Pharaoh Sun God – were also petrified memorials to the mountains and to the first pyramids or mountains of people rising above the chaos of the waters and out of the sands. They were also the petrified epitomes of the Egyptian pyramid of power. The Sun that shone Providentially upon the *Homo sapiens sapiens* few near the source of all Light, shone but dimly upon the multitude of *Homo sapiens non sapiens* reaching up from the bottom of the pyramid towards that Light. (See figures 8.2, 8.3)

Part I: fig 8.2

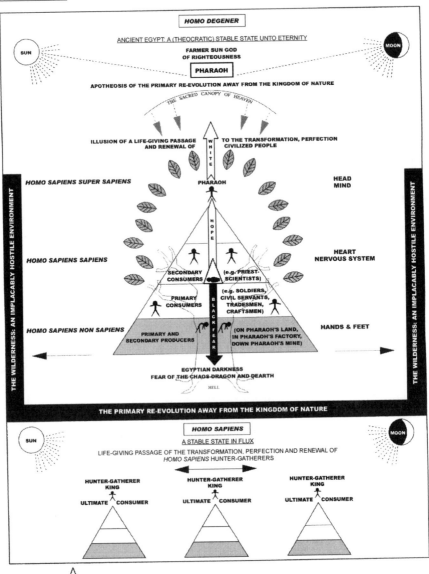

KEY: PHARAOH IN PYRAMID

Part I: fig 8.3

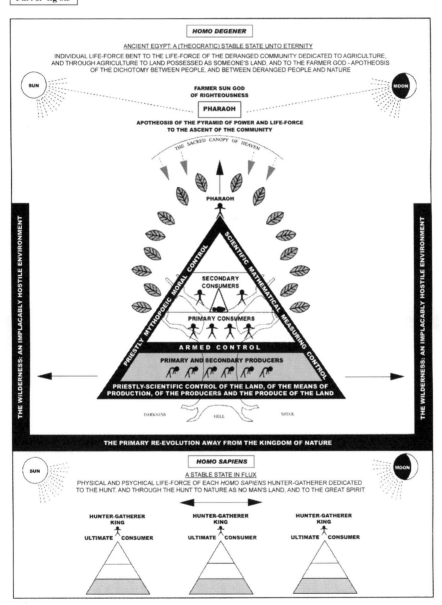

Where previously all people as hunter-gatherers had walked freely and providentially under the sun, heirs to the whole world as no man's land, now many toiled beneath a Sun God, or altogether out of the rays of Sun God and sun, as slaves of the Sun God's State and extremely partial Providence. They were bound within a parasite pyramid by an overwhelming combination of private and State ownership of the land, of the producers and the produce of the land; by the priestly-scientific mediators of moral and measuring control; by the intimidating presence of their great buildings and walls; and by the armed men. Above all revolved the all-seeing eye of the Sun God. The only hope of many of release from a present state of bondage lay in their hope of resurrection into an after-life bathed eternally in the Light of that self-same Sun God. Ironically, in that very hope of resurrection into an after-life, as the reward for right behaviour in this, lay the ultimate bond binding the people to the State in this life.

Here, then, was the penultimate unreality, the expression of a collective primary schizophrenia, the deluded conviction of the Egyptians that their head, the Pharaoh – whether living or immured within a pyramid – was a Son of the Sun God, and the promise of Resurrection into an eternal after-life. Divorced from the natural arena and source of their true stability, perfection and specific immortality, deranged people had lost the universal meaning and measure of themselves. The raising up of Pharaoh and pyramid to the sun fulfilled the collective urge to create a society – and buildings reflecting that society – that was perfectly ordered, stable, predictable and lasting. Pharaoh Sun God, priestly-scientific experts, parasite pyramidal society and pyramids thereafter provided the vertically oriented meaning and measure of people and of the land beneath them: as Pharaoh's subjects and land, they were something lower and less than the Pharaoh, and so on down the hierarchy. In the sun and in its daily rebirth above the sands of Egypt lay their hope of survival in this world and the promise of Resurrection into a life hereafter.

Eventually, whether for social or environmental reasons, the rule of the Old Kingdom dynasties suffered eclipse. Central government was restored by new dynasties during the Middle Kingdom (2055–1650 BC). There followed the deeply humiliating invasion by the Hyksos c.1650 BC. After reigning for some 100 years, the Hyksos were expelled. Militant Pharaohs of the New Kingdom (1550–1069 BC) that followed their expulsion initiated the period of greatest Egyptian expansion and empire.

As the power of Pharaonic Egypt spread down the Red Sea and up the eastern Mediterranean coast, Egypt in its turn became a super-power.

Thereafter the civilizations of Egypt and Mesopotamia, like the city-states of China, began to tear themselves apart with aggressive war. The Suns that shone down on Egypt and Sumeria were eclipsed, only, in the case of the former, to shine again in the 20th century over an independent kingdom of Egypt.

In China, however, Qin Shi Huangdi, who died in 210 BC, ended 500 years of strife between the warring states. He pacified and merged them into a united China, built the Great Wall and established an imperial system with himself as the first Emperor of China. That imperial system, of whatever dynasty, received its Mandate to rule from Heaven – each Emperor was the 'Son of Heaven', the Sun that illumined China – and survived throughout many vicissitudes from 221 BC until its eclipse in 1911 AD. In 1949 the new ideological Sun of Communism rose over China as victorious communists proclaimed the People's Republic of China under Chairman Mao Zedong.

Meanwhile, in the West, an after-glow from the ancient civilizations remained. The new civilizations and empires of Greece and Rome drew energy and warmth from the embers of the old, as when Alexander the Great was welcomed in Egypt in 332 BC – a country regarded by Greek minds with semi-mystical awe – where he was installed as Pharaoh and received confirmation of his divinity as Son of Ammon, beloved of Ra. The Greeks bequeathed to Europe a search for wisdom, a love of beauty and a pressing need to define the good; Rome passed down lasting values relating to law and order and the disciplined pursuit of objectives most conducive to the elevation and well-being of élites.* The Greeks and Romans rose to new heights of learning and conquest. Their Suns illumined more of the Earth than any heretofore – but not for long. As waves of barbarians advanced into western Europe, the Roman Empire of the West was engulfed (476 AD).

A man-made flux was now in operation across the world. The superposition of parasite pyramid on parasite pyramid, building empires ever higher against the natural flux and in violation of the basic rule of a harmonious environment with its primacy of horizontality, gave rise to a man-made flux – the rise and fall of empires combined with the waxing

---

* Though the Greeks and Romans bequeathed great literary, legal and artistic traditions to the West, it is noteworthy that the Greek and Roman edifices were built by slaves. In the Greek mining camps during the 5th and 4th centuries BC, slaves were worked to death. The slaves who built Rome and provided the comforts of its citizens lived in dungeons underneath their masters' houses. Their lives were lived in constant fear of retribution; while their masters feared the slaves around them. (The gladiators who entertained them were often slaves who lived in a nightmare world of blood.) Indeed, they lived and died under a black Sun.

Both Greece and Rome also destroyed their forests in their pursuit of wealth and power.

and waning of man-made Suns which spread devastation and destruction across the land.*

The rise and fall of successively larger and more widespread empires (whether territorial or commercial) has increasingly overlaid and replaced the natural flux and succession of innumerable natural food pyramids and the royal beings at their summits, the whole contributing to a disharmony and imbalance of the world. For whereas the natural environment and flux are generally life-enhancing and perfecting under the true sun, the artificial environments and flux are generally life-degenerating and destroying under the man-made Suns of nations. And it was the rise of the black monotheistic Suns of Christianity and Islam over the nations in the first millennium AD that further obscured the light and meaning of the true sun for humankind, encouraging more widespread destructive behaviour than any heretofore as Christians and Muslims indulged in religious wars and spread their parasite pyramidal structures across the world in the furtherance of their ascent to the sun. I shall examine the growth and spread of Christianity in detail because of its key rôle in the shaping of the modern world. BC/AD (Before Christ/Anno Domini) was a psychical watershed in the history of humankind. *Christianity raised the collective primary schizophrenia and paranoia inherent in stratified societies to new levels of intensity.*

Christianity arose 2,000 years ago as a sect within Palestinian Judaism, the faith and practice of the Jews who themselves originated as a recognizable group c.1800 BC in Ur in Chaldaea. Their God, Yahweh, first announced His presence to Abraham, making a Covenant with him, promising him that in return for his allegiance He would give Abraham and his heirs the land of Canaan, and that his issue would grow into a multitude. Abraham's descendants went down into Egypt, where they were later oppressed and eventually enslaved. Their flight, or Exodus, from humiliating oppression into the desert was aided by Moses, on whom Yahweh bestowed the gift of the Ten Commandments engraved on two stone tablets. These Commandments, the Covenant with Abraham and the subsequent history of the Hebrews – or Israelites as they called themselves – were transcribed in alphabet writing in the Bible. Thus it was that between the polytheistic Mesopotamian and Egyptian empires, which were centres of early literacy, of cuneiform and hieroglyphics respectively, there appeared the Hebrews who embraced two revolutionary concepts: the monotheistic male God of Abraham and alphabet writing.[11]

Following the establishment of a kingdom in the Promised Land under

---

* See Part II, Chapter 7, for an amplification of this argument.

King Saul and his successors, David and Solomon, the kingdom was divided into Israel (north) and Judah (south). Israel was destroyed as a political entity by the Assyrians (722 BC) as was Judah when Jerusalem was sacked by the Babylonians (586 BC) and part of the population transported. Although Babylon was overthrown by the Persians, and the captive Jews allowed to return to Judah, subsequent vicissitudes led to its incorporation in a Roman province in 63 BC. It was there that Jesus of Nazareth grew up.

Jesus was born in 4 BC. He became a penniless, peripatetic prophet living on casual gifts of food. His teaching in the last few years of his life called people into an altogether more promising life that would reveal their present state as intolerable slavery. He called his hope, his vision, 'God', 'Father', 'Lord'[12]. 'He who has seen me has seen God.' 'I am the way, the truth and the life.' Jesus had the courage to meet people as their God, refashioning God in the image of human hope. Jesus broke tradition, the Sabbath and the Law. He held the two fundamental Commandments to be to love God with all your heart, and to love your neighbour as yourself. He brought healing and forgiveness to others by giving them hope, that they might take up their beds and walk, thereby inspiring others with hope, that together they might realize the Kingdom of Heaven – that is, the vision, hope, dream, aspiration – that is within each. Jesus compacted God into the flesh of humans, into any individual, 'the least of my brethren', the despised Samaritan. Jesus was the Christ, the Messiah, only to those who understood, who were prepared to reject as irrelevant everything in their society that enslaved them – in particular, the shackles of nation and religion and everything they stood for, including power, property, privilege, precedence, pride, the dead weight of possessions and the burdens of toil which so corrupt the personality of the individual – and to follow him; to follow his example by becoming, as he was to them, the son of God to others. I meet God in the person who gives me a new chance, who inspires me to be born again, to recover the lost inspiration, to do the impossible, to become an eternally hopeful wanderer towards a retrieved paradise, to walk freely under the sun. In the absence of any knowledge of the past of all men and women as hunter-gatherers obedient to the Great Spirit, Jesus' hope for humankind was the revolutionary transformation of the profoundly repressive pyramid of power into something that placed the love of neighbour above even that of family or nation, and which embraced even the enemy in love.

Jesus' message was regarded by the Jewish religious authorities as blasphemous and a threat to their own position, for he was sweeping away all the securities underlying Judaism. The priests realized that unless he died the nation and priesthood would perish. Jesus' crucifixion occurred in 30 AD. In his death the life of Jesus was completed, becoming a parable of hope to everyone who is made truly hopeful through it. In that sense, it became eternal, immortal. However, his followers tragically believed that a Messiah, both human and divine, had died and risen again like the gods of old, a faith which thereafter lay at the heart of the earliest Christian teaching. Christianity turned a man and his prophetic vision into a deity, Christ, whose teaching, death and Resurrection constituted the core of the new priestly religion. He who called himself the Son of man was deified as the Son of God.

I have expounded at some length on the prophetic status and vision of Jesus because of the tragic repercussions that followed his death and the subsequent birth of Christianity. For not only was the prophetic vision of Jesus opposed to the priestly religion *per se*, but it was so perverted to serve the self-righteous priestly ends of Christianity as to cause illimitable confusion and conflict – as the remainder of this chapter will show – giving rise to a host of warring Christian sects within Christendom, and to war against the non-Christian world and wilderness without, all in the name of Christ.

It was Saul of Tarsus who, as Paul and between 40–50 AD, created the religion called Christianity – a Church which included Gentiles as well as Jews – by combining Judaism with elements of Mithraism* and the Greek mystery religion Orphism. (If the mythical Christ story is reminiscent of the pagan Orphic/Dionysian myth, it also resonates with Egyptian myth. The Trinity of Father, Son and Holy Ghost that Paul created are strongly reminiscent of the centuries old Trinity of Serapis (Father), Isis (Mother) and Horus (Son),† while the Christian offer of immortality to those who believed in the divinity of Christ reflects a similar offer extended to the worshippers of Serapis.) Contrary to the prophetic teaching of Jesus, Paul preached the ancient religion of priest and altar and sacrificial lamb – i.e. Jesus mythologized as the Christ, the Lamb of God – offered up to God as an atonement for sin: that is, the idea of the redemption of sins through a Saviour who would rise from the dead. Paul's Epistles were joined to the Four Gospels (written c.60–110

---

*Originating in Persia, the worship of Mithras, the sun, was adopted by Rome and spread across most of Northern and Western Europe during the first three centuries AD. It was the principal rival at that time to Christianity. Christians adopted Sun-day as their principal day of worship instead of the Jewish Sabbath.

†With the elevation c.800 AD of Jesus' mother Mary as the mythical Mother of God and Queen of Heaven, the similarity becomes even more striking. A thousand years later, in 1854, the Papacy declared that Mary had been conceived by Immaculate Conception.

AD) to form the New Testament. Paul, as well as advocating the creation of bishops to oversee the laity's spiritual life, to all intents and purposes established an all-male hierarchy, with Jesus, mythologized as the Christ, at the apex. The bishop of Rome, or pope, became Christ's Vicar on Earth. These were the orthodox Christians. Between 150 and 450 AD men like Tertullian (c.155–222 AD), Jerome (c.340–420 AD), Ambrose (c.339–397 AD), and Augustine (c.354–430 AD) helped shape the doctrines of the Church. These law-making Fathers of the Church turned the teaching of Jesus into a legalistic religion. Jerome translated the Old and New Testaments into Latin (the Vulgate); Augustine was mainly responsible for the theological framework of Catholicism up till the Reformation, and even for the leading principles of the reformed religions, including in particular the doctrine of Original Sin.

In 313 AD the Roman Emperor Constantine declared Christianity to be the state religion, administered by the orthodox. Constantine looked to the orthodox to revitalize Rome's military standing, inscribing on his cross the motto *in hoc signo vinces*: by this sign (i.e. the Cross) thou shalt conquer. Aided by the military and police, the orthodox forced the closure of pagan temples and the destruction of centres of Gnosticism.

For several centuries sharp divisions had existed between those who were orthodox Christians and those who were Gnostics. The latter believed in a corpus of secret spiritual knowledge surrounding the Christ, and derided the literal interpretation by the orthodox of the Gospels. Their beliefs combined elements of Greek legend, Orphic mysticism and Platonism, and tended towards extreme spiritualism at the expense of all things material, including the body. In Leonard Shlain's terminology* they split along the lines of the hemispheres of the brain: the orthodox favoured left-brained male dominated patriarchy, while the Gnostics favoured intuition, imagery and egalitarianism. The destruction of Gnosticism, and the branding of Gnostics as heretics, expressed the triumph of words over images, of patriarchical hierarchy over egalitarianism, throughout Christendom. However, it is important to understand that the power of the word over the image already lay at the heart of orthodox Christianity, with potentially disastrous consequences. For the Word of God in the Old Testament and that Word made Flesh in Jesus Christ (i.e. the image of God in the New Testament) were not complementary but antithetic and antipathetic to the minds of the orthodox Christian hierarchy. For they rejected the egalitarian image of Jesus (and those

---

* See Appendix iii.

words most in harmony with that image) and selected those words of the New Testament (e.g. Paul's Epistle to the Romans) most suited to securing and enhancing the power of the orthodox hierarchy. Hence Jesus, who was crucified, not only as a threat to the Jewish hierarchy under their invisible male monotheistic Farmer God, but to hierarchy *per se*, was – irony of ironies – elevated as the Christ by the orthodox hierarchy to a seat at the right hand of that self-same God of the Israelites. God and Jesus were united in underwriting the orthodox hierarchy.

The same underlying contradiction may be seen if Christianity is viewed from the standpoint of the peaceable, egalitarian image of Jesus. For the Israelites' God was primarily their vengeful God of Battles, whose very first act on their behalf was to encourage the extermination of the innocent Canaanites. When Christians adopted the Bible as their own, and added the New Testament witnessing to the life, death and resurrection of Jesus, they adopted that self-same God, but now masked and garbed in the robes of Love. It was a mask that would inevitably fall, to reveal the true face of their Farmer God, in the event of a threat to the orthodox hierarchy.

This may help resolve the problem that people have in reconciling a God who is reputedly loving and omnipotent with the suffering of the innocent and the good. Not only does a monotheistic Christian God permit such suffering but His very existence promotes it. Because He was created by farming peoples in their own deranged hierarchical image to sanctify and promote their subjugation of peoples and of land (initially the land of Canaan), He, an entirely fictitious creation, has inevitably appeared to side with those who created Him, siding with the strong against the weak, with the landowning rich against the landless poor. Jesus of Nazareth, himself a penniless, peripatetic prophet, attempted to break the hierarchical mould with his denunciation of the Pharisees and their God, but was instead, with the aid of myth, elevated on high to sanctify the ends of a new pharisaical élite, the Christian orthodox Church.

Whichever way the Christian message is viewed, there is a profound contradiction at its heart which has reinforced the two-fold dualism inherent in all deranged cultures. It was inevitable that the Christian world view, and so Christian behaviour, would be deeply ambivalent, veering wildly between love and hate, tolerance and tyranny, peace and war, forgiveness and revenge, self-righteously attributing all their acts – whether peaceful or warlike – to the will of their Farmer God. Inevitably the overall effect of such a dualism and patriarchal left-brain dominance was to accelerate the process of conquest, persecution and exploitation throughout the second millennium AD in the joint names of God (i.e.

the vengeful God of Battles) and Christ (of the Cross – *in hoc signo vinces*), the black Christian Sun whose baleful light has illumined the path of the Bible and the gun.

Following the destruction of the Western half of the Roman Empire in 476 AD,* the civilized way of Roman life collapsed. Cities and towns became isolated and commerce virtually ceased. The majority of people lived as serfs in small settlements separated from one another by miles of wilderness, home of the chaos-dragon – in their case, raiders from neighbouring tribes and threats from Huns, Vandals, Ostrogoths, Visigoths and wild animals. The serfs were both protected and oppressed by the landowning rulers of petty fiefdoms and the Church, paying tithes to both. These so-called Dark Ages lasted some 500 years, during which time the Church became the dominant institution. The founding of the Benedictine Order in 529 AD saw the beginning of the monastic movement. The monasteries 'possessed all the books there were in Europe',[13] and were therefore the key to literacy and advancement, letting down ladders up which intelligent men might ascend to escape the drudgery and oppression of serfdom. But their spread heralded a significant advance of agriculture and associated demise of European forests. One further most important result of the rise of the monasteries was that, despite the rule of celibacy, monks cohabited with women, siring innumerable offspring out of wedlock.

> Monasteries spawned so many illegitimate children that, in exasperation, the Council of Pavia declared in 1018 that all children born to clerics were to be condemned to perpetual slavery and disbarred from any inheritance...
>
> Born without legal status, many misbegotten boys who grew into manhood felt they had no further option but to try to seize power by force. Medieval history is filled with the names of bastards: Arthur, Gawain, Roland, William the Conqueror, and many a knight in Froissart's *Chronicles* among them. Many became brigands or, like their fathers, joined monasteries. For girls born out of wedlock, menial jobs, poverty, or slavery was their lot. Some emulated their mothers and became concubines; others turned to prostitution, creating a social malaise that frequently overwhelmed local authorities.[14]

---

*The Eastern half flourished for another thousand years, until the Eastern capital, Byzantium (Constantinople), fell to the Ottoman Turks in 1453 AD.

Such a pernicious effect on society reflected the existing illegitimate status of a *Homo degener* humankind born not only outside the evolutionary union of the Great Spirit and Earthmother, but also out of the prostitution of the Earthmother subjugated as Mother Earth, foundation of *Homo degener's* power to ascent. That power has been reinforced by those, such as the clerics' bastards, who have suffered massive humiliations down the millennia at the hands of those in power, driving them in turn to seek legitimacy and power in ascent, so extending and perpetuating the parasite pyramids of humiliating power.* One outstanding instance at this time concerns the appearance of the Prophet Muhammad on the stage of history and the rapid rise of the Arab Empire.

Muhammad was born c.570 AD in Mecca: he was orphaned at six. In 610 he had a dream, a revelation conveyed to him by the Angel Gabriel, that he, Muhammad, was the messenger of Allah. His words were repeated to converts and written down, to form the Quran.† His Muslim followers were promised life after death in Paradise if they rejected idol worship and venerated only Allah, the monotheistic God of Islam. Threatened with humiliating eclipse, the guardians of Mecca's idols persecuted Muhammad, threatening Islam in its turn with eclipse. Muhammad was forced to flee to Medina (a flight known as the Hegira, from which the Muslim era is dated). From there he launched a Holy War against the enemies of Islam in Mecca. By 630 AD he had defeated the Meccans, acquired recognition as chief and prophet, and gained control over all Arabia, thereby avenging his, and Islam's, earlier humiliation at the hands of the Meccans. The Prophet died in 632 AD. Within a decade Muslim Arabs – inspired by religious zeal and a desire for plunder – embarked on wars of conquest. By the middle of the 7th century AD they had established the Arab Empire, eventually converting diverse peoples as far west as Spain and as far east as India. The Arab (Muslim) conquest of the Mediterranean in the 640s forced northern Europe eventually to unite for protection under the Carolingians. The Islamic threat also accelerated the consolidation of the Western Catholic Church around the authority of the Pope in Rome. Already Christendom had divided into the Western Catholic Church under the Pope and an Eastern Orthodox Church led by a Patriarch in Byzantium. Following the Great Schism in 1054, it

---

* See Part III, Chapter 2, and Appendix v, for an amplification of this argument.

† Just as the orthodox Christians became divided from the Gnostics (or as the Western Catholic Church was divided from the Eastern Orthodox Church), a similar division occurred between Sunni Muslims who strictly observed the tenets of the Quran, and the Shiites (who traced their lineage from Muhammad's son-in-law, 'Ali' and youngest daughter, Fatima) who also subscribed to an oral tradition arising from periodic reinterpretations of the Quran.

was Byzantium that maintained the literary and artistic traditions inherited from Greece and Rome.

In 800 AD Charlemagne took control of most of Christian Western Europe, promoting culture to such an extent that the period became known as the Carolingian Renaissance. And just as the Great Goddess arose out of the darkness and chaos of the early Neolithic, so now Christianity experienced a temporary pendulum swing away from the legalistic orthodox creed towards the feminine, when Mary, the mother of Jesus, was elevated in c.800 AD as the mythical Mother of God. As I argued in Chapter 6, she was venerated as the Queen of Heaven and became the centre of devotion of the largely illiterate peoples of Western Europe.[15] In times of adversity the long-suffering poor would call upon her to intercede for them in the face of what they saw as the wrath of God. Many churches and cathedrals began to be built throughout Europe in Mary's name.

Meanwhile, by the year 1000 AD, iconography represented Jesus as the mythical Christ, Emperor of Emperors, King of Kings, Mediator and High Priest, the justification and sanctification of Christian Emperors, Kings and prince Bishops at the summits of pyramids of power, and of the corporate state beneath them. He was the Light of the World, the Sun that would increasingly obscure the light and meaning of the true sun for humankind evolving as kings of natural food pyramids. For whatever the attraction of Mary and of the image of Jesus as egalitarian and peace-loving over the next thousand years, it would be the mythical male monotheistic Trinity of Father, Son and Holy Ghost – the black Christian Sun – that would illumine and sanctify Western nations in their aggressive expansion and ascent away from the humiliating darkness of the past towards the sun.

Christianity, like Islam, like every other religion or ideology, was open to as many interpretations as there were States growing up to embrace them in their competitive ascent to the sun: each had its own Farmer God, its own black Sun. As new States arose Phoenix-wise in the second millennium AD out of the ashes of the old, they employed similar methods to those of the earlier civilizations to raise the apices of their pyramids of power and to maintain their stability as vertically-orientated structures: ruthless exploitation of the primary producers, dispossession, enclosures, slavery and war. They also employed similar methods to sanction and sanctify their parasitical-cum-perverted predatory activities: the invocation of their Farmer Gods, the black Suns that illumine their Providential Stable States, whose most powerful mythopoeic manifestation has been the Sun – and now also the Christ. Instead of inspiring men to walk freely under the sun, Jesus, mythologized as the Christ, was made the spearhead of an ascent of humankind on the backs of their fellows to the heavens, towards the sun.

By the 10th century, force of arms had raised many warrior chiefs to kingship. National states began to emerge. Their kings created what is known as feudal government – that is, the granting of land in return for military service – in wide areas of Western Europe, including England, France, Germany and Scandinavia. Generally the king was regarded as owner of all the land within his domain, granting estates to his vassals in return for a given number of fighting men. The greatest vassals were dukes and counts, who often had vassals of their own. As kings began to indulge in the profitable waging of wars and as feudal lords required men to protect their properties, the need arose for professional fighting men and knighthood originated. A European aristocracy thus arose whose origins were military and whose titles were generally military ranks. Its rise was accompanied by the building of castles. Medieval castles were bases for the projection of physical power, threatening, dominating and controlling the surrounding countryside. In that countryside, at the bottom of the feudal pyramid, were thousands of peasants and serfs. Medieval law recognized two kinds of peasants: freemen and serfs. The former usually held their land in return for part-time military duties as men-at-arms. Serfs, who made up as much as 95 per cent of Europe's population, were neither allowed to work nor to travel where they pleased, nor even to marry without their lord's permission. They and their descendants were required to farm their lord's land and pay him special dues. However, they had rights dating from when they first accepted serfdom in return for military protection, rights that included the grazing of cattle on common land. Feudalism reached its zenith in the Middle Ages, though it survived until the late 19th century in much of Eastern Europe.

In 1095 the First Crusade was proclaimed by Pope Urban II, ostensibly to defend Byzantium against the Muslim Turks. In 1099 the Crusaders, including many of the aforementioned knights, captured Jerusalem from the Turks, establishing the Latin Kingdom of Jerusalem, only to lose Jerusalem again to Saladin (Sultan of Egypt and Syria) in 1187. There followed, between 1189 and 1291, some six further Crusades against the Muslims in Palestine, Egypt and North Africa, which ended with the Christian Latins being driven out of the Holy Land.

However, the crusading movement continued well into the 17th century, as evinced in the resistance to the Muslim Ottomans and their defeat before Vienna in 1683. Expeditions against the pagan Slavs and Lithuanians in the north were treated as crusades (that against the Lithuanians from the 1220s on being dubbed the 'Perpetual Crusade'), as were expeditions to crush heresy. The end of the 12th century saw the rise of anti-clericalism amongst the lower classes in Western Europe seeking escape from a corrupt and indifferent hierarchical control of their lives and a return to the egalitarianism and simplicity of early Christianity. The principal groups who thus posed a serious threat of humiliating eclipse to the Catholic hierarchy were known as Cathars or Albigensians. The Albigensian Crusade was launched against these heretics in southern France (1209–29), while Pope Gregory IX (1227–41) set up the machinery for the Inquisition, sanctioning the torture and burning at the stake of all such heretics.

Further devastation followed with the breaking out of a land dispute between the kings of England and France, which degenerated into the Hundred Years War (1337–1453). This was shortly to be accompanied by the Black Death (1347–52) which hit a population already debilitated by war and a series of poor harvests, resulting in the loss of over a third of the population of Europe. There followed a severe disruption of agricultural and industrial production and trade. These, together with the increase in the incidence of warfare, induced social tension and revolts, including the Peasants' Revolt in England in 1381.

In contrast to the romantic view so often presented of the Middle Ages (5th century AD–15th century AD), Pennethorne Hughes argues that

> The people, except perhaps in Italy, trembled under a religion which was built on fear, and a political system which was based on selfish force. The whole period was, with only minor exceptions, one of physical, moral, and intellectual degradation and atrophy...
>
> There was no sort of social freedom, and there was a level of semi-starvation, particularly in winter – when there was no meat – so bitter as even to provoke sporadic cannibalism...
>
> This situation was the result of an ascetic religion which was both all-powerful and profoundly pessimistic. This world was held to be a vale of blood and tears preparatory to the next, which was, for the majority, to be one of eternal torture and damnation. It was, indeed, a culpable heresy to hold that more than a tiny minority were likely ever to escape hell fires...
>
> Round humanity clustered devils, for ever seeking to clutch men and drag them down to hell. The ascetic preoccupation had indeed made a religion of love into one – in many hearts – of terror.[16]

Throughout this period men were reaching up, straining their eyes towards Heaven in expectation of the delayed millennium, in widespread paroxysms of communal yearning for the Second Coming of Christ. 'Even Sir Thomas More, by the time of the high Renaissance, orthodoxly believed the last stage of the world to be imminent.'[17]

Earlier, the 13th century had seen the re-creation of the lost legacy of classical learning and art (rediscovered during the Crusades) that finally resulted in the Italian Renaissance. There have been three periods involving significant revivals of interest in the classical past, all of which, of course, helped further conceal the true evolutionary past of human-kind – their learning and art as hunter-gatherer kings of natural food pyramids. Following the Carolingian Renaissance there was a Renaissance in the early 13th century when Christian learning was fused with the rediscovered works of Aristotle in the great intellectual synthesis known as Scholasticism. Thomas Aquinas (1225–74) was a prime mover in fusing the words of the pagan philosopher with the Christian message. He provided such a reasoned defence of the faith in his *Summa Theologica* that Thomism came to represent the general teaching of the Catholic Church. However, he viewed women as inferior to men, and even as having no souls, thereby writing off 50 per cent of the world's population. He also upheld Augustine's animadversion that Eve was responsible for the blighting of the whole human race with Original Sin. The third and principal Renaissance occurred in the 15th and 16th centuries in Italy, when art and architecture, music and science flourished. It gave those who were not clerics a new sense of history and of their creative powers. In 1454 Johannes Gutenberg patented the printing press; presses began to copy and disseminate ideas. Literacy rates soared. Together, the Renaissance and printing gave rise to a philosophy called Humanism. During the revival of learning in the 14th–16th centuries, humanists devoted themselves to the study of the language, literature and art of Greece and Rome, generating advances in the arts and sciences. How-ever, as Leonard Shlain points out, although people throughout Europe were now inspired to demand rights, while universities broke free from the Church and a wealthy middle class began to grow, Humanism was primarily a male credo, glorifying men in every cultural sphere at the expense of women. Women were ill-served by the Renaissance and printing.

Linked in the subconscious with the fear of wild nature – the fear of the 'other' – the innate power of women has always haunted men down the millennia, but none more than the ascetic Catholic orthodox hierarchy. Women who practised witchcraft – deriving from the early

Neolithic fertility cults of the forests of Europe combined with the later traditions of magic of Egypt and parodies of Christian worship – were much in vogue amongst the peasantry of Europe. Witchcraft became particularly attractive to a peasantry reacting against a Catholic religion of ascetic dogma and corrupt practice, which promised salvation to a few at the cost of a life and death of hell for the majority. Pennethorne Hughes[18] denotes three peak periods when witches, like heretics, suffered persecution. First, around the time of the Albigensian Crusade against heretics, witches were also singled out by the Inquisition as a threat to Christendom – heretics threatened Church dogma but witches were believed to possess supernatural powers. They were the Devil's* agents, accused of causing not only pestilence and other physical and mental ailments, but also of being responsible for destructive natural phenomena. There followed a second wave of persecutions after the Black Death and Hundred Years War, and a third in the 16th and 17th centuries following the combined threat to Catholicism of the Renaissance and the Reformation. In 1490 the Chief Inquisitors for Germany produced a guide to the extermination of witches and witchcraft, called *Malleus Maleficarum* (The Hammer of Witches). Following the Reformation, the Reformed Churches were even more fierce witch-hunters than the Catholics in their efforts to protect the new orthodoxies against perceived threats from heretics and witches. Between the late 15th and early 17th centuries untold numbers of women in Europe were hunted down, tortured, mutilated and burned to death as witches at the instigation of both the Church and the State. Altogether, over 500 years, generations of women throughout Europe must have lived in constant dread of the approach of the witch-hunter and his chains. Hughes[21] hints that a suggested figure of nine million women dying as witches may be a conservative estimate. Generations of children were orphaned.†

---

* 'Theologically speaking, the Devil was first defined by the Council of Toledo in AD447.'[19]

With the personification of evil in the Devil, Christianity now had its own dualistic concept of the world, as between the works of God and those of the Devil (or between those of Christ and those of the Anti-Christ), a dualism resembling that between Yahweh and Beelzebub. Both dualisms are expressions of the same sacred Tree of Knowledge of good and evil of the Old Testament, itself resembling the sacred World Tree of the Teutons – Yggdrasil, the sacred tree of knowledge whose roots and branches bind together Heaven, Earth and Hell – that is found in different forms throughout the world. (Pennethorne Hughes argues that the sacred tree reappeared 'as the Cross – the sacred tree of the Crucifixion, miraculously renewed throughout time'.[20])

It should be recalled that all such dualistic thinking originated with that between the perceived good of the farming settlement and the evil of the wilderness, home of the chaos-dragon.

† See Part III, Chapter 2, and Appendix v, for the effects of parental deprivation.

1517 saw the birth of the Reformation,* when Martin Luther (1483–1546) attacked the sale of papal indulgences. The reforming Protestants inspired a Biblical revival, translating the New Testament into the vernacular. They emphasized the sovereignty of God, insisting that faith and the Bible, rather than works, were the key to salvation, placing emphasis on those passages from the Old Testament that expressed the wrathful aspect of God as against the loving message of the Gospels. (Here again, we see evidence of the profound contradictions at the heart of Christianity, itself founded on the two entirely fictitious creations of God and Christ.) Luther endorsed Augustine's conception of Original Sin and of predestination, that predestined the salvation of an elect and the consignment of the majority to hell. He saw wild nature as the abode of devils, and natural phenomena such as thunder as Satan's handiwork. John Calvin (1509–64), with the aid of his book *Christianae Religionis Institutio* (1536), invented a more extreme form of Protestantism. He systematized Protestant doctrine and organized its ecclesiastical discipline. He argued that the civil government existed solely to carry out the Word of God. To that end he provided Protestantism with an organization comprising an all-male hierarchy, requiring the total submission of women to their fathers and husbands. It was this more extreme form of Protestantism that inspired the English Puritans, Scottish Presbyterians, French Huguenots and Afrikaner Boers.

In the mid-16th century the Vatican launched the Counter-Reformation, a general movement of reform and missionary activity whose most influential figure was the Spanish theologian Ignatius de Loyola (1491–1556) who, in 1534, founded what in 1540 was legitimized by Pope Paul III as the Society of Jesus (the Jesuit Order). The Counter-Reformation provided for the enforcement of disciplinary measures by the Roman Inquisition, while in 1563 the Council of Trent laid down its doctrinal formulations. These measures halted the tide of Protestantism and inspired

---

*It was in fact, as Leonard Shlain has argued[22], the fourth protestant reformation (or 'wrenching reorientation in a culture's religion') to affect the West. The first occurred in Sinai c.1800 BC when the Israelites revolted against the icon worship of Egyptian polytheism, and adopted the first sacred alphabetic book. The second occurred some 2,000 years later in the Roman Empire when Christians, having adopted the second sacred alphabetic book, the New Testament, rejected the images of the polytheistic state religion. The third occurred in the deserts of Arabia when the followers of Muhammad rejected idolatory and adopted the third sacred alphabetic book, the Quran. All these reformations derogated the religious and property rights of women.

Members of these religions, and of their offshoots, have tended to regard themselves as the chosen of God. All who have subscribed to this belief, and who have regarded and persecuted others as heretics, are victims of what I describe as a collective primary paranoia: they cherish collective delusions of grandeur and associated fears of conspiracy and persecution. See Part II, Chapter 3, for an amplification of this argument.

Catholics with new confidence. By 1650 more than two-thirds of Europe had returned to Rome, leaving the Reformation to retain a hold in the North.

There now occurred a series of religious wars and persecutions, the conflicts of the Reformation (1517–1648). In the early years of the Reformation the Anabaptists – German-speaking peasants – committed themselves to the baptism of believing adults only and embraced religious tolerance and non-violence, establishing self-sustaining communities on shared land. They believed that the teachings of Jesus Christ and strict Church discipline ranked higher than the laws of the state. Perceived by the nobility as a threat to the social order based on the inheritance of land, they were denounced both by the leaders of the Reformation and the landed gentry. Furthermore, in 1528, the Holy Roman Emperor outlawed the practice of adult baptism on pain of death. The Anabaptists suffered horrific persecution. Meanwhile, thousands of peasants in Germany, motivated by the New Testament which they interpreted as a revolutionary message of social reform, and believing – wrongly as it transpired – that they had Luther's support to that end against the nobility, refused to pay taxes. There followed the Peasants' War (1524–25) in which thousands died. This was followed by the Thirty Years' War (1618–48) which, though German in origin, involving Lutherans and Calvinists killing each other, also involved a long power struggle between the Kings of France and the Habsburg rulers of the Holy Roman Empire and Spain, spreading throughout Europe. It was further complicated by conflict between Protestants and Catholics, throughout which both Protestants and Catholics continued to hunt down and burn witches. More than one-third of Germany's population perished.

Meanwhile in France the Reformation gave rise to Protestants known as Huguenots. In 1535 King Francis ordered the suppression of the growing heresy. Persecution of Huguenots reached its apogee following the Saint Bartholomew's Day Massacre (1572) of Protestants in Paris, when a number of other cities murdered thousands of their Huguenots. The Netherlands too suffered a reign of terror lasting nearly a century. Not only did agents of the Spanish Inquisition in support of Dutch Catholics burn Protestant heretics, but Calvinist Protestants persecuted other Protestants whom they accused of heresy. In Spain, in 1483, King Ferdinand and Queen Isabella appointed Torquemada as Chief Inquisitor, unleashing a reign of terror against all those suspected of deviating from the Catholic faith. Jews and Muslims – even those who had converted to Christianity – were caught up in the dragnet, tortured and burned. The Jews were expelled from Spain, and in 1502 some 3 million Spanish Moors were likewise expelled.

When, in 1509, Henry VIII ascended the throne of England, he was at first a staunch supporter of the Catholic Church against Luther, receiving from the Pope the title 'Defender of the Faith'. However, following the failure of his wife, Catherine of Aragon, to produce a son and heir, Henry VIII petitioned the Vatican for a divorce. The Pope refused, and in 1533 Henry married Anne Boleyn. In 1534 Henry's marriage to Catherine of Aragon was invalidated by Acts of Succession, which declared that the King was the sole and supreme head of the Church of England. This break with the Vatican was followed by the banning of Catholicism and the suppression of the monasteries (1536–39). These acts led to a great unrest throughout a country already profoundly affected by the Reformation and Tyndale's 1525 translation into English of the New Testament. Henry VIII died in 1547, to be succeeded by a son, Edward VI, and then, in 1553, by Mary, his daughter by Catherine of Aragon. Mary, an ardent Catholic, reversed the Acts of Succession and instituted a Catholic reign of terror. Many Protestants were persecuted for having supported Henry against the Papacy, earning Mary the sobriquet 'Bloody' in Protestant hagiography.

Elizabeth I (only daughter of Anne Boleyn, Henry's second wife) ascended the throne, following Mary's death, in 1558. She supported a moderate Protestant Church settlement which promoted stability and firmly established the Anglican Church. Numerous Catholic conspiracies, however, forced Elizabeth to persecute the Catholics in the 1580s and 1590s, in turn provoking Philip of Spain's unsuccessful attack on England with the Armada (1588). Following the death of Elizabeth in 1603, James I ascended the throne. He had already published a book on witchcraft, *Daemonologie,* and was accompanied by a number of Scots 'imbued with their own dogmatic and cruel variant of the continental hysteria'.[23] James immediately proceeded to legislate against witchcraft, making it punishable by death on first conviction. James was succeeded in 1625 by Charles I. War with France, unpopular economic policies, and 11 years rule without a parliament alienated much of the country. Then Charles' attempt to unite the three realms of England, Scotland and Ireland (each of which resided under its own exclusive black Christian Sun) led to almost simultaneous revolts throughout the three realms. There followed two Civil Wars (1642–46, and 1646–48), when Anglicans, Catholics, Puritans and Presbyterians tortured and butchered each other indiscriminately. King Charles was executed in 1649.

Holy wars arising from religious zealotry and dynastic and constitutional disputes, and economic dislocation and hardship, were the principal forces destabilizing the nations of early modern Europe. During the 16th century in Europe there were only five years of complete peace, and only four in the 17th.[24] It was against this background of 1,500 years of massive humiliation, mayhem, madness and human sacrifice that had already consumed so many millions across Europe in the name of Christ that the black Christian Suns which had arisen over Europe now began to shed their baleful light across the world.

Christopher Columbus discovered the New World in 1492. The Spanish began to settle and exploit the Caribbean islands, which provided a base for the exploration of Central America. They carried with them both the virus of the black Sun of Catholicism and of disease. Hernán Cortés established Spanish rule over the Aztec Empire in Mexico in 1521, while Francisco Pizarro crushed the Inca Empire in Peru during the 1520s. Over the next 300 years European colonists – Spanish, French and British – together with the diseases they spread, exterminated some 40 million out of an original 50 million inhabitants of the New World, together with their great variety of cultures.

In the West, amongst the mythical Suns that have sanctioned and sanctified the parasitical-cum-perverted predatory activities of rulers and élites at the summits of pyramids of power – Mithras, Apollo, or Christ – none had shone more brightly in the second millennium AD than that which illuminated the *ancien régime* in 18th century France. Louis XIV, who reigned from 1643–1715, became 'the greatest expression of absolute monarchy in the world'. Louis Dieudonné, Le Roi Soleil, the Sun King – the names of Louis XIV are synonymous with the magnificence of his great creation and monument to his own regal glory, Versailles. Versailles became a symbol of the enduring power and glory of the monarchy; an expression of an Age of Genius, the age of Molière, Racine, Pascal, Lully and Couperin. But above all Versailles was a tribute to Apollo, the Sun God, who seemed not so far removed from the Sun King. Once again, as in Ancient Egypt and Sumeria – whose Sun Gods and Sun Kings and their monuments provided the earliest and most profound expression of absolute monarchy and pyramidal power to ascent – a *Homo sapiens super sapiens* Sun King, together with a *Homo sapiens sapiens* élite (talented musicians, artists, writers and intellectuals), was raised up on the backs of a *Homo sapiens non sapiens* majority. Before the end of the century the *ancien régime* would be destroyed in a bloodbath of its own making, the French Revolution, revealing its mythical Sun in its true light – as black.

It was between c.1690 and c.1790 in Europe that the certainties surrounding absolute monarchy and religion began to be undermined by a philosophical movement called the Enlightenment. Increasing philosophical and radical criticisms of the existing order opened the way to the growth of science which, through the use of reason and experiment, provided an alternative world view to that of religion, arguing that the world functioned in accordance with consistent physical laws, as opposed to the belief in a world governed by supernatural powers. Francis Bacon (1561–1626) had already developed the concept of scientific induction. He opined that truth is not derived from authority, stressing the importance of experiment in the interpretation of nature. In his book, *Novum Organum* (1620) he

> ...used metaphors derived from the witch hunt torture chamber to describe how scientists should force nature to relinquish her secrets.[25]

Bacon neatly summarized the (anti-evolutionary) processes by which science should advance:

> ...we propose to show nature not only in a free state, as in the history of meteors, minerals, plants, and animals; but more particularly as she is bound, and tortured, pressed, formed and turned out of her course by art and human industry.[26]

Science had now joined the black Sun of Christianity in perverting the course of evolution.

In 1637 the French mathematician René Descartes (1596–1650) wrote a book, *Le Discours de la Méthode,* that provided a conception of the universe operating under mathematical laws. His views – the Cartesian dualism – accentuated the old dualism between mind and matter, by focusing on the split between the mental and the physical, thus reinforcing the ancient split between *Homo sapiens sapiens* head and *Homo sapiens non sapiens* hands and feet, and between both and *Homo sapiens.*

It was in 1687 that the English natural philosopher Isaac Newton (1642–1727) published his *Philosophiae Naturalis Principia Mathematica* in which he set out three laws of motion. In astronomy he formulated the universal law of gravitation. The advance of mathematics and physics was greatly accelerated by these discoveries.

Although science reduced the power of the Church, it reinforced the parasite pyramidal structure, while its effect upon women and wild nature was dire. In Leonard Shlain's terminology,* scientists used the left brain's faculties of reason and mathematical skills to discover the laws of nature.

---

* See Appendix iii.

Anything that could not be comprehended by reason was 'other', less than real. Many men placed women in this category. Their conviction that men were 'naturally' superior to women was not only reinforced by 'natural law', but it complemented the earlier view expressed by Thomas Aquinas that women were inferior to men.

> Women's rights and the attributes associated with the right brain suffered accordingly. Thus, European civilization passed from a patriarchal society based on laws handed down three thousand years earlier by a male deity into a new version of patriarchy founded on 'natural laws' discovered by male scientists.[27]

And just as Constantine had allied orthodox Christianity with the military, so now science allied itself with contemporary hunter/killers. As with the priest-scientists of yore, religion and science reinforced one another in enhancing and defending the wealth and power of élites of stratified societies, eventually transforming the instruments of conquest into the Bible and the space rocket. Religion (or ideology) and science were now combined to increase immeasurably the power of the black Suns illumining stratified societies to energize their ascent to the sun.

The Enlightenment and its associated scientific discoveries made possible the Industrial Revolution, which eventually spread across both Northern and Southern Hemispheres. It was another watershed in the history of humankind, a revolution energized by the black Sun of Protestantism.* It began in Britain, the greatest slave trading nation on Earth. It was this indescribably cruel trade which provided the impetus to the Industrial Revolution. The slave trade involved the transportation, between 1650 and 1850, of some 12 million West Africans to work on sugar, cotton and coffee plantations in North America and the Caribbean. It was a triangular trade involving the export of manufactured goods (including brass and copper products and glassware) to West Africa, thence the

---

*In Britain evangelical Protestantism provided moral and emotional support to emergent industry. It preached the values of thrift and self-advancement through hard work, as well as promising heavenly rewards beyond the poverty and misery of this life. Piety, the work ethic, submissiveness and progress were equated with salvation; sloth, insobriety and disobedience were equated with sin and damnation. Evangelical religion became the moral cement of English society. Ironically, though the evangelicals were to the forefront of the movement to abolish slavery, they were at the same time helping bind workers together as 'wage-slaves' in factories and in mines. They also initiated a universal mission to the heathen, particularly in Africa. Evangelical missionaries saw the homelands of native peoples (and too the wilderness) as territories of the Prince of Darkness to which they were bringing the Light of Christianity and associated work ethic, binding the natives together as 'wage-slaves' in colonial industries.

transportation of slaves to the Caribbean, returning to the ports of Bristol and Liverpool laden with sugar, rum, tobacco, cotton and money. It was the fabulous profits accruing from this trade, together with the growing need for iron for machinery for the West Indian plantations and for processing their products in Britain, coupled with the need to provide long-term credit to sustain the slave trade which in turn led to the growth of specialized banking houses, which provided the impetus to the Revolution.

The Industrial Revolution began in the mid 18th century and took off following the development of coal and coke as sources of energy,* the mechanization of the cotton and wool industries of Scotland, Lancashire and Yorkshire, and the invention of the steam engine as a source of power. Already a steam engine had been invented by Thomas Newcomen (1663–1729) for pumping water from mines; its design was improved by James Watt (1736–1819). His early steam engine was bought by some wealthy West Indian planters, while money from the slave trade enabled Abraham Darby to perfect the smelting of iron with coke, to produce a metal that was both robust and machinable. Following the harnessing of steam power, cotton and wool factories were increasingly concentrated in towns. Around 1830 the Industrial Revolution entered its second phase, with the mechanization of the heavier iron and steel industries.

If slavery provided the impetus to the Industrial Revolution, the deprivation of thousands of tenant farmers and labourers of their livelihood and way of life as a result of the 18th century Enclosure Acts also helped make the Industrial Revolution possible. The driving of the small farmers, cottagers and labourers from the village common land, in order to establish 'enclosed' farms owned by the richer farmers and landed gentry, was both the precursor to, and helped consolidate, the Industrial Revolution in Britain, providing labour for the new industries. In other words, *the descendants of people who were doubly deprived of their hunter-gatherer way of life and wilderness home as Neolithic farmers were now further doubly deprived of their farming way of life and common land.*† Because industrialization, and in particular the steam engine, substituted inanimate for animate sources of power, by converting heat into work through the

---

*The forests of Europe, as well as being cleared away for agriculture, had by this time been severely depleted to service the building and ship-building trades, as well as being used as a principal source of fuel. They were not therefore available to supply the increasing amounts of energy needed to fuel the Industrial Revolution.

†Each was *forced* to adapt as farmer and as factory-hand respectively in order to survive.

use of machines, people were able to exploit not only vast new sources of energy but even vaster numbers of workers deprived of land. Many of the dispossessed and deprived were transformed into 'wage-slaves' in factories or buried deep in mines. People, from being enslaved *en masse* as work-machines in earlier civilizations were now also enslaved *en masse* as machine-workers, to the same ends: the ascent to the sun of élites of pyramids of power.

Finally, as well as being built on the backs of slaves and wage-slaves, industrial civilization has been described as being built on the back of the whale, as shore-stations near whaling grounds grew into cities – in the Americas, in Europe, in Russia and in the Far East.

> Millions and millions and millions died in a marine holocaust,
> Generating the implacable human appetite for electricity, petroleum
>   and plastic...
>
> Without the blood-letting of the whale:
> Prime source of light and lubrication,
> The industrial revolution would have been scantily equipped.
>
> A spectral colossus haunts the inflated myth of progress,
> So keen to brush aside its hidden costs,
> In the cause of pure profit;
> So forgetful in the bright name of novelty.[28]

Like the agricultural revolutions in Egypt and Mesopotamia, the Industrial Revolution was initially based upon water power. Like them, it led to the self-aggrandizement of new breeds of élite – the elevation and ennoblement of great industrialists and scientists, just like the earlier elevation and ennoblement in Egypt of great landowners and priest-scientists – and to the enslavement of the masses to the machines they created. Industrialization, in substituting inanimate for animate sources of power – and in particular the introduction of the steam engine – began to transform the economic and social circumstances of men and women between 1780 and 1820, constituting the basis of the modern megamachine.* Steam power was the driving force of the Industrial Revolution, driving hundreds of machines grouped together in factories and thousands of men and women who had to work to their rhythm.

---

*With the introduction of the machine men came to be seen and treated as machines, and the work-force itself came to be seen as a machine – a megamachine.

Unlike their hunter-gatherer ancestors, who had obeyed the natural rhythms in their daily lives, *Homo sapiens non sapiens* workers were forced to obey rhythms imposed upon them by *Homo sapiens sapiens* managerial and engineering élites. They were forced into subservience to a megamachine that compelled them to obey the demands of the 'rapid, regular, precise, tireless' machines.[29] While the machines were running they had to work, and the machines were controlled not by the workers but by the bosses. So the workers became doubly enslaved, enslaved to the controlling bosses and to the controlling machines. Furthermore, following Michael Faraday's invention of the electric dynamo in 1831, the workplace was transformed, enabling the employer to work his employees day and night, as artificial sunlight turned night into day.

Manchester was to be the characteristic, the dominant city of this new capitalistic civilization of dominant factories, in which people were absolutely submerged – under a power of water and of steam, as it were – in the pursuit of industrial wealth. (The ownership of the means of production was replacing the ownership of land as the principal source of wealth.) As De Tocqueville wrote of Manchester,

> From this foul drain, the greatest stream of human industry flows out to fertilise the whole world. From this filthy sewer, gold flows. Here humanity attains its most complete development, and its most brutish; here civilization works its miracles and civilized man is turned back almost into a savage.

Recall the analogy of the dammed up and polluted waters of the primary re-evolution, which led eventually to a stream and then a deluge destroying the wild world. Now a new deep lake of static and even more polluted water (that is, imbued with all the characteristics of a primary re-evolution and of the Industrial Revolution) enabled a new breed of *Homo sapiens sapiens* to exploit their fellows to raise their heads above the water, followed by a stream and then a deluge of filthy water spreading out over both domesticated land and the wilderness.

In the 19th century, this new capitalistic civilization spread first across England, then across Europe and finally across the world – a wave of advance 'miraculously', Providentially, raising a few on the bent backs of the brutalized many. No-one can doubt that, by the beginning of the 19th century in England, a new world of pleasure was opening up for the middle classes. But this new world was built on the slave labour of millions of brutalized men, women and children who had no access to such pleasures. Their sole concern was survival.

Like the roads that spread a primary re-evolution and deluge of destruction across the world, the Industrial Revolution was now greatly assisted in its progress by the railroad. The destruction caused by the coming of the railways and by road improvements was savage. According to Dr H.J. Dyos, 76,000 Londoners were evicted in the second half of the 19th century for railway clearances.

> Those worst hit by the clearances were casual and poorly paid workers. Factory, railway, and dockland extensions were almost exclusively achieved at the expense of the poorest neighbourhoods. As William Denton wrote in 1862:
> 'The special lure to the capitalists offered by the railway projectors, is that the line will pass only through inferior property, that is, through a densely peopled district, and will destroy only the abodes of the powerless, and the poor, whilst it will avoid the properties of those whose opposition is to be dreaded – the great employers of labour.'[30]

The railroad, forerunner of industrial civilization, opened up both domesticated land and wilderness, particularly in North America. As it progressed across North America from east to west, the railroad helped wholly to change 'the law and custom' of the Native American hunter-gatherers by enabling the destruction of the buffalo, foundation of their economy. Like the road, the railroad led to a 'particular kind of deluge'. The Native Americans were drowned in a deluge of white men – they were dispossessed, deprived of their land, consigned to imprisonment and death and their wilderness home destroyed. The same deluge Providentially raised up the railroad owners to eminent positions in American society.

It will be appreciated that the Native American hunter-gatherers underwent a process of multiple deprivation similar to that suffered by the hunter-gatherer ancestors of the Europeans, except this time the deluge comprised multitudes of Europeans. Their devastating advance across the world was accelerated with the arrival of the Industrial Revolution.* That

---

* Subsequent revolutions and roads, like the Xavantina road referred to above, and associated activities such as logging and cattle ranching, are helping decimate what little remains of the rain forests, destroying the last of the forest inhabitants. Because of the effect of this destruction on the atmosphere and ecosystems of the world, it is meet and proper, if ironical, that such activities, intended as they are to improve the wealth and well-being of *Homo degener* peoples, instead now threaten their very survival. One of the main reasons why *Homo degener* peoples behave as they do is because their vertically structured, or layered, societies resemble to a marked degree those of a forest, with which they are in competition for space and resources. In this connection, see Part II, Chapter 5.

revolution reduced people to a state as naked as that of their primitive farmer forbears stripped of their hunter-gatherer characteristics and confronted by an unknown wilderness, 'a forced rebirth from one age to humble status in the unknown of another'[31] – all for the sake of the enrichment and ascent of secondary and ultimate consumers at the summits of pyramids of power.

Power has been gained and maintained by violence. The history of ancient and modern civilizations is dominated by human conflict and the domination of one human group by another through the process of conquest; that includes colonialism.

> There was a time when religion was one of the great causes of international strife. Later, the possession of colonies brought wealth to the colonial powers of western Europe, wealth which was gained by armed strength; it was commercial rivalry that then pushed nations into conflict.[32]

As Woodrow Wilson declared,

> Since trade ignores national boundaries and the manufacturer insists on having the world as a market, the flag of his nation must follow him, and the doors of the nations which are closed against him must be battered down... Colonies must be obtained or planted, in order that no useful corner of the world may be overlooked or left unused.

Conquest and colonialism by stratified societies – the use of 'terror and physical violence unsparingly against competitors and enemies'[33] – have caused socio-economic disintegration and deculturation throughout the world. The subjugation and exploitation of weaker people by the stronger, and of wild animals such as the whale, made possible further agricultural and industrial revolutions, while subsequent similar revolutions heralded a further concentration of power, as stratified societies in the Northern Hemisphere extended their bases laterally, or right down into the Southern Hemisphere, whence they have drawn the sustenance (both from other nations and from nature) necessary to their ascension.

The release and arrogant use of the new power to self-aggrandizement – of Industry and Science harnessed to the chariot of the Christian Sun – enabled and encouraged Kings, Emperors, Napoleons, Presidents and Dictators and their subjects in the Northern Hemisphere aggressively to acquire and exploit the necessary land and wealth of primary producers to launch themselves into the sky, trailing clouds of lesser consumers in their wake. Their lunatic ascent, even as high as the moon, is still often justified by appeal to the myths of Creation that had their origins in Mesopotamia. (The first American astronauts read out extracts from Genesis as they climbed towards the moon.) We are just finishing 300 to 400 years of world domination by the Christian powers, whose ferocity in the use of the Holy Bible and the gun – and their devastating introduction of disease, deliberately or unwittingly – to acquire and exploit no man's land or someone weaker's land, and to sanction, sanctify and protect their acquisition, is quite without parallel in history.* This was particularly the case in the 19th century.

> In the year 1800, Europeans occupied or controlled 35 per cent of the land surface of the world; by 1878 this figure had risen to 67 per cent, and by 1914 to over 84 per cent.[35]

Europeans imposed their industrial civilization on the world through exploration, through economic relationships – including trading, shipping, construction, railways and mining – through the establishment of infrastructures of buildings, ports, roads and railways, through the dissemination of the Christian faith, through the diseases they brought with them, but above all through terrorism, rapine and conquest and the subsequent delineation of colonies whose artificial frontiers have generally survived their transformation into the nation states of today. The whole modern world, if not simply the creation of Europe, is the product of European imperialism, by conquest, by intellectual penetration, by economic development. According to *The Cocoyoc Declaration* (1976),

> Much of the world has not yet emerged from the historical consequences of almost five centuries of colonial control which concentrated economic power so overwhelmingly in the hands of a small group of nations. To this day, at least three quarters of the world's income, investment, services and almost all of the world's research are in the hands of one quarter of its people...

This is, of course, in accordance with the structured inequality within any one parasite pyramid in the Northern Hemisphere. The withdrawal

---

*It has been estimated that the total losses suffered by tribal societies during their conquest by Europeans amounted to more than 50 million people over 400 years, a process described by Mark Cocker as 'the greatest, most persistent act of human destructiveness ever recorded'.[34]

of the colonial Powers brought little change, at least at the economic level, for they had already forced the developing world into a global economy on their own terms: the great multi-national companies succeeded the earlier maritime empires and are today's new imperialists.

Christian nations in the Northern Hemisphere, with the aid of the colonized and enslaved peoples to the south of them, were enabled to create and use an energy surplus to build up and feed factory industries, wage slaves and power machines. These in turn have created further energy surpluses necessary to raise the summits of the industrial nations ever higher in the vertical. If our concrete monuments are rocket launching sites, nuclear power stations, skyscrapers and high-rise office blocks rather than henges, obelisks and pyramids, they still epitomize the monumental pyramids of power which created them. In the Northern Hemisphere, prior to the Industrial Revolution, nations generally consisted of primary, secondary and ultimate consumers parasitizing primary and secondary producers. By their invasion and parasitizing of peoples to the south of them, these nations have been able so to raise their general standards of living away from the primitive as to have become mainly rich consumer nations, while those peoples whom they parasitized have become mainly poor producer nations.* The First World/ Third World† structure may be described as the ultimate class system. All the aid and investment in these mainly poor producer nations has only helped to make the rich donor countries richer and the poor recipient countries poorer. Exploitation of the people in these countries has continued as it did during the colonial era. For instance, in the second half of the 20th century, a large part of Peru's most fertile land was devoted to cash crops – for export. In the slums around Lima children starved while Peru exported millions of tons of fish protein to feed European pigs. The spectacular high Andes are the source of the potato, one of the world's most important food crops. Yet in Peru potatoes

---

* Britain, for instance, established an empire with an industrially developed core surrounded by a periphery comprising a quarter of the world's population producing food and raw materials. Britain was thereby enabled to become a wealthy *Homo sapiens sapiens* consumer nation through the exploitation of poor *Homo sapiens non sapiens* producer peoples throughout the empire.

See Fig. 5.6 above representing the parasite pyramid of energy and numbers, described as a pyramid of structured inequality as power to an élite. It is this structured inequality that has spread across the world. Fig. 5.6 may now therefore also be seen as the picture of a world of nations being inexorably integrated by the forces of globalization into a single parasite pyramid of power to the ascent of an élite of mainly rich *Homo sapiens sapiens* consumer nations through the exploitation of mainly poor *Homo sapiens non sapiens* producer nations.

† It was called the 'Third' world because, during the 1950s, its members insisted on distancing themselves from both the American and the Russian dominated blocs.

have been scarce and expensive, and malnutrition has been widespread there.*

Tsarist and Communist Russia, on the other hand, acquired a similar power to vertical ascent by the enslavement of large numbers of her own people and by the parasitizing of her neighbours in Eastern Europe and in Asia, while Communist China welded together the majority of her enormous population – 800 million labourers and peasants – as primary producers.

It was in the midst of the Industrial Revolution that Karl Marx (1818–83) appeared on the scene. In 1848 he finalized the *Communist Manifesto* which attacked the state as the instrument of oppression, declaring religion and culture to be ideological products of the capitalist class.† In 1867, aware of the desperate plight of the working class, he published *Das Kapital.* His writings predicted imminent social revolution in the industrialized Western part of Europe. It occurred instead in agrarian Russia.‡

After 500 years of autocratic, often tyrannical, rule by a series of Tsars, Russia experienced the Bolshevik revolution, instigated in 1917 by Lenin (1870–1924), who became head of the first Soviet government. Leonard Shlain[36] has argued that Communism was a 'religious' revolution, whose bible was the *Communist Manifesto*, Western culture's fourth 'sacred' alphabetic book (after the Old and New Testaments and the Quran). It was the West's fifth 'protestant reformation', which violently overthrew the Russian aristocracy and Church. Though Marx's 'Force of History'

---

* In the new millennium such exploitation without regard to the cost proceeds apace. For instance, the insatiable demand for diamonds has led to the opening up of the Central Kalahari Game Reserve in Botswana to diamond mining and to the eviction and persecution of the Bushman (San) whose ancestral land it is. (*Survival Newsletter* 42, 2000.)

The demand for tantalum, a rare and valuable metal used to make capacitors for the developing mobile telephone and aerospace markets, fuelled a civil war in the Democratic Republic of Congo over the possession and control of the tantalite mines. The companies that processed and bought Congolese tantalum preferred not to see the connection. (*New Scientist*, Vol. 170, No. 2285, 7 April 2001.)

† Marx rightly declared (in the manifesto of the First International, 1864) that 'the subjection of the man of labour to the man of capital lies at the bottom of all servitude, all social misery, and all political dependence'. This is the inevitable outcome of the imprisonment of people within parasite pyramids of power: it accords with their structured inequality, in contradistinction to the natural equality of people moving at the summits of natural food pyramids.

‡ If Marx was wrong in the short term he will surely be proved right in the long term. If his predictions are viewed in the light of the globalization of the world economy, and in the light of its First World/Third World structure – the ultimate class structure of rich consumer nations and poor producer nations – he was right in assuming the rich would become richer and the poor poorer, until revolution threatens.

replaced the Eastern Orthodox God as the black Sun sanctifying and guiding the USSR, the development of Communism in the USSR would owe more to the pragmatic interpretations by Lenin and Stalin of Communist ideology than to the writings of Marx. Like the earlier Christian Suns, that of Communism energized a reign of terror. The murder of millions of the property-owning class of Kulaks for the sake of 'collectivism', the condemnation of members of a variety of professions as 'heretics', and the public trials, 'confessions' and executions resembled earlier religious persecutions aimed at preserving the purity of the new dogma. But, following Stalin's implementation of a series of crash industrial programmes, it was nature

> ... that suffered the most grievous wounds at the hands of the Communists, who irretrievably despoiled much of Russia's pristine landscape.[37]

Stalin's reign of terror was resumed after the Second World War, and Stalinism extended over Eastern Europe. Stalin died in 1953, to be succeeded by Nikita Khrushchev, whose confrontationist foreign policy led to the Cuban Missile Crisis (1962) and near nuclear catastrophe.* Subsequent vicissitudes at home and abroad, and catastrophic environmental damage, led Mikhail Gorbachev, who came to power in 1985, to initiate democratic reforms which ended the Soviet control of Eastern Europe. In 1991 the Soviet Union split into fifteen independent republics, leaving a core Russian Federation which had abandoned Communism. Threatened with further nationalist fissure, Russia faces an uncertain future as it strives to maintain its place in the sun.

Like Christianity and Islam, Marxism gave rise to a wide range of interpretations – to as many in fact as there are nations that have embraced Marxism. The Marxism-Leninism of the USSR was a distinct variant of Marxism. China embraced another variant when, following the defeat of the Japanese invaders and the unification of the country under one government, the Communists, in 1949, proclaimed the People's Republic of China under Chairman Mao Zedong. Under the light of its newly

---

* At that moment in history two men – President Kennedy of the USA and Nikita Khrushchev of the USSR – held the fate of the world in their hands. Such is the pass to which the two-fold fall has brought us. Two pyramids of power, each illumined by its own Sun of self-righteousness, were each evil in the eyes of the other, threatening one another with humiliating eclipse. In fact, each was to the other illumined by a black Sun, while both were black from an evolutionary standpoint.

What we were witnessing was a convergence of composite animals to a point of near violent conflict, a phenomenon which I shall examine further in Part II, Chapter 9.

arisen Sun, China followed the Soviet model of economic development and social change until 1958. Then Mao introduced an extremist five-year plan, the 'Great Leap Forward', based upon a Chinese interpretation of Communism that included the development of peasant labour collectives running small-scale iron and steel foundries. These not only produced sub-standard products, but removed labour from the agricultural sector. A consequent decline in food production, combined with a 'strong' El Niño (ENSO) event which caused widespread drought (1958–59), led to a nationwide famine – twenty million peasants died.* A further decline, in industrial production, forced the government to de-industrialize the economy, bringing China's economic growth to a temporary halt.

In 1966 Mao launched the Cultural Revolution. His ideology was outlined in *The Little Red Book*. China underwent its own convulsive 'protestant reformation',[38] when the religions of Confucianism, Taoism and Buddhism were swept away and a reign of terror ensued. Ten years of persecution at home were accompanied by intense xenophobia abroad. Though China lost support abroad following its invasion of Tibet, *The Little Red Book* nonetheless became a symbol of revolutionary zeal both in China and around the world. Following Mao's death in 1976 China's leaders became more pragmatic and more concerned with economic growth, becoming, in the 1980s, more open to Western economic principles and ideology. Strict party control is now uneasily combined with a trend towards a semi-capitalist society as China seeks to establish its place in the sun.†

So with the aid of the Industrial Revolutions and Christianity in the West and Communism in the East, nations and agglomerations of nations in the Northern Hemisphere either acquired – or, in the case of China, will shortly acquire – the enlarged bases and energy surpluses and resources necessary to extend their summits even to space stations, the moon and beyond. (See figure 8.4)

As the world has moved from one world integrated in a freedom of movement of all in obedience to the Great Spirit to the atomized world of thousands of deranged tribes, and now moves to the still atomized world of some 200 separate States of deranged men obedient to their peculiar Farmer Gods and Ideologies, empires like America, Europe, Russia

---

*Once again climate change, as in the ancient world, played a major rôle in the destruction of vulnerable, sedentary peasants.

† 'China is following an approach to development that measures progress only through economic growth, while ignoring the disastrous effects on the environment. Economic growth is supposed to solve the problem of poverty, but it causes so much environmental destruction that poverty continues and development is undermined. It is a vicious circle.'[39]

Part I: fig 8.4

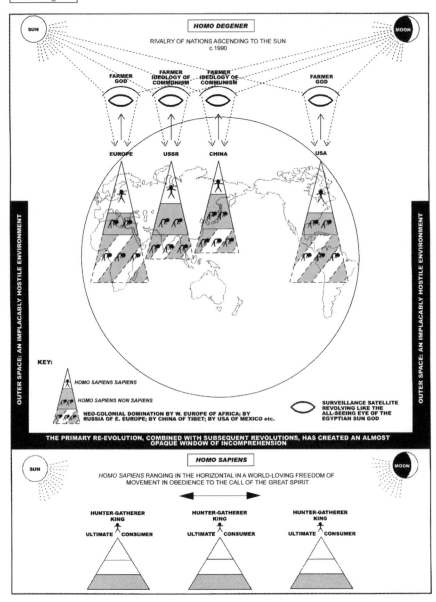

and China conspire to throw a wall of intelligence or spy satellites – revolving like the all-seeing eye of the Egyptian Sun God – around the world to safeguard and promote their interests. If these various nations often feel themselves threatened militarily or economically by their neighbours, all are threatened with an unparalleled rapidity of population growth, inroads into non-renewable resources, the widening gulf between rich and poor nations, global warming and the deterioration of both our natural surroundings and the man-made environment. These threats arise to a considerable extent from the effects of globalization, which forces countries to open up their national economies to transnational corporations. This makes them subject to the rule of market forces which, by moving resources only towards those with money, increases social inequality and environmental devastation. Globalization is the latest stage in the 'battering down of closed doors' of nations so aptly described by Woodrow Wilson, including the 'closed doors' of the remaining nature reserves. Only a small minority of people at the summits of parasite food pyramids, together with those most intimately connected with the economic process, benefit in the long term, while the majority live in violent communities in search of fewer jobs in the decreasing space of a devastated world. In other words, whatever *Homo degener* appears to have achieved in the economic integration of the world is greatly outweighed by its malign consequences.

Because the wilderness had become an alien and hostile place to them, and because they built physical and psychical structures of self-elevation and self-protection against the wilderness and against their own wild natures and the natural flux, they have turned the world into an alien and hostile place of their own making, a wilderness of warring peoples, hostile not only to themselves but to wildlife as well. In the 20th century, and following closely on the First World War, which saw the loss of some 8 million lives, the Second World War caused the deaths of some 55 million people as virtually the whole planet went to war. Now the world is involved in what is seen by evangelical Christians in the USA as a Third World War – a war against terrorism, itself a by-product of globalization, for many Islamic fundamentalists see the USA as leading a Crusade that aims to humiliate and subordinate Islam to the Christian capitalist ethic, particularly when that ethic is subsumed under the Christian apocalyptic vision contained in the *Book of Revelation.*

The modern world has rightly been described as the inevitable construct of a whole series of wars, but I would add in particular the endless war against wild nature, now also waged on a world-wide scale, and so against true human nature. This cannot be regarded as a success story but rather as an unmitigated failure. *In destroying the wilderness we destroy the only ground of the real freedom and relative perfection of humankind. More than that, we destroy the only ground of reality and of the real memories of humankind.* In this process, history has been a principal purveyor of false memories overarching and undergirding stratified societies, whitening *Homo degener* while blackening *Homo sapiens,* falsely celebrating the passage from 'primitive' hunter-gatherer through the early civilized societies to modern civilization as a progressive ascent towards perfection; it is in fact the precise opposite. The whole process may truly be regarded as mad!

The union of the alphabet and war resulted in generations of suffering and provides a metaphor for history that is both mythic and true. Every time there has been a great advance in science and knowledge assisted by alphabet literacy, it has been associated with war. The periods that historians most admire – Classical Greece, Imperial Rome, Renaissance Italy, and Elizabethan England – were born in strife and carried within them a vein of terrible madness. Indeed, whenever the alphabet appears, so too does madness. Roman history is replete with mad rulers such as Caligula and Nero. The Renaissance and the Elizabethan Age produced tremendous advances in the arts and sciences, along with witch hunts and ferocious religious wars. The French Revolution, child of the Enlightenment, ended in the mad Jacobin Reign of Terror. In the twentieth century, the Germans, who glorified reason, produced the madmen Nazis.

More recently, we have witnessed staggering advances in exploring the frontiers of knowledge. Yet we came perilously close to destroying ourselves and the planet in a nuclear holocaust. It is fitting that the Pentagon program charged with the massive buildup of thermonuclear weapons, far in excess of what could ever be needed to destroy any enemy, was named Mutual Assured Destruction, known more familiarly by its acronym, MAD.[40]

History is the story of escalating madness, of cultures of deranged people born in strife with the wild world. It is the record of their demented struggle to recover from the humiliation of their fall and failure as humans. Driven always by the fear of humiliating eclipse, *Homo degener* peoples began so to alter and adapt their own natures and the natural environment to their parasite pyramidal needs as to compound their failure, inhumanity and incomprehension with every subsequent revolution on the original re-evolution. They carved Kingdoms for themselves out of the one true kingdom of nature, which they then endowed with a legitimacy and stability which their origins and vertically oriented structure-building behaviour have ultimately and inevitably denied them. The fact that their civilizations have persisted and 'progressed' for 6,000 years or more does not legitimize their illegitimacy and the basic illegality of their usurpation. Nor does it alter their natural status as doubly deprived degenerate peoples. Nor does it obviate the fundamental evil of their anti-evolutionary ways. Yet their progression and lunatic ascent are nevertheless described, in self-congratulatory terms, as the Ascent of Man. In truth, after overwhelming evolutionary *Homo sapiens*, it is anti-evolutionary *Homo degener* subhumans who ascend.

Under the circumstances, the world is moving inexorably towards a new climax, when it seems likely either that it will destroy itself in a biological, chemical or nuclear holocaust* or, more likely, perish through the perversion of our natural support systems. Hence, a further revolution is called for by members of the scientific community.

This may take one of two main forms. The first is the attainment of a sustainable environment by means of advanced technology and the establishment of a World Government that would still have as a principle aim the ascent of humankind to the stars. The second involves the return to a simpler life-style within a world of self-sufficient village communities living in accordance with an ecological world-view that embraces the Way of the ancestors and renounces the way to the stars.†

The first form would require international control of nuclear, biological and chemical weapons, the restructuring of the global economy in order to ameliorate the effects of globalization – thereby reducing the gap between the overconsuming rich and the burgeoning poor and ensuring an environmentally sustainable future – and major changes in human reproductive behaviour, in values and in lifestyles. In order thus to restore and preserve Earth's environment, and to enable civilization to continue reaching up towards the stars, a planetary policy and planetary unity will be needed, a unity which transcends the merely selfish concerns of nation states and transnational corporations. The world's statesmen and scientific community will be under increasing pressure to bring the planet under the control of a single World Government as the only solution to their problems. (In this connection, see Part III, Chapter 3, Fig. 3.1.)

---

*If civilization were to be destroyed in a Third World War, many believe that a saner and finer civilized world would be built on the ashes of the old. (In particular, fundamentalists of all faiths are infatuated with the redemptive power of destruction). Such a dream is as old and as self-delusory as civilization itself, and one which merely helps pave the way to just such a catastrophe. The only sane world was that populated by *Homo sapiens* hunter-gatherers.

† See Appendix x for an exposition of the second main form of revolution.

To achieve the maximum possible power to that end, members of the international scientific community will be permanently raised to the heavens in space stations and on the moon. (In ancient and medieval societies the priestly religious aspect of the priestly-scientific experts was a guarantor of the stability and growth of nations; in modern societies it is the scientific and technological aspect that has come to the fore to guarantee stability, control of the environment and growth.) Already a series of agricultural and industrial revolutions have provided the energy that has made it possible for *Homo degener* finally to realize the ancient myths, enabling them actually to travel to the moon, towards the sun, and possibly to the stars, towards which pyramids of power have been growing ever since their inception. It was the Pentagon in Washington, arguing that the nation which first got control of the moon would be able to dominate the Earth, that persuaded President Kennedy of the USA, in 1961, to call forth the extraordinary technological effort that landed Americans on the moon eight years later. So, whereas in Ancient Egypt the priest-scientists could only *imaginatively* raise a Pharaoh to the sun, whence he could dominate and control the world – the penultimate unreality and expression of a collective primary schizophrenia – technology will enable scientists *actually* to raise the apices of their stratified societies into space, to circle the heavens Pharaoh-wise in solar-powered space stations (chariots of the sun) and on the moon, from which they may, like gods, dominate and control the world – the ultimate unreality.* Already, as if in pursuance of that aim, scientists in the developed nations are currently embarked on what may be described as the third Industrial Revolution, following on from an original Industrial Revolution and a second revolution into automation and mass production.

The third revolution is based on biotechnology, nanotechnology, robotics (the industrial 'serfs' of the factory systems of developed nations will be replaced by robots) and information technology and telecommunications – that is, based on intellectual energy rather than physical energy. Previously, machines replaced human muscles; this time machines will replace human minds, to bring about a machine dominated, computer controlled world. Computers containing information about the whole planet – both people and the environment – would enable scientists to control the world in order to secure an environmentally sustainable future and their own ascent

---

*The elevation and mythical ascent of the Pharaoh to the Sun was the ultimate achievement of the agricultural revolution. It would require the Industrial Revolution to take place before the mythical ascent of the Pharaoh would become transformed into the actual ascent of men to the moon and beyond. A material space industry has begun to fulfil the ancient expectations of a mythical space industry. See Appendix viii.

to the stars. Having conquered and colonized the world of wild nature, *Homo degener* now seeks to conquer and colonize the Galaxy. Just as the Pharaoh, ostensibly circling the heavens in the Chariot of the Sun, was seemingly enabled therefrom to monitor and control all the people and the lands of Egypt in a single Theocratic Stable State, scientists and technocrats, circling the heavens in solar-powered space stations and on the moon, controlling and filtering the organization and flow of information in relation to the world, would actually be able to monitor and control all the peoples, lands and seas of the world in a single world-wide Technocratic Stable State.*

Such a Universal Authority over all people and the environment would effectively replace the universal authority of the Great Spirit to manage the Earth as a primarily horizontally integrated economic unit of natural food pyramids with the authority of *Homo degener* élites to manage the Earth as a primarily vertically integrated economic unit of parasite (food) pyramids of power. It would replace the intelligence and understanding of all people as hunter-gatherers, obedient to the evolutionary edict that 'nature knows best' in a self-regulating wilderness, with the intelligence of ruling bureaucratic and scientific élites dominating an uncomprehending mass of humankind and the kingdom of nature. This is surely both a likely scenario and a logical outcome of a primary re-evolution, for it would mark the culmination of 12,000 years of the redirection in the vertical and perversion of the physical and psychical energies of *Homo degener* and of the true energy flow of the biosphere. The light of the sun energizing the evolutionary growth of natural food pyramids would be neutralized, eclipsed by the black Sun energizing the growth of an anti-evolutionary hierarchy of pyramids of power.

---

* See Part III, Chapter 3, and Fig 3.1, for an amplification of this argument in the light of the convergent evolution of nations to the stars.

PART II
THE COMPOSITE ANIMAL

Chapter 1

The Birth of New Species of Composite Animal

Part I examined the ascent of *Homo degener* primarily from the standpoint of the stratified society, showing that *Homo sapiens* and *Homo degener* peoples down the ages and throughout the world have been the victims of a madness which has escalated with every revolution on the original re-evolution. However, that is only one major outcome of the re-evolution that occurred. For the second major aspect of the fall, which relates to the growth and spread of stratified societies as parasite pyramids of power, may also be viewed as a growth and spread of new (pioneer) species of composite animal comprising

Homo sapiens sapiens	head and brain,	
Homo sapiens non sapiens	hands and feet	

that are subject to a convergent evolution.

Humankind is believed to have evolved in Africa, spreading slowly around the globe, eventually to become *Homo sapiens*. When some people were forced to adapt to agriculture, they did not do so in one place and diverge; rather, different groups are believed to have made this adaptation in several different places around the world within a few thousand years of one another, a case of parallel development.

I believe that the events leading up to the emergence of agriculture in various regions of the world demonstrate remarkable parallelism, and I believe that this parallelism not only permits but demands that some common underlying force or factor be found operating in all world regions, not necessarily to the exclusion of local variables, but in conjunction with those variables.[1]

That force comprised environmental and population pressures, combined

239

with a consequent food crisis and subsequent loss of hunter-gatherer characteristics. Thus we find geographically isolated enclaves of primitive farmers in different parts of the world splitting off from the main body of humankind who remained hunter-gatherers. Such enclaves formed the nuclei of entirely new kinds of composite animal.

New species usually arise by the splitting off of small populations from an unchanged ancestral stock, rather than by the slow and steady transformation of entire ancestral populations. This is what happened, following the Mesolithic, to people de-ranged as primitive farmers. As they slowly developed hierarchies of leaders and led, these groups began to multiply and grow as stratified societies or composite animals. By composite animal I mean the settlement, colony, clan, tribe or nation: the organism created by a group of farming people (together with their domestic animals, plants and machinery) who, in combining for greater security, forfeit certain individual functions in order to specialize as thinking head, fighting arms or cultivating hands, legs and feet of that greater animal which may be portrayed as

Homo sapiens sapiens   head and brain,
Homo sapiens non sapiens   hands and feet

a (rudimentary) composite animal resembling a giant human being.*

An example of such an organism at the most rudimentary level may be found in Hindu India, whose caste system, manifested in four divisions – *Brahmanas* (priests), *Ksatriyas* (administrators), *Vaisyas* (merchants or farmers), *Sudras* (labourers) – forms the community in a way often described as analogous to the way parts of the body form an organism. The *Brahmanas* represent the head and intellect, the *Ksatriyas* the power of chest and arms, *Vaisyas* the energy or stomach, and the *Sudras* the legs. As each body part is necessary for an organism to function

Part II: fig 1.1

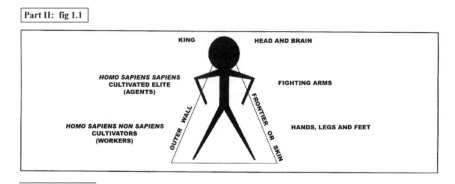

---

* In England, for generations, workmen and sailors have been known as *hands*.

properly, so each caste is necessary for the satisfactory functioning of the community.

These were composite animals characterized by a division of labour which made the whole greater than the sum of its individual parts. The relationship between the parts has been mainly one of parasitism. Multitudes of plant-like primary producers have been parasitized by a smaller number of secondary consumers, and by a few ultimate consumers (such as Chiefs and Kings), who have exploited the physical energy of the producers and also, by means of taxes and so on, have robbed them of their energy store. All these in turn have parasitized domesticated animals and plants, to form pioneer species of composite animal.*

As tribal villages and towns grew into cities, and cities into city-states and nations, there followed a process of adaptive radiation and divergence within their composite animals, and of convergence between them.

With the multiplication of different specialities within each enclave, the environments were more finely apportioned between them. With the increasing divergence of the ways in which each specialized group in each enclave fitted into their habitats went increased divergence in their appearance and behaviour. Compare the differences in dress and behaviour between nobleman and slave in many early civilizations. It is also noteworthy that at the end of the 19th century in Russia the habit of command, hierarchical Table of Ranks and cosmopolitan culture of the nobles so separated them from the more egalitarian world and parochial culture of the peasants, whose paramount priority was survival, that their very different life-situations generated mentalities which were often mutually incomprehensible.[2] This divergence was particularly to be found in the deep attachment to one tiny three-dimensional domain, as it were, a limited range that was an adaptation for survival, and within which most settled peoples have lived out their whole lives. Their adaptive radiations were more akin to the evolutionary adaptations of monkeys than to those of true human beings.

Members of these composite animals faced the wilderness and world as corporate bodies of subhumans resembling giant human beings, forests or termitaries. In their protected environments they were like cells enclosed in the outer skin of a giant human being, like monkeys in family trees growing within the confines of a forest, or like termites imprisoned within the outer skin of a termitary. Amongst other characteristics, these have in common a vertical structure, a greenhouse atmosphere and an exclusive selectivity over life forms within their boundaries. In each case, the world

---

*See Appendix xi for examples of composite animals in nature.

beyond the bounds of the composite, or super-animal, is fundamentally hostile to the individual life forms within.

The human family was to all intents and purposes split into different

Homo sapiens sapiens
Homo sapiens non sapiens

composite animals which have tended to treat members of other composite animals, and the hunter-gatherers, as though they were different species. Each was made different from every other by the peculiarity of its Gods, its different language, laws, culture, history, institutions and traditions, the different quality, shape and size of the land it occupied, and the different types of animals and plants it domesticated and minerals it mined. They were collectively as different from each other, and from the hunter-gatherers from whom they were descended, as were, for example, the Old World catarrhine and the New World platyrrhine monkeys from each other, and from the prosimians from which they were descended. The observations of Helmut Hemmer on domestic animals in relation to the selective measures applied by their keepers are, I believe, applicable to the generality of the domesticated masses within composite animals in relation to the selective activities of the governing bodies and experts (the agents or keepers) of those animals.

> Over the course of numerous generations, influences on growth and reproductive success, tending in different directions and arising from different keeping conditions and different selective measures applied by the keeper, lead to different stock developments typical of wild animals kept in zoos or of domestication.[3]

As well as the process of adaptive radiation and divergence within their different composite animals, these separate artificial environments had certain resemblances which were solutions to the shared problem of the loss of their evolutionary identities and their struggle to survive and to prosper. They were made similar by their foundation in agriculture, their domestication of animals and plants, their great irrigation systems, their emperors and god-kings at the summit of political and religious life, their cults of the Sun, Moon or Heaven, their monumental structures and temples, their social stratification and the division and specialization of labour, and their protected environments behind high walls. The divinely appointed Emperors of China, the Pharaohs of Egypt and the Incas of South America adorned similar but entirely separate stratified societies. Given that these unrelated composite animals developed similar features and habits, making them superficially very alike, they have been the subject of convergent evolution.

Where two unrelated (or at least not closely related) groups of animals living in similar but separate environments in different parts of the world have both developed similar features and habits and have come to look superficially very alike – in other words, where similar demands of the environment have evoked similar phenotypic responses, or where they have certain resemblances which are solutions to a shared problem – they are the subject of convergent evolution. Notable examples are the unrelated cassowary, emu, ostrich and rhea, which have all adopted running on the ground as a way of life.

An example of the parallel or convergent evolution of societies as unrelated and as far removed from one another as those of South America and the Middle East was in the mining and use of gold as the metal of Kings and God-Kings. Its mining was often exclusively in the royal domain, its use the exclusive adornment of the court and King, while its colour and sheen equated it with the Sun God and sun, and its incorruptibility made it a symbol of permanence. It was a visible expression of status, power and immortality. Another noteworthy example of convergence was the appearance of snake motifs, with their phallic and fertility association, in the art of Mesopotamia, India, China and Mesoamerica.

It is this re-evolutionary change in behaviour, from being members of the climax communities of the single species of *Homo sapiens* to being members of pioneer communities of *Homo degener* composite animals that are the subject of convergent evolution, that has initiated a new evolutionary trend: *the regressive evolution of Homo degener which also contains the seeds of speciation.*

The very fact of domestication amongst geographically isolated peoples, as amongst domesticated animals generally, has tended towards speciation. The following observations of Helmut Hemmer on speciation amongst domestic animals may, perhaps, be equally well applied to a domesticated humankind:

> Domestication as a special kind of regressive evolution also contains the seeds of speciation, i.e. the origin of new species. The formation of two or more new animal species from a common initial species presupposes in principle the development of isolating mechanisms which, with increasing efficiency, prevent mutual reproduction.[4]

This has been the case amongst the generality of domesticated humankind in relation to the hunter-gatherers. Many *Homo degener* colonies developed in isolation from one another, but in particular in isolation from the species *Homo sapiens*, during which time they built up cultural isolating mechanisms. When they eventually met the hunter-gatherers they viewed and treated them – in North America, in South Africa, in Tasmania – as though they were a different and inferior species of animal. For instance, during the 19th century the San in South Africa were hunted down and shot like vermin.

> Soon they were eliminated. Not one San survives in South Africa today.* A few still cling to existence on the fringes of the Kalahari Desert of Namibia and Botswana, where land dispossession, unemployment, and liquor are rapidly destroying the last vestiges of their traditional life and turning them into an endangered species.[5]

Allister Sparks may have been using the expression 'endangered species' metaphorically, but the increasing spread of *Homo degener* across the land, their change from being hunters of animals to being hunters of people and the consequent annihilation of *Homo sapiens* as though they were a different species implies that members of *Homo degener* composite animals are – or, with the increasing efficiency of isolating mechanisms, will become – themselves a different species. This regressive evolutionary process, containing as it does the seeds of speciation, arose as the direct result of the building up of cultural isolating mechanisms.

Such mechanisms were transmitted down the generations by what have been described by Richard Dawkins as *memes*.[6] These are the cultural equivalent of genes and constitute a form of evolution analogous to genetic evolution, though greatly faster than the latter.† It is important to examine this mechanism in some detail because memes underwent an extraordinary transformation following the Mesolithic. It was the memes of *Homo degener* that built the survival machines, the giant human beings we now call nations.

Susan Blackmore has compared genes and memes as follows:

> Genes are instructions for making proteins, stored in the cells of the body and passed on in reproduction. Their competition drives the evolution of the biological world. Memes are instructions for carrying out behaviour, stored in brains (or other objects) and passed

---

*With the exception of a group of Khomani Bushmen who, in 1999, were given back 100,000 acres of land in Northern Cape Province.

†Meme, *n. Biol.* (shortened from *mimeme* ... that which is imitated, after GENE *n*). An element of a culture that may be considered to be passed on by a non-genetic means, esp imitation. (*OED*)

on by imitation. Their competition drives the evolution of the mind. Both genes and memes are replicators and must obey the general principles of evolutionary theory and in that sense are the same. Beyond that they are ... very different – they are related only by analogy.[7]

Blackmore argues that

The turning point in our evolutionary history was when we began to imitate each other. From this point on a second replicator, the meme, came into play. Memes changed the environment in which genes were selected, and the direction of change was determined by the outcome of memetic selection. So the selection pressures which produced the massive increase in brain size were initiated and driven by memes.[8]

These included the development of language, the natural laws and rules, stories, songs, ceremonies, customs, social mores and ethical standards, the skill of making stone tools and the portrayal of animals in rock art: almost certainly these and a variety of other skills were developed by early *Homo sapiens* through imitation, both of their fellows and of the animals around them, and through enhanced memory, leading to increased brain size.* Because life changed infinitely slowly in hunter-gatherer societies, the transmission of memes, like that of genes, was largely from parent to child within the wild environment. Memes were transmitted alongside genes to the benefit of the health, longevity and reproductive success of their human vehicles. In conjunction with genes, memes so improved the design of the meme-copying and meme-spreading brain as to make for the relative perfection of *Homo sapiens* as a wild animal.

... memes are driving human behaviour... Memes provide the driving force behind what we do, and the tools with which we do it. Just as the design of our bodies can be understood only in terms of natural selection, so the design of our minds can be understood only in terms of memetic selection.[9]

This statement is true in the case of *Homo sapiens*, but requires qualification

---

*The large size of the brain has long puzzled scientists. The truth is that no one who is not a hunter-gatherer has need of so much processing capacity, hence the modern brain appears to its possessors to be too large for its quotidian purposes.

in the case of *Homo degener*. For underlying the memes of *Homo degener* is the far deeper driving force of humiliation: the initial humiliation and hatred of the wilderness, combined with humiliation and self-hatred, arising from the void of the Mesolithic. These, in conjunction with subsequent humiliations down the millennia, comprise *the* fundamental driving force behind *Homo degener*'s search for power to ascend to the stars.* Furthermore, in the case of *Homo degener*, memetic selection was perverted to raise up stratified societies, a process which was described earlier as a perverted cultural selection. Imitation no longer occurred in its evolutionary setting, but in the anti-evolutionary domestic setting of the stratified society, in which the interests of the memes began to pull in the opposite direction to those of the genes. They began to build for themselves ever more powerful and secure vehicles, survival machines resembling giant human beings, governed by the collective brains of the most powerful men in each stratified society. To the extent that they have generally been governed by males, these giant human beings may themselves be regarded as male.†

Thereafter, a perverted memetic selection, instigated mainly by the élite of each stratified society, functioned both inside and outside each, selecting for *Homo sapiens sapiens* agents and *Homo sapiens non sapiens* workers within, and against other stratified societies and the wilderness without through war and conquest. If, as Susan Blackmore argues, the turning point in our evolutionary history was when we began to imitate each other, a turning point in our anti-evolutionary history was when nations, as giant human beings, began to imitate each other, giving rise to such phenomena as the arms race between nations. The design of our minds – the minds of *Homo degener* – has been principally influenced by this perverted memetic selection, a perversion arising mainly from the maintenance and pursuit of power, primarily over the land and its resources.

Amongst the most important memes of hunter-gatherers, were those dealing with food and sex. To those were now added memes relating to status, wealth and power as pursued within stratified societies. Part I was much concerned with the acquisition of power by those *Homo degener* peoples who were rendered powerless in a powerful land following the two-fold fall of humankind. It is people in positions of power, particularly men – rulers, aristocrats, great landowners, professionals, experts, artists – who, down the millennia, have been amongst the principal spreaders

---

*I shall explore this phenomenon more fully in Part III, Chapter 2.

† See Appendix iii for the transition of societies to male dominance and subsequent rape of the wilderness.

of memes within stratified societies. These have included the development of language, religious and political views, laws, social mores, ceremonies, customs, skills, songs, architectural trends and technologies as these reflect the hierarchical systems of wealth and power within stratified societies. Such memes are passed on by imitation, by one person copying another, and through our main sources of information, which today include schools, radio, television, newspapers, books, magazines and the Internet. Above all, memes within stratified societies protect and enhance power as an expression of collective security against the threat of humiliating insecurity and powerlessness.

The evolutionary algorithm of variation, selection and heredity as applied to memes lay increasingly in the power of the *Homo sapiens sapiens* agents or élites of each composite animal as they guided and governed its behaviour and interactions with other composite animals, and with the wild environment as an arena to be possessed and exploited. Memes beneficial to élites of composite animals began to spread through the populations as co-adapted meme-complexes, which Richard Dawkins has described as stable sets of characteristics similar to the stable sets of genes in animal gene pools:

> Perhaps we could regard an organized church, with its architecture, rituals, laws, music, art, and written tradition, as a co-adapted stable set of mutually-assisting memes... I conjecture that co-adapted meme-complexes evolve in the same kind of way as co-adapted gene-complexes.[10]

Susan Blackmore has described these co-adapted meme-complexes as memeplexes. Most memes are contained in widespread memeplexes which are groups of memes that come together for mutual advantage – that is, 'co-operate' in mutually supportive memeplexes that include the languages, religions, political ideologies, etc, peculiar to each composite animal. Once together, they form a self-organizing, self-protecting structure which is both divided from, and hostile to, rival memeplexes in the outside world. Thus memeplexes imitate precisely the hostile relationship of the self-protecting composite animal to others of its kind in the outside world and to the wilderness. This applies particularly to the religious memeplexes which predominated throughout the early civilizations. Everything in the lives of the early civilizations was saturated in religion: all the architecture, every person, every product, every written word reflected the power and the glory of the peculiar God and élite of each stratified society, thereby perpetuating as God-given the relationship of

superior   *Homo sapiens sapiens*
inferior   *Homo sapiens non sapiens*
devilish   wilderness

In other words, while the memeplexes of *Homo sapiens* reflected the sacredness of the wilderness, those of *Homo degener* reflected the sacredness of each composite animal and the malignant nature of all others and of the wilderness.

Richard Dawkins has rightly described memeplexes such as religions and cults as 'viruses of the mind' or viral memeplexes. This description may, however, be applied to all the memeplexes of *Homo degener*, since all derive from a two-fold fall of humankind. They are the product of the collective brains – for instance, those of the priest-scientists of Babylon and Egypt – of these giant human beings growing under the aegis of their black Suns. As viral memeplexes have evolved and become more complex, new niches have been created within these composite animals in which new kinds of meme can thrive. They in turn have brought about the design of better and better meme-copying machinery – first writing, then books and now computers. So whereas, amongst hunter-gatherers, natural selection and memetic selection may be said to have functioned originally alongside one another, a perverted memetic selection, operated principally by *Homo sapiens sapiens* élites of stratified societies, now governed *Homo degener*'s behaviour, to produce behaviour that is memetically adaptive but biologically maladaptive, and therefore evodeviant.

In sum, each composite animal has its own meme pool, arrived at over thousands of years of a perverted memetic selection. Each, under its Farmer God memes – that is, its own version and representation of God, or an ideology such as Communism with its different interpretations – has regarded itself and its authority as sacred, an authority and sacredness pervading the whole of its meme pool. Just as genes propagate themselves in the gene pool by moving from body to body by means of sperm or eggs, so memes propagate themselves in the meme pool by passing from brain to brain, and from collective brain to collective brain of each composite animal, by a process of imitation, association and learning. In that memes govern the behaviour of generations of members of composite animals, they may be said to govern their combined life-forces as *a collective memetic inheritance*. Instead of inheriting genes and memes relating to the architecture of the wild world, they have inherited genes relating to the wilderness and memes relating to that of their composite animals which are inherently in competitive conflict with one another and with the wilderness. These have made each not only different from all the others, but as different from their *Homo sapiens* forbears as the solitary locust is from the locust swarm.* The latter are not different species, though they look and behave as though they were. Similarly *Homo sapiens* and *Homo degener* populations look and behave as though they were different species.

If, as posited by E. Mayr,[11] new evolutionary trends amongst animals may be initiated by behaviour, the primary re-evolution into composite animals that has occurred is surely such a trend. For, as I argued above, the regressive evolution of *Homo degener* composite animals, arising from geographic isolation and the subsequent building up of cultural isolating mechanisms, contained the seeds of speciation. It may now be seen that, though they are not species in the biological sense, they may be so described in the cultural sense.

Geographic speciation means the genetic reconstruction of a population during a period of geographic (spatial) isolation.[12]

Similarly, just as the memes of composite animals are the cultural equivalent of genes and constitute a form of evolution analogous to genetic evolution, so the original geographic isolation of composite animals, which guaranteed their independent development and permitted the accumulation of memetic differences and the development of isolating mechanisms, may also be said to have initiated geographic speciation – that is, speciation through memetic reconstruction into what may be described as *separate Sacred Species of composite animal,* whose whole was greater and more sacred than the sum of its individual parts.

In animals behavioural barriers are the most important of the various isolating mechanisms.

In the human species, however, conditioning is an important isolating mechanism. The free interbreeding of individuals coexisting in a geographical region is strongly influenced by religious, economic, and cultural barriers.[13]

I argued earlier, in Part I, Chapter 4, that the father/children relationship between a god and the people implied that they were literally of his stock. It is this prehistoric relationship – or that where the god was seen as king and the people as his servants – that formed the core of the peculiar memeplexes and uniquely sacred nature of each, to create fundamental barriers between societies. Altogether a recognition of the

---

* See Appendix xii.

Sacred as being characteristic of, or specific to, a particular stratified society – together with its antithesis, a recognition of the profane nature of all other stratified societies and of the wilderness – might be said to have characterized it as a composite animal that behaved as a separate Sacred Species in its relationships with other composite animals and with the hunter-gatherer peoples.

All states and nations of *Homo degener* peoples are the descendants of pioneer Sacred Species of composite animal comprising

Homo sapiens sapiens.

Homo sapiens non sapiens

domesticated animals and plants

One hallmark, for instance, of the pioneer species is a population explosion. Another is instability, as the pioneer species attempts to establish a degree of stability in competition with others. Competition occurs when

> ... *two species seek simultaneously an essential resource of the environment* (such as food, or a place to live...) *that is in limited supply.* Consequently, competition becomes more acute as the population of either species increases.[14]

In the case of other unrelated groups of animals that are the subject of convergent evolution, natural selection has tended to emphasize the similarities between them, to the extent that if they lived in the same place they would compete for space and resources. In the case of *Homo degener* composite animals, however, it is a perverted memetic selection, in imitation of a natural selection, that has tended to emphasize the similarities between them. So when they eventually met, inevitably they competed for ideological and territorial space and resources. When, for instance, the Spaniards met the Inca Empire, almost their first act was the destruction of the Inca and the melting down and transportation of Inca gold to Spain.

It is the purpose of the following chapters to examine the main contributory factors to the development and growth of these composite animals, and to their convergent evolution, a convergence that threatens the existence of every other species on Earth.

Chapter 2

The Nation, a Composite Animal

A nation is a society united by a delusion about its ancestry and by a common hatred of its neighbours. (Dean Inge)

This study of the nation as a composite animal will show how, throughout history, the individual has been absorbed in the collective; how this incorporation has been achieved by the perversion of the individual life-force to serve the Life-Force of the nation; what the socio-biological implications of that perversion are; and finally the hostile relationship of nations.

First, however, it is necessary to recall what it has meant to be an individual under the evolutionary circumstances of hunter-gathering. The core of individuality lay in the hunter-gatherers' independence as kings of natural food pyramids. They were neither the subject of hierarchy nor of man-made law. Rather, they obeyed the culture and natural law of the land that imposed their controls from within. At each point along the seasonal round each and every individual has had to assess and process for themselves immense amounts of information, making thousands of critical decisions each year. Each individual had to master 'a multitude of diverse physical and intellectual skills'. Hence the exhilaration and joy experienced and expressed by hunter-gatherers – their whole beings were totally integrated, involved and fulfilled as hunter-gatherers, to make for their relative perfection. With the arrival of farming and the stratified structure, people who had evolved as independent hunter-gatherers now became deeply dependent members of stratified societies, in which dominant élites determined the bases of economic, moral and social life. They were no longer relatively perfect individuals in the evolutionary sense, but formed anti-evolutionary colonies of grossly imperfect beings.

Throughout history the individual has been submerged in the mass. In the early urban phase, a majority was born into a subservient condition of life, while the very process of domestication requires that each generation of domesticated people is brought into bondage, first by the suppression from childhood of evolved true characteristics, and secondly by their physical, mental, moral and spiritual subjection to the requirements of their stratified societies. It is axiomatic, therefore, that ever since the days of Ancient Egypt and for most of history, the great majority of ordinary people have been treated by the authorities as if they were a congealed mass, without differentiating personalities, let alone individual rights and aspirations. Rome, for example, organized its subjects by class, trade and occupation that were legally binding on present and future generations: people's rights related to their class and trade. The corporation was paramount, while the individual counted for nothing. The image of people as mere living components of a collective social body persisted into and through the Middle Ages in Europe. The classes were sharply differentiated; people were categorized, making it difficult to change their status, occupation or place of residence. This was particularly the case in Eastern Europe, where the peasantry remained in a state of feudalism until the mid–19th century; in England there was greater mobility. A.P. Thornton argues that the Church of the 12th century in England

> ... played a rôle not unlike that fulfilled by 'government service' in twentieth-century colonies in Africa; it set down a ladder into the lowest reaches of society, up which the natives might climb.[1]

Not until the 20th century were women in England enfranchised, transformed from mere chattels and possessions of men – like wives in a harem – into independent individuals. Their independence, however, has been tempered by the necessity to join the men as wage-slaves to survive. In many Muslim countries women remain chattels.

In effect, people have formed mere living components of composite animals. If the Industrial Revolution and the present democratic environment in the West appear to be more conducive to a greater individual freedom than heretofore, such freedom is illusory and is rapidly being eroded by the growing power of giant corporations, bureaucrats and the advanced technologies of control at their disposal.

Following on from the 19th century, when workers became doubly enslaved – enslaved to the controlling bosses and to the controlling machines of factories – industry and bureaucracy between them have built what the historian, Neal Ascherson, once described as 'a precise prison' around people, in which the tyranny of clocked time, simultaneous behaviour throughout the nation and linguistic conformity reveal a cult of precision and standardization that argues for only one right way of doing things.* For thousands of years the grip of the priestly caste over agrarian societies was total; the early Temple and modern Church used a transcendental authority to keep people 'doing the right thing'. Now, with the increasing mechanization of all aspects of modern societies, that power is transferred to the scientist and technocrat. Furthermore, the controlling and imprisoning categorization of people – whether by caste, class, income or occupation – remains a predominant feature of stratified societies everywhere. People in the United Kingdom, for example, are becoming increasingly locked into a computer-controlled system which categorizes them socially according to their financial status: A, AB, B, C, etc. They are now imprisoned as much by financial strictures as they are by the imprisoning effect of machines. It is of the nature of stratified structures that they change only in appearance, not in substance: as ever, deference to authority – whether it be a monarchy, a Communist dictatorship or a democratic government – is the norm, while economic opportunity and its accompanying social status remain 'open to all, like the Ritz Hotel'. It is the necessary acceptance of this ongoing social situation – a stratified structure comprising a decision-taking minority governing a passive majority, and the privileges and rewards accruing to the former at the expense of the latter – that breeds conformity.

> The dictatorial systems use threats and terror to induce this conformity; the democratic countries, suggestion and propaganda. There is, indeed, one great difference between the two systems. In the democracies non-conformity is possible and, in fact, by no means entirely absent; in the totalitarian systems, only a few unusual heroes and martyrs can be expected to refuse obedience. But in spite of this difference the democratic societies show an overwhelming degree of conformity.[2]

Whether people choose to conform or are forced to conform, in every

---

*The world of *Homo sapiens* was timeless. Time began to be measured by *Homo degener*, as with the invention of sundials in ancient Egypt around 1500 BC, while the desire to measure time in less sunny climates led to the invention of devices like the sandglass and water clock. Monasteries at the end of the first millennium AD divided the day into hours and minutes with their regular cycles of prayer. With the introduction of mechanical clocks in 13th century Europe, man-made time has increasingly governed the movement of people and materials world-wide, though their relatively safe movement at sea was only made possible when John Harrison, in the 18th century, finally harnessed time to the accurate measurement of longitude. Now most of the world resides under the twin tyrannies of time and money. Standard Time, for instance, was adopted throughout Britain in 1847 in order to meet the requirements of Bradshaw's Railway Time Tables.

State, above all the imprisoning factors of their daily lives, the mode of operation is coercive, in that it lays down laws which are backed up by the threat of violence, incarceration or death.

> In all hierarchically structured societies obedience is perhaps the most deeply ingrained trait. Obedience is equated with virtue, disobedience with sin. To be disobedient is the arch crime from which all other crimes follow.[3]

Obedience in the earliest civilizations was demanded in the name of, and in response to the edicts of, the Farmer God and King who, together with wealthy and powerful élites, formulated and sanctified laws in their own interests. It was an obedience – and thus conformity – of the great mass of inferior citizens to the wealthy and powerful superior to them and exercising divine authority over them. Obedience thus formed a most important element of the religious memeplex, and thereafter of the collective memetic inheritance of each composite animal – it formed an important constituent of the cement binding the people hierarchically together. Subsequent obedience to superiors – whether at the level of the State or of the work-place – became second nature and a characteristic of the citizen in the maintenance of the stability of the State, particularly in the time of war. No such degrading relationship pertained amongst hunter-gatherers, whose obedience was an entirely individual response to an inner imperative arising from the oneness of their natures with wild nature and its laws.

Meanwhile, liberty, equality and fraternity remain the grand illusions they have always been. They are concepts that have been used to disguise the true situation of the imprisoned mass of humankind. The British people, for instance, are not free but under coercive constraint:

> This is coercion by the mass hypnosis of custom and organised propaganda: in education; in the media, especially television; by the church and by all major political parties.

They are not equal because the monarchy

> ... epitomises conspicuous consumption and personal indulgence on a grand scale, while millions of compatriots lack the wherewithal to meet basic needs.

And British citizens are

...deferential, not fraternal.[4]*

Nevertheless, contemporary society preaches an ideal of unindividualized equality

> ...because it needs human atoms, each one the same, to make them function in a mass aggregation, smoothly, without friction; all obeying the same commands, yet everybody being convinced that he is following his own desires. Just as modern mass production requires the standardisation of commodities, so the social process requires standardisation of man, and this standardisation is called 'equality'.[5]

A true individuality, freedom and equality were the evolutionary possession of the hunter-gatherers. With their loss, our doubly deprived ancestors cohered in rudimentary composite animals organized in defence against the outside world, whose members now number millions and tens of millions. To describe any one or all of these as individual or as a collection of individuals would be to devalue the word and to deny the reality of human evolution. People's potential for growth and development as individuals can only properly be realized in the right physiological and psychological climate, which is the wild environment in which they evolved. The protected environments in which people now find themselves are essentially enormous prisons, hospitals or zoos full of those whose potential and development are suppressed and perverted to conform to the conditions of their confinement within more or less rigid and repressive hierarchies – just as their economies founded on agriculture require the suppression of the wilderness.

All in all, therefore, the power relations in the society into which we are born so affect what we become as to make the individual a romantic fiction. In every State throughout history the fundamental relationship has been between rulers and ruled, a relationship which, to a greater or lesser extent, has implied, 'You can do what you want as long as you do what we say'. From Socrates through to the present day, philosophers have described humankind in terms of the herd or as sheep to be led by a shepherd, and the herdsman does not consult his herd. To find the right shepherd, who will best control the environment in order to gratify the need for a great national identity and for security, is what politics is all about. As Hitler said: '...leading means: being able to move masses'.[6]

---

* It is noteworthy that, unlike the inhabitants of France and the USA, the British are not, technically, 'citizens' but 'subjects'.

The tragedy is that there are such masses waiting to be moved.

Hitler succeeded in releasing pent-up energies in the nation, and in re-creating a belief in the future of the German people. It is wrong to lay stress only on the element of coercion, and to ignore the degree to which Hitler commanded a genuine popular support in Germany – so much less, as Mill once remarked, do the majority of the people prefer liberty to power.[7]

The egalitarian individualism and independence of the hunter-gatherer has thus been replaced by an 'equality' in mass standardization and conformity. Conformity is essential to the survival of the nation as a composite animal: the incorporation and conformity of the individual as the component part of a composite animal has been achieved by the perversion of the individual life-force to serve the Life-Force of the nation, a process that has been in train ever since the primary re-evolution of people following the Mesolithic. As I argued in the last chapter, because memes govern the behaviour of generations of members of composite animals, they may be said to govern their combined life-forces as a collective memetic inheritance, activating the Life-Force of the society. When this happens the collective combined physical and psychical energies for survival – as exemplified, for instance, in the release of 'pent-up energies' and in the re-creation of a belief in the future in the German nation referred to above – may be mobilized to expand territory to acquire the resources necessary to the building up of physical and psychical structures conducive to their well-being and security (see figure 2.1).

In the Middle East and S.W. Asia, the community Life-Force was personified in a Farmer God, apotheosis of the Life-Force of their society, and beneath him in the Chief or King, divine embodiment on Earth of the Life-Force of the community. For instance, an act of great political importance in the conquest of any of the cities of Sumeria by another was the carrying off of the city Farmer God of knowledge and power to become a subordinate in the city temple of its conqueror, to work on its behalf against its enemies. Like the primitive head-hunters of S.E. Asia who took an individual human head in order individually to gain its life-force, the taking of the God Head of a Sumerian city added to the Life-Force of one community while diminishing that of another. This was far more important than the subjugation of king by king. More recently, it is interesting to recall the ugly rush by head-hunting Russians and Americans at the end of the Second World War to recruit German scientists, who were supposed to hold in their heads secret knowledge of

Part II: fig 2.1

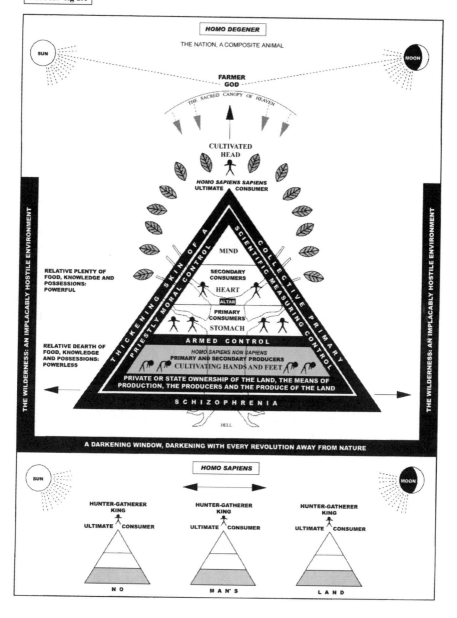

rocket propulsion and nuclear fission. This was in order to enhance their national Life-Forces (through growth in wealth, power and security), raising some of their members up to the moon, up towards the heavenly home of their God, where the hopes and fears of *Homo degener* peoples have been transporting them ever since the early Neolithic.*

There are now some 200 states, countries with recognized governments and boundaries, whose economies are founded on agriculture/industry, that requires the suppression of the wilderness. Each is a greater or lesser stratified society, a pyramid of power. The word *state* is often used interchangeably with the word *nation* (as in the name of the United Nations). However, though traditionally *nation* refers to a distinct people who may be identified by certain characteristics such as a common language, I shall generally use it to denote the state, which may contain a number of nations – Nigeria, for instance, comprises at least 250 nations, while Indonesia has over 300. I shall also use the term nation in its traditional sense, to denote a people belonging to the same ethnic family and speaking the same language who comprise a minority within the larger nation, and who could, if they so wished and were able to, establish a government and territory of their own. The Welsh nation is a case in point.

The Life-Force of the nation has two main aspects, one positive and the other negative. The positive aspect is the presence of the Farmer God, Culture Ancestor or other bloodless or long-dead founder of the nation – such as Muhammad in many national guises, the ancient lineage of Emperors of Japan, Atatürk or Lenin – sanctified in myths of Creation or Constitutions of State as the Sun and ultimate embodiment of the corporate identity of the nation, drawing and holding the people to it: symbols of national legality, unity, stability and security. In America, the Declaration of Independence, the birth certificate of the USA, serves the same function as did Lenin in the USSR, and is as sacred an icon as was Lenin's tomb. In addition, most nations have a formal head of state who serves as a living focus of national unity, performs ceremonial rituals and promotes voluntary participation in the life of the nation. In Britain, for instance, in most of the 19th century, Queen Victoria embodied the corporate identity of the nation. Now that identity is more to be found in the combination of monarch and the Crown-in-Parliament.

The monarchy in Britain is a living personified symbol of the nation. The monarch is the legitimate Head of State and the elected parliament

---

* See Appendix viii for the contribution of myth and science to this thrust of deranged peoples in the vertical.

governs in the monarch's name. Official ideology maintains that the monarchy exemplifies the highest standards of public and private morality, is above the strife of classes and political factions, and contributes to political stability. As the head of every major department of the nation's life, including the Church of England, the monarch is the symbol of the nation's unity. In respect of value and unity, the royal family is the putative model for all other families in Britain.*

Just as members of the royal family in Britain are married at the altar of their God, many citizens in Britain, as in many other countries, are likewise married at the altars of their God, thereby binding themselves to the Life-Force of the nation. In Communist Russia many newly married couples started life together paying homage to the Father of the Revolution and founder of the Soviet Union, Lenin, whose dead body was exhibited in the Kremlin. The undergirding and overarching presence of religion was, however, still all-powerful. For Moscow itself was built as a Christian city, in order to produce a likeness of Heaven on Earth. The buildings were turned towards the Kremlin, the holy place, above which there was nothing except Heaven. By association, Lenin, entombed in the Kremlin, transformed it into a gigantic altar of worship, communion and sacrifice to Communism.† Communism was a State church: Leninism became the chief religion in Russia. For example, it was reported that a concert hall in Moscow was decorated with a banner reading, 'Let the name and deeds of the great Lenin live for ever'. Likewise in Moscow, offices exhibited his picture and often his bust as well; schools had each a Lenin room and a Lenin 'shrine', consisting of a large bust of Lenin, which was surrounded with flowers on his 'birthday'. Newly-weds also liked to have themselves photographed before a large statue of Lenin outside the Finland Station in Leningrad.

In each case, whether the wedding has been blessed in Britain, Russia or wherever, these are unions that have been blessed by the ascendant black Sun of the nation. The children of such unions are no longer children as by nature, born free to fulfil their needs as kings of natural food pyramids within the one kingdom of nature. Rather they are the Farmer God's or Lenin's children, whose second nature it is, as subjects of the law-giving and law-abiding father-figures ranged above them, to further and fulfil the religio-socio-economic needs and laws of their composite animal.

---

*The people of Thailand imitate their royal family even more than the people of Britain do theirs.

†It is noteworthy that Lenin's tomb, like Mao Zedong's mausoleum, are like pyramids and are expressions of behaviour similar to that of societies thousands of years ago.

Everyone must obey the State authorities, for no authority exists
without God's permission, and the existing authorities have been
put there by God. Whoever opposes the existing authority, opposes
what God has ordered, and anyone who does so will bring judgement
upon himself.[8]

The Farmer God or Ideological Father of the nation, its formal Head of
State and its flag,* represent the spirit of the nation and are thus symbols
of the principle of national unity through obedience and conformity to
hierarchical order. They imprison us in an imagined past. Under them,
the dominant major institutions of a society form a centre which defines
and radiates throughout society a pattern of rôles, values, beliefs and
symbols, making it a principal source of social order. Its authority bears
the aura of the sacred (in this sense, every society has an 'official' religion,
making each a Sacred Species) thus placing a stamp of legitimacy on the
values and beliefs which it espouses. The extent of integration under one
government, one law, varies as between nations. Some, like China and
North Korea, have been tightly bound together: their institutions and
people have had to conform within very narrow limits, wide deviations
from the norm being unacceptable. Other societies, such as the United
Kingdom and France, have been more diverse and free, permitting
departures from the norm. In every case, its Sun and formal Head of
State, combined with its dominant major institutions, provide (divine)
justification of a nation's status, its wealth and its power, and sanctify its
efforts to enhance its status, wealth and power.

As well as the positive aspect, the energy flowing from the Sun of the
collective aspirations of the people, particularly to national prosperity and
greatness, there is also the negative aspect, the collective fear of forces
within and/or outside the nation that threaten to eclipse its Life-Force
and Sun, endangering the corporate identity of the nation. This is the
energy flowing from the darkness of its collective fears arising from the
original degradation during the Mesolithic, from 'the terrifying maw of
chaos that yawns beneath the feet of civilized man'. Anyone or anything
threatening a resurgence of anarchy or chaos, whether from within or
without, has been seen as the Devil. In short, it is the energy flowing
from the threat of humiliating eclipse, the threat to survival. This negative
aspect of the Life-Force is the original or primary one, the positive aspect

---

* During the South African flag debate of 1926, Dr D.F. Malan stressed the power of a national
flag as a unifying factor in the life of a nation, when that nation comprises different sections.

being secondary and dependent upon the primary. For it was out of humiliation, powerlessness and fear of the wilderness that the Life-Force and aspirations to ascent of each composite animal were born.

These combined aspects of the Life-Force – the aspirations to aggrandizement, combined with the fear of eclipse – form the vital energy or dynamic for growth and security of the nation. The Life-Force of the nation – which incorporates the five-fold concentration of power to the self-aggrandizement of élites, and to the security of the community, together with the vertically oriented structure-building behaviour of the stratified society – is impelled by its collective memetic inheritance. As well as being imitated and imprinted through obedience and conformity, that inheritance is transmitted from generation to generation primarily through education, through the suppression, bending and merging of the individual life-force of each generation of children with that of the nation.

Learning through imitation and teaching no longer occurred in its evolutionary setting, but in the anti-evolutionary domestic setting of the stratified society. Hence the earlier transmission of memes down the generations of hunter-gatherers was replaced with the transmission of viral memeplexes down the generations of *Homo degener* peoples. *Homo degener* children were now inculcated into the collective memetic inheritance of the nation. This process started long before the appearance of schools, being initiated by parents who have been, even after the appearance of schools, still the primary perverters of the life-force of the child as it has fought for a freedom such as that enjoyed by hunter-gatherer children.

The revolutions that have occurred in history must not obscure the fact that infants and children also make revolutions, but since they are powerless, they have to use their own methods, those of guerrilla warfare, as it were. They fight against suppression of their freedom by various individual methods, such as stubborn negativism, refusal to eat, refusal to be toilet trained, bed-wetting, up and on to the more drastic methods of autistic withdrawal and pseudomental debility. The adults behave like any élite whose power is challenged. They use physical force, often blended with bribery, to protect their position. As a result, most children surrender and prefer submission to constant torment. No mercy is shown in this war until victory is achieved, and our hospitals are filled with its casualties. Nevertheless, it is a remarkable fact that all human beings – the children of the powerful as well as those of the powerless – share the common experience of once having been powerless and of having fought for their freedom. That is why one may assume that every human being

– aside from his biological equipment – has acquired in his childhood
a revolutionary potential that, though dormant for a long time,
might be mobilized under special circumstances.[9]

This powerlessness of generations of *Homo degener* children, and consequent
acquisition of revolutionary potential, reflects precisely the powerlessness
of the new-born *Homo degener* populations in face of an all-powerful
wilderness following the Mesolithic and their subsequent re-evolutionary
behaviour.

Schools probably came into existence about 5,000 years ago, and are
known to have existed in Sumeria c.1780 BC. With their appearance the
inculcation of the young into the stratified society became institutionalized,
forcing them even more drastically to change direction away from their
phylogenetic propensities as individual hunter-gatherers to become absorbed,
at whatever level, into the collectivity of the stratified society. Children
were now forced, by a new kind of specialist, the school teacher, by strict
discipline, by fear of retribution and by artificially introduced competition
– as they are still – to spend much of each day practising tasks and
memorizing items which had no relevance to their evolutionary inclinations.
Such evodeviation was made most apparent in the 19th and 20th centuries
in the USA, where Native American children were removed from their
tribal reservations and placed in boarding schools where they were forced
to imitate the language and culture of their conquerors at the expense
of their own languages and cultures which had evolved over thousands
of years of living in harmony with nature. Fear replaced excitement and
fun as a motive for learning. As their inherently wild natures were subdued
they have suffered, down to this day, a forced evodeviation and initiation
into the adult world of *Homo degener*.

It is indisputable that however humane the educator – or, come to
that, however committed to organic or 'natural' farming the farmer –
both suppress and pervert the true natures of the subjects of their work.
A principal concern of education has been to inculcate children into the
work ethic of the stratified society. The disciplined work in school, and
the general discipline, have led inexorably to the world of work outside:
disciplined work in the factory, the mine, the office and the store,
imprisoning them under the twin tyrannies of time and money. More
recently, children in the West have become a prime target of television.
It seeks to become part of the fabric of their lives, enticing them from
the earliest age to mimic the behaviour of high profile representatives of
the consumer ethic. Television thus reinforces the two widespread elements
of *Homo degener*'s cultural psychology: that people tend to copy the

majority (further reinforced by the fact that the majority watch television), and secondly that people tend to mimic the most successful individuals. Together these make for co-operation and conformity within composite animals, fostering aspirations appropriate to each.

The schools lead to qualifications, such as degrees, which enable a minority to distance themselves from the labouring majority within the work settings, perpetuating the dominant/subservient relationship that is now second nature to members of stratified societies. The teaching of history, like the teaching of myth in the early agrarian societies, is a major factor contributing to the seeming 'naturalness' of the hierarchical order. History, like the ancient myths, bonds people to their past – which has been a past itself founded in, and built on, myth – bonding them to their society and manufacturing social unity. It is above all the embodiment of the country's corporate memory and an important part of its collective memetic inheritance.

As in the ancient agrarian civilizations, members of nations are bound from birth by national élites and their myths to the Life-Forces of the nations they govern: each generation is inculcated into its country's corporate memory. (For the Jews, as the children of God, 'memory is the Commandment underlying all Commandments'.) Those who control the present control the past; those who control both present and past control the future. As ever, the quintessence of that control over the past – as a source of identity, legitimacy and a standard against which to appraise the present – is the God or Ideology of the nation, the moral guarantor both of the head and Life-Force of the composite animal. This is the ideology which promotes the belief that the secular rulers of the state owe their position to a higher than human authority, and that God in any one of his many national guises is in complete alliance with the government, and is the source of the morals preferred by that government. Poland in the 19th century, partitioned and humiliated, even saw itself as the collective reincarnation of Christ, awaiting its resurrection to redeem all nations.

The nation resembles a giant human being whose Life-Force exists apart from, and is greater and more enduring than, the perverted life-force and span of any one member of the nation, binding such members to itself in order to survive and prosper as a collective unit. This is most noticeable when nations are dispersed over the face of the Earth. Dispersed peoples such as the Kurds and the Jews often retain their cultural heritage and identity, defying all attempts at assimilation. The Jews, for instance, have been bound by a Book (containing the experiences, hopes and fears of their ancestors) to a bloodless Farmer God, the God of Abraham, the

Sun of their cultural separateness and superiority, that was in earlier times the quintessence of the Life-Force of their nation. Like the original nuclear enclaves of deranged men, that were embryonic nations surrounded by alien wilderness, groups of Jews formed similar enclaves of survival and salvation in the midst of alien cultures, enabling them, when the opportunity arose, to come together again in the composite animal that is Israel.

Though often divided by regional loyalties and animosities within – competition between sectional linguistic, religious, social and economic interest groups often takes precedence over the national interest – the nation is best revealed as a composite animal in the reaction of its members to the natural unknown, and when it is threatened by invasion, that is to say, when the nation is threatened by forces similar to those which originally assailed its prototype, thus reactivating the negative world-fearing aspect of the Life-Force.

Homo degener members of nations, except for a few intrepid explorers, have stood in fear of the natural unknown, the Land of No Return. They have not only feared the unknown, they have shunned it. Even as late as the last few centuries in their own country, the English built walled gardens around which they might promenade in safety, while Europeans in general filled wild nature with imaginary beasts. As late as 1723 a serious scholar wrote a treatise on Alpine wingless dragons; children's fairy-tales have implanted a fear that wild nature was out to get them. Western fairy-tales have portrayed the wild world as foreboding and dark, as a place where Hansel and Gretel were lost, where Sleeping Beauty was encircled by thorn bushes and a vast forest, where the unwary could become lost forever and be assailed by innumerable wild animals and starve to death. The wilderness, which had been totally accessible to *Homo sapiens*, became, to *Homo degener* peoples, the '...undiscover'd country from whose bourn/No traveller returns,...'

In 1759 Edmund Burke wrote an essay, 'On the Sublime and the Beautiful', relating the traveller to wild nature as experienced in the mountains of Europe, in the vastness of desert or in a gale at sea, which Burke saw as awe-inspiring realms of the sublime. To him, whatever in wild nature inspired terror was a source of the sublime. 'Indeed, terror is in all cases whatsoever, either more openly or latently, the ruling principle of the sublime.' The gentleman traveller, in his turn, went in search of the sublime in the wilderness, seen as a place of chaos and the great Abyss. By this time, however, at the end of the 18th century in Europe, the traveller could be more certain of being guided safely home.

A similar fearful attitude to the wilderness prevailed in China which, for 2,000 years, under most dynasties, was a sacred empire, the Celestial

Kingdom ruled by the Son of Heaven. It is now the home of almost a fifth of the world's population. The Chinese universe is still a network of outer and internal constraints against disorder, demanding conformity. China's appearance has been that of a giant composite animal, grown up in the midst of a frightening unknown wasteland, whose mouth vomited out its exiles. That mouth was the Ming fortress of Jiayuguan, beyond which, to the west, lay the wilderness. Exiled officials were ejected through its gateway, condemned to live 'outside the mouth', to die tormented by demons in exile in the unknown wasteland of wilderness.

Now that the forests and wilderness have almost disappeared, and the mountains have been conquered, the old collective fears have been largely overlaid with the new: the anxiety and fear surrounding the intentions of the nations that now confront each other. The fears surrounding the latter are nonetheless often clothed in the garments of the former. For instance, when the USA felt herself threatened by Germany in 1916, she issued propaganda posters depicting a black gorilla, reminiscent of King Kong, holding a swooning white woman in its arms, representing their threatened invasion by German Kultur, in order to whip up anti-German feeling prior to declaring war in 1917. Germany, in the same vein, issued an anti-Bolshevik poster employing a similar image in 1918: an image of terror, threatening war, unemployment and hunger. More recently, Russia was portrayed as a giant bear bestriding the continent like a colossus, or on the prowl through the man-made wilderness of nations.

The uncanny and the frightening unknown beyond the bounds are equated in the collective unconscious with the wilderness – or rather, with a myth of the wilderness and of the dangerous nature of the wild animals lurking therein. For in reality, an animal such as the gorilla is the most peace-loving of herbivorous animals, which, before its true nature was revealed by George Schaller, was nevertheless regarded by European hunters as the epitome of ferocity, to be shot on sight. Old fears, old bogeymen arising from past relationships with other nations, overlie even older fears of the wilderness. The mode of expression of present insecurities in relation to other nations is peculiarly revelatory of past insecurities in relation to the wilderness. During the First World War, as one British soldier observed,

... the field grey of the German uniforms 'seemed always to call up the grey wolf of Nordic literature'[10] ... To the Germans, the ochre of the British tunic appears as 'a brownish-yellow fleeting shadow', constituting one of the 'signs that we puzzled over as though they were ... the spoor of some mighty and unknown beast that came nightly to drink'.[11]

The resulting atavistic animosity that comes to the surface in the form of vehement denunciations or acts of war may be expressive of any one or all these different layers of humiliating insecurity and fear. The division between nations and the kingdom of nature – with which they have been in a perpetual state of war – not only underlies but may be compared with that between two nations at war, such as Britain and Germany during the First World War. That war produced extraordinary divisions in the minds of British men and women. The most obvious was that which continuously haunted the imaginations of men at the front: 'Them and Us', with No Man's Land between. Though the trenches were some-times only 50 yards apart, the distance seemed as great as that between the Earth and the moon. The British seldom saw the German soldiers, except during a successful raid or a general assault. Everything on the other side was strange, sinister and ultimately unimaginable. A front-line officer, Charles Carrington, looking back on that time, said:

> In fifty years I have never been able to rid myself of the obsession with No Man's Land and the unknown world beyond it. This side of our wire everything is familiar and every man a friend; over there, beyond their wire, is the unknown, the uncanny.[12]

He might be speaking of any war in the last 7,000 years, as hostile tribe faced hostile tribe, or as the citizens of the separate cities of Sumeria threatened each other across the intervening No Man's Land. Or he might be speaking of the day when settled peoples first walled themselves in against the wilderness without; when animals, seldom seen, were made monstrous in myth. Ever since, every unknown people and place has tended to be tarred with the same brush of world-fearing and perverting myth. In this connection, it is significant that a Governor of Hong Kong, Sir Crawford Murray MacLehose, was able to say in 1980 that China had ceased to be 'a feared and unknown place'.

The primary division between mutually hostile enclaves of *Homo degener* peoples and wilderness underlies the division in the vertical between the ruling minority and the majority of ordinary citizens within any one nation – or between sectional interest groups within the nation – and in the horizontal between nations themselves. Amongst the sectional interest groups there is also the division between those made comfortable by their economic circumstances (who may be in the majority, as in the

USA, or in the minority, as in many Third World countries) and the poor, whom the comfortable tend to regard as 'the enemy', a feeling that is usually reciprocated. In countries that are not under one party rule or a dictatorship, this division is usually reflected in the political parties, which tend to divide into those of the Left (including the radical and poorer sections of the community) and those of the Right, a division which ensures that the nation is continually riven by political conflict. Which division – the vertical or the horizontal – assumes the greater importance at any given moment very much depends on the balance of the stresses and strains within nations and strains between nations themselves. For instance, between 1815 and 1850 governments in Europe feared revolutionary uprisings within their own countries, whereas from the early 1850s until 1870 European governments came to fear other governments more than revolutionary uprisings, and armies fought five major wars against other armies rather than revolutionaries at home.[13] Meanwhile, on the other side of the Atlantic, shortly after the outbreak of the American Civil War in 1861, the American Secretary of War, William H. Seward, expressed the hope for a war with some European power. Such an outside threat, he argued, could not substantially harm the United States, and yet would probably cement the nation, bring the errant southern states back into the Union, and so end the Civil War. 'If the Lord would only give the United States,' he prayed, 'an excuse for a war with England, France or Spain!'

The nation is most obviously a composite animal when it is threatened by circumstances similar to those which initially brought nations into being, uniting all against the common enemy. Amongst other things, the Second World War is remembered in Britain for fostering the rare sense of belonging to Britain as 'one nation', united against the common foe, despite the fact

> ... that the traditional enmity between management and worker in Britain ran so deep, and sectional interests were so strong (even within the work-force), that people in British industry were not prepared to sink their differences and suspend their quarrels even under the spur of a total war for national survival.[14]

The Labour victory after the war brought into the open the feeling of 'us' and 'them' which had existed during the conflict, yet was contained by the demands of the larger and external threat. New nations are born in similar fashion to the threat from without. For example, the historical experience of the Palestinian people, their sense of nationhood, was shaped not just by colonial conquest but also by Zionism, with its own programme of national and religious regeneration. For years many Palestinians called attention to the Zionist threat. They came to nationhood in their attempts to oppose it and in the common experience of loss and exile which followed.

The merging of the individual self into the greater whole, the nation, in order to control the environment to survive is thus most noticeable under circumstances of external threat or war.

> National identity becomes particularly important when a polarised situation turns into open strife. In the Israeli case, involving frequent wars, a study by a group of psychiatrists found that Israeli behaviour displays an attachment to the nation so profound as to be virtually inseparable from the individual self. In the case of the Palestinians there has been a similar tendency to see the nation as part of the extended self. Personal and national identity have been merged: the nation and the homeland have become part of the extended self. As a group of American psychiatrists who studied the conflict in Israel phrased it: to lose the homeland 'is to risk the fragmentation of the self, an eventuality which people will resist with their very lives'.[15]

The original 'fragmentation of the self' occurred with the loss of the hunter-gatherer way of life and homeland, and consequent loss of the unity of the individual – of one body and one mind – with nature. The freedom of the individual identity within its natural setting has been exchanged for the absorption of that identity in that of the nation, whose cohesion, and consequent behaviour as a giant human being, is most easily assured by the threat of an enemy without, causing the nation to rally behind a leader and his Farmer God or Ideology.*

Nothing ties tighter the in-group bonds than an out-group threat.[16]

The greater the threat, the stronger the response. Whether the threat is actual or imaginary makes no difference; it soon becomes actualized because the rallying response will be seen by the 'adversary' as a threat, leading to a confrontation. War, and the threat of war, have provided not only the incentives to modernization and technological revolution

---

*A general fear of the unknown has a similar effect, as when, in October 2001, following the terrorist attack on the World Trade Center in New York in September 2001, the United States was terrorized with anthrax.

which the market and the pursuit of profit do only fitfully and by accident, but they have provided an urgent and continuous pressure towards the growth of nations, reshaping territorial boundaries and inducing national consciousness in a negative fashion, in that the protagonists learned to hate one another.

> The post-1450 waging of war was intimately connected with 'the birth of the nation-state'... Military factors – or better, geostrategical factors – helped to shape the territorial boundaries of these new nation states, while the frequent wars induced national consciousness, in a negative fashion at least, in that Englishmen learned to hate Spaniards, Swedes to hate Danes, Dutch rebels to hate their former Habsburg overlords.[17]

'Them and Us' situations between nations have ritually reactivated their original conflict behaviour, further stimulating the Life-Force to ascent and to offensive-defensive measures of environmental control.

What then are the socio-biological implications of the perversion of the individual life-force to serve the Life-Force of the nation? I argued in the last chapter that the body of the nation is, as it were, a permanent survival machine constructed by the memes of *Homo degener* to fight for their survival and propagation in a world regarded as an implacably hostile environment; while the members are like cells enclosed in the outer skin of a giant human being within which the memes operate. Japan has been an outstanding example of the cell-like condition of *Homo degener*, where the employee in one of Japan's big firms has resembled a single cell which adapts itself to the requirements of the organism. Or, in the case of France,[18] the basic cells are not so much individuals as groups of individuals or *pays*. These are small informal districts acting as cells in which the past is stored. Local culture thereafter slowly and inexorably imprints that past on each inhabitant.* France is thus the sum of its *pays*, a patchwork of individual cells. In similar vein, we speak of terrorist cells, such as those of al-Qaeda, that function like cancer cells within the organism.

The specialization of function of cells within individual human beings, that enabled them to evolve and adapt as self-governing hunter-gatherers,

---

* 'It is not the literal past that rules us, save, possibly, in a biological sense. It is images of the past. These are often as highly structured and selective as myths. Images and symbolic constructs of the past are imprinted, almost in the manner of genetic information, on our sensibility. Each new historical era mirrors itself in the picture and active mythology of its past, or of a past borrowed from other cultures. It tests its sense of identity, of regress or new achievement, against that past...'[19]

was now replicated at the macrocosmic level of the nation as *Homo degener* peoples became highly specialized as functional parts or cells of a giant human being. Like the cells of the human body, which possess an adaptability, plasticity and variability that have allowed the remarkable specialization of function that we see at the microcosmic level in the human liver or brain cell, the adaptability, plasticity and variability of the members of a nation, as cells of a giant human being, have allowed the similar and equally remarkable specialization of function that we see at the macrocosmic level in the head (the government), in the eyes, ears and senses (the priests and scientists and their world view), in the brain (including universities, schools, libraries and the media acting also as a collective memory),* in the bureaucratic nervous system, in the fighting arms, in the energy or stomach (the main body of citizens), and in the legs and feet (the labourers) of the nation. It is a composite animal that uses fossil fuel as part of its metabolism: it defecates tons of rubbish a day onto waste disposal sites. Amongst features feeding the organs and linking them to the whole are the rivers, the canals, the main railway lines and trunk roads which form the arteries,† while branch lines and secondary roads are as capillaries from an artery; the life-blood that flows through the arteries and veins of the nation is commerce. In Britain, London is the heart of the nation – the social, financial, commercial and political centre that acts as the pump governing the circulation within the country. The postal services, telephone, wireless and television – together with the new information-handling computer networks at the heart of banking, business, science and social accounting – form part of the collective nervous system of the composite animal, via which messages pass to and from the brain, handling millions of the members' problems and causing them to conform to its requirements. Here the nervous system and brain are mainly concerned with the internal environment of the composite animal.

In Britain during the Second World War, the whole network of national communications – road, rail, telephone and telegraph – centred upon London. Since then, a degree of unity has been maintained by television, a mass medium which above all others passes on to the public a shared sense of values, encouraging conformity to the values it espouses. This process will be carried a stage further with the proposed introduction of

---

*In this connection, the poet Ted Hughes once observed that 'Decay of libraries is like Alzheimer's in the nation's brain'.

† In Canada, the transcontinental Canadian Pacific railway was a main artery that so knit the nation together that it came to be regarded as 'the father of the nation'.

'information technology superhighways' which will connect members of nations to electronic networks, comprising perhaps 500 television channels connecting every office, school and home to centres of communication.

Such a heritage as I have described above has been transmitted to successive generations by the dominant priestly and scientific mediators and educators, and below them by the heads of establishments at every level, including the heads of households.* They have transmitted, as it were, the sequence of coded messages – including the 'corporate memory' – that have spelled out the memes of a particular nation, and the nature of the values handed on to the next generation. In short, they have transmitted the collective memetic inheritance of the nation.

It is not as individual men and women that we now face the world, but cloaked in a national persona, members of psychotic giant human beings called Britain, Russia, China, Germany or France. Descriptions of the nation in anthropomorphic terms rightly abound. The nation 'stands on its own two feet', 'speaks to nation', 'flexes its muscles', 'is driven to its knees', etc. We speak of 'a national consciousness', 'a national psyche' and 'the national character'. Leaders have 'their fingers on the pulse of the nation'. Each nation is a different Sacred Species of composite animal, each energized to grow by the power of its black Sun. Each is a corporate body that treats the external world as a hostile environment, just as the organs and cells of the human body must be protected from the alien environment outside the skin.

One means available to cells to safeguard themselves against deleterious changes around them is to come together in communities large enough to permit the development of an internal environment, together with mechanisms that will respond to changes in the external environment, thereby ensuring them a measure of freedom and stability. For instance, following the centralization of the nervous system and the development of the neo-cortex, the ancestors of humans were enabled to deal with environmental changes and so to insulate their internal environment. This was the basis of the wide-ranging freedom and success of the hunter-gatherers, who relied on their ecological understanding to recognize, and an unpossessive mobility to counteract, environmental change. (If unpossessive mobility was their most important mode of adaptation, physical and cultural adaptations were also available to them.) And here it is important to recall that hunter-gatherer communities

---

*All education, in all stratified societies, accepts and defends the dominant institutions of that society, whether it be the Sovereign, the Constitution, Parliament, the Law, or Communism. 'Corporate power is early subdued in our consciousness as the powerless servant of the people, and thus protected.'

were seldom larger than fifty persons. In other words, they did not cohere in sufficient numbers to create an internal social environment, for they did not need one. From time immemorial, the wild external environment was their home. They were individuals born free – individuals whose own internal environments were sufficient to secure them freedom within the wilderness. In sharp contrast, settled people lost that freedom and ability to counteract environmental change. Their individual internal environments were thus set gravely at risk, forcing them to congregate in communities sufficiently large to create artificial internal environments for themselves. Like cells confined within the protected internal environments of their composite animals, they then developed mechanisms to stabilize those environments. The frontier, like the skin of a human being, has been a principal guarantor of the climate within. In addition, national survival has depended on the development of means of protecting their internal environments against threats to their vital interests, against invading change.

Before the invention of the telegraph and telephone, fire-signals were much the quickest and most sure method of sending an alarm over long distances to members of the composite animal. In England the use of fire-signals to give warning of seaborne attack goes back at least to the final stage of the Roman period, and was part of the Saxon defensive system against the Vikings. During the Middle Ages beacons were again prepared at various times of invasion scare. They were prepared against Napoleon in 1804. These were the call to arms, the ultimate in the nation's armoury of conformist requirements. Today, Science, by increasingly sophisticated means, provides similar warning. These now include the development of defence surveillance systems, reconnaissance satellites, complex networks of intelligence-gathering and communications installations operated both by intelligence services, the armed forces and the police. All these, together with the Immigration Authority, may be said to comprise the nation's immune system. Like those systems concerned with the internal environment, this information-processing system, together with its key decision-makers, constitutes an essential function of the central nervous and immune systems and brain in their interactions with the external environment of the composite animal.

The priestly-scientific experts, together with their Farmer God, were once the eyes, ears and other senses in the interaction of the composite animal with the outside world – its world-fearing 'windows to the world'. Their descendants, the intellectuals and scientists, now fulfil that function. Soviet science, for instance, was the main channel of Soviet Russia's knowledge about the outside world – it represented its eyes, ears, and all other senses in its interaction with the external world. It was also the instrument of development of Soviet economic and military power. This is increasingly the case with the other industrial nations.

Note the extraordinary change that has taken place in terms of the individual human destiny. Before the Mesolithic all hunter-gatherers were true scientists in nature's natural laboratory, their brains and sensory apparatus integrated in a holistic ecological understanding of the wild environment. Now highly specialized *Homo sapiens sapiens* scientists and technocrats – their brains dominating and repressing their greatly diminished and desensitized sensory apparatus – provide the sensoria of composite animals, supplying knowledge of the outside world the better to control the protected environments of subhumans ascending to the skies.

Science controls and interprets the flow of information and dictates, through its control of technology, the development of measures of offence-defence. And if the ultimate aim of the scientific community is international co-operation, it is nonetheless a fact that offensive-defensive competition is still a principal motivating force behind scientific research and development – recall the intensity of the competitive recruitment of German scientists by the Americans, British, French and Russians after the Second World War for exploitation in their national interests – just because it is a principal motivating force behind nations whose economies thrive both on the making of arms for their armed forces and for the arms trade, and which are fundamentally at war with the world.

A UNESCO symposium held in Ajaccio (Corsica) in February 1981 stated that some 40 per cent of all research and development world-wide was undertaken for military ends. In Britain, some 48 per cent of all UK government-funded research and development has had a military purpose, and some 50 per cent of scientists have been personally committed to developing and perfecting weapons of destruction or extermination. Solly Zuckerman likewise has argued that science and industrial research are in the main committed to technological development for military purposes; that the decisions that scientists 'make today in fields of science and technology determine the tactics, then the strategy, and finally the politics of tomorrow'.[20]

Ernst Chain, when Director of the Microbiological Institute at Porton Down, provided the ultimate justification for this use of science when he wrote the following:

Throughout the ages wars have been won by superior weapons, and in modern war technology based on science is a bigger factor than ever before. Capable scientists are therefore the most precious asset which a nation possesses to give it superiority over its enemies, and victory or defeat is in their hands...

It is often said that science is universal and international, and scientists have the responsibility to see to it that all advances in knowledge are freely made available to mankind as a whole. This is a gross over-simplification. The first responsibility of the scientist is to the nation of which he is a member. It is quite obvious that the very nature of the development of war weapons is such that the results of this research must be kept secret from the enemy, and this applies both to the defensive and aggressive methods. It has been so ever since the beginning of organised society, and must be continued in modern times as long as the threat of armed aggression by an enemy nation exists.[21]

Homo degener peoples have undergone an extraordinary change in behaviour in face of threats to survival precisely because, unlike *Homo sapiens*, they have had to safeguard sacred hierarchies and exclusive territories, while their aggression has been uninhibited and uncontrolled.

Intraspecific disputes and aggression amongst animals arise either to establish dominance in a social hierarchy or to establish territorial rights over an area of land. Some species are primarily hierarchical, having no fixed territories; others are primarily territorial and have no hierarchies; yet others have hierarchies on their territories and experience both forms of aggression. However, intraspecific aggression amongst animals is inhibited and controlled in order to safeguard the survival of the species. The normal outcome of intraspecific aggression is not the killing of the enemy but his submission or flight.

The brains of *Homo sapiens*, like those of other animals, are phylogenetically programmed to mobilize defence mechanisms in the event of a threat to their vital interests, to their very survival. Phylogenetically programmed aggression has been termed 'biologically adaptive, life-serving, benign aggression'.[22] It is a biologically adaptive defence reaction to threat, but it is not the only means of reaction available to *Homo sapiens*. Other options are fission of the band, submission or flight. Flight has generally been the favoured option with animals, except when the animal has no chance to flee, when it might assume an effective threatening posture or, failing that, fight. However, not only have hunter-gatherers been restrained by inhibitions against intraspecific aggression, but they had really no reason for such aggression. Given their absence of social hierarchy, their intermingling between hunter bands and their free-ranging movements in pursuit of game, their aggressive tendencies were, in the main, outward directed in their hunting of game, with little need to direct them against their own kind. Had those aggressive tendencies been directed against their fellows, they would surely have been portrayed in their art. Not only is there an absence of intraspecific strife in their art prior to the Mesolithic but, equally, intraspecific strife occupies a most important place in the cultures, literature and art of civilized people.

For with the development of composite animals, a completely different and more complex situation arose. Unlike *Homo sapiens*, the territory on which *Homo degener* peoples grew belonged to them, and therefore required protection. The collective memetic inheritance of each composite animal was programmed to wage war on the wild world, and by extension on anyone or anything looming over the horizon and on anyone threatening the composite animal from within. With the accretion of territory, hierarchies, institutions and possessions the range of its vital interests grew, as did potential threats to those interests and so the need to develop further measures of protection. Increasingly the territorially-based composite animal lacked the ability to flee in the face of threats to its survival, necessitating total reliance on measures of offensive-defensive aggression. Any flight impulse would often be deliberately repressed by leaders with threats of death to those inclined to flight. So one whole aspect of the biologically adaptive defence mechanism available to *Homo sapiens* in face of a threat to survival was lost to *Homo degener*. Instead, caught between flight and fight, nations have often engaged in offensive-defensive displacement displays (sabre rattling), such as the building of ever larger fortifications, warships, etc., causing potential enemies to imitate them. Because the survival and vital interests being protected are thus no longer those of *Homo sapiens* but those of composite animals, man's phylogenetically programmed aggression, his 'biologically adaptive, life-serving, benign aggression', has been perverted to serve the collective memetic inheritance of the nation: it is the survival of the *Homo degener* nation that is at stake, not *Homo sapiens*. In addition, in their sedentary situation caught between flight and fight, *Homo degener* élites have developed means of killing and cruelty against subversive elements within who might threaten, not the vital interests of the nation as a whole, but those of élite groups within the nation. Although Erich Fromm uses the phrase 'biologically nonadaptive, malignant aggression'[23] to describe killing and cruelty that is not defence against a threat, I use the phrase to describe *all* the aggressive activities of *Homo degener*, whether seemingly benign or malign, because all are malign in that they are concerned with the survival of anti-evolutionary composite animals at the cost of *Homo sapiens*, wildlife and wilderness.

Unlike the hunter-gatherers, who were the regular prey of none, each nation has been the regular prey of others. If hunting animals and the absence of war were principal characteristics of *Homo sapiens*, the hunting of people and the waging of war have been salient features of *Homo degener* nations. For instance, war was virtually a permanent feature of Greek and Roman societies, as it has been of more modern European societies. Hence the activities of other nations and of nature have automatically been regarded with suspicion and hostility, forcing societies to develop mythopoeic and technological measures of environmental control and to launch pre-emptive strikes against the sources of threatening change.

Principal mythopoeic measures of offence-defence of the early priest-scientists were the imagined emanations from their Omniscient, Omnipotent and Omnipresent Farmer Gods – that is, space support. Now, while still appealing to their Farmer Gods for help, nations ask for space support from spy satellites, weather satellites, etc., in conjunction with nuclear weapons, the products of an increasingly omniscient, omnipotent and omnipresent science, whose actual emanations are even more to be feared. It was, and still is, the humiliating threat of change, of invasion by other and unknown nations and ideologies or by unknown natural forces, that evokes a profound collective response amongst settled peoples, emphasizing the underlying dichotomy and difference between *Homo degener* peoples and *Homo sapiens* ranging within the natural habitat, and between nations.

So separate, so different are they, that Wilfred Trotter, writing of the First World War between Britain and Germany, was able to see it as a war between virtually different species.

> Nature has provided but few roads for gregarious species to follow. Between the path that England finds herself in and that which Germany has chosen there is a divergence which almost amounts to a specific difference in the biological scale. In this, perhaps, lies the cause of the desperate and unparalleled ferocity of this war. It is a war not so much of contending nations as of contending species.[24]

It was in fact a war between separate Sacred Species of composite animal, the one called Britain and the other Germany, which, while appearing to diverge, have in reality been converging.

Finally, when they have established new colonies in the wilderness, the collective memetic inheritance of the colonizers has programmed the behaviour that will govern the actions of the new colony, overriding the true genetic and memetic inheritance of each member. An example of a collective memetic inheritance operating to bind people together as a rudimentary composite animal against a hostile wilderness may be seen in the covenant for political organization drawn up by those who sailed to America in the *Mayflower*. Thirty-five members of the Leyden congregation of religious exiles from England left Holland and joined sixty-six West Country people at Plymouth, England, and in September 1620 they set sail. During the voyage there was dissention over the enforcement of discipline. Whereupon

> ... it was thought good there should be an association and agreement, that we should combine together in one body, and to submit to such government and governors as we should by common consent agree to make and choose, and set our hands to this that follows, word for word...
>
> In the name of God, Amen. We whose names are under-written, the loyal subjects of our dread sovereign Lord, King James, by the grace of God, of Great Britain, France and Ireland King, defender of the faith, etc., having undertaken, for the glory of God, and advancement of the Christian faith, and honour of our King and country, a voyage to plant the first colony in the Northern parts of Virginia, do by these presents solemnly and mutually in the presence of God, and one of another, covenant and combine ourselves together into a civil body politic, for our better ordering and preservation and furtherance of the ends aforesaid; and by virtue hereof to enact, constitute, and frame such just and equal laws, ordinances, acts, constitutions, and offices, from time to time, as shall be thought most meet and convenient for the general good of the colony, unto which we promise all due submission and obedience.[25]

The Mayflower Compact was signed by forty-one members of the new body or pioneer species. In December they founded the town of Plymouth in Cape Cod Bay on the North American coast. They were bound together under their Farmer God in a bitter struggle with the wilderness, to create the colony of New England. As the new composite animal grew larger, Thanksgiving Day, which celebrates the first harvest of the Plymouth colony, and has thereafter acknowledged the divine favours received during the year, became as essential a part of the American collective memetic inheritance as the Farmer God and agriculture on possessed land.

These colonists formed the embryo of a new Sacred Species of composite animal that would eventually displace the indigenous inhabitants.

Brothers! I have listened to many talks from our great father. When he first came over the wide waters, he was but a little man ... very little. His legs were cramped by sitting long in his big boat, and he begged for a little land to light his fire on... But when the white man had warmed himself before the Indians' fire and filled himself with their hominy, he became very large. With a step he bestrode the mountains, and his feet covered the plains and the valleys. His hand grasped the eastern and the western sea, and his head rested on the moon. Then he became our Great Father. He loved his red children, and he said 'Get a little further, lest I tread on thee...'[26]

Regardless of whether they had chosen, or been forced, to leave, and regardless of where they went, colonists have recreated the internal protected environment of their homeland, clinging for security to their familiar culture which they deploy as protective armour against the humiliating presence of an alien world, as when settlers in Australia tried to recreate England. In the case of the Americans, they eventually began to dominate the alien landscape of the New World with visible expressions of their Life-Force to ascent, as exemplified in their sky-scrapers. These are the modern equivalent of the aspirations to ascent that generated the Gothic cathedrals throughout Europe six hundred years ago. Today that ascent is accentuated by the cathedral-like rockets ascending to the moon and to the stars.

There is a most important corollary to this perversion of the life-force of the individual to that of the nation. It concerns the levels of instability inherent in nations which are Stable States in stasis. Their origins and growth were substantially in response to their view of the external wild environment as hostile. Ever since, the nation has required an enemy to give it cohesion and unity and to make sense of its members' lives: an enemy without gives it maximum cohesion and unity, while an opposition party within the nation may be seen as an enemy, uniting the majority against the opposition minority accused of threatening national survival. This has made for an inherent rigidity and instability, a condition exacerbated by the inefficiency and vulnerability of its internal protected environment. In effect, the collective inherited reflexes of the nation, a giant human being, replaced the plasticity and adaptability of the *Homo sapiens* individual. And this generalized pattern of behaviour has predominated over individual learning. Nations so depend upon collective reflexes and myth that they can never learn from history: they are programmed to repeat the same mistakes on an increasingly world-wide scale down the millennia.*

Several consequences arise from this, all making for the fundamental instability of nations. First, the suppressed genetic and memetic inheritance of all human beings evolved as hunter-gatherers – their true human nature – tries to reassert itself in every generation through violence and disease. Secondly, the suppressed forces of nature must always try to reassert themselves – through catastrophe and disease – against the alien farming bases of these stratified societies that block the selection and succession of true life-forms. Thirdly, because they were pioneer species of composite animal, their descendants are still experiencing population explosions as they spread throughout the world – as for instance in South America and Africa – forcing them to domesticate and adapt the remaining wilderness to their growing religio-socio-economic needs. Fourthly, their vertical structures, vertically oriented behaviour and ascent and related territorial demands have caused disharmony and instability world-wide. They have caused such stresses and strains within nations and strains between nations themselves, that external pressures, as well as threatening the survival of the nation, have paradoxically often been essential to ensure that internal pressures do not destroy the nation. Earlier I instanced the hoped for aggressive intervention by foreign powers to reunite the North and South of the United States during the Civil War. In addition, virtually none of the existing 200 or so nations, nor those in the past, have consisted of peoples who form a coherent ethnic group within the national boundaries, with common interests and a common background, so they have been consistently at one another's throats and a cause of foreign intervention. Take, for instance, the situation in Europe following the First World War:

> Because of the geographical dispersion of the various populations under the former multinational empires, it had not been possible in 1919 to create a territorial settlement which was ethnically coherent; large groups of minorities therefore lived on the wrong side of every state's borders, offering a source not only of internal weakness but also of foreign resentments.[27]

Such an observation could equally be applied to those nations created after the withdrawal of European colonialists in Africa and Asia following

---

*Hegel once said: 'What experience and history teach is this – that nations and governments have never learned anything from history, or acted upon any lessons they might have drawn from it.'

the Second World War, and to those nations created following the more recent collapse of Yugoslavia and the Soviet Union.

Lastly, following on from the above, composite animals that originated in a continual war against the feared and hated wilderness have subsequently continued to expand and to grow in continual wars – both military and economic – against other equally feared and hated composite animals. Because they have behaved towards one another down the millennia as though they were different species, the essence of warfare between nations is that it is primarily *interspecific*. Relatively speaking, an endless battle of 'individual' giant human beings against one another and against the wilderness replaced a potential unity of true and individual people living in relative harmony in the wilderness.

There are conflicts within and conflicts without as members of nations seek to establish and perpetuate a steady state, which, because they are converging as pioneer species, remains at present beyond their powers to achieve. For instability is a prime characteristic of pioneer species as they attempt to establish a degree of stability amongst contending species. As unrelated Sacred Species of composite animal they must, by virtue of their similarities, compete for space and resources. Prime factors contributing to their instability and convergence are their self-aggrandizement and search for stability and security, and associated delusions of grandeur and fears of conspiracy.

Chapter 3

The Pathology of the Nation

Paranoia is a form of mental illness characterized by fixed delusions, usually of persecution... In paranoid delusions, others, human or supernatural, are intent on harming the person, although there is no basis in reality. Delusions of grandeur or of having remarkable attributes are typically associated with mania. (*Black's Medical Dictionary*)[1]

In order to reveal more fully the pathology of the nation, it is first necessary to examine its origins and relationship *vis à vis* the kingdom of nature, then the pressures within the nation, and finally its behaviour in the external world beyond the confines of its protected environment, together with its relationships with other nations.

Because the early farming communities were eventually isolated from contact with, and no longer able to communicate with, other animals and the whole natural world as hunter-gatherers, they suffered a near total sensory deprivation, giving rise to complete disintegration and loss of evolutionary identity, and hence to a dichotomy and distortion of their thinking and their feelings, coupled with a distortion of their perception of reality. In effect, they suffered from a primary derangement of the self and of the senses which has been described as a collective primary schizophrenia.

Schizophrenia is generally described as a genetically inherited disease, mediated through the body's chemistry. A collective primary schizophrenia is a memetically inherited disease, mediated through the 'chemistry' of the body of the composite animal. The consequent distortion of *Homo degener*'s perception of reality has inevitably brought in its train a host of anxieties and fears and paranoid delusions.

These peoples were effectively crippled survivors – crippled physically, mentally and emotionally – who were attempting to survive in what they

281

now perceived as an alien and malignant land, whose language was entirely incomprehensible to them. They began to create make-believe worlds for themselves, reinforcing the fundamental alienation, isolation and incomprehension: they created composite animals which institutionalized fear. This was first of all a fear of the seemingly chaotic wilderness. Their stratified structures behind high walls, their Farmer Gods and associated behaviour were expressive of, and institutionalized, their fear of chaos. The frontier wall that arose between them and the wilderness was a petrified outward expression of their inner fears of natural chaos, consolidating the dichotomy between farming peoples and the wilderness. Their basic premise was that the wilderness was a hostile environment, hostile and alien to humankind: they imagined the wilderness was persecuting them. They transformed in their imaginations their own inadequacies, fears and hostility towards wild nature into a hostility on the part of nature towards them, and then by their very beliefs and behaviour made nature hostile, thus confirming their original mistaken belief. They thereafter transformed that hostility on the part of nature into a supernatural one, into a conspiracy of the Powers of Darkness to destroy them.

Trapped in fear and suspicion of the intentions of nature, their perception of reality distorted, the deluge appeared as an instrument for the destruction of their ancestors because of some wrong-doing on their part, which is of course a perversion of the facts. Such a distortion of the facts, however, became immortalized in myths such as that of a Fall and Flood. Their subsequent experience of natural catastrophe and disease convinced *Homo degener* peoples that they were being punished for further wrong-doing on their part. Without any real understanding as to how they had arrived at their debased and dangerous condition they could only punish ostensible wrong-doers and perform ceremonies around Divine Powers that might rescue them from the devilish Powers that conspired to destroy them. Thereafter the unknown wilderness remained the prime catalyst of their fear of chaos. They were alone in the world, and the wild environment was conspiring to destroy them. The world was suddenly full of terrifying monsters out to get them. They were the victims of what I have described as a collective primary paranoia. The paranoia in relation to wild nature is still apparent today. A commentator on a programme on Bangladesh described the devastation caused in 1989 by the flooding of the Ganges and Brahmaputra rivers as 'the malicious conspiracy of nature'.

At the same time they suffered systematic delusions (false ideas not amenable to reasoned argument) of grandeur, as evinced in their myths of Creation and later delusions of a Manifest Destiny or divine commission to rule, benefit and save the world. Each stratified structure, as well as being a mountain of escape and protection from the hostile world without, was a stage for displacement displays of grandeur against the unknown. This was evinced in their physical and psychical constructs – for example, in the glittering figures, God Kings and Pharaoh Sun God, at the summits of their social pyramids, in the associated monumental structures such as temples and pyramids, and in their myths of a new Creation certifying them as the chosen of their Farmer God. Indeed, many later civilizations have undergone similar psychical transformations. Just as the myth of Noah's Ark, the lifeboat that saved a chosen few from the Darkness of a sinful humankind and consequent Flood, refracts even as it reflects the origin of civilizations, new nations have originated in similar circumstances of humiliating oppression, deprivation and dearth and passed behind similar refracting lenses of myth – as when the Israelites escaped from the Darkness of Egypt and crossed dry-shod over the Red Sea into the Promised Land of Canaan; or when the Pilgrim Fathers fled the Darkness of a sinful Europe and sailed across the Atlantic to the Promised Land of America; or when the Boers fled from the British in the Cape Colony, crossing the mountains by wagon into the Promised Lands of the Orange Free State and Natal. The Boer settlers explicitly saw in their Great Trek a parallel with Israel's exodus from Egypt. In each case, from the point of view of those forced to flee, the States from which they fled were threatening lands of Darkness. They were moving from Darkness into Light. In each case, they offered Thanksgiving to a Farmer God for their safe deliverance. All reflect the Noah salvation myth, in which a Covenant is established in perpetuity with a Farmer God, thus establishing their chosen condition, divinely ordained State and superiority. All these examples express the primacy and power of the religious memeplexes that undergird and overarch infant nations, comprising the core of the collective memetic inheritance of each.

The first arrivals of Europeans in North America were known as the Forefathers, the term Pilgrim Fathers not coming into general use until 1820. Like the later Scots-Irish settlers in North America, all the early immigrants may be described as God's Frontiersmen. On arrival, many Scots-Irish wrote back to Belfast likening Ulster to the land of the Pharaoh and America to the land of Canaan, a land provided by God for His Chosen People, a land of plenty for the poor man. Like the Scots-Irish settlers, many rose from being poor radicals to being rich ultra-conservatives, a success ascribed to God's Providence. They believed in the righteousness and moral goodness of their own cause under the guidance and protection of their Farmer God, while believing that everything pertaining to the wilderness was morally evil as well as a material threat to their protected environment. As Dee Brown argues, after driving out or destroying the Native Americans on the eastern seaboard, the white Americans established a 'permanent Indian frontier'[2] between themselves and the Native Americans to the west. In 1834, Congress passed an Act to the effect that no white persons would be permitted to trade without a licence, nor permitted to settle, beyond the 'permanent Indian frontier'. However, even before these laws could be effected, white settlers had already moved further west, forcing the policy makers in Washington to re-establish the 'permanent Indian frontier' at the 95th meridian. Notwithstanding, following the war with Mexico, in 1847, and the subsequent annexation by the United States of territory west of the 95th meridian, and then the discovery, in 1848, of gold in California, thousands of settlers invaded the territories west of the 'permanent Indian frontier'. Washington justified the invasion by appealing to a Manifest Destiny, a grandiose term which sanctified greed for land and wealth by proclaiming that the Europeans were ordained by destiny to govern the whole continent.

A Manifest Destiny, or delusion of a divine commission to rule, benefit and save the world, is prime evidence of the paranoid delusions of grandeur that characterize nations. From the outset they have cherished collective delusions of grandeur, and associated fears of conspiracy and persecution, primarily in relation to the wilderness, and subsequently in relation to other nations.

Delusions of grandeur and fears of conspiracy and persecution became inherent within the psyches of members of composite animals growing up in the wilderness, and so in their institutions. And whether the actual holder of any one Office of State has delusions of grandeur or fears of persecution is less important than the fact that such established Offices of State – and, of course, the State itself – are themselves expressive of a collective primary schizophrenia and paranoia. These terms in fact describe precisely the pathology of the Life-Force to ascent and collective security of the nation. They represent the polarization of their petrified fears of chaos, the energy flowing from the Darkness of their collective fears arising from their original degradation during the Mesolithic.

When the Church was the predominant organization in Europe, paranoia was evident amongst all those Christians who believed they were, like the Jews and Muslims, the chosen of God. They were victims of a collective primary paranoia – they cherished collective delusions of grandeur and associated fears of conspiracy and persecution. Their paranoia was evident in the hunting down of heretics and witches, and in general in what was described in Part I as 1,500 years of massive humiliation, mayhem, madness and human sacrifice that consumed so many millions in the name of Christ. Yet their paranoia did not begin with the belief that they were the chosen of their Farmer God, but rather with the delusion that such a God, who sanctified such inhuman behaviour and associated devastation of the environment, could exist at all.

All a nation's relationships, whether internal or external, are suffused with the two aspects of a primary derangement, i.e. a collective primary schizophrenia and paranoia. Consequently, any one Office of State, or other position of power within the nation, is liable not only to attract the paranoid person but is also liable to infect the holder with the incipient paranoia inherent in the system. More and more studies are revealing the paranoid nature of leaders of organizations and of nations.* They are the most prone to paranoia, being quick to sense a slight and to feel that they are the victims of conspiracy.

Two leaders who were patently paranoid and who had the most profound effect on the fortunes of nations in the last century were Stalin and Hitler.[3] Both exhibited chronic suspicion, narcissistic self-absorption, hypersensitivity and megalomania. Their narcissism sprang from an infancy similar to that experienced by the infant farming societies of the Neolithic. In other words, both men grew up feeling isolated in a hostile world, seeking an inner security from their anxieties by forming idealized images of themselves which they adopted as their true identities, just as did the early farming societies in a hostile wilderness. In such a state only they themselves, *their* needs, thoughts and feelings were experienced as fully real, while everyone and everything else lacked reality or interest. The only human beings who existed for them were themselves. The rest of humankind were seen either as instruments with which to accomplish their purposes, and therefore to be exploited to those ends, or as obstacles to be eliminated. These were precisely the narcissistic perceptions of farming peoples of wildlife and wilderness, primary perceptions out of which sprang the secondary ones towards human beings. As to their megalomania, Stalin planned to build the Palace of the Soviets, which was to be the largest building in the world surmounted by a 100 foot high statue of Lenin, a plan which was prevented only by the onset of war. Hitler's palace in Berlin was to be, according to Albert Speer, the largest residence ever built, and one hundred and fifty times the size of the chancellor's residence at the time of Bismarck. Others of his planned

---

*In his book *We and They: Civic and Despotic Cultures* (Temple Smith, 1980), Robert Conquest suggests that some 10% of Members of Parliament are paranoid, while in a book entitled *The Paranoid Style in American Politics* (Jonathan Cape, 1966), Richard Hofstadter shows that a conspiratorial view of the world has pervaded American politics since the 18th century.

buildings were to be two to four times as large as their counterparts elsewhere.

> Like so many tyrants from the pharaohs onwards, he saw his equivalent of the pyramids as providing the 'imperishable confirmation' of his power.[4]

Under the circumstances, both Stalin and Hitler became convinced of a providential mission and claimed an infallibility of judgement and a monopoly of power in relation to that mission, any challenge to which was perceived as a threat to both their private and public image of themselves. Both suffered delusions of grandeur combined with the conviction that they were the victims of persecution and conspiracy. Both raised up the spectres of internal and external enemies engaged in conspiracies to pull them down, if they did not strike and destroy them first. In Stalin's case, internal enemies included the kulaks, seen as class enemies on whom he eventually declared war. In Hitler's case, as well as internal enemies whom he accused of stabbing the German Empire in the back in 1918, spectres of external enemies rose up in the shape of Jews, Marxists and Slavs. Many Germans shared the same paranoid fears, seeing Hitler as their saviour.

The paranoia of these leaders, like that of so many before them, and more recently like that of the leaders of the fissiparous parts of the former Yugoslavia, tends to activate the incipient collective primary paranoia of their nations. Because all the relationships of the nation, both internal and external, are suffused with a collective primary schizophrenia and paranoia, the imagining of enemies, both internal and external, is a constant theme of those in power, provoking offensive-defensive conflict behaviour that is both irrational and inhuman. Before examining some of the internal pressures and related aggression in greater detail, it is necessary to recall what I mean by the term 'aggression'.

As I argued earlier, the phylogenetically programmed urge to attack (or to flee) on the part of *Homo sapiens* in the event of a threat to their vital interests, which may be termed defensive or 'benign' aggression, has been perverted by the collective memetic inheritance of the separate Sacred Species of composite animal in the service of their survival, against that of the species *Homo sapiens*, thus rendering all their aggression malign. I use the phrase 'biologically nonadaptive, malignant aggression'[5] to describe *all* the aggressive activities of *Homo degener*, including the propensity to destructiveness and cruelty and the craving for absolute control. 'Malignant' aggression is not an instinctual drive – that is, a drive instinctive to the individual – but a passion rooted in the perversion of the individual life-force by the Life-Force of a composite animal. It is not just one isolated behaviour trait but part of a syndrome, in that it is found regularly combined with other traits that form the social character, such as strict hierarchy, class division and dominance. 'Malignant' aggression may be described as an 'innate' characteristic of the stratified society viewed as a composite animal, forming part of the collective memetic inheritance of the nation. It constitutes what has been described as 'institutionalized violence', that is, the overt or covert presence and use of force to ensure the stability and security of the nation. It is precisely because *Homo degener* lives in zoo-like or prison-like conditions – that is, in various degrees of captivity – their life-forces perverted by that of the nation backed by the veiled threat of 'institutionalized violence', that they are under constant internal and external pressures, or threats to their vital interests, both physical and psychical. The latter is particularly important, as psychic equilibrium involves not only their frames of orientation, but their sense of identity. If they feel threatened by ideas that question their own frame of orientation, they will react to those ideas as to a vital threat. This applies equally to the nation as a whole.

Virtually every society since the beginnings of civilization has relied upon institutionalized violence to consolidate its vertical structure and ensure its stability and growth. This is the violence that originated under the stresses of the enclosure and deprivation of deranged people following the Mesolithic, which was perpetrated initially against the wilderness, and which thereafter became institutionalized in their stratified structures. In the words of Archbishop Oscar Romero of El Salvador, whose assassination in March 1980 caused such outrage in the West,

> This violence finds its expression in the structure and daily functioning of a socio-economic and political system which accepts it as normal and usual that progress is impossible unless the majority of the people are used as a productive force under the management of a privileged minority.[6]*

---

* As declared by a meeting of Brazilian bishops in 1966, called by Archbishop Helder Camara, concerning the more recent exploitation and depression of the workers and peasants of Brazil to achieve the successful capitalist development of that country – the famous 'economic miracle': 'Limitless ambition and boundless selfishness have created the present situation in which the poor are sacrificed for the benefit of the privileged.'[7] This declaration could as well apply to the behaviour of the privileged of any number of nations past and present – whether capitalist or Communist – or to the exploitation by the privileged nations of the poor nations of the world. 'Poverty,' as Gandhi said, 'is the worst form of violence.'

He might as easily have been writing of the violence practised against the populations of England, Scotland and Catholic Ireland during the hundreds of years of enclosures by a privileged minority, and their exploitation as a productive force for the sake of industrial development and progress. It is a violence which begets violence. In England, for instance, the peasants were driven from the village common land in order to create large 'enclosed' estates belonging to the local gentry. These land-deprived peasants were forced into towns to earn their livings, an act of class deprivation which was followed by another, when the Industrial Revolution transformed men into 'wage-slaves'. This ongoing process of deprivation and growth of industrial towns has led to the soulless monoliths of modern society, where those whose livelihoods are now at the mercy of market forces and faceless multinationals can only express their fear and hatred arbitrarily by venting their anger on each other and on strangers in the street.

Institutionalized violence and its concomitant, the arbitrary violence of those deprived, are inherent characteristics of the parasite pyramidal structure. As well as being the agents of an institutionalized violence, *Homo sapiens sapiens* élites of nations are the agents of a continual competitive conflict, which may be controlled or uncontrolled, and which may either help relieve or merely exacerbate the fundamental institutional pressures and violence.

From earliest childhood, in most *Homo degener* cultures, competition is encouraged, a controlled conflict that is a main product of their ritualized conflict behaviour that drives them to ascend in the vertical. To foster competition, societies and the international community have established a whole range of alluring prizes – e.g. school prizes, university degrees, knighthoods, Olympic Gold Medals and Nobel Prizes – whose attainment enhances the status and prestige of persons and nations. Such an obligation to be competitive provides members of nations and nations themselves with an aggressive drive which helps project them into the limelight on their national stages and on the international stage respectively. The prime motive is self-interest. Most organizations within a nation – the navy, the army, the civil service, etc. – are run for the benefit and prestige of those who run them, as is the nation itself.

Aggression and competition, in various forms, in the pursuit of status and prestige are themes running through most *Homo degener* cultures, raising some people head and shoulders above their fellows.* In the process,

---

* It will be evident that such aggression and competition underlie the Life-Force to vertical self-aggrandizement in ascent of nations. In every sphere of knowledge, for instance, men compete to be luminaries, standing on the shoulders of their immediate predecessors as they reach up, like their ancestors, towards luminaries such as the sun, the moon and the stars.

the natural co-operative behaviour is subverted by, and made subordinate to, competition, when members of teams co-operate in competition with other teams. The sum total of such aggression and enhanced prestige enhances the prestige of one clan or nation in relation to others. Like a giant human being, it adds cubits to its stature, putting it ahead in the race to prosperity and power. Here again, controlled competitive struggle is the primary objective of co-operation within the nation. It is when control breaks down, in the face of circumstances similar to those in which nations were born, that controlled competition may turn into violence.

In the absence of mobility and ecological understanding to disperse like hunter-gatherers to seek a generous environment elsewhere, deranged societies are always and inevitably vulnerable, particularly when the society numbers millions and there is a great disparity and distance between *Homo sapiens sapiens* top and *Homo sapiens non sapiens* bottom of the social pyramid, placing society's range of glittering prizes and prestige quite beyond the reach of many. Within such societies a *Homo sapiens sapiens* few have basked in the Providential Light of their Sun – a generous environment for them, no doubt – while a *Homo sapiens non sapiens* majority has remained in a religio-socio-economic limbo, denied not only the prestigious limelight of the Sun of their society, but often the light of the true sun as well. Such a displacement and perversion of the life-force of the individual has given rise to a feeling of entrapment and sense of 'sinking beneath the waters' similar to that experienced by their forbears, 10,000 years ago, continually reactivating their conflict behaviour as they have sought likewise to 'keep their heads above water'.

David Sheppard, Bishop of Liverpool, in the 1984 Richard Dimbleby Lecture, pointed to the gross disparity in living conditions between what he described as Comfortable Britain and the Other Britain – city areas where poverty and unemployment are realities; pointing out that people are imprisoned in spirit by relative poverty.

> In describing this poverty I imagine a whole series of locked doors which imprison the spirit. There isn't just one factor which creates deprivation in urban life. The door of unemployment clangs shut against you. So does the door of neglected housing. So does the door of poor opportunity in schooling. The list of shut doors is a long one. If you live in the inner city you are likely to have the poorest service in health care, in transport and in leisure facilities, even sometimes in policing. Together, these locked doors make very large numbers of people feel powerless and unable to make any real choices about their destiny.

I admire more than I say those who keep their head above water; as one inner-city person said to me: 'You need an A-level in survival'. An honest observer must say that many survive only in the sense that their head bobs up above water every now and then.[8]

Here again is evidence not only of the imprisoning character of parasite pyramids of power, but also of the relative deprivation that is endemic to them, and which is, of course, in addition to, and consequent upon, the double deprivation already sustained following the Mesolithic and the double deprivation sustained – at least in Great Britain – following the enclosure of land prior to the Industrial Revolution. Life for the oppressed – that is, the vast majority of men, women and children over the last 10,000 years – has been a monotonous striving against extinction.

The behaviour of deranged people has been the behaviour of people alienated and imprisoned in a variety of degrading circumstances, under a variety of recurrent environmental pressures (whether natural, or man-made in the form of oppressive measures and laws), whose experience has been predominantly one of violence. In every generation since the first re-evolution, deranged people have struggled to escape the incapacitating, alienating and imprisoning circumstances of their environment, seeking to move from the lower end of the spectrum to the upper end, out of Darkness into the Light, seeking a superior identity, stimulus and security on stage in the Sunlight of their society. Others, as in religious, ideological or dynastic disputes, seek forcibly to change the principal actors, stage and very Sun itself – as when the Bolsheviks overthrew the Tsar of Russia. Yet others flee abroad, there to establish a new stratified society under another Sun, as in the USA. Others may seek relief from the religio-socio-economic pressures at the level at which they are forced to reside, often resorting to violence – particularly if they are unemployed workers who are nonetheless pressurized to conform to images, to compete, to acquire – taking things which they need as well as avenging themselves on a society which will not give them work or money, and therefore status.

These victims of manifold alienation – alienation from their wilderness home, then from the farmed land and now their social alienation – react in a number of different ways to their plight. Like the rudimentary communities of alienated early farmers who waged territorial wars on one another in the wilderness, the alienated unemployed and slum-dwellers in the city wilderness may organize themselves into street gangs, thereby acquiring an identity and goal structure within a rudimentary community which wages wars over territory with other gangs. (The powerless –

whether as individuals or groups – sometimes seek power through the barrel of a gun: therewith they become 'somebodies' rather than 'nobodies'.) Others may arbitrarily relieve their anger on casual victims from the street, while there are many cases of fathers, overwhelmed by pressures of an authoritative society upon them, revenging themselves on their children or pet animals – or they may seek ways of enduring pressures,* including indulging in vicarious violence. For institutionalized violence is also to be found in national spectacles of violence. Since long before the days of Ancient Rome, spectacles of cruelty and violence have been cornerstones of political and social life. Such spectacles in amphitheatres, theatres, bullrings and market squares, and now pre-eminently on television, entertain and excite the mass of *Homo degener*, and serve as vicarious outlets for their own frustrated feelings of violence. Yet others merely sink apathetically to the bottom of the heap.

There is another major effect of such pressures, particularly amongst those to whom aggressive competition is inappropriate or impossible, or those who do try to escape to prosperity but fail. Social competition abuses the life-saving stress response in such people, often transforming it into a life-threatening condition of drug addiction or disease. Consider, for instance, the adverse effects that those in authority can have on those beneath them under even the most advantageous conditions of a modern democratic State such as Britain – in factories, in schools, in society at large. People holding important positions in society, senior executives, factory managers, teachers, doctors, lawyers and others in positions of authority can so play with the self-respect of subordinates that they help create any one of a variety of stress disorders, from cardio-vascular disease or ulcers to feelings of insecurity, depression, alcoholism and drug dependency, or even retreat into schizophrenia,† while a minority of individuals with personality defects in the armed forces can inflict on their fellows depths of misery and pain far beyond that in other walks of life.

Given a parasite pyramid of ascent and control, there are always many suffering a greater degree of alienation and entrapment than those raised above them. The higher the latter climb on the backs of their fellows, the higher the pyramid, the greater the delusions of grandeur (and the

---

* As David Storey has said of the society in which he grew up: 'It was ignorant, vicious and ferocious, lived in by men who were not responsible for it but who sustained it by going on enduring it.'

† It will be appreciated that the retreat into schizophrenia, which is the retreat of the individual into his own world of fantasy, occurs in societies which are themselves already suffering from a collective primary schizophrenia.

greater their accompanying fears of conspiracy), the greater the pressures and feeling of oppression and powerlessness amongst those below, of sinking as it were beneath the rising waters, and so the greater the disturbed reactions, including a whole range of self-abusing behaviour and violence. They meet institutionalized violence with the violence of despair.*

This state of affairs is exacerbated when the nation consists of two or more nations divided by ethnic, linguistic and religious differences. Nations are in fact often made up of two or more nations (tribes), which, because of their bitter conflicts, may at any moment split up into their constituent parts, inviting tyranny to hold the fissiparous parts together. The state of Zimbabwe, for instance, is inhabited by at least two mutually hostile nations, Mashonaland in the North East, which was settled in antiquity by Shona speaking Mashonas, and Matabeleland, which was settled by the Ndebele, an offshoot of the Zulus who fled there from Chaka's armies. In Israel one nation has dominated another. In Northern Ireland, where the hostility between Catholics and Protestants has been passed off as a purely religious dispute, the hostility has also been between two different ethnic groups, the indigenous Irish on the one hand and the descendants of the 17th century Scottish and English settlers on the other. In all these cases and in many others two nations are imprisoned as one by the domination of one over the other. Such a situation of ethnic domination affects people's sense of personal worth, thus vitally affecting their behaviour. Under the circumstances, individual and communal group esteem are entirely dependent upon whether the communal group is dominant or suffers the humiliation of subjugation. Conflict between them makes communal group esteem of central importance.† Religion

---

* In 1977, at the height of a fuss about violent picketing, Sir Robert Mark, Commissioner of the Metropolitan Police, pointed out that 'violence has always been a natural aspect of society and, indeed, many social changes now regarded as wholly acceptable have been achieved by it.'[9]

This is also the case at the international level. Only after terrorists had bombed the World Trade Center in New York in September 2001 did the United States and Britain pledge themselves urgently to resolve some of the problems that may have given rise to terrorism, including problems besetting the Middle East, such as re-thinking the strategy towards Iraq and resolving the Arab-Israeli conflict by the establishment of a 'Palestinian state'. Violence on the part of the powerless can so concentrate the minds of the powerful as to achieve results.

† It is important to recall that the original communal group esteem of *Homo degener* peoples arose out of the protracted struggle against the wilderness, and that the domesticated majority within each stratified society suffered the humiliation of subjugation. Conflict amongst those so subjugated, as well as being fuelled by religion and race, is also fuelled by class differences. Those only one step above the poor are liable to hate them and fear them, fearing the humiliation of descent into the abyss of poverty, dispossession and despair. Religion and race often serve only to exacerbate what is fundamentally a class conflict.

helps heighten group esteem, accentuates the ethnic differences, and adds fuel to the conflict.

Religion, worship of a Farmer God, has been a principal instrument to the growth and survival of nations. It has been the Sun that nourished and caused the nation to grow in status and prosperity and has protected it as with a Sword and Shield of Light against those who have threatened the stability of the existing order. The relationship of the individual to religion and God is subordinate to the relationship of the nation to God. The point can be made by quoting some words of Sir Ieuan Maddock, Secretary of the British Association for the Advancement of Science, who said of the situation in Northern Ireland:

> It would be presumptuous to try and prescribe an instant formula for a subject which has baffled so many for so long. What baffles me particularly is that two allegedly Christian communities, believing in 'Love thy neighbour' and 'Turn the other cheek', should be furiously destroying each other.[10]

Baffling indeed, yet there is an answer. The Irish Roman Catholic minority and the Protestant majority are members of different tribes fanning the flames of one another's insecurities. They throw up leaders who, with the aid of religion, activate the incipient paranoia of their respective tribes. Their religions – that is, the Sun of each – emphasize the differences between them, enhancing the superiority and prestige of each the better to enable each to survive in the face of the conspiracy of the other to destroy it. Tribal or national differences are fundamental to the survival of a people, and to be able to appeal to a God in justification and defence of *any* act, however fiendish or foul, is the ultimate weapon in a nation's moral armoury. God and country make an unbeatable combination – they take first prize in terms of oppression and bloodshed.*

That then is the primary function of religion, to assist the nation to preserve the stability of the existing order, at the same time celebrating its separateness and superiority over all other nations, and of course over the kingdom of nature. Only after that primary function has been fulfilled does the secondary function, such as the individual 'loving his neighbour', come into play. As long as the primary function is fulfilled and the

---

*Nations also appeal to nature to suit their own social and economic purposes. Each major cultural revolution tends to give rise to a new concept of nature which serves to undergird the new order, making out that it accords with nature's grand design. Appeals to a 'natural order' – reinterpreted to suit the new cultural revolution – may accompany or replace appeals to a Farmer God to legitimize both the élite of the stratified society and its unjust and oppressive acts.

secondary function does not interfere with or undermine the primary function,* priests (and prophets) are usually free to pursue the individual neighbourly aspect. Regarding Northern Ireland, where the enemy was at the gate, the secondary function was nugatory in face of the urgent need to fulfil the primary function – particularly when the neighbour from the other nation was seen as a disciple of the Devil.

Linguistic differences also accentuate ethnic differences, and, when allied to different faiths, breed savage hatreds in many parts of the world. They can sever neighbour from neighbour and trigger murderous violence. An early symptom of any nationalist struggle is the re-establishment of the subordinate language, as in Wales, where Welsh is fiercely guarded against the English official language. Gaelic is now creeping into Scottish schools. In Belgium, Dutch-speaking Flemish and French-speaking Walloons once confronted one another across a language barrier so bristling with antagonism as to threaten the future of Belgium as a nation. A similar virulent confrontation between French-speaking and English-speaking Canadians resulted in French Canada seeking autonomy.

Whether the conflict is controlled, as when individuals compete for a range of alluring prizes set up by the State, or uncontrolled and violent, as is more often the case when different ethnic groups are involved, status, prestige, reputation and honour – that is, the attempt to attain or retain a place in the Sun of their society – are the motivating forces behind the struggle, the overt expressions of an underlying aggression and rivalry. It is most often when ethnic groups feel humiliated and oppressed, when their status, prestige, reputation and honour are at rock bottom and they are prevented from acquiring the wider society's range of glittering prizes – as has been the case with the Irish Roman Catholic

---

*In the case of Jesus of Nazareth, the primary function of religion was threatened. His appeal to the individual undermined the nation, and he was destroyed. He was eventually raised on high by his followers as the Christ, to become the King of Kings of pyramids of power. Ever since, his 'down to earth' appeal to the individual has been subverted to serve the nation 'from on high'; his words and deeds are made to serve both the primary and secondary functions of religion. Is it any wonder that Ieuan Maddock was baffled, and that confusion reigns throughout Christendom!

Religion (or ideology such as Communism) and Science are primarily servants of the ruling élites of the nation, energizing it to maximum growth (in status, prosperity and power) and security. They are primarily concerned with dominance over nature and over people; their search for knowledge is directed to that end. Only secondarily are they concerned with the individual. The prestigious sciences, those on top, are those which hold out the promise of the greatest profit, prestige, power and security to the nation. Both Religion and Science hold the collective to be paramount, and the individual of secondary importance. Both willingly sacrifice the interests of the individual to those of the nation. Both Religion and Science preach the human while often practising the (grossly) inhuman. This paradox will continue for as long as nations shall last, if only because the individual is but a conforming cell within a composite animal, while yet believing himself to be truly human.

minority in Northern Ireland – that conflict is liable to become uncontrolled and violent, when violence tends to be used to control violence.

In short, all these pressures and related acts of violence are the outcome of the ritualized conflict behaviour of people deranged as

Homo sapiens sapiens
Homo sapiens non sapiens

members of pyramids of power. The nation – whose origins lie in the alienation of deranged people from nature, the fission of the (potential) unity of all people as hunter-gatherers, and the apparent conspiracy on the part of nature to destroy them – tends automatically to propagate further conspiracy, alienation and fission. It is liable at any time to break up into conspiring groups, whereupon group loyalties become all too easily a basis for rivalry and strife. All these divisions and the tradition of mutual hostility within and between nations are in turn symptomatic of the wider rift between anti-evolutionary nations and an evolutionary kingdom of nature.

Civilization is always but a thin veneer covering the two-fold fall. That fall constitutes a dark basement room in the depths of all our beings. Subsequent agricultural-cum-industrial revolutions on the original re-evolution have merely deepened the dust of millennia covering what may be described as the rotten timbers that form the ground floor of civilization, which conceals the dark basement beneath. Civilization has also rightly been likened to a skin of ice that covers deep dark waters, or to a crust of lava that covers a volcano below. In terms of the individual, a corporate persona of cultivated refinement overlays and suppresses an earlier primitive corporate condition, which in turn overlays and suppresses the truly regal character of the highly developed individual as hunter-gatherer.* Widespread collapse of the timbers, increasingly large cracks in the ice, or greater eruptions out of the fiery depths are inevitable, as seen in such abominations of tyranny and annihilation in the Gulag Archipelago, two World Wars and Auschwitz. The continual collapse of structures and eruptions out of these depths – as in Lebanon in the 1970s and in the Balkans in the 1990s, where the contestants were in the grip of a sort of psychopathic disorder – lies at the heart of the extraordinarily irrational and inhuman behaviour of every generation of deranged people, as the past comes alive and takes its revenge.

Each nation is in effect a *protopathic composite animal*† – i.e., one that is suffering from a primary disease – whose members, all doubly deprived

---

* See Appendix xiii for an amplification of this argument.

† See Appendix xiii.

delinquents, are physically and psychically damaged and imperfect animals unable to live in the wilderness. Given their utterly non-human and inhuman conditions and parasite pyramidal relationships, it is hardly surprising that the members of nations should continually be in conflict with one another. For where one dominant group manipulates and controls the destinies of others, to whatever ends, there is liable to be a measure of conflict as people compete for a place in the Sun of their society, or struggle merely to survive.

As well as these mainly internal pressures on the inmates of nations, there is the behaviour of nations in the external environment as they seek to aggrandize themselves and their Suns under the real sun. This collective behaviour has two main components, a horizontal one and a vertical one: a horizontal expansion to ensure a vertical growth of nations. The horizontal expansion has been mainly one of robbery with violence; the subsequent vertical growth has been achieved by the parasitization or perverted predation of those peoples and lands subjugated by the conquerors, by 'the crowning of the Chief of the robbers' and by the placing of the mantle of a Divine approval upon the principal actors and their actions.

Cromwell, for instance, advertised the colonial policies of the Commonwealth as '...promoting the glory of God and enlarging the bounds of Christ's kingdom; which, we do not doubt, will appear to be the chief end of our late expedition to the West Indies.' Whether justification was sought in Genesis I or in the New Testament, the actual result of such expansion was to promote a large British interest in slave-trading and slave-plantations. They were driven by self-interest and greed, combined with contempt, whether they were Europeans or Africans. As Conor Cruise O'Brien has pointed out of the slave trade:

> ...Europeans, more successful than Africans, despised the latter comprehensively and bought, sold and exploited those available, usually without mercy. The more successful African peoples and polities likewise despised the less successful ones, attacked them and sold their prisoners, either directly or through African middlemen, to the Europeans.[11]

The immense disparity between rich and poor, between cultivated head and cultivating hands and feet, as found until recently in Jamaica,* is a legacy of such exploitation and a hallmark of civilization.

---

*At the beginning of 1977, there was a yawning gap between the 70 per cent poor and the 30 per cent whose living standards often surpassed those of Europe.

More recently Ulysses S. Grant, as a Lieutenant in the US Army, was caught up in the Mexican War of 1846–47. Mexico had the misfortune to stand in the path of US expansion in obedience to what it saw as its Manifest Destiny, and Grant has been quoted as saying: 'I do not think there was ever a more wicked war than that waged by the United States on Mexico. I thought so at the time, when I was a youngster, only I had not moral courage enough to resign.'[12] Following the war, Mexico lost Texas, New Mexico, Arizona and California to the USA, which thereafter came to believe in its right to exploit both the North and South American continents.

America was by no means alone in this drive to territorial expansion. Britain, France, Italy, Germany, Russia and Japan, in imitation of one another, were all announcing their country's Manifest Destiny. As Gilbert Murray observed in 1900, each country appeared to be declaring, 'We are the pick and flower of nations ... above all things qualified for governing others.' The overseas conquests of nations were, as Admiral Tirpitz said of Germany's expansion, 'as irresistible as a natural law'.

Like offensive-defensive displacement displays (sabre rattling) by nations that cause potential victims or enemies to imitate them, thereby instigating an arms race, the competitive drive to overseas expansion (whether commercial or territorial) in imitation of rivals in order to avoid being left behind in the self-righteous pursuit of status and power, is another example of the propagation of memes passing from collective brain to collective brain of composite animals.*

Civilization has also been spread abroad by the flight of the victims of persecution, dispossession and dearth, as in the case of the flight of Europeans to the USA; also by the transportation of convict-settlers to such countries as Australia. They habitually mythologize criminal acts such as the original thefts of no man's land, and subsequent thefts of someone weaker's land, as just and progressive and the acts of righteous men – an abiding hypocrisy that is itself evidence of individual and collective dementia. For instance, His Most Catholic Majesty, King Leopold II of the Belgians, described the acquisition and opening up of the dark Congo to the light of civilization – one of the most scandalous examples of colonial exploitation in history – as constituting 'a crusade worthy of this century of progress': fine words that masked his actual intentions. The Congo produced some 60,000 tonnes of rubber. But 10 million of

---

* See Part III, Chapter 2, for an exposition of the driving force behind such conquests, in terms of what is described as the historical imperative of reaction to humiliation, to the fear of being eclipsed.

its 20 million people perished in the process. Change only came about after Leopold had been unmasked by Roger Casement and E.D. Morel.

The judicial theft and exploitation of land, together with the enslavement or genocide (actual or attempted) of the indigenous peoples – as in Tasmania,† North America and more recently Brazil – is the cornerstone of each new pyramid of power, and the fundamental act and ground by and upon which are raised up the deeply ambivalent Temples and Judicatures of national self-deception and self-justification, one of the principal rôles of which has been to justify and legalize thefts by individual landowners, and by nations themselves. The following rhyme is still quoted in parts of Suffolk:

> They hang the man and flog the woman
> Who steals the goose from off the Common;
> But let the greater criminal loose
> Who steals the Common from the goose.

At a different level it was La Rochefoucauld who said:

> Some crimes get honour and renown by being committed with more pomp by a great number; and hence it is that public robberies, plunderings and sackings have been looked upon as noble achievements and the seizing whole countries is dignified with the glorious name of conquests.

And why not, when the myths of Creation, Declarations of Independence and Constitutions of States, in sanctifying their respective States in the present, sanction and sanctify the means and behaviour that led to their establishment? As the first security of tenure and indefeasible title-deed to land and control of land, and of people and animals on that land, the Creation myths of Egypt, of Sumeria and of Israel and their modern counterparts, the official histories and Constitutions of State, have performed a vital rôle in the perpetuation and proliferation of civilizations. They have placed the Divine seal of approval – the stamp of the Farmer God of Providence – upon what can be seen in retrospect as successive acts

---

*Between the years 1803 and 1876, Tasmanian Aborigines, with the support of the Tasmanian Government, were gunned down, poisoned, imprisoned or deported out of existence. The hunting down, deportation and extinction of the 4,000-odd Tasmanian Aborigines until the last death in 1876 is probably the most complete act of genocide the world has known. There remained, however, on the islands of the Bass Strait (between Australia and Tasmania) a mixed race community which established its Tasmanian Aborigine identity in the last quarter of the 20th century.

in a drama that moves from an accretion of many small acts of larceny by early settlers, through the theft and enclosure of great swaths of territory by robber Chiefs, to the later acts of grand larceny that would form the bases of such as the Babylonian, Egyptian, Roman, Arab, British, Belgian, American and Russian Empires.

Here let me emphasize that I am using the word 'theft' from the evolutionary standpoint of *Homo sapiens* and wild nature, which is the only objective standpoint from which to view the morality and behaviour of humankind down the ages and throughout the world. For it was upon the original theft of no man's land from the control of the natural flux and wild nature that settlements of primitive farmers were made possible at all. All subsequent anti-evolutionary settlements, morality and behaviour of *Homo degener* peoples are founded upon that initial theft and criminal destruction of no man's land. So one Canadian was right to observe of the constitutional conflict in Canada that threatened to tear it apart:

> For the aboriginal inhabitants of Canada, the constitutional conflict between the provinces is a 'quarrel among thieves'. Any new constitutional settlement will have to make reparation for the primal crime of white settlement.[13]

What, then, is the pathology of these composite animals, that has persuaded each of its manifest destiny to steal no man's land and someone weaker's land, and to sacrifice or enslave their populations? In the certainty of its own God-given or Ideological chosenness and superior right to steal territory, to enslave the inhabitants or put them to the sword, each nation has been a psychopathic thief and killer of people, and despoiler of the kingdom of nature, while pretending that its crime was no crime at all but the behaviour proper to the progress of humankind.

Generally speaking, a psychopath is a mentally deranged and morally irresponsible person with a tendency to outbursts of violent and anti-social behaviour. He feels he is different and does not belong. He is against the world. He shuts himself up in a world of his own, a dream world which is more important to him than reality. His own persona fills his horizon: everything is 'I', entirely self-centred and narcissistic. His concept of right and wrong is built up solely in relation to himself. He may appreciate the difference between right and wrong at a superficial level, but he is unable to internalize that difference. He suffers from a blunted conscience. He shows an apparent inability to learn, and an inordinate capacity for aggression, dishonesty, plausibility and persuasiveness. Emotionally, he is cold and callous; he treats his fellow human beings with indifference. If he is of a more aggressive type, he may have explosive outbursts of anger which can lead to seriously irresponsible anti-social behaviour.

In a recent case, for instance, a psychopathic man went to the house of a Roman Catholic priest, who had earlier befriended him, and killed him – while a classic example of psychopathic behaviour at the collective level is that of the early European settlers of North America. They survived their first winters on American soil only with the generous help of the Native American inhabitants. No sooner had they acquired a collective strength, however, than they turned upon their benefactors and hosts, robbed them of their land and killed them. Their success was unequivocally attributed to the workings of Divine Providence.

Every aspect of the behaviour of *Homo degener*, instanced in this chapter, and particularly as discovered in the self-interested and self-righteous behaviour of the nation as a composite animal, may be described as psychopathic. As in the case of the psychopath, the *Homo degener* nation has turned against the world, in its case the wilderness. Its own persona fills its horizon, an artificial dream world which has proved so much more important than the real wild world that little of the latter remains. The hunter-gatherers, on the other hand, were obsessed with the wilderness around them, and not at all with themselves. Their cave-paintings, for example, are almost entirely devoid of portraits of people. They had a truly objective, scientific and real understanding of the world. Nations, however, are obsessed with themselves, self-importantly exhibiting themselves in their every artefact and art. They are all caught up in a narcissistic distortion of reality, arising out of the experience of the wilderness as a frighteningly empty, unreal and dangerous world. Unable to see the external world objectively, nations, like psychopaths, have viewed it in terms of their own deranged imaginations. Hence, while one's own nation stands for everything that is noble and good, others are tarred with the same brush as the wilderness, and viewed as potentially evil.

Just as behaviour, which in the individual might be described as criminal and a threat to the stability of the State, has been regarded as honourable when committed with more pomp by a greater number, behaviour, which in the individual might be described as psychopathic, has been described, in the case of the nation, as glorious and necessary to the progress of civilization.* In fact, they are romanticizing a psychopathic killer. Behaviour

---

*Gibbon wrote that history was 'little more than the register of the crimes, follies and misfortunes of mankind'. History also 'appears to many artists as a surreal fiction, invented by idiots and madmen'.

that is psychopathic in the individual is likewise psychopathic in the mass.

Finally, in order to reveal more fully the pathology of the nation, it is necessary to examine the relationship between nations, each of which, in its origins, is a protopathic composite animal, each a psychopathic thief, killer of humankind and despoiler of the kingdom of nature; yet each of which is equally certain of its own rectitude and of the moral turpitude of the others, and that other nations are conspiring to destroy it.

For instance, like the wilderness to earlier colonists, Ireland has posed a constant threat to England over hundreds of years, activating a collective primary paranoia. Ireland, from the 16th century to the 19th, had a large population, some 8.5 million against 12 million in the rest of the United Kingdom. As a potential ally at one time of Spain, and then of France and the United States at a later date, Ireland posed a threat and a source of phobic fear to England. In addition, the English were in the main ignorant of conditions in Ireland. For three centuries England, in its ignorance and fear, regarded Ireland with a paranoid hatred, a reaction which had a profound effect on its attitude to the Great Hunger of the 1840s, when a million and a half people died. One political economist, Nassau Senior, was reported as saying that he feared the famine of 1848 in Ireland would not kill more than a million people, and that would scarcely be enough to do much good. The general attitude was 'let them starve', an attitude which foreshadowed the horrors of 20th century genocide.

Ignorance and fear of the wild world, the growth of composite animals and a consequent collective primary paranoia, has led inexorably to collective ignorance and fear of other composite animals growing up in that world. Because each nation in relation to the others is to a greater or lesser extent ignorant and fearful of the others, even measures of defence are often seen as measures of offence: the ever-present and persistent ambiguity of measures of defence to preserve peace and a balance of power that are yet felt as intimidating and offensive. As one nation, impelled by delusions of grandeur and fears of conspiracy,* grows in power, it can appear as an intimidating threat to others; like

---

* If the megalith builders were guilty of the folly of grandeur (or grandiosity), so are we today with our grandiose energy projects, nuclear arsenals and exploration of space. National prestige – delusions of grandeur – and military requirements, arising from fears of conspiracy on the part of the unknown and frightening other, provided the most important motivation for the US and Soviet space programmes. Each, in imitation of the other, was reaching for the 'high ground' the better to control the world environment to its own ends.

the stars in the presence of the noonday sun, their Suns are threatened with eclipse.

For instance, from quite early in the 20th century the rulers of Germany looked with apprehension at the rising might of Russia. As the German Chancellor, Bethmann-Hollweg, said on 8 July 1914: 'The future belongs to Russia; she grows and grows, and weighs on us like a nightmare.' The experts of the German general staff reported that by 1917 the Russian army would be greater than the German. This would upset the Balance of Power and enable Russia to dominate Eastern Europe. Viewed from this aspect the Great War of 1914 was, on the German side, a preventive war. Yet there is another aspect. For at the same time as she feared Russia, Germany entertained delusions of grandeur of her own. It has been generally accepted that there was a German conspiracy to precipitate war in Europe, with the aim of economic hegemony in Western and Central Europe and the acquisition of territory in the East. The murder of the Austrian Archduke Franz Ferdinand was merely an excuse to wage war to that end. Hitler's aims and foreign policy essentially continued those of the Imperial Government.

So the Sun that shines warmly and brightly upon those at the summit of one parasite pyramid may appear cold and threateningly dark to those at the summits of others. That is to say, what is God and order to one nation can appear as chaos-dragon, devil and disorder to another. For example, following the Second World War, the ideological nature of what became known as the 'Cold War' between Communist Russia and the West caused international affairs to be presented

> . . . as a Manichean struggle; in Eisenhower's words, 'Forces of good and evil are massed and armed and opposed as rarely before in history. Freedom is pitted against slavery, lightness against dark'.[14]

Later, President Reagan of the USA would talk of the Soviet Union as an 'evil empire' and of the USA as a 'shining city set on a hill'. The increased intensity of the Light and heat generated by a nation's offensive-defensive activities, viewed through the world-fearing 'windows' of the others, appears as an increase in intensity in the Darkness and cold void surrounding it, threatening to upset the balance of power, extinguish their Suns and overwhelm them. This differential lighting and heating gives rise to fears of conspiracy on their part, causing what may be described as a pendulum of paranoia to swing between nations that are themselves possessed of a primary paranoia, which may be followed, as so often in the past, by a pre-emptive strike or by mobilization and war (see figure 3.1).

Part II: fig 3.1

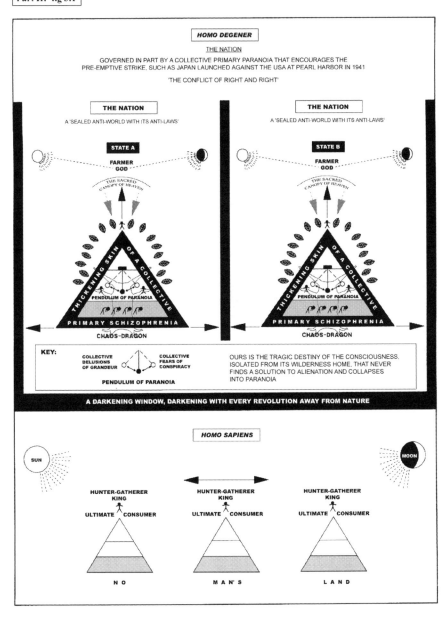

The balance of power, like the stability of the Stable State, is an illusion. It is always an imbalance of power, an imbalance between separate Powers whose efforts to maintain a balance in the hierarchy of power between nations tends to be negated by optimistic opportunism on the part of one or more nations, causing the pendulums of paranoia to swing violently, to be followed by an almost inevitable explosion. Carlyle described the 18th century European wars as 'A Balance-of-Power delirium not to be comprehended by any man'. Such a delirium may also be described as a ritualized conflict behaviour between right and right. As the world contracts to the size of a global village, and the clamour of the conflicting claims of right and right grows louder, a world-wide explosion seems ever more likely. And this is also because the primary communal derangement revealed in this chapter is also the fundamental cause of much of the secondary physical and mental illness to which stratified societies are notoriously prone – including schizophrenia and paranoia. The fate of millions can depend upon the secondary derangement or dementia of a single individual. In the event of a nation being taken over and led by a megalomaniac or psychopath, the fate of millions – even the fate of the whole world – could depend upon the whim of that one demented person. Such is the extraordinary pass to which a re-evolution into nations has brought us.

Behaviour based on the denial and destruction of the real evolutionary world of *Homo sapiens* and wilderness is distorted, psychotic, mad. Melanie Klein's observations are relevant.

> The assumption in Klein's work is that we all have psychotic dimensions to our personality, and these will vary in strength from person to person, place to place and time to time. I am talking about 'psychosis' in the sense of an 'everyday psychosis', a way of perceiving the world that leaves us out of touch with aspects of external and internal reality, but not in a way that makes everyday life impossible; indeed, it might make everyday life more manageable.[15]*

With every agricultural-industrial revolution and expansion of territory on the original re-evolution away from reality towards the skies, the refracting lens of a collective primary schizophrenia has grown thicker; the pendulum swings from the consequent heightened delusions of grandeur to deepened fears of conspiracy between nations – and cycles of violence or build-ups towards aggression within nations – have grown more violent

---

* See Appendix ix.

and widespread, reinforcing their psychopathic behaviour as protopathic composite animals committed to a competitive struggle across the world, resulting in '... wholesale slaughter on a scale unheard of in any other species'.[16]

The nation is a composite animal at war within itself and at war with the world without. In its appearance and behaviour it resembles, to a marked degree, an autistic person.

Chapter 4

The Empty Fortress

...our greatest pretences are built up not to hide the evil and the ugly in us, but our emptiness – the hardest thing to hide is something that is not there. (Eric Hoffer)

The strongest guard is placed at the gateway to nothing... Maybe because the condition of emptiness is too shameful to be divulged. (F. Scott Fitzgerald)

The nation, as I have shown, is like a giant human being comprising failed people who, no longer able to live as self-reliant hunter-gatherers within the wilderness, were reduced to an emptiness within and faced with a nothingness without. It is a protopathic composite human being whose behaviour, particularly in relation to the wilderness, may be shown to resemble that of an autistic person in relation to modern society.* This is not to say that the attributes of *Homo degener* composite animals that I have already revealed are to be found in autistic people, but rather that the analogy of the autistic person can reveal further aspects of the individual and collective behaviour of *Homo degener* that could probably not be revealed in any other way. I am viewing the development of the composite animal primarily from the standpoint of *Homo sapiens* and the wilderness.

Autistic children are those who show extreme aloneness from the beginning of life, apparently rejecting their parents and being unresponsive to their proffered affection.

The common denominator in all these patients is a disability to relate themselves in the ordinary way to people and situations from

---

* Autism now affects approximately 1 in 100 children in Britain.

the beginning of life... The case histories indicate invariably the presence from the start of extreme autistic aloneness which, wherever possible, shuts out anything that comes to the child from the outside.[1]

Many autistic people describe themselves as feeling as though they come from another planet, aliens marooned in the modern world. Though sensory information reaches them, it does so only in a fragmented, meaningless and unpredictable fashion, and is therefore often frightening. They suffer from acute, excessive anxiety, investing often ordinary phenomena with terrifying characteristics. Unable to make sense of the world, they reject reality and are obsessed with small repetitive activities, exhibiting an anxiously obsessive wish for the preservation of sameness, and strive in the event of change to restore sameness. They feel the world is about to disintegrate, and they have to impose their own order on the world. Some autistic people collect and classify objects the better to impose their own order and make sense of the world around them. Others make calendars relating to natural events and phenomena; they find a haven in the impersonal world of numbers, which gives them a sense of control. (Calendrical obsession may be accompanied by millennial obsession.) Still others develop a creative interest in other worlds, portraying cathedral-like structures rising towards the stars; they exhibit great interest in the star constellations and space, insisting that the night sky be painted absolutely correctly in its dark vacuum. They are morbidly self-absorbed and out of touch with reality. They give vent to great anger if their fragile defences are broached by an unwanted person or question. Against this background of seemingly severe retardation there are a few with normal or even exceptional intellectual function or skill.

All these characteristics of autistic people have been, and are, principal characteristics of early and modern *Homo degener* societies in their relationships with the wilderness and universe, and with one another. In its origins, appearance and behaviour, the rudimentary nation can be shown to resemble the autistic child.* It too originated in isolation and

---

*That is, some autistic children. For the range of behavioural characteristics associated with autism is as great as that associated with nations. Autistic children are often extremely bright – about half of all autistic people do talk – but are trapped inside bodies that they cannot always control. Similarly the members of nations have been trapped inside their greater bodies whose stability has often been subject to violent religio-socio-economic upheavals beyond their control. 10 per cent of autistic people are said to be gifted savants: similarly, nations produce geniuses. But the one is still autistic and the other is still a protopathic composite animal whose members are divorced from their true evolutionary potential. Deprived of the true outlet – that of the hunter-gatherer – and true ground – the wilderness – of their evolutionary potential, both autistic child and members of nations are empty vessels. All strive to fill that emptiness without success, for all their artefacts [*Continued over*]

extreme aloneness, shutting out anything coming from the (wild) outer world: it rejected its spiritual parents (the Great Spirit and Earthmother) and was totally unresponsive to their proffered affection. Aliens marooned in the wilderness, it was as though they too had come from another planet. (This might also serve as a description of the first European settlers in North America.) Because the five senses of the members of *Homo degener* communities were disintegrated from their evolutionary integration within the wilderness, sensory information reached them only in a fragmented, meaningless and unpredictable fashion, and was therefore often frightening. They suffered acute, excessive anxiety, investing phenomena such as the forests and gorilla with terrifying characteristics. Unable to make sense of that world, the rudimentary nation also rejected reality and became obsessed with small repetitive activities, exhibiting an anxiously obsessive wish for the preservation of sameness. The rudimentary nation became morbidly self-absorbed, obsessed with calendrical calculations based on observations of the stars, giving rise to repetitive ritual activities in order to control the threatening world without. Just as the autistic child is unable to live in, or communicate with, the civilized social world around it, the rudimentary nation comprised failed men no longer able to live in, or communicate with, the wilderness. Failure to communicate leads to misunderstanding and conflict, and ultimately to violence and war. Faced with mirror-images of themselves, both autistic child and rudimentary nation have been liable to react violently to the threatening presence of the other – a mindless, emotionless behaviour. Both tend to present a beautiful face to the world that conceals the void within. Like the autistic child, the nation is an animal inherently at war within itself and at war with the world without.

The cause of autism is still uncertain. It apparently arises from a form of cerebral dysfunction: genetic factors may also be involved. As I argued in Part I, stratified societies (rudimentary composite animals) of primitive farmers arose under circumstances of severe dietary deficiency (or nutritional stress), with probable deleterious effects on their brains, which were already affected by the loss of environmental sensitivity and degeneration of their sensory apparatus. As their composite animals grew their collective

---

[*Continued from previous page*] and activities merely serve to distance them ever further from their true evolutionary path.   Autism has been described as a kind of survival mechanism designed to protect hypersensitive people from the world, just as the composite animal has protected its profoundly vulnerable members from contact with the wilderness. Some autistic children exhibit modes of perception beyond what our debased five senses can provide: they may be able, at birth, to recapture aspects of the earlier hunter-gatherer insights and abilities, including telepathy. For all aspects of hunter-gatherer life are interconnecting components of a vast spiritual network which a supersensitive child could tune into.

brains developed a world view based on the two-fold dualism of sacred society/hostile wilderness and sacred ruling élite/potentially hostile masses. It has been the predominantly left hemisphere – the patriarchal hunter/killer left hemisphere – of the brains of the ruling classes which has governed the actions of the growing composite animals throughout the last two millennia, with little input from the right hemisphere. Instead of the two hemispheres of the collective being opposite and complementary – which they usually are only when a nation is threatened from without – they are almost invariably opposite and antithetic. In England, for example, there are Left and Right wing political parties which, particularly at their extremes, may be said to represent the right and left hemispheres of the collective brain respectively. On every major issue, both at home and abroad, these two main governing parties tend to be diametrically opposed.

Throughout their existence nations have been plagued with disharmony and a marked imbalance of power at every level: power struggles within – both within and between religious sects, political parties, companies and so on – as well as power struggles between nations. Each, like the autistic child, has been obsessed with possession and control as if against 'a Titan waiting terribly to break forth',[2] striving to preserve or restore sameness in the face of threatening change. Like the autistic child, the nation has been alone in the sense that it has been governed by an inner secret world protected by Official Secrets Acts etc. into which it has dared not let outsiders intrude. (Japan even went so far as to exclude all foreigners from its shores from early in the 17th century until the end of the 19th.) It has held its personal world together precariously, feeling itself manipulated by insensitive overwhelming powers. Imagine, for instance, how members of the Mayan, Aztec and Toltec civilizations must have felt with the knowledge that tomorrow might bring the end of the world. Unlike the hunter-gatherers, who evolved and thrived precisely because of their mutable adaptive behaviour in obedience to the flux of natural forces, autistic child and nation have stood in dread of a breakdown of an insecure inner world: each has been easily distressed by any change in the balance of power within the environment. For the autistic child, inanimate objects and repetitive ceremonial are much safer than are people, because they do not behave unpredictably, make no demands and can be manipulated without difficulty. In the same way, uncertainty, unpredictability and unlimited horizons of wilderness and night sky have been delimited and demarcated on charts and maps by rudimentary nations. Each established a core of certainty – for instance, changeless Farmer God, Temple and altar on possessed agricultural land – around which it cohered. (In the face of subsequent threats to that established core of sameness and certainty, people have tended to turn to any leader, however crazy, who has offered a return to absolute certainty.) In obedience to that core of changeless certainty and orderly continuity of the nation, people and the environment were graded, classified and made as predictable and as safe as possible. This was achieved with the aid of the census and classification of the people, land measurement, observation and measurement of the heavens, the raising up of buildings through whose windows the outer world was safely framed and contained – just as today it is so safely framed and contained on the television screen – the classification of wildlife, and so on. Such obsessive delimitation, demarcation, classification and contraction of horizons, while making the world more predictable and less perplexing for *Homo degener*, had the effect of imposing upon deranged people a static, hierarchical world view (mimicking their own social hierarchies), an imprisoning stereotype that tended to affect all their dealings with the outside world. For this compulsion on the part of *Homo degener* systematically to arrange all animals and inanimate objects in hierarchies extended to the definition of boundaries of one's social group and the placement of outsiders – foreigners and other races – lower down on the human scale. Furthermore, when they went forth in the service of their nation as traders and explorers, they carried with them, as it were, the stratified structure of their homeland as a self-protective stereotype – exhibiting, like an autistic child, a sustained resistance to change in the environment and a striving to maintain sameness – assuming a universal model of the world based upon their own station within a social pyramid and the supposed superiority of their stratified structure over all others. Early accounts of travellers and explorers in Africa, Asia and the Americas describe kings and chiefs who more often than not did not exist; European colonial officials were often similarly intent on finding political leaders amongst aboriginal peoples. The misconception has arisen partly through the need of finding someone with authority to speak for his people and to make deals, and partly because Europeans have believed that their own form of hierarchical political organization, comprising dominant/subordinate offices and rôles, is universal.

Similar stereotypes appear in art, as in the depiction of the Australian wilderness by the first colonial artists.

The comparison of the harbor landscape with an English park is one of the more common, if startling, descriptive resources of First Fleet diarists. Partly it came from their habit of resorting to familiar European stereotypes to deal with the unfamiliar appearance of things

Australian; thus it took at least two decades for colonial watercolorists to get the gum trees right, so that they did not look like English oaks or elms.[3]

Such stereotyping formed an essential part of what I have described as the collective memetic inheritance of each composite animal, imposing an imprisoning self-protective view of the outside world. Such stereotyped behaviour both within each composite animal and in relation to the outside world was further achieved by a mushrooming of mutually exclusive languages, together with the growth of specialist mythopoeic and mathematical languages of domination and control.

It has been argued* that before the catastrophe of the Mesolithic, the languages of all peoples were founded in an understanding of the secret language of nature – the human mind was in great part created by the hunter-gatherer's use of language in relation to an ecological understanding of nature. Language developed as a means of co-operative communication and survival in the wilderness. The diversity of language was based on the diversity of climate, landscape, animals and plants experienced by each hunter-gatherer band. With the loss of their stability and *raison d'être* as hunter-gatherers, *Homo degener* peoples lost the ability to speak, to interpret and to understand the secret language of nature. In effect, they awoke in a world which they could no longer interpret nor understand: they had lost their evolved way of perceiving the world. Like autistic children in relation to modern society, they were caught up in a seeming conspiracy of non-meaning, in a world become frighteningly alien and obscure. With their adaptation to a primitive agriculture, these voided men began to develop related languages that gave meaning, albeit an illusory meaning, to an otherwise frightening and incomprehensible world. Like autistic children, they began to develop and to use language for the purpose of manipulating the environment to their own ends. A prototype Indo-European language now began to grow up and spread outwards from S.W. Asia.

The languages of literate and articulate élites of nations found their most profound expression in their myths and mathematical formulations that guaranteed and justified their dominion and superiority over the masses beneath them and over the kingdom of nature – and justified too their sense of moral superiority in relation to other nations.

A noteworthy relationship between language and the stratified societies that were growing up was the imposition of socio-economic order by

---

* See Appendix viii.

means of daily, weekly, monthly and yearly recitations of myths and the associated enactment of rituals and religious festivals relating to human, animal and plant fertility, death, rebirth, etc. These memeplexes were achieved with the aid of astronomical observations by priest-scientists.

Meanwhile, the languages of the illiterate and inarticulate masses – that knew neither the literature and languages of the highly specialized élites, nor the secret language of nature – remained impoverished and debased. The masses were literally imprisoned by the memes transmitted down to them by the priestly-scientific élites of their societies. Beyond their obeisance and obedience to those memes, all was meaningless in a meaningless land.

Language changed from being a principal means of communication and expression of a natural self-consciousness to the co-operative survival in equality of all humans as hunter-gatherers, to being a principal means to the exploitative power of dominant élites over subservient masses of each stratified society, and over wild nature. Language also became a principal means to the competitive expansion and growth of nations in the Northern Hemisphere, as they bulldozed the languages of weaker peoples out of existence. The growth of the Word has been central to the growth of pyramids of power.

As composite animals have grown, head over hands and feet, their languages have reflected that growth and division of labour. The languages of *Homo degener* peoples and the ideas and information they convey, whether written or by word of mouth, tend to be socially divisive. They are no longer expressive of a coherence of all people as kings of natural food pyramids, but of increasing specialization and division within and as between stratified societies. Whether in the vertical between dominant employer and subservient worker, or in the horizontal as between nations, a wall of blankness, infantile gesture or sheer silence often cuts us off, like autistic children, from our fellow men, just as it did our ancestors from their evolutionary language, fellows and past. We are either encapsulated in a cultural envelope of language that offers an exclusive identity of superiority and security against the void within and without, or adrift in that void.

This situation has been further complicated and exacerbated by the development, by the head and brain of the nation, of technical languages peculiar to each division of function within that brain, and as different again from those of every other nation. For instance, a few millennia after they had been forced to abandon their wild, wandering life as hunter-gatherers, the peoples of the Middle East were beginning to express the new intellectual concept of their relationship with nature in the form of neologisms – the Creation myths. They used secret symbols and hieroglyphs, as in Ancient Egypt, that were intentionally incomprehensible to all but the experts concerned in their efforts to maintain intact their fixed value systems and stability in hierarchy against change. Ever since, the specialized languages of the experts of nations have been, like the language of autistic people, secret group monologues, mainly incomprehensible to the outside world, and forming an invisible barrier against the unknown. These experts have taken, and take, an excessive interest in word forms and neologisms, permutations and combinations of verbal mythopoeic and mathematical language only intended to serve a particular intellectual élite in its search for prestigious control over things and people manipulated as things, and largely incomprehensible to those not working in their specialized fields. Computing, for instance, is a closed world, with a jargon all of its own, shrouded in the mysteries of inputs and print-outs; it is a world that is having more and more effect at every level on every aspect of society. Science, too, is a closed world, guarded by its arcane language – mathematics, 'the language of science' – and impenetrable literature against intrusions by the lay public. Even within Science, molecular biologists, physiologists and psychologists, for instance, have marked difficulties of communication, partly because they have to use different concepts: scientific books and papers are so arcane that scientists can understand only those of their own speciality. Equally arcane are the language and techniques of Religion and Law. British Law, it has been said, is 'lawyer's law', highly technical and designed for experts in a specialized and remote language. All specialists are laymen in the specialities of others. Each language, like the hieroglyphs of the theatrical priest-scientists of Ancient Egypt, like the linguistic and ritual flummery of Freemasonry, like the jargon of the theatre today, is a semi-secret language designed to mystify, to keep insiders for ever separate from, and superior to, outsiders. It further removes people from an already remote reality.

Most important of all, the highly specialized languages of élites within any one nation, and the common tongues of nations themselves, have combined to suppress and destroy the real languages of co-operation through an understanding of the secret language of nature, that speaks of an infinite wealth and variety of natural food pyramids and enchanting Earth to be experienced and explored. In naming the wilderness as empty, as the home of the chaos-dragon, and nature as a realm to be conquered and tamed, nations have been persuaded to spread over the face of the Earth, destroying the infinite wealth of natural food pyramids and their kings. In so doing, they have stamped on the true linguistic inheritance common to all as hunter-gatherers and have substituted competitive élitist, socially divisive and fractured forms of verbal and written non-communication; fractured too from other art forms of interpretive communication such as painting, sculpture, drama, music, song and dance, which, in being separated from their true ecological setting and unity within nature, are also divorced from each other and perverted to the gratification and amusement of élites.

As *Homo sapiens*, the people, their arts and their technology were one in a relative perfection of their world-loving adaptations within nature, speaking to and serving all equally in, as it were, a brotherhood of kings. Art amongst hunter-gatherers was a system of communication operating throughout the entire group; art in *Homo degener* societies has tended to be something that is enjoyed by a minority, using it as a means of private pleasure to fill the emotional void in their lives. (Leo Tolstoy reputedly rejected the plays of Shakespeare, Beethoven's symphonies and his own novels, because they spoke only to an élite.) Furthermore, art, in its presentation, is most often experienced in architectural buildings – in churches, art galleries, libraries, museums, concert halls and country houses – whose construction, as I argued in Part I, has depended upon the subjugation of nature to the requirements of the ruling classes. Whether as cathedrals or great music, architecture and art co-exist as viral memeplexes. Wittingly or unwittingly, they celebrate *Homo degener*'s war against wild nature – like the often extraordinary creations of autistic people, they are *fleurs du mal.* This accords with Samuel Beckett's view that art is merely colluding in what he considered to be our tragic destiny: he saw life as having no real meaning, and the tragedy lay in living, and representing in art, a meaningless life. It is indeed only the hunter-gatherer culture that is truly meaningful, that conveys the spirit of peace and unity of peoples through its art and technology.

Altogether there has existed within nations a staggering sum total of incomprehension and source of misunderstanding, forcing people to rely on stereotypes – particularly that of the wilderness as an alien void – prejudices and slogans in their dealings with their fellows, with other nations and with the kingdom of nature, in order to minimize anxiety and uncertainty and to maximize stability and control against invasion by the unknown. Pathological utterances such as 'imperialist aggressors', 'communist thugs', 'fascist hyenas', 'red barbarians' and 'running dogs' have been regularly exchanged between the accredited representatives of nations possessed of opposed paranoid faiths – responses as gross, vague, irrational and incoherent as those of autistic people. Such stereotyped, prejudiced and slogan-filled language of non-communication, like that of the autistic person, 'stamps on language, pulverising it to gibberish or maniacal silence'.[4]

Each nation has been a prison of ignorance and fear, first in relation to the threatening wilderness, then in relation to threatening nations. Each has been fundamentally blind and ignorant as to what has been going on beyond its borders. In the absence of knowledge, a vast syndrome of distortion and propaganda, which is both deceitful and self-righteous, emanates from nations all over the world, revealing, in the proper sense of the word *autism*, a 'morbidly abnormal admiration of themselves'. Like the autistic child, a travesty, they are travesties of human beings, living as they do encapsulated in artificial worlds within and without which all is blurred and obscured, where ambiguous communications are used to conceal the fact that it is not person to person communication that is intended at all, but distance and control for the sake of the self-interested prosperity, power and security of national élites.

Finally, both the autistic child and nation, as if to counter an inner life of fear and panic, present an exterior that is often exceptionally orderly and beautiful. The nation achieves this by myth and ceremonial, and by the use of rose-tinted spectacles worn by the official chroniclers and historians when they recall great people, heroic deeds, Golden Ages and great art of the past.

Their histories, that speak of great individuals and of national greatness, are myths of deception and self-deception. They deny the reality of people ordered and imprisoned within parasite pyramids of power. Lord Acton was nearer the mark when he said: 'Power tends to corrupt and absolute power corrupts absolutely. Great men are almost always bad men.'

Golden Ages and heroic deeds are equally suspect. Philip Toynbee has pointed out that Chaucer's 'verray parfit gentil knyght', was atually one of those English mercenaries who were such a curse to Europe, the Middle East and North Africa during the 14th century. A close examination of Chaucer's 'Prologue' shows the kind words used by the poet about his knight are either ironical or had a very different meaning from that which they have now. His knight is revealed as quite the opposite of a paragon of chivalry and virtue, in a period that was the very opposite of golden.

It is fashionable to look back with nostalgia to so-called 'golden ages' which, on closer inspection, invariably reveal the perennial vices of greed and cruelty, together with the arrogance of the privileged and brutalized suffering of the oppressed. In fact, there have been no golden ages amongst farming communities organized as pyramids of power or composite animals. But there has been an unrecognized and unsung golden age of humankind as hunter-gatherer evolving within a paradisial land – that is, if the happiness and joy so obviously experienced and expressed by such peoples as the Native American, San and pygmy hunters are anything to go by. On the evidence, it was a time when all people were self-reliant socio-economic equals; a time which the myths of a Paradise or Golden Age, now lost, distort and conceal. Ever since, rose-tinted spectacles have been used to make the ignoble appear noble, the unacceptable acceptable, the illegitimate legitimate and respectable, the inhuman human, the guilty innocent. Like the beautiful exteriors of Leonardo da Vinci and Robert Oppenheimer, Father of the Bomb (and the beauty and perfection of their respective mythopoeic artistic and mathematical fabrications) that masked the void and torment within each man and the devastating end products of their visions; like the beautiful features of El Glaoui that masked his cruel vendetta against his opponents in the Atlas Mountains, a beauty, so we are told, strikingly similar to that of a Christian Saint who has cruelly repressed his emotions; each nation has tended to present a deceptively self-righteous persona and image of itself that masks the inhumanity and void within. 'How many of us,' writes Michael Delahaye, 'at the mention of the "Sun King", picture Louis (XIV) enthroned in all his glory amid the splendours of Versailles? How many of us remember – know even – that the same man bankrupted his country, sanctioned the persecution of the Huguenot Protestants, was finally trounced by the Duke of Marlborough, and – in the opinion of many historians – personally paved the way for the horrors of the French Revolution by his uniquely egocentric style of monarchy?'[5] In Britain, many mansions were built in ports like Bristol on the profits of the slave trade (1660–1810). The gracious facades of the mansions, and the titles their owners purchased from the King with their profits, concealed their brutal origins – slaves in the Caribbean survived on average for eight years. In America, too, rose-tinted spectacles are used to make the inhuman human, the guilty innocent – like the ambivalent Father-figure of Thomas Jefferson,* whose ambience is used to mask the Hamiltonian activities of the American rich, and whose declaration that 'all men are created equal' meant white men only, and *men* only; or like the Statue of Liberty that stands at the gateway to the All-American Dream (as exemplified in Hollywood motion pictures), that masks the plight of the many for whom the dream remains a nightmare.

---

* Thomas Jefferson and James Madison were prime movers in the shaping of the American Constitution (at the Constitutional Convention at Philadelphia in 1787) who, while speaking of the inalienable rights of liberty, were themselves slave-owners.

The image, the illusion, masks the appalling plight of many of the members of nations forced to the bottom of the heap: the poor whites and blacks of the Southern States of North America, for example, whose greatest tragedy is that they become indifferent and innured to tragedy that is a constant factor in their lives, and against which they build up defence mechanisms else they would not be able to stand life as it actually is. Most important of all, the illusion masks too the destruction of the very real freedom and dream of aboriginal peoples such as the Native American hunter-gatherers.

> The United States has never been innocent since the time it began cruelly to persecute those who had remained loyal to the Crown. It has indulged in a classical imperialism that compares morally with our own. And it did less physical good in the process. It has indulged in the social perversion of slavery and its aftermath. It has worshipped great wealth as we worshipped hereditary or royal honour. It has had its own hereditary aristocracy and cities run by oligarchies composed of the rich or the élite or by those men ruthless enough to take up power as if it were fruit for pleasure and enrichment and selective distribution. In all this the United States hardly differs, in anything but scale, from the nation of which it is a majestic offspring.[6]*

The United States had not in fact been innocent from the day the first white men stepped ashore and began cruelly to persecute the Native American hunter-gatherers, who had remained loyal to the Great Spirit. Americans may be said to suffer from a permanent identity crisis. They profess freedom while all around are the sad relics of those whom they robbed of their freedom and their land – the Native Americans. Under the circumstances, is it any wonder that their conquerors should suffer a permanent identity crisis, for they only succeeded in conquering their true hunter-gatherer selves. The first farmers were the first to conquer their true selves and to re-invent the self, by the will of and in the image of their Farmer God, in their myths of Creation. Americans today believe in the ability to re-invent the self by act of will; genetic engineering will make such re-invention practicable, in an image created by Science. Nevertheless, there remains a widespread feeling that at the centre of one's being there is a nihilistic void – the heart of darkness in all deranged human nature.

---

*Democracy has been rightly described by the actor Jack Shepherd as being 'like a nice dress on top of a ruthless regime'.[7]

The illusion of people being fully human within stratified structures – an illusion which in reality surrounds an awful emptiness both in the person and in the stratified society as a whole – is maintained by a number of artifices.

> I think here of a supporting structure, a scaffolding as it might be around a building, propping up something that would otherwise fall down. The scaffolding is, let us say, a structure of distinctions, of office, decorations, honorary degrees, membership of learned societies, and the like. There are systems of scaffolding so complete that it's now virtually impossible to distinguish what's inside. It's no longer even possible to say whether there is anything inside at all. It's like the Emperor's new clothes, but in reverse. The clothes are there all right, bright with jewels, ribbons and stars, but where is the Emperor? The higher you go, the fewer – or the less. There's always room at the top – perhaps there's nothing else. Can it be that the whole business is managed by non-people operating in a structure of non-events?[8]

The nation is an empty fortress, its members emptied of their original humanity and understanding, protected physically by external walls or frontiers and armed men, and psychically by armour-plated ideologies and memeplexes – the fortress mentality. The nation is a damaged composite animal whose outward show of advanced development, orderliness and greatness is but a mask, behind which there is not only a 'skull and crossbones whining to get out' (to use a phrase that Neal Ascherson applied to the Swedish nation), but a behaviour in relation to the wilderness like that of 'a brutish infant'.

The nation portrayed as a pathological giant human being is only one of several models which may be used to reveal the regressive anti-evolutionary condition of *Homo degener*.

Chapter 5

Ecological Analogies of the Nation

I have tried to show how and why the magnificent complexity and self-reliance of the hunter-gatherer gave way to the corrupting interdependence of subhumans cohering in a rudimentary nation, a composite animal which bears many of the characteristics of a psychotic giant human being. There are, however, other models that may be used to explore more fully different aspects of the origin, evolution and behaviour of composite animals, particularly in relation to the wild environment. They include the rain forest and the termitary. These analogies are important because altogether they help reveal more about the various aspects of the individual and collective behaviour of *Homo degener* – especially by comparison with the truly human behaviour of *Homo sapiens* – than can be revealed by any one analogy alone. They reveal striking similarities because the nation sustains biological and physical processes that are a perversion of their natural counterparts.

Each city and town is an ecological representative of the nation as a whole. Each is a network of biological relationships tied to, while perverting, the laws of the physical world. Physical aspects that act upon and influence each other, just as they do in the wild, include air chemistry, a water system, flow of energy and a mixture of species, including *Homo degener* peoples. Each is an artificial ecosystem whose sum total makes up the artificial ecosystem of the nation, itself both resembling, and in competition with, natural ecosystems such as those discussed below. In addition, scientists and engineers are pursuing a policy of improving the efficiency of their artificial ecosystems by deliberately imitating certain characteristics of these natural ecosystems. They include the use of artificial photosynthesis to harness sunlight to produce limitless quantities of energy-rich fuels such as hydrogen, and the design of buildings whose ventilation systems mimic those of termitaries. In general, the behaviour of the inhabitants of our artificial ecosystems tends to imitate that of the

319

inhabitants of the ecosystems discussed below rather than that of *Homo sapiens*.

First, the structure of a nation may be shown to resemble that of a rain forest. There are three great rain forest areas of the world – African, Asian and American. As pointed out by Archie Carr,

> The most striking feature of the rain forest as an ecological structure is its vertical stratification.[1]

The green canopy at the top of the forest is exposed to the full sunlight – it may be described as the powerhouse of the forest, the layer where nearly all the photosynthesis occurs. Because the top canopy shuts out direct light from the ground, a layered structure develops, depending mainly on the amount of sunlight that each layer filters through to the next. All the layers are interconnected, both by the constant movement of animals from layer to layer, and by the movement of water and chemicals within the trees themselves. The enormous growth of the trees is engendered primarily by an abundance of sunlight and an abundance of water. The combination makes for a laborious reaching upward of trees towards the light. Each tree grows in a silent and slow, though fierce, competition with the others, its shape determined by the space available, and its leaves twisting on their stems to find a place in the sun, falling to the ground in the event of failure. The top canopy thereby created far above the forest floor is responsible for much of the greenhouse-like stability of the climate of the rain forest, within which a fine balance is struck between the processes of competition and co-operation.

The rain-forest animals live mainly in the trees or beneath the ground; the forest floor is only sparsely inhabited. In order to harvest the best of the forest products animals such as monkeys and rodents must either climb towards, or traverse, the higher levels of the forest. The top floor, as it were, of the building is where the most spectacular action takes place. However, an animal able to leap and grasp branches and twigs can travel indefinitely through the forest at whatever level, and establish a home range and territory for itself just as does an antelope on the ground. An animal that lives in the tree tops may never cross the path of a different species that lives on the forest floor. On or below the ground are to be found insects and bacteria which convert fallen organic material – dead leaves, twigs and animal detritus – back into living tissue.

In contrast to the savannah where the eye is drawn to scan the horizon, in the rain forest the eye is drawn upwards, towards the light and the sun, mirroring the reorientation of human behaviour in stratified structures, and the consequent striking resemblance between these and the rain forest. For thousands of years, throughout the world, stratified societies have likewise grown up from the ground, with the aid of an abundance of Sunlight from their Farmer Gods and an abundance of manpower and water power – a ponderous ascent towards the Light of their Farmer Gods.

Compare the main characteristics of the nation with those of the rain forest. Pre-Christian tribes in western and northern Europe, for instance, with the aid of chiefs and shamans, sought well-being and security through the medium of trees. Their god, Odin, with the help of other gods, breathed life into two trees and thereby created the first mortals. Thereafter the cult of Odin, and of other gods and goddesses, spread and caused the tree, and the worlds above it, to become sacred. Such trees and associated ceremonies, rituals and sacrifices were manifestations of the sacred: they formed ladders to other worlds. They were the first trees of shamanic knowledge as magical power of healing and over future events.* Over the generations, and in the shadow of their sacred trees of knowledge, farming settlers took possession of the ground, planted their families thereon, took root and grew family trees. As colonies of family trees expanded, smaller trees gave rise to larger, and eventually the forest-like stratified society came into being. Like the forest, its most striking characteristic is its vertical stratification. It may be described as a forest of cultural and social trees, a forest dominated by trees of religio-scientific, social and economic knowledge and their innumerable branches – business trees, with branches spreading out all over the country, and great family trees, beneath which grow the more diminutive family trees.† An example of a cultural tree, and its variety of branches, is that sheltering the pictorial arts. The development of pictorial art may be seen in terms of the development and growth of its particular tree of knowledge.

The first great abstract painters like Kandinsky and Mondrian did not believe that abstraction would supersede figurative art, but that the two would continue together, complementing each other. Kandinsky wrote that abstract art was not 'the abnegation of all earlier art' but a 'vitally important division of an old trunk into two main branches

---

* I argued in Part I Chapter 4 that the temple and church replaced the tree as the take-off point to other worlds in space in pursuance of humankind's highest aspirations. Science and spacecraft have now provided *Homo degener* with the vehicles with which to realize those aspirations, enabling their trees of knowledge to reach up into the cosmos.

† Winston Churchill has been described as a 'great tree' towering above all the others in the political forest.

from which other branches grow that are essential for the formation of the green crown'.[2]

It is indeed the sum total of such green crowns, representing every aspect of cultural and economic activity within the nation, that make up the top canopy of the nation. The evergreen top canopy comprises the Crowned Head or President, the Government and landowning and priestly and scientific élites – organized in Universities, the Civil Service, the Church, the Law etc. – which form a tightly set mosaic that is exposed to the full Light of its super-dominant Sun. As in the forest, the most spectacular action takes place on 'the top floor of the building'. The top canopy is the mental power-plant and umbrella of power of the nation. It is the layer in which almost all the photosynthesis, as it were, takes place. As a huge super-plant the nation manufactures its own food through the agency of the Light of the super-dominant Sun and top canopy of priestly and scientific dominants. It manufactures food and materials for the bodies, minds and imaginations of its members in agricultural, industrial and academic plants.

With the aid of its ideological Sun, the top canopy of the nation perverts the light of the true sun and life-forces of its members to irradiate and grow the nation in the vertical. Like the tree canopy, the Crowned Head and élites shut out the direct Light of the Sun of religio-socio-economic consequence from the ground, and the lower one descends the social tree the darker and more satanic the environs. This makes possible the development of a layered structure as in the forest, based primarily on the amount of Sunlight – on the wealth of knowledge, possessions, status and power – each level filters through and permits to the next. *Homo sapiens sapiens* members of nations – whether individually, or organized in institutions – are like trees reaching up towards the sun, grappling over lower regions where *Homo sapiens non sapiens* primary producers are buried in factories and underground in mines, amongst whom there will be some trying to grow like trees towards the Sun of their society. With most of them, however, as with the leaves of a tree, there comes a point at which, deprived of the Light of their Sun, they resign themselves to accepting some less advantageous place, or simply give up and fall into the darkness below.

As in the forest, the top canopy of the nation is responsible for much of the greenhouse-like tranquillity of the climate within, allowing relatively long-term adjustments to evolve without setbacks from violent internal eruptions or external invasion, whether by natural or human agency. Like the evolution of animal life in the greenhouse atmosphere of the forest, where the animals live mainly in the trees or beneath the ground, the members of forest-like nations have evolved as *Homo sapiens sapiens* in the trees of knowledge and great family trees, and as *Homo sapiens non sapiens* on the ground and beneath the ground, growing more and more adept at surviving and reproducing their kind by increasingly specialized and refined adjustments to one another (see figure 5.1).

Metaphor has been much concerned with trees: trees of life (the two-dimensional tree is used as a metaphor for natural phenomena in general, and biological evolution in particular*), trees and branches of knowledge, family and ancestral trees† and position on social trees. *Homo degener* peoples occupy and work in forest-like cities of houses, churches, cathedrals, skyscrapers and high-rise office blocks, where they attempt to add cubits to their statures, seeking superior identities and security in spiritual and financial rewards and status above their fellows. The growing and climbing of imaginary trees has in fact been a principal means of escape from primitiveness, captivity and dearth to a heightened identity and greater freedom and security, just as the climbing of actual trees is a means, through diversification, to the survival of monkeys.

If the nation thus resembles a rain forest, and if its overall cultural pattern resembles that of trees growing tall or short, straight or stunted, the day to day behaviour of its members also resembles that of animals within the rain forest, particularly that of monkeys climbing within the vertical structure. For in order to harvest the highly partial Providence of the stratified society one must climb as the monkey climbs, or fly as the bird flies. For example, the higher up the office building an executive resides, the more senior and important he usually is, and the more often he takes to the air on foreign business or travel. Like monkeys moving transversely at different levels through the leaf canopy of the rain forest, people move in the horizontal at different levels within the social pyramid – those at the top may never, or scarcely ever, meet those at the bottom. Those at the higher levels often behave like monkeys in their ritual defence of territories, whether the territory be that of a landowner, the field or branch of knowledge of a scholar, or a territory of governmental,

---

*Biologists are beginning to map what is described as the Tree of Life, revealing how all living creatures are related to one another. This 'will help researchers conserve species, restore ecosystems and control invading species. Medical researchers can use evolutionary data to trace the origin and spread of diseases, and to develop new medicines'. (*New Scientist*, Vol. 176, No. 2368, 9 November 2002, p. 7).

† In this connection, the evolutionary history of various languages is described in terms of the construction of family trees of languages that are comparable with the genetic family trees based on differences in DNA.

Part II: fig 5.1

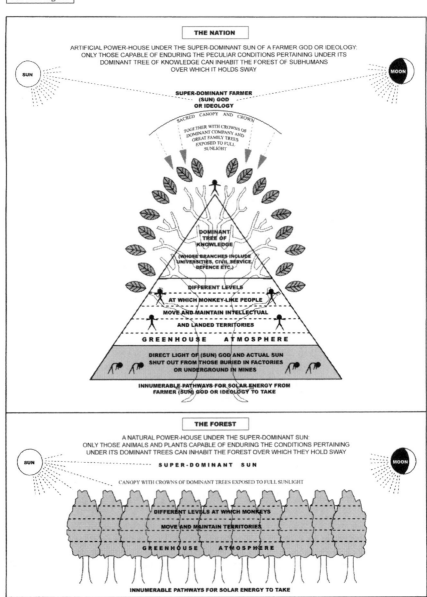

professional or managerial control, guarding that territory in one or more of many ways: with high walls, examination and initiation procedures, apprenticeship barriers to the professions (particularly with respect to the arcane nature of their language), Official Secrets Acts, ritual signs ('trespassers will be prosecuted') and sounds.

> Troops of howler monkeys have a way of standing each on their own side of the territorial boundary and howling at each other in fierce and deafening concert: departmental managers and craft union officials often behave in a very similar way.[3]

So do intellectual and scientific protagonists of branches of knowledge – established to retain territories over which they have control – in their papers and periodicals. For instance,

> All studies of the human record since we parted company with the chimpanzees must inevitably be based on the flimsiest of foundations. It is not surprising that the views of experts are so diverse or that the quarrels can be so virulent... A quarrel of palaeontologists and palaeoanthropologists might be the appropriate collective noun.[4]

In their ignorance and fear of the world beyond the bounds of their own specialized fields, that epitomizes the ignorance of any one nation of the others and of the kingdom of nature, they have jealously guarded the boundaries of their territories of knowledge against the external world, just as the nation has jealously guarded its own territorial bounds, guarding the boundaries of the known against the threat of the unknown. Nations have seen the outside world, the world of nature and of other people, as a continual threat to be mastered. Their members began to indulge in forms of artificial jungle behaviour – including climbing and cutting down company trees, laying waste the real jungle and jungle warfare.

In the Philippines, for example, following the Second World War, Muslims became a minority in the south, outnumbered four to one by Christians. Lush Muslim lands and rich fishing grounds were 'gobbled up' by Manila-based businesses and Christian migrants from impoverished northern regions. Muslim family trees, as it were, became engaged in a desperate struggle to retain some of the Sunlight of prosperity and power of their forest-like society against Christian threats to cut them down and uproot them. Armed Muslim rebels – in particular the Moro National Liberation Front – took to the hills, whence they conducted offensives against government forces. It is significant that a general, following a pre-emptive strike against the Muslim rebels, used the analogy of a plant to describe the strategic situation. He said that whereas before the roots had been many and shallow, and the foliage abundant, now some of the roots had been cut and there were fewer leaves, but that the remaining roots had grown deeper.

Such behaviour has been entirely at variance with the behaviour of *Homo sapiens*. It was as though their earlier adaptations out of the forests into the wider world, and their evolution as hunter-gatherers, had never occurred. Yet it was just because the ancestors of man came down from the trees and moved vulnerably and unpossessively through the unknown wilderness that he became *Homo sapiens* at all. *Homo degener* has indeed sunk below the normal high standard of behaviour of *Homo sapiens*. Just as the ape became the prisoner of the forest, *Homo degener* peoples have become the prisoners of forest-like nations. Their artificial jungle existence was, and is now – in the jungles of Brooklyn and Harlem, of London, of Tokyo and of Rome – a parody of the true forest existence of their earlier monkey-like ancestors, and a perversion of the behaviour of true human beings.

Whether regarded as animals residing and moving at different levels within a forest or as greater and lesser trees within the forest, the survival of the top canopy of great trees is assured in the event of the threat of invasion, or when the country is planning for war. The contingency war plan of one of Britain's Regional Health Authorities brings into direct focus the nation as a super-plant, in which great dominant trees are selected to survive.

> In its way a nation is like a forest and the aim of war-planning is to secure survival of the great trees... If all the great trees and much of the brushwood are felled, a forest may not regenerate for centuries. If a sufficient number of the great trees is left, however, if felling is to some extent selective and controlled, recovery is swift... There will remain brushwood enough, if 30 million survivors may be so described. The planning policy is clearly élitist.[5]

As well as resembling a rain forest in its structure, the nation itself may also be shown to resemble a giant tree within an international forest of giant trees, each competing for a place in the sun as it struggles for wealth and power; a few giant trees become the Great Powers forming the top canopy of the international forest of trees. Around them has grown a forest of interconnecting international religio-socio-economic organizations and associations.

... In recent years, for example, the Commonwealth Secretariat has achieved formal observer status at the UN and at a number of other international organisations and meetings – thereby more formally enmeshing the Commonwealth within the growing forest of contemporary international institutions and associations.[6]

The rain forest is a product of natural selection, of slow evolution; each part of it raises the life expectancy of every other part. It is probably its efficiency in use of energy – requiring, as it does, 'less energy, per pound of live stuff, to support its organization than any other kind of terrestrial environment'[7] – that has made for the success of its design. Some rain forests have had a stable history over many millennia.

Homo sapiens was likewise the product of natural selection, of slow evolution; whose increased efficiency in the use of energy from the sun within and beyond the confines of the forest increased the success of the non-specialized human design. Quite simply, our hominid ancestors, in ranging freely under the sun, both within and beyond the confines of the forest, had innumerable pathways open to them, leading to an infinite variety of natural food pyramids and experience. As they became more diverse, giving rise to a great variety of specialized and non-specialized forms, the latter gained efficiency in their use of energy, maximizing their life-expectancy and quality of life in the long-term, to give rise to *Homo sapiens*, the least specialized and most adaptable of their kind. They had a stable history of over fifty thousand years.

The nation, on the other hand, is the product of sudden re-evolution, when every one of the innumerable pathways in the horizontal was closed to primitive farming peoples. In opening up new pathways in the vertical, and as it grew more mature, the nation gave rise to dominant *Homo sapiens sapiens* consumer experts at the top and *Homo sapiens non sapiens* producers at the bottom, losing efficiency in its profligate use of energy – just consider the untold millions of people consumed in the growth of their stratified structures, and in the prosecution of wars to extend and protect those structures – requiring more and more human and material energy and resources to support its organization to ascent and environmental control than any other terrestrial environment. Nations have a history of great instability in their internal and external relationships.

Unlike plants, plant-like people are ill-suited to their rôle as dominants.

It is significant that in non-anthropocentric systems of any size the dominants are almost always plants – the 'A' stratum trees in the rain-forest, the algae in the reef, the grasses of the savannah. Plants, because they are without conscious purpose, are well-suited to be dominants: their *mere existence* fills the rôle, and the conditions which they set for other species tend to be stable. Men, on the other hand, must *act and act continuously* to maintain their dominance, and the action of men is less to be relied upon than the stolid existence of oak trees or algae. Men, unlike oak trees and algae, are also capable of making mistakes, and since the self-interested purposes of men may not coincide with the requirements of the systems they dominate, the conditions set by men tend towards instability.[8]*

Just as the dominants in a rain forest are the 'A' stratum trees, the dominants of forest-like nations are the plant-like Alpha, socio-economic grade 'A' or 'A' stratum people at the tops of trees of knowledge, great family trees, and so on. Their self-interested purposes, their continuous action to maintain their dominance as plant-like people cultivated at the top canopies of their societies, their consequent instability and serious disruption of the environment: all these are the direct outcome of their re-evolutionary selection and development as members of separate Sacred Species ascending to the skies. The nation is in fact so structured as to raise the life expectancy and quality of life of *Homo sapiens sapiens* at the top of the stratified society at the cost of *Homo sapiens non sapiens* at the bottom – that is, unless the nation parasitizes another to create an empire, thereby raising the quality of life of the whole at the cost of the other – and at the cost of the flora and fauna of the kingdom of nature.†

Nations are now aiming to make their industrial plants more forest-like, and therefore less wasteful and more efficient, by adopting a philosophy known as industrial ecology. In industries, materials move in a linear manner from factory to consumer, and thence go to waste. In a forest ecosystem, materials flow cyclically from the plant producers to animal consumers, to be recycled by decomposers such as microbes and termites. The aim of industrial ecology is to mimic the forest ecosystem by creating a network of symbiotic factories which behave like organisms adapted by natural selection to exploit the different niches in the forest ecosystem. They will recycle resources and feed off one another's by-products, thereby eliminating waste and pollution. However, their greater efficiency, through

---

* See Appendix xiv for a diagrammatic representation of the cumulative effects of anthropocentric nations on the environment.

† I shall explore in depth the devastating effects of these dominants in Chapters 6 and 7.

imitation of the forest ecosystem, which emphasizes the similarities between them, will make them increasingly the subject of convergent evolution and competition.*

In effect, the law of co-operation of the true jungle of natural food pyramids has been replaced by a law of competition governing the man-made jungle of pyramids of power. Within nations people, like trees in a forest, compete for a place in the Sun of their society; nations themselves, like giant trees in an international forest of trees, compete both with each other and with the true forests for a place in the real sun.

In the second analogy I will show that if individual behaviour resembles that of monkeys, and the corporate structure and behaviour of the nation that of the rain forest itself, they also resemble the behaviour and structure of the termite and the termitary respectively.

Termites and termitaries predominate throughout much of Africa, particularly in the rain forest where, because they carry leaves and other food materials underground, termites accelerate their conversion into food. Termites are the most prevalent of the forest insects, their colonies are amongst the most highly organized and efficient, and their inhabitants the most specialized. Their colonies start below ground and grow upwards, usually up the side of a tree, both in order to ensure good ventilation for their increasing numbers, which may be many millions, and to escape periodic floods. Buried deep inside the termitary, in total darkness, are the queen and her consort, the former being the sole reproductive organ of the community. Her millions of progeny supply and tend the fungus gardens that feed the young and help maintain the internal moisture and even temperature of the termitary. They build an elaborate air-conditioning system of chimneys that discharge warm humid air at the top of the termitary and draw in cool air from lower down; if the air drawn in is too warm, it is cooled with the aid of water carried up from a well sunk into the water-table. Air conditioning keeps the termitary within 1° of 31°C, with ambient temperatures between 3°C and 43°C. The hidden queen and colony of termites, their phrenetic activity and their regulated temperature and stable climate are protected and preserved, as in a fortress, by an outer skin. In the event of a breach of the hard wall and the entry of light, strong-jawed soldiers assemble to repel the attacker and defend the nest, while smaller workers rush to mend the breach. The queen meanwhile receives a detailed chemical report from passing termites on the state of the termitary, and reacts accordingly. If, for instance, a number of soldiers have been killed protecting the termitary, she will

---

*I shall amplify this argument in Chapter 9.

give birth to an all-soldier clutch of eggs to redress the balance in the colony.

It is, perhaps, difficult to imagine animals more poorly adapted to life on Earth than the slow, soft-skinned, blind and weak termites that are so vulnerable to sunlight or changes in temperature. Yet, by enclosing themselves in a hard-shelled fortress they survive floods, droughts and predators. Such was, I believe, the equally hard to imagine condition of some hunter-gatherers, reduced, as it were, to blindness and powerlessness by the loss of their ecological understanding and hunter-gathering skills. Like termites, they survived by enclosing themselves in hard-shelled fortresses whose walls helped maintain the religio-socio-economic culture and stable climate within against a hostile world without. They tunnelled and mined resources and sank wells for water; and extended their walls or frontiers outwards to enclose and exploit more and more of the surrounding wilderness to sustain the composite animal growing like a termitary (see figure 5.2).

Eugene Marais[9] has likened the termitary to the organism of an animal, and particularly to the human body, the queen functioning as the brain and central nervous system, the fungus gardens as the digestive organs, the workers and soldiers resembling red and white blood corpuscles, and the sexual flight of swarms of princes and princesses analogous to the escape of spermatozoa and ova. But the termitary also resembles to a startling degree the organism of the nation as a composite animal.

> A termitary operates on a caste system, a strict division of labour among builders, soldiers, foragers, cleaners and nurses. There may be several million individuals in one colony, but there is no thought process or reasoning among them: each works or fights instinctively, according to the genetic information programmed into it.
>
> The remarkable order and efficiency resulting from this fact has led to the popular conception of the termite colony as a 'being' in itself – a sort of 'super organism', in which the individual termites are analogous to cells and the duties of the castes to physical functions: the foragers are the bloodstream carrying nutrients through the organism; the cleaners are its excretory organs; the soldiers, its claws and fangs; the king and queen, its sex organs. It is a compelling metaphor because it *describes* a termite colony so well...[10]

Like the termitary, the nation is a 'super organism' whose Farmer God or Ideology, Head of State and Government function like the queen. For just as all termites are the children of their queen, working according to

Part II: fig 5.2

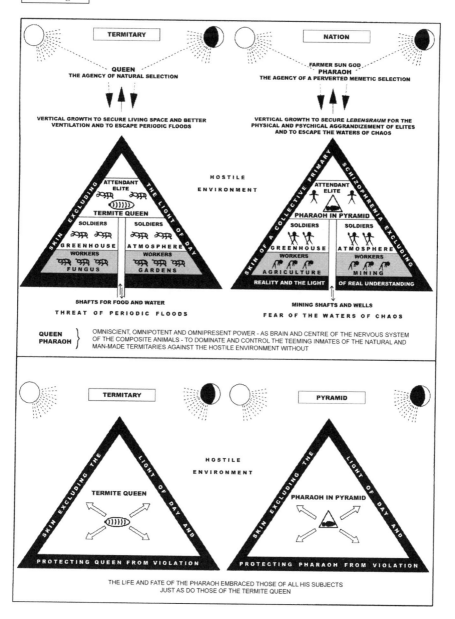

the genetic information programmed into them, members of nations have been treated as children of their Farmer God, and manipulated through the collective memetic inheritance of each. The identification of the nation with a termitary has been most apparent in regimented societies such as those of the Incas, Ancient Egypt, China and Japan. In Egypt, the Pharaoh, ostensibly circling the Heavens in the Chariot of the Sun, installed within a city and immured within a Pyramid as the apotheosis of the pyramid of power, was, like the queen termite, the Omniscient, Omnipotent and Omnipresent Controller of all the people and the lands of Egypt. He was the super-dominant Sun, heart and nerve-centre of the human termitary, whose attendant priest-scientists kept the people on the 'straight and narrow' by persuading them that the Pharaoh saw, knew and controlled everything at all times and everywhere, even in a life hereafter.

The Ashanti of West Africa have believed that their queen-mother was the source of life.[11] She has been compared with the queen termite, the source of all life within a termitary. Just as all termites are the children of their queen, so too members of the Ashanti community have regarded themselves as children of one mother. And just as each termite instinctively functions in obedience to the genetic information programmed into it, each member of the Ashanti community has been duty-bound to function in accordance with the dictates of the queen-mother. As well as ruling the state, she has been the supreme war leader.

Many Japanese still see themselves linked to each other by blood, all having come from the belly of the Sun Goddess, Amaterasu Omikami, while the Emperor is seen as the centre of this eternal cycle of life. However, whether or not such beliefs and behaviour overtly persist today is less important than the fact that it is through such beliefs and termite-like behaviour down the millennia that nations have spread throughout the world and achieved their present shapes and conditions as superorganisms. German citizens, for instance, from 1933 were taught blind obedience. In Germany few questioned the Fascist ideology. Japan has been noted for the blind obedience and conformity of its people under their Emperor. Within its rigid hierarchical system individual desires have been subordinated to the good of the collective, the nation. Both Nazi Germany and Japan exemplify nations whose members were programmed to the collective memetic inheritance of the superorganism.

The nation is a composite animal characterized not only by a division of labour which makes the whole greater than the sum of its individual parts, like a termitary, but also by a degree of termitary-like specialization that is utterly unlike the non-specialization of the hunter-gatherers. The nation's industrial workers, cultivators and agents of distribution, policing and protection function like the worker and soldier termites. The farms and irrigation systems that have fed the children of nations down the millennia, and helped maintain a balanced religio-socio-economic climate, have functioned like the fungus gardens of a termitary. The despatch of small groups of colonizers, in the name of their Farmer God and King, are analogous to the sexual flight of prince and princess termites. Their subsequent resettlement in the wild environment has led to the creation of a new composite animal whose essential characteristics and existential requirements imitated those of their homeland.

The flight of the Pilgrim Fathers to the North American continent is a good example of this ritualized conflict behaviour. Unable to survive real wilderness conditions and weather unaided and alone, it is ironical that they did survive their first winter on American soil only through the timely intervention and aid of local Native Americans. They regarded the Plymouth colonists as helpless children. Little did they know that they were helping the bearers of the collective memetic inheritance of a new composite animal whose actively destructive behaviour would ruin them utterly. Evidence of a collective memetic inheritance overriding their individual genetic inheritance and learning (as hunter-gatherers) lies in their prior belief that the wilderness was empty and its Native American inhabitants 'savage and brutish men'; in the carrying with them of implements of agriculture and the Holy Bible, instruments of their dominion over nature and over the natures of humankind; in the covenant they drew up binding them into a civil body politic under a God and King; and in the attribution of their safe deliverance to the Divine intervention of their God of Providence. These European colonists – rendered as blind and defenceless as termites by the original loss of their ecological understanding and hunter-gatherer skills – were indeed like helpless children – that is, until they, like termites, had built their hard-shelled forts, and begun to spread abroad like successive generations of prince and princess termites, establishing a string of forts across the continent. Only when the whole continent of North America had been purged of the Native American 'menace' within, and had itself become a hard-shelled fortress against a hostile and threatening world without, could the inhabitants safely leave their earlier forts behind and begin to consolidate their greater fortress, the United States of America.*

---

*This is an excellent example of the fortress mentality which has governed the activities of nations, primarily in relation to the wilderness. In England, the power of the early Barons was likewise established over the countryside with the aid of castles.

The existence of the termitary appears to depend mainly on five things: the living presence of the queen, the constant supply of food and water to feed the fungus gardens which nourish the progeny of the queen, the exclusive possession and exploitation of the ground on which the termitary stands, a system of air-conditioning that keeps the superorganism at an approximate temperature of 31°C, and the preservation of the outer skin against invasion and the entry of light and lowering of the regulated temperature. Similarly, the existence of the nation depends mainly on the living presence of a Farmer God and/or Founding Father and Head of State of the community, the constant supply of materials, food and water to house and to nourish the population, the exclusive possession and exploitation of the land upon which the nation stands, the maintenance of a stable religio-socio-economic climate, and the preservation of the outer skin or frontier against invasion.*

As regards work on behalf of society, *Homo sapiens non sapiens* workers have generally suffered a dehumanizing regimentation for thousands of years all over the world. It is only now, with the birth of automation and robots – or mechanical serfs – that workers in the richer nations are being relieved of some of the more onerous tasks demanded by society – often only to be thrown out of work altogether. Scientists are now trying to develop robots that mimic termites and ants. Each ant lays a pheromone trail which others use and reinforce. Similarly, one robot with expensive sensing equipment could be used to mark a trail which would be followed by cheaper slave robots.

The maintenance of a stable religio-socio-economic climate is perhaps the most contentious aspect of the nation. As in a termitary – whose members, as children of a single queen, may be described as one race that so differs chemically from members of other termitaries as to make intermingling unlikely – there has always been a tendency within nations for the majority race either to exclude from mainstream society, to expel or even, as in the case of Nazi Germany, to eliminate unwanted minorities, in order to establish and maintain a stable racial and ideological climate acceptable to that majority. Post-1945 independence movements, for instance, have increasingly defined themselves by the race of the majority, while expelling minorities. The Lebanese were forced out of Egypt, many Palestinians out of Israel, and the *pieds noirs* out of Algeria; ethnic riots in Caucasia and 'ethnic cleansing' in the Balkans aimed likewise at the expulsion of minorities. The Iraqis attempted to eliminate and to expel

---

*These five characteristics resemble those I described in Part I, Chapter 5, as the fivefold concentration of power of the stratified society.

the Kurds from their territory. What is known as nationalism is essentially the racial purification of the human termitary, thereby establishing a stable religio-socio-economic climate acceptable to the majority. The Japanese, on the other hand, were isolated for two centuries and have been committed to racial homogeneity, seldom marrying with other ethnic groups. They have avoided conflicts arising from the importation of large numbers of guest workers, which European nations are now finding so embarrassing, by their use of automation and robots. Japan already possesses some three-quarters of the world's robots and more automated workplaces than anywhere else.

As well as an overall racial, ideological and general climate stabilization within nations, there are temperature control mechanisms governing the actual temperature of the members' workplaces and homes. Amongst Western nations in the Northern Hemisphere, some 40 per cent of energy is used for industrial purposes: 60 per cent is used to create and to maintain the warm, well-lit environment to which Western people have grown accustomed, and for refrigeration and air-conditioning against the environment becoming too warm. Like termites, *Homo degener* prefers to work in a controlled climate. But because air conditioning is expensive and uses a lot of energy, architects are designing office blocks that stay cool using termite-inspired ventilation systems. At the same time, scientists and engineers are thinking about buildings that can sense internal and external conditions in a way analogous to termitaries. They predict that the city of the future will be one whose anatomy – its buildings, bridges, roads and other urban structures – will be able to feel, with the aid of optical fibres that act as 'glass nerves', the pain of material injury and structural deterioration and warn its human users through a neural network of computers. Altogether, such temperature control mechanisms, structural controls and an overall climate stabilization will make for a physical and psychical setting peculiar to each nation, constituting its protected internal environment and greenhouse atmosphere. It will be recalled that *Homo sapiens* communities hunted and gathered in the external environment to whose changes in temperature and climate they were both physically and psychically adapted.

Such artificial internal environments of nations will, however, not only increasingly resemble one another, but will do so precisely because of their growing resemblance to termitaries, a process of convergent evolution that is tending to merge the nations into one termitary-like superorganism.*
Already the termitary-like appearance of many cities is enhanced by their

---

*In this connection, see Part III, Chapter 3, and Fig. 3.1.

use of underground rail systems to transport their workers; soon it is hoped to link the whole of Europe by a similar network of high-speed underground trains. At the level of the transfer of information, the termitary-like 'nervous systems' of the separate European nations are being merged in the single 'nervous system' of a super composite animal, Europe.

The identification of the nation with a termitary is also most apparent in times of external threat and war, when a nation's military command centre may be compared with the royal cell. Hitler, for instance, in his Berlin Bunker lived in a cell far from the light of day, while above him was a large upper bunker, inhabited by secretaries, leading Nazis and a considerable armed force. Above that again were the Old and New Chancelleries, both in constant use. Here then were housed the super-dominant head, heart and nerve centre of Germany. From here – if only in imagination – Hitler directed military operations against the invading Allies.

Saddam Hussein and the Iraqi high command had a command centre built 200 feet underground, allowing them to direct military operations from there and to survive underground for up to six months. Other nations – including Libya, Syria, Iran and North Korea – have likewise been building deep bunkers to shelter their political and military leaders, together with their key installations.

Compare these with the queen termite in her cell surrounded by her attendants – the super-dominant head, heart and nerve centre of the termitary. Pierce the outer skin or frontier protecting the vertical structure and greenhouse atmosphere within, and a host of soldiers and workers appear to defend and mend the breach in the defences. In most *Homo degener* societies men have been trained from an early age to play out, like soldier termites, their sanctified rôle as killers-to-order – a vicarious type of aggression deriving from identification with the society and its system of beliefs. It is when this identification is total and at its most extreme – as seen in the 20th century in the absolute obedience and ferocity of the Japanese Army, whose lives belonged to the Emperor – that the behaviour of *Homo degener* most closely resembles that of termites.

The beginning of the 21st century has witnessed a marked extension of this termite-like behaviour. Following the world-wide threat of terrorism, secret underground cities built in Britain during the Second World War, and nuclear bunkers built during the subsequent Cold War,[12] may be brought back into service to house key personnel and material from a variety of political, military, financial and cultural institutions. In other words, external threats – nuclear, chemical and biological – may force more and more people to seek safer living and working conditions underground.

Such resemblances as have been described above are neither superficial nor coincidental. They are the direct result of a perverted memetic selection by agents of stratified societies growing up in isolation around agriculture in a hostile environment, causing them to regress to forms of behaviour similar to those found in rain forests and termitaries. I shall explore these relationships in greater depth in the following chapters.

Chapter 6

Victims of a Perverted Memetic Selection

All humanity seeks power, and to have power you must have victims. (Wole Soyinka)*

In through the gates, out through the chimneys. (A devastating comment on the Holocaust)

Just as a wood or forest may be regarded as a huge super-animal in which all the parts are alive and respond dynamically to each other, the nation may be regarded either as a super-animal (for example, a giant human being) or as a huge super-plant. It even manufactures its own food – by photosynthesis, as it were, through the agency of the Light of its super-dominant Sun and top canopy of dominants – in agricultural, industrial and academic plants, manufacturing food for the deranged body, mind and imagination. The nation forms a perverted biome and biotic community (see figure 6.1).

It is by studying in greater detail the nation in its resemblance to a great forest that we can appreciate not only the inter-relationship of members of nations but also those of nations and nature. Because of the need for each of these unnatural biomes and biotic communities to survive and prosper in a world that is essentially hostile to them, each tries to grow increasingly wealthy and powerful, which in turn makes it ever more destructive of the natural environment. For, as artificial forests, they overrun not only other artificial forests of people but also the true forests. It is for this most important of reasons – the inexorable destruction

---

* This aphorism is true of *Homo degener*, but not of *Homo sapiens*. The extraordinary lengths to which *Homo degener* will go to gain power are a measure both of his loss of humanity and the depths of his inhumanity. The aphorism neatly encapsulates the essence of the parasite pyramid of power. (Wole Soyinka is the pen-name of Akinwande Oluwole Soyinka, Nigerian dramatist, poet and novelist.)

Part II: fig 6.1

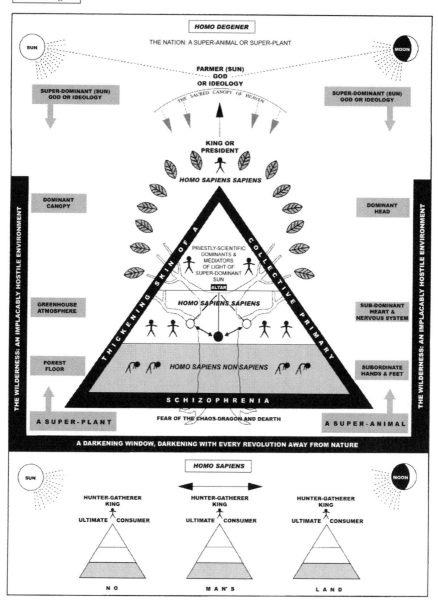

of the natural environment by the artificial environments of composite animals – that it is imperative to understand in detail the processes of a perverted memetic selection constantly at work to enhance the dominants of these artificial biomes at the expense of all other life on the planet.

As argued above, a natural biome is distinguished by dominant types of plants, while there are dominant species in any community.[1] In a forest in which beech trees predominate, the beech uses the sun to manufacture energy, providing for growth. As it grows it helps create a canopy to shade the forest floor below which keeps it moist and a suitable dwelling place for a myriad creatures which also feed on its fallen nuts and rotting leaves. The beech is *the* dominant which creates conditions that enable only certain animals and plants to flourish. Nearer the ground there are innumerable sub-dominant plants which shelter a variety of communities. These sub-dominants must also adapt to the conditions established by the beech dominant, while yet further modifying the communities below them, which in turn give shelter to societies comprising, for example, fungi and insects. In other forests other trees are dominant, providing life conditions for other plant and animal life.

The close resemblance between the different natural biomes and biotic communities and the different perverted biomes and biotic communities of nations is immediately evident. Each occupies a different geographical area on land controlled by an entirely different set of environmental conditions and climate, which, though giving rise to different growths of different kinds of dominant trees and sub-dominant plants, produce growths with similar vertical structures and greenhouse conditions, each under its own super-dominant Sun – Abraham and his Farmer God that were met together in the Book and Temple at Jerusalem, Christian Farmer God and Christ, Muhammad in some 26 different national guises, or the Marxist Ideal. Their Providential Light is mediated to the layered masses below by a top canopy comprising the dominant Crowned Head, President or Party Chairman – whether Charlemagne, Süleyman the Magnificent ('Sultan of the Ottomans and God's Viceroy on Earth'), Jefferson, Peter the Great (still regarded by many Russians as the Father of modern Russia), Lenin or Mao Zedong – together with dominant landowning farmer-industrial and priestly and scientific élites who govern and control the manufacture of food for the deranged body, mind and imagination by the Light of the Sun of the community. (In Britain, they include bishops, judges, politicians, vice-chancellors, senior civil servants, defence chiefs, BBC mandarins, chief executives and other Establishment figures.) These are the dominant trees of the forests of deranged men. Their superior adaptations and utilization of the available Light, space, water and natural resources limit the growth of other types of plants – and strongly influence the population of plant-like people.

As the layer in which almost all the 'photosynthesis' takes place, the top canopy is the power-plant of the forest-like nation. It is also responsible for much of the greenhouse-like tranquillity of the climate within, maintaining, through the medium of innumerable sub-dominants – such as bankers, managers, magistrates, doctors, priests, lawyers, teachers, police, etc. – maximum and minimum religious, social, economic and political temperatures, religious seasons and holy-days and even changes in the length of day – e.g. BST – urging obedience and conformity (through imitation) to the Sun of the super-plant. So, just as the beech is the dominant of its forest, the dominant landowning farmer-industrialist and priestly and scientific élites are the dominants of the nation, even to the extent of disposing of dominant trees to secure their own survival. In England, for instance, the dominant oaks were cut down and made into ships to defend the human dominants against being cut down in their turn by foreign invaders.

Hearts of oak are our ships, jolly tars are our men...

This example provides an instance of the convergent evolution of a forest-like nation and the true forest, to the detriment of the latter.

The dominants of the nation not only control but justify the *modus operandi* of the society. By whomsoever and whatever the controls and modes of justification, the overall pattern of the stratified structure generally remains the same: the upward flow of wealth and possessions as power, away from the producers towards the top canopy. Each stratified structure comprises a number of hierarchies competing for wealth and power, competing for a place in the Sun of their society. Many hierarchies exist within each nation – governmental, religious, scientific, academic, military, commercial – and all, throughout the world, reveal a positive correlation between material wealth and position in the power structure. The dominants at the top canopy are the principal agents of a perverted memetic selection, perverting the light and energy of the sun to irradiate and raise up their stratified structures. Only those people, animals and plants acceptable to, and capable of adapting to, the conditions and laws they create and mediate can inhabit the land over which the dominants hold sway. There are four principal aspects of this perverted forest-like behaviour to be considered. Each is an expression and example of memes relating to wealth and power as pursued within and between stratified societies; each involves memes primarily beneficial to élites of stratified societies; each creates victims of the pursuit of power, victims of a perverted memetic selection; each is the result of nations as forest-like structures wittingly and unwittingly mimicking the behaviour of the variety of life within the forest, and that behaviour as it is affected by climate changes.

First, through what I have already described as the fivefold concentration of power, the dominants tend to create a vast disparity as between top and bottom of the stratified structure by concentrating a wealth of knowledge and/or possessions as power at the top, and ignorance and poverty as powerlessness at the bottom.

Secondly, those newly arrived at the top canopy through the competitive process – particularly if they have acquired their superior status through conquest, by force of arms – tend to use their newly acquired status to impose a new rigidity of structure and a rigid stratification of society beneath them, thereby ruling out further competition and creating distinctions that amount to specific distinctions similar to those found in a rain forest.

Thirdly, and following on from the above, dominants and sub-dominants of nations have not only deliberately sacrificed those below them *en masse* in wars, but habitually oppress and cause immense suffering amongst them, often actively treating those below them and other nations and races as though they were different species of animal, including experimenting on, and sacrificing, humans regarded as rodents.

Finally, and underlying these three principal ways, there has been the more profound super-dominant: the atavistic fear of the wilderness.

The discussion which follows relating to a perverted memetic selection is in effect the description of the collective memetic inheritance that impels the Life-Force of the nation, seen as a giant human being, reinterpreted mainly in terms of the nation seen as a forest-like stratified structure. The super-dominant Sun and top canopy, together with the atavistic fear of the wilderness and wild nature, are the equivalent of the positive and negative aspects respectively of the Life-Force of the nation.

First, regarding the top canopy, in the early civilizations it was the priest-scientists who held the key to knowledge and dominated society. As the principal enemies of the ancient world were climate change, plague, famine and war, they were primarily concerned to dominate nature, and to assist the ruling classes in their efforts at domination, accumulation and security. Science has since been developed, virtually independently of its priestly aspect, by the ruling classes and for their benefit in a way which has fostered the reproduction and strengthening of its domination. Hierarchy in production and in society generally has been preserved by making expertise the prerogative of those who are socially selected (often by those whose ancestors originally acquired a pyramidal power by force of arms) to hold such knowledge and authority. This social selection – or perverted memetic selection – of the knowledgeable and expert is performed primarily through the medium of education. The teachers include the knowledgeable and the experts themselves.

As well as concentrating a wealth of knowledge as power at the top of the structure, dominant élites within a society use the power so gained to make laws concerning property which help consolidate their power. Adam Smith has shown how government limits the freedom of the majority in order to ensure the rights and liberties associated with property:

> Laws and government may be considered in this and indeed in every case as a combination of the rich to oppress the poor, and preserve to themselves the inequality of the goods which would otherwise be soon destroyed by the attacks of the poor, who if not hindered by the government would soon reduce the others to an equality with themselves by open violence.[2]

Adam Smith has called government 'the orderly oppression of law'. Many of the descendants of those who were thrown off the Common land by Enclosures, who were forced into the drudgery of industrial work, are now thrown altogether out of work by new technology into the humiliating and degrading dependence of permanent unemployment. (By the same process they have been entirely alienated from the land.) An extraordinary division now exists between landowning-cum-intellectual élites and the mass of technologically unemployed.

It might appear at first sight that competition should change all this for the better. Competition is fostered early in a child's life, both at home and by teachers, but is also operative throughout the lives of the members of almost all *Homo degener* societies. If society is viewed as a man-made forest, its overall cultural pattern is like that of trees grappling over gloomy lower regions, struggling into the limelight, competing for the Light of the Sun of the society; while the day to day behaviour of its members resembles that of animals climbing trees. But by its very nature only a relatively few in every generation can avail themselves of the opportunities to climb to the top of the social tree. Competition has little effect on the overall structure of society. The fact that a few individuals may move up the social scale – particularly in times of economic expansion and growth – may serve only to blind the working class to the fact that, as a class, they are destined to remain where they are.

By the very nature of the design and vertical energy flow of the stratified structure there will be a relatively small number of dominant people of relatively great wealth of knowledge and/or possessions, status and power at the top, and a relatively large number of subordinate people who are relatively poor in knowledge and possessions, who lack status and are powerless at the bottom. *The structured inequality of parasite pyramids of power almost invariably ensures that the top one-fifth of the people will own four-fifths of the wealth.* In other words, at the top reside those upon whom the Sun of a Providential prosperity shines brightly, and in the shadows at the bottom reside those upon whom the Sunlight of prosperity may never reach at all. As Disraeli wrote of Britain in the mid 19th century:

> Two nations; between whom there is no intercourse and no sympathy; who are as ignorant of each other's habits, thoughts, and feelings, as if they were dwellers in different zones, or inhabitants of different planets; who are formed by a different breeding, are fed by a different food, are ordered by different manners, and are not governed by the same laws... THE RICH AND THE POOR.[3]

The people who have lived for the past 200 odd years in poverty and disease in the East End of London have been described as 'the people of the abyss'. While income distribution in the UK has grown steadily more unequal, income differentials have grown yet greater in London. A similar widening of the income gap is evident in New York and Tokyo.

The shadows at the bottom are deep and long. In those shadows lurk the so-called 'guest-workers' of Europe. Germany, in common with Britain and other European nations after the Second World War, found its pyramidal base too narrow and brought in hundreds of thousands of migrant workers to undertake the lowliest and dirtiest tasks of society. They became the real poor of Europe, whose status was one of servitude.

Relative and extreme poverty and associated deprivation of every kind, together with an immense disparity between very rich and very poor, between dominant and subordinate, are inherent characteristics of stratified societies.* Lit by its own Sun of prosperity, each engenders a structured

---

*For generations the unequal distribution of the goods of this world has been seen as a special dispensation of Divine Providence. Calvin justified this state of affairs by alleging that only when the workers were poor did they remain obedient to God. This justification accords with my argument in Part I, Chapter 8, that the monotheistic Farmer God was created to sanctify and promote the subjugation of peoples and of the land, siding with the landowning rich against the landless poor, thereby perpetuating by psychical means the stranglehold of the rich over the poor.

inequality as between dominant *Homo sapiens sapiens* and subordinate *Homo sapiens non sapiens*. If the standard of living appears generally to have been raised throughout the Western world, this is largely because of the enormous influx of millions of darker skinned migrant workers from poorer southern countries into the lower reaches of the North American and European societies, and because of the extension of their structures down into the Southern Hemisphere, which drew the less developed and weaker peoples of the Northern and Southern Hemispheres in as additional power bases to ascent in the Northern Hemisphere.

In the past 300 years the shadows of stratified structures growing up in the Northern Hemisphere have extended right across the Southern Hemisphere in the wake of European colonialism and neo-colonialism, spreading conditions comparable to, or worse than, those attendant upon their own Agricultural-Industrial Revolutions. This is mainly because the operation of market forces, and the allocation of resources in favour of urban sectors, now occur on a macrocosmic scale.

When a market economy first began to develop in Europe in the 13th century, and grain began to be stocked in the cities, there were some dramatic effects amongst the populations affected. One such was that for the first time people had to buy their food. Whether they ate or starved no longer depended only on the vagaries of the weather and climate, but now also on the even less predictable ones of the market. A classic European example is that of the Great Famine in Ireland between 1845 and 1849 – to which I referred earlier in a different context – when many hundreds of thousands of men, women and children died of starvation following a blight of the potato crop. One-third of the Irish population of about 8.5 million lived off potatoes. The Irish small farmer did grow cereal crops, but records show that these were almost all used to pay his rent. He lived off his potato crop, depending wholly upon it for survival. When news reached London of the potato blight, Peel, the Prime Minister, imported a large supply of maize from the USA, which was stored in government depots in Ireland, not primarily as food to be eaten immediately by starving people but for occasional sale as an economic lever to balance the free market forces of supply and demand. Peel also tried to lower the price of bread by repealing the import duties on corn. But lowering the price of bread in Ireland was of little use to the one-third of the population who lived off potatoes, for they did so because they could hardly afford bread, whatever the price. Eventually, by early 1846, the poor were becoming desperate. Food such as flour, wheat, oats and barley was available in great quantities, but only for export. It was not available to the Irish poor who lacked the money to pay for it. Many emigrated to the United States, while a million and a half died of starvation and disease.

Further afield, the great famines of India during the British Raj were likewise mainly due to the operation of market forces. W.A. Dando[4] argues in his book, *The Geography of Famine*, that there had always been crop failures, but these were largely catered for, as farmers would conserve sufficient stocks, either in their homes or in village store-houses. Such famines as did occur were the result of food shortages due to a breakdown in this support system. In a market economy, however, their grain was sold to merchants and stocked in the city. When there was a crop failure, Indian farmers and villagers were forced to buy grain at an inflated price and with much reduced incomes. This resulted in famine in the countryside, though not in the cities.

Two major factors that have affected the provision of food have been climate change and the world market. A recent study of famine by Mike Davis,[5] *Late Victorian Holocausts*, shows that famines in India, China, Brazil and elsewhere have not been food shortages *per se* but economic crises arising from the effects of drought and crop failure on the market. Droughts (or, indeed, sometimes floods) in great areas of Asia, Africa and northeastern South America have been shown to be associated with the rapid warming of the eastern tropical Pacific (known as the El Niño event); a cooling of the eastern Pacific (known as a La Niña event) is associated with heavy rainfall and flooding in those same regions. This interrelated movement of air mass and ocean temperature is called the 'El Niño Southern Oscillation' (ENSO). Drought arising from an El Niño event has had devastating effects upon poor producers who were already victims of the world markets.

European colonization of Asian, African and South American countries so transformed their systems of production as to make them vulnerable to adverse climatic changes. Export economies based on wheat, rubber, cotton, coffee and so on were developed at the expense of subsistence farming and animal grazing rights on common land. In India, for example, the traditional system of household and village grain reserves was replaced by a merchant-controlled market, enclosures and the displacement of fields of grain by cash crops such as cotton, thereby reducing local food security. These market orientated changes, together with extortionate taxes, debt and rising prices resulting from food shortages, combined to make the poor producers even more vulnerable to drought and flood than were their farming ancestors.

The frequency of famines increased dramatically during the British Raj – legends and records mention more than 90 famines in that country in the past 2,500 years, but 60 per cent have taken place since 1701 –

mainly because the underlying nature of famine had changed. In pre-European India famines occurred because of a shortage of food, whereas in British India they were due to inability to buy food. Although the British built railroads, ports and canals which might have aided indigenous development and prevented starvation, they were financed by taxes which pauperized the peasantry and were used for resource extraction. Food surpluses, as in Ireland during the Great Famine, were exported to England or hoarded by speculators in heavily guarded depots.

According to Mike Davis, waves of drought, famine and disease in 1876–79, 1889–91 and 1896–1902 are estimated to have killed at least 30 million people. All were selected to die – a perverted memetic selection – as the direct result of a London-centred world economy which spread memes based on the principles of Adam Smith, Jeremy Bentham, John Mill, Herbert Spencer and Thomas Malthus. Together their theories constituted a socio-politico-economic memeplex governing the education and behaviour of generations of East India Company and Government officials. A late Victorian holocaust could have been averted – almost everywhere there were grain surpluses that could have been made available to the starving – but the prevailing memeplexes of Utilitarianism and Social Darwinism (including the theory of *laissez-faire*, which taught that any artificial interference with the iron laws of supply and demand, including interference by the government with the price of grain and with private trade, could not be other than harmful, and the belief that over-reproduction on the part of the poor would negate any efforts to ameliorate their situation) prevented such intervention. Where relief was given it was only in exchange for labour on the part of those who often had not the strength to do any sort of work. Brazil imitated the example of the British government in India by giving relief only in exchange for labour. Work camps in India and Brazil became outbreak centres of cholera and smallpox respectively.

Famines in Russia have mainly been man-made.

In essence ... all of the famines which have occurred in Russia from 971–1970 can be predominantly attributed to human factors.[6]

Recently in Russia some 9 million people died of famine between 1921 and 1922, some 6 million between 1933 and 1934, and perhaps 2 million between 1945 and 1947.

As well, therefore, as the threat of famine through crop failure, climate change or over-population, people starve because the world's agricultural systems have been designed primarily to create wealth and not to feed people. In effect, the majority of the people who are hungry are hungry, not only because there is insufficient food available, but also because they have not the money to buy food. This accords with the 'structured inequality' which is the essence of the parasite pyramid of power.

The structured inequality that favours the wealthy at the summit of a national pyramid has now spread in the wake of colonialism across the world, to make for a structured inequality between nations that favours the rich nations in the Northern Hemisphere. The greatest quantity and the best quality food is consumed by the wealthiest one-fifth of the people within the wealthiest one-fifth of the nations of the world. And this has only been made possible because food is controlled by the rich, by the new breed of supra-national merchants. Its production and distribution are in the hands of the supra-national agribusinesses, led by those based in the USA and supported by the international aid industry, headed by the World Bank.

Aid has typically benefited the donors politically and economically, and the ruling élites of the primary producer nations. Countries receiving aid have most often been forced by the donors – whether the World Bank or the International Monetary Fund (IMF) – to cut public expenditure and wages, and to devalue their currencies to generate money through cheaper prices for export commodities. It is the poor who have suffered from these 'structural adjustments'. Many people have been forced to clear forests or to farm marginal lands to survive. The power hungry big business concerns of the West – which, as well as multinational corporations and international agencies which control the world-wide food cartel, includes their allies in the petrochemical, agricultural machinery, shipping and distributive industries – have achieved the ultimate weapon: the power to decide what the rest of the world will eat, and at what price – or even whether they will eat at all. Theirs is the ultimate power of life and death.* It is the power that enabled

---

*This is the case in several other spheres of economic activity. For instance, the giant drug companies, by stifling competition from generic drugs manufacturers in developing countries, are placing life-saving drugs, on which they hold the patents, beyond the reach of the poor in developing countries. As a result, as pointed out in a report in the *New Scientist* (Vol. 171, No. 2300, 21 July 2001, p. 18) a thousand children a day world-wide die painfully from dysentery through the inability to afford life-saving drugs. That the poor of the developing world have little or no money to buy even the barest necessities of life is also the responsibility of multinationals who site their operations where labour is cheapest, paying the lowest possible wages for products whose sale generates huge profits to the governments and corporations concerned. As pointed out by John Pilger in a television programme on 18 July 2001, a maker of shoes, Nike, pays a golfer, Tiger Woods, more to advertise its products than it pays its entire Indonesian workforce that produces them.

The memeplexes that have governed the behaviour of business élites in the Western world over the last 300 years – that have been primarily beneficial to those élites, enabling them to thrive on the profits arising from slavery and factory wage-slaves – are now operating on a world-wide scale: the globalization of Western business memeplexes enables multinationals to thrive on profits derived from similar conditions of slavery and sweat-shops, giving rise to poverty, malnutrition and disease in environmental hells even worse than those exposed by Charles Dickens 150 years ago.

Homo sapiens sapiens landowning élites in Scotland to enclose the land against the *Homo sapiens non sapiens* peasants, and that enabled the big landowning corporations in North America to seize and mechanize thousands of smallholdings, a process of dispossession which John Steinbeck immortalized in his novel *The Grapes of Wrath*. It is this power of *Homo sapiens sapiens* over *Homo sapiens non sapiens* within any one nation in the Northern Hemisphere that has now spread over the face of the Earth, enabling predominantly *Homo sapiens sapiens* nations in the Northern Hemisphere to wield an anonymous and utterly impersonal power of life and death over predominantly *Homo sapiens non sapiens* nations, or primary producer countries, in S.E. Asia, sub-Saharan Africa and Central America.

As a direct result of their selective manipulation of world markets, of their control over land use, and because of the structured inequality inherent in stratified structures, which concentrates the greatest quantity and the best quality food towards the top canopy, they have widened the gap between the wealthy 'haves' and the poor 'have-nots' to such an extent that widespread man-made famines, as against localized famines brought about by natural catastrophe, now dominate the world scene. There are an estimated 1 billion people living in extreme poverty, most living on less than £250 a year. Some 850 million people are chronically malnourished. The future promises to be even more bleak. Not only is the world population expected to grow by some 2 billion to 8 billion by the year 2050, but most of that growth will be in the poorest developing countries – the population of sub-Saharan Africa will almost double over the same period to 1 billion people. It is hoped that biotechnology will help alter this situation by transforming agriculture in the same way as did the Green Revolution. However, as has been the case with all previous technology-driven revolutions, biotechnology will produce winners and losers: the genetic engineering of plants is most likely to contribute to existing inequality.* The gross inequalities arising from the control of production, distribution and price by affluent minorities and their privileged position as primary consumers of food are directly related to their control of the production and dissemination of information, and their privileged position as primary consumers of knowledge and developers of advanced technology. Modern Western technologies can only be operated by élites, resulting in the rich becoming richer and the poor poorer. The computer culture, as well as being used to increase

---

*More important still, however, and as pointed out by Peter Melchett of Greenpeace UK, is the fact that the introduction of genetically modified foods (GMOs) is an attempt on the part of the chemical industry, in their words, to 'escalate the war against nature'. (Greenpeace Letter, April 2000).

centralization and control over individuals, is increasing the gap between rich and poor within nations; at the same time it is widening the gulf between North and South as wealthy nations organize and use information in their favour commercially.* The introduction of robotics will further exacerbate this situation. As developed nations undergo a robotics revolution in manufacturing industries, societies in the developed world will once again be better placed to compete than those in the developing world, weakening the poorer nations still further.

In imitation of the structured inequality that has existed within parasite pyramids of power – which, as I argued above, almost invariably ensures that the top one-fifth of the people will own four-fifths of the wealth – *a structured inequality of nations has come into being as the rich and powerful consumer nations parasitize the poor and powerless producer nations, ensuring that the top one-fifth of the nations will own four-fifths of the wealth, while four-fifths of the world's population live in poverty.*† Nevertheless, a global campaign to eradicate poverty and starvation, called the Millennium Development Goals, has been launched by the United Nations which, in the light of my argument concerning world-wide parasitism, will in no way affect the relative deprivation suffered by the *Homo sapiens non sapiens* majority of humankind.

It is noteworthy that famine was relatively unknown amongst hunter-gatherers. It was only with their degradation to a sedentary agricultural way of life that famines began to occur.

> Famine is a characteristic of crop and livestock agriculture, and was not a facet of preagricultural systems.[7]

One further important point should be made. It is the extent to which religious taboos have prevented people turning to other food sources in their efforts to stave off hunger. In India, for instance, Hindus have been prohibited from killing the holy cows that wander so freely across the land in order to supplement their diet.

As well as guaranteeing the continuity of the extremes of wealth/

---

*Pope John Paul II claimed, in *The Social Concerns of the Church*, that Marxism and capitalism were both 'structures of sin' exploiting the poor.

†The long-term socio-economic effects of the parasitism of one nation by another may be deduced from Mike Davis' book *Late Victorian Holocausts* (Verso, 2001). He shows that not only did India's per capita income between 1757 and 1947 remain static, but that it probably declined by more than 50% during the latter half of the 19th century, while life expectancy amongst ordinary Indians between 1872 and 1921 was reduced by 20%. Davis argues that these trends vindicate the claim of 19th century nationalists 'that British 'Progress' was Indian ruin'.

power and poverty/powerlessness, there is a second principal way in which the super-dominant Sun and dominant élites of each nation are the principal agents of a perverted memetic selection. It is that those newly arrived at the top canopy through the competitive process have tended throughout history to use their newly acquired status to impose a new rigidity of structure and a rigid stratification of society beneath them, thereby ruling out further competition and creating distinctions that have amounted to specific distinctions similar to those found in a rain forest. For just as the dominant trees of the rain forest are the agents of selection of different species of wildlife moving at different levels within their domain; just as the cells of the human body allow the remarkable specialization of function that we see at the microcosmic level in the human liver, heart or brain, each organ a different species of animal, as it were, within the human body; or just as the queen termite is the agent of selection of different castes of termite within a termitary, *the dominants of the nation are the agents of selection of different levels, castes or classes of people who tend to treat those far below them, and members of other nations, as though they were subspecies or wholly different species* (see figure 6.2).

Originally *Homo sapiens* was differentiating all over the world within hunter-gatherer cultures, and had already differentiated into a number of varieties, but had not differentiated into different species. A 'species', in biological terms, is distinguished from a 'variety' (or subspecies) by the fact that varieties can interbreed, while species either do not do so or, if they do, produce offspring which, like mules, are sterile. (A species may also be defined as a group of individuals which is unable to exchange genetic material with the members of another group.) All humankind can intermix and interbreed freely, can learn and understand the same speech, can adapt itself to co-operation. The world-wide hunter-gatherer cultures were an expression of just such a co-operation and potential unity of people moving within the kingdom of nature. But – and it is a vital 'but' – a state of affairs has come into being between people that has ensured the treatment of one person by another *as though he or she were of a different and inferior species.*

For instance, throughout the Middle Ages England had a warrior aristocracy, a rich warrior caste trained specifically for war, who held their lands through right of conquest, and whose poor peasant producers were cast in the rôle of serfs. Their accumulation and control of territory, their constitutional rights and privileges, their modes of dress and address, made them as different in appearance and behaviour from their producer fellows as are monkeys in the treetops from rodents or termites on the

Part II: fig 6.2

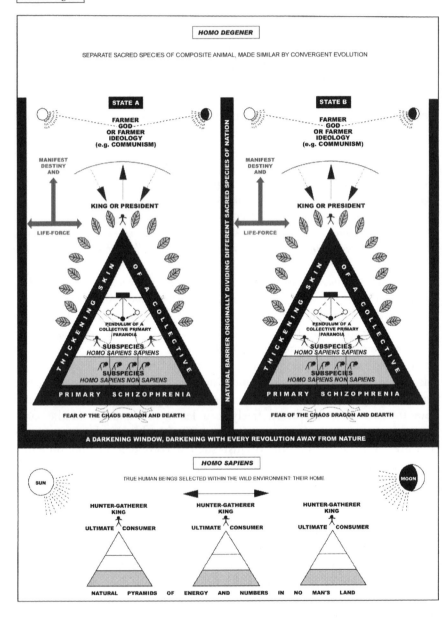

forest floor – or as are soldier termites surrounding their queen from their worker termite fellows within the same termitary. Their dominant presence, and the super-dominant God and King they represented, guaranteed their superior station acquired through expropriation and conquest, and thereafter ensured the evolution of different levels of such inferior beings to work for them and to serve them – but not to mix with them nor to marry them – as virtually to constitute different species of animal.

Civilized élites, by dint of their fivefold concentration of power, have become what may be described either as the *Homo sapiens sapiens* dominants of a super-plant or as the subspecific head of a super-animal. Thereafter they have segregated themselves and segregated and legislated against other men as though they were different species. The necessity of the Pharaoh and other Royal Houses to marry those of royal descent, the caste system in India, and in particular the Outcaste, and the laws against miscegenation in apartheid South Africa are cases in point. Thereby the ruling party – whether light skinned Egyptian or Hindu or White Afrikaner – has been able to preserve intact its wealth, its cultural and racial purity and superiority, and so its power.

In this context it is necessary to appreciate the importance of 'whiteness' amongst agricultural peoples. For an essential connection between barriers of class, caste, race, etc. – and so the treatment of others as different species – has been the degree of whiteness as a symbol and expression of legitimacy, of cultural superiority, moral purity and perfection: that is, of likeness to the Sun God, the Great White Hope to national wealth and power. This is governed first by the position of a group within any one structured society in relation to the White Light of its super-dominant Sun, and secondly, by the elevation, whiteness or brightness of a particular nation's belief-system and Sun in relation to others.

Many élites of ancient civilizations, with the aid of Farmer (Sun) Gods and myths of Creation, legitimized or whitened themselves with superlative identities, while at the same time heightening the illusion of righteousness and whiteness by denigrating or blackening their forbears and the kingdom of nature in myth. These myths of the earliest priestly-scientific élites constituted the core of the earliest religious memplexes of *Homo degener* peoples, which in turn formed the core of the collective memetic inheritance of each composite animal. On this foundation dominant élites operated a perverted memetic selection to perpetuate the social order and division of labour beneath them, ensuring the accretion of wealth and power at the top canopy, a process that has favoured white over black, relatively white *Homo sapiens sapiens* dominants illumined by the White Light of their Farmer (Sun) God or Moon Goddess over the relatively black *Homo sapiens non sapiens* on the forest floor. For thousands of years since, in every part of the world, stratified structures have been growing towards the White Light of mythical Farmer Gods of Providence and Perfection, and away from Darkness, Dearth and Death in environmental hells. All civilizations have been, and are, at bottom, hells on earth, as in the case of the reduction today of millions of children to slavery.* All civilizations have risen up towards the sun on the bent backs of men blackened – or of black men – working in appalling conditions on the ground and underground. Less than 200 years ago, for example, Scottish miners were serfs.

> As serfs, they were beaten and tortured at their pit-owner's will. As 'free' men and women, they at first lived not much better. Pray for forgotten Janet Cumming, aged 11, who carried coal underground at Fordel colliery from 5 a.m. to 5 p.m. except for Fridays, when she worked on through the night until Saturday noon – a case from the 1842 Royal Commission report.[8]

In the Border country between England and Scotland, women were still being treated as bond slaves up till the onset of the First World War. Quite simply, untold millions of poor devils have lived and died on the ground and underground – buried alive in iron, tin, copper, coal, bauxite, lead, silver, gold and diamond mines – for the benefit of élites exploiting them and their products in their ascent to the Sun. This is their inescapable heritage, a regenerative Life-Force to ascent. Thereafter, legitimate landed, intellectual and technical authority, inasmuch as these reflect a cultural superiority, moral purity and perfection, have been linked with whiteness at the top of the structure; illegitimacy, disorder and low grade manual work status, inasmuch as these reflect a cultural inferiority, moral impurity and imperfection, have been linked with blackness, darkness and death at the bottom of, and beyond, the stratified structure.† Altogether, these

---

* See below this Chapter.

† The dichotomy, dualism and polarity existing within stratified societies, which is depicted in Part I, Chapter 5, is particularly noticeable in the perceived opposition of white and black.

> White   denotes purity, simplicity, and candour; innocence, truth and hope... Generally, the priests of antiquity wore white vestments, and Bardic costume, supposedly derived from the DRUIDS, is always white. OSIRIS, the ancient Egyptian god, wore a white crown; the priests of JUPITER were clad in white, and at the death of a CAESAR the national mourning was white. The Persians affirm that the divinities are clothed in white.
> *The white bird.* Conscience, or the SOUL of man. The Mohammedans have preserved the old idea that the souls of the just lie under the throne of GOD, like white birds, till the resurrection morn.[9]   [Continued over]

characteristics have constituted a most important memeplex, forming a major element of the collective memetic inheritance of nations world-wide.

The degree of whiteness is most often, though not necessarily, related to the whiteness of dress – e.g. the white robes of legitimate (pure) priest and scientist, the white wedding dress of the legitimate (pure) bride, the white collar of the manager and clerk – and the whiteness of the skin. The importance of the whiteness of the skin, in conjunction with the degree of whiteness as an expression of legitimacy, status and aspirations to perfection, is all too apparent throughout the world. For instance, an estimated 60 per cent of Japanese women whiten their skins in an attempt to attain their cultural ideal of beauty and perfection, and as a passport to success in the East. Marriage advertisements in Mumbai newspapers, as until recently in Mombasa, repeatedly emphasize the whiteness of the skin as a major attraction. Lightness of skin has long been a status symbol amongst South African Coloureds, and darkness a stigma. Trevor Phillips, chairman of the Commission for Racial Equality, pointed out that in Britain, in 2004, the negative impact of race (whether Asian or black) on people's chances in life is increasing with time: their colour increasingly traps them in the place into which they were born. The American writer James Baldwin has spoken of the urgency with which black bodies in Harlem were scrubbed in order to whiten them and to achieve some measure of acceptance in the white world outside. In Mexico, 'the darker the skin, the closer to the ground'. Whiteness of the skin has also been decisive in matters of punishment and death. In several states of the USA the murder of a black man – even by another black – has been

[*Continued from previous page*]

Killing an albatross, or a white hart, used to be considered bad luck.

Black   (In symbolism etc.) *In art*, signifying evil, falsehood, and error.
As a mortuary colour, signifying grief, despair, death.
Its use for mourning was a Roman custom ... borrowed from the Egyptians...
In several of the Oriental nations it is a badge of servitude, slavery and low birth. Our word *blackguard* seems to point to this meaning, and the Lat. *niger*, black, also meant bad, impropitious.[10]

Black   5. *fig.* Having dark purposes, malignant; baneful, disastrous, sinister
6 *fig.* Foul, iniquitous, atrocious
8 *fig.* Indicating disgrace, censure etc. Cf. BLACK BOOK, LIST etc

(Extracts from *Shorter OED*)

For example, it was a common belief in Scotland, as evinced in several witch trials, that the devil appeared as a black man. Black cats were used in devil worship in medieval England, and were often connected with witchcraft in Europe in the Middle Ages. Those who deviated from the norm of the family were often known as 'black sheep'. Those in China accused of conspiring behind the scenes of the Tiananmen demonstrations in 1989 to overthrow the government were described as 'black hands'.

only one-tenth as likely to be punished by death as the murder of a white man.

However, the degree of whiteness is not necessarily related to the whiteness of the skin. A black man may be 'whitened' by becoming the earthly embodiment of the hopes of the nation. Robert Mugabe became – ironically – the 'great white hope' of the people of Zimbabwe after independence in 1980. President-For-Life Dr Hastings Banda of Malawi was a self-confessed despiser of black people, considering himself as pre-eminently a white man.

It has been the certainty of cultural and moral superiority – of selection by one's Farmer God or other ideological Sun, the White Hope of the nation – on the part of those occupying the top canopy of the forest-like structure that has encouraged the treatment of others as though they were different species, particularly through sanctions against intermarriage and miscegenation.

The escape towards the White Light of the Sun, away from the blackness and chaos of the Mesolithic, achieved its first zenith in the Egypt of the Pharaohs, who became *Homo sapiens super sapiens* Sons of the Sun God, apotheosis and quintessence of a civilized Legitimacy and Whiteness. One of the longest surviving hierarchical systems in the world, however, is the caste system of the Hindus, which originated c.1500–1200 BC when Aryan tribes from the North West overran North India and the Deccan. With the gradual Aryan colonization of the sub-continent Brahmanism (a form of Hinduism) developed, together with the four-caste system – outlined in Part II, Chapter 1, above. At a later date the Outcastes were altogether excluded from this system and assigned such tasks as street sweeping, scavenging, transporting and skinning carcasses and the execution of criminals. Around 200 BC this system was codified in a Hindu scripture, *Manusmriti*. This decreed, amongst other things, that the dress of Outcastes 'shall be garments of the dead', 'they shall eat from broken dishes', and 'they shall live outside the village', an edict that still prevailed at the end of the 20th century. For although untouchability is formally outlawed – Untouchables are now known as dalit (or oppressed) Indians – it is still a brutal fact of life in India.* For caste still regulates life in the villages where some 70 per cent of Indians live. It defines what they may wear, what trade they may follow, where they may live and sometimes even what colour they may paint their houses (blue, for instance, is often reserved for Brahmins). This system, though restrictive, ensures stability and is divinely ordained. Hindus believe that their caste reflects their behaviour in a previous life, good behaviour being rewarded by

---

* The poor and excluded almost invariably have dark skin in India.

high caste and bad behaviour with untouchability. This behavioural aspect of untouchability, compounded with the traditional trades assigned to them, has persuaded the higher castes that they are polluted merely by touching them – or an object used by them. Any attempts by individuals or the government to raise the status of the lower castes is seen, particularly by the upper castes, as breaking the cosmic cycle, defying nature.

This is an excellent example of a perverted memetic selection which forms an important element of the collective memetic inheritance of India, the achievement of power by the upper castes being perpetuated by religious memes, to form a viral memeplex which new memes, such as raising the status of the lower castes, have found it hard to invade. Furthermore, this viral memeplex is considerably reinforced by the belief entertained by the lower castes that they will, by good behaviour, ascend to a higher caste in their next lives, thereby making this life more endurable.

The image presented by the caste system is that of animals constrained to live out their lives at a single level within a rain forest, with species as far removed from one another on the evolutionary scale as monkeys and ants occupying the sunlit top canopy and darkest subterranean regions respectively. The latter form part of the multitude of small scavengers which convert fallen organic material back into living tissue. Without them, the pile-up of detritus would be so great that the whole community would eventually come to a standstill. Similarly, the dalit are the scavengers of the forest-like nation. So are the 2 million Burakumin of Japan. In feudal times they were called 'eta hinin', which means 'filthy' and 'subhuman'. Today they still do the worst and meanest jobs – slaughtering, handling rubbish, clearing the drains and day labouring. For some 300 years now they have been forced to live in separate communities. They were forbidden to intermarry with the rest of the population, and even physical contact was avoided. Like the dalit, they have been the termites and ants of the forest-like nation.

A somewhat similar situation arose in South Africa, where some of the conquering Afrikaners came to view the black population below them, with whom they were in a more or less permanent master-servant relationship, as belonging to a different and lower species. This is most apparent in their folk-tales and legends, where black farm labourers change into baboons and vice versa.* They enacted

---

*The attitude of the Germans to the Herero people in German South-West Africa, at the beginning of 20th century, was similar:

At best, the Herero who worked for the Germans had to suffer systematic humiliation. They were called 'baboons' to their face. The settlers told the government in a petition that it was 'almost impossible to regard them as human beings.'[11]

laws against miscegenation and deliberately segregated them, so reinforcing their view of them as different species. As far removed from the black man as Brahmin is from dalit in India, the Afrikaners had the makings of an economy that would be characterized by 'black roots and white fruit', and of a caste system as effective as that dividing soldier and worker termite in a termitary, ruling out any competition between the races.

So as well as competition for society's glittering prizes and associated prestige there has been a parallel process at work: the pursuit of cultural superiority, moral purity and perfection – a process of whitening oneself towards the Sun of the society,* to win the ultimate prize and prestige of the certainty of being one of the Chosen and Elect of the Farmer God or other Ideological Sun. The process of whitening may operate in conjunction with, or independently of, the competitive process. More often it is directly opposed to the competitive process, in that it has encouraged those who are thus whitened to place barriers of class, caste, religion, race, etc. between them and those below them. The caste system supplied a religious basis for the inequalities of the parasite pyramidal division of labour; so too did apartheid. So too did Christianity in England, as the hymn 'All Things Bright and Beautiful' illustrates:

> The rich man in his castle,
> The poor man at his gate,
> God made them, high or lowly,
> And ordered their estate.

In Britain, a hierarchy based on caste – that is, on hereditary relations between castes established since the Norman Conquest and virtually incapable of change – overshadows and entwines a hierarchy of class based on occupation and wealth and open to mobility. Amongst the 20 per cent of poor on the forest floor of society, however, there is a silent army of cleaners – working at night, cleaning offices, streets and public lavatories – who, because they are never going to do anything else, form a caste almost as rigid as the dalit Indians. In the USA some eight million Americans live in security zones or 'gated communities', creating an embryonic caste system which depends on a total separation from the poor. In Christian Yugoslavia, the Muslim Albanians of the Kosovo region

---

*In alchemy, 'whitening' is a process whereby a base metal may be transformed into gold, and, by extension, the soul of the sinful man may be purified.

were the untouchables in the Yugoslav caste system. They were the poorest people in the country, having a Third World income of about £200 a year.

Within nations there have been, to a greater or lesser degree, two subspecies: the one superior, relatively white, wealthy, knowledge-able and powerful, the other inferior, relatively dark, poor, ignorant and powerless. They are as different in appearance, function and behaviour as are king and queen termites from soldier termites, and as are both from worker termites. To the extent that they perform entirely different functions, the one performing high grade intellectual work, the other low grade manual work, they live in separate and different worlds, enabling those on top to exploit those below with arrogant indifference, as though they belonged to a different and inferior species. White élites have so treated their white brethren on the forest floor, just because they were 'black', as representatives of primitiveness, disorder and outer darkness. This difference is most acutely felt when, as old people, they fulfil no function at all, and become the object of bureaucratic 'care'.

> One of the fearful developments in the consciousness of many old
> people is that, in the eyes of society, they have become another
> species.[12]

The degree of whiteness as a symbol and expression of the legitimacy, cultural superiority, moral purity and perfection – and so the treatment of others as different species – is governed first by the position of a group within any one pyramid in relation to the White Light of the super-dominant Sun at the apex of that pyramid. It is also governed, as I pointed out earlier, by the elevation and whiteness of a particular nation's belief-system and Sun in relation to others.

Each nation has tended to see itself as the Centre of the World, as *selected* by *its* Farmer God or Ideology, as culturally and morally superior to its neighbours, viewing others as inferior and dark. For instance, in an interview in May, 1968, David Ben-Gurion said this of the Israeli nation:

> The thing which I try to explain to my friends all the time is that
> our ability to survive depends on one condition – if we preserve
> our spiritual superiority. Our spiritual superiority means two things.
> In olden times it meant one thing – moral superiority. But in our
> time it means two – moral superiority and technological superiority.

We are more developed, we have made more progress in science
than they, and we are morally superior.[13]

Ben-Gurion was speaking of the superiority of the 'civilized' Israeli
over the 'less civilized' Egyptian, of Israel over Ishmael, a rivalry of
brothers. Each nation has tended to view others through its world-fearing
windows of myth as inferior and Dark, relying on myth, prejudice
and stereotypes developed over thousands of years of alienation both
from other nations and from the kingdom of nature. The Pharaohs, for
instance, regarded the ancient Greeks as obese, hook-nosed, piratical
barbarians, while the Greeks viewed all non Greeks as 'barbaroi', as
barbarians who could only go 'ba-ba'. Pericles saw democracy as a privilege
confined to Athenians, a privilege not to be granted to barbarians outside the Attic Law. Aristotle perpetuated this theory, and practice, when
he propounded that less rational beings exist in order to serve more
rational humans, proposing the inhuman racial thesis that Greeks
were born to be the master race and that barbarians were destined to be
their slaves. The Chinese have regarded outsiders as Fan Kwei (foreign
devils) and viewed what they regarded as 'the red-faced drunken European'
as barbarian. The present Chinese occupiers of Tibet have been shown
to be genuinely afraid of the Tibetans: they believed their own myth
that the Tibetans were dangerous barbarians. The Japanese have regarded
other peoples as less than human. This was made apparent, both during
the Second World War when they experimented on European prisoners-
of-war and used them for bayonet practice, and when a Japanese,
Issei Sagawa, killed and ate a young Dutch woman in Paris in the early
1980s and was deported to Japan in 1984. Japanese curiosity about
Sagawa was rooted in their perception of his victim as less than a person.
'It would be very different if his victim had been Japanese,' commented
one expert.

Western travellers, from Burton to Naipaul, caricatured the East as a
place of lascivious sexuality, violence and sloth, a caricature which
encouraged the spread of Empire, since in the presence of such obvious
anarchy 'the imperialist could feel himself justified in stepping in
and ruling'. Imperialism has even been defined – by Christopher Hichens
– as 'the habit or practice of treating another country as if it
were uninhabited.' The last part of that definition could as well read
'as if it were inhabited only by species of animal different from themselves.'

The belief of the élite of any one nation in its legitimacy and cultural
superiority – or whiteness – in relation to those below and to other

nations, that makes for the treatment of others as though they were different species, has in fact been greatly strengthened by the acquisition of empire. Colonial expropriation and exploitation, which is the process that encouraged the spread of famine over the face of the earth, is also the process by which prohibitions against miscegenation have built up and spread across the world, and so by which different races have come to be treated as though they were different species. It may be seen in the forest-like spread of the structured inequality of the Spanish culture over Peru (see figure 6.3).

Peru was conquered early in the 16th century by Francisco Pizarro.* He subjugated the Incas (the ruling caste of Quechua Indians) who had risen to power some 500 years earlier. Peru remained under Spanish rule for almost three centuries. At first, Spaniards mixed with and married Indians. But by the 17th century Peru had changed from being a frontier society into a stable parasite pyramidal community intent on imitating the customs and manners of contemporary Spain. The relationship between conqueror and conquered, which has been a principal one between peoples down the ages throughout the world, has also been a prime factor in the perverted memetic selection of peoples. For

> Those who are conquered always want to imitate the conqueror in his main characteristics – in his clothing, his crafts, and in all his distinctive traits and customs.[14]

It is noteworthy that an important change had recently taken place in Spain affecting its memes. At the beginning of the 16th century Spain had purged itself of Jews and Moors. Such physical and spiritual cleansing – a perverted memetic selection under the black Spanish Sun – together with a rejuvenation and strengthening of the Catholic faith in the face of the threat from Protestantism, would have profoundly affected Spanish relations with the Indians of Peru. Not only would Spanish newcomers in the 17th century have entertained a degree of racial prejudice, but also religious memes, insisting on strict observance of canon law, would have brought into question the legitimate status of the marriages between Spaniards and Indians, causing many lighter skinned Peruvians to conceal their Indian forebears and to distance themselves from the Indians, while attempting to integrate themselves into white society. The result of such a perverted memetic selection, particularly in the Sierra (or mountain

---

*Conquest was made easy because the Indians were profoundly fearful of the white men whom they saw as gods wielding instruments of thunder and lightning.

Part II: fig 6.3

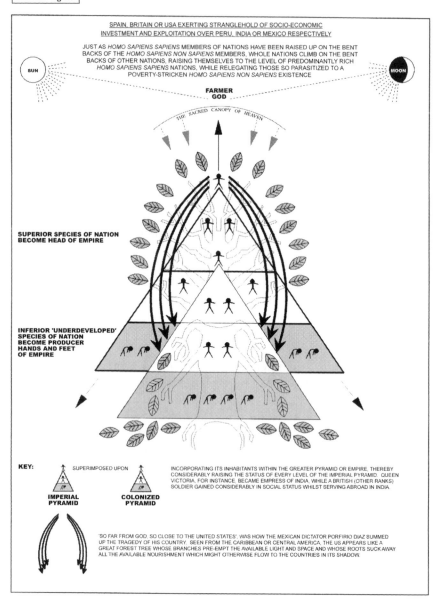

SPAIN, BRITAIN OR USA EXERTING STRANGLEHOLD OF SOCIO-ECONOMIC
INVESTMENT AND EXPLOITATION OVER PERU, INDIA OR MEXICO RESPECTIVELY

JUST AS *HOMO SAPIENS SAPIENS* MEMBERS OF NATIONS HAVE BEEN RAISED UP ON THE BENT
BACKS OF THE *HOMO SAPIENS NON SAPIENS* MEMBERS, WHOLE NATIONS CLIMB ON THE BENT
BACKS OF OTHER NATIONS, RAISING THEMSELVES TO THE LEVEL OF PREDOMINANTLY RICH
HOMO SAPIENS SAPIENS NATIONS, WHILE RELEGATING THOSE SO PARASITIZED TO A
POVERTY-STRICKEN *HOMO SAPIENS NON SAPIENS* EXISTENCE

SUN

MOON

FARMER
GOD

THE SACRED CANOPY OF HEAVEN

**SUPERIOR SPECIES OF NATION
BECOME HEAD OF EMPIRE**

**INFERIOR 'UNDERDEVELOPED'
SPECIES OF NATION
BECOME PRODUCER
HANDS AND FEET
OF EMPIRE**

KEY: SUPERIMPOSED UPON

IMPERIAL
PYRAMID

COLONIZED
PYRAMID

INCORPORATING ITS INHABITANTS WITHIN THE GREATER PYRAMID OR EMPIRE, THEREBY
CONSIDERABLY RAISING THE STATUS OF EVERY LEVEL OF THE IMPERIAL PYRAMID. QUEEN
VICTORIA, FOR INSTANCE, BECAME EMPRESS OF INDIA, WHILE A BRITISH (OTHER RANKS)
SOLDIER GAINED CONSIDERABLY IN SOCIAL STATUS WHILST SERVING ABROAD IN INDIA.

'SO FAR FROM GOD, SO CLOSE TO THE UNITED STATES', WAS HOW THE MEXICAN DICTATOR PORFIRIO DIAZ SUMMED
UP THE TRAGEDY OF HIS COUNTRY. SEEN FROM THE CARIBBEAN OR CENTRAL AMERICA, THE US APPEARS LIKE A
GREAT FOREST TREE WHOSE BRANCHES PRE-EMPT THE AVAILABLE LIGHT AND SPACE AND WHOSE ROOTS SUCK AWAY
ALL THE AVAILABLE NOURISHMENT WHICH MIGHT OTHERWISE FLOW TO THE COUNTRIES IN ITS SHADOW.

ranges of the Andes), was to create a rigid division between the whites, the white-Indian half-breeds and the pure Indians. Those half-breeds excluded from white society, while not interbreeding with the Indians, became established in the Sierra as a race apart, as minor officials and traders.*

Following the spread of forest-like nations in the Northern Hemisphere right across the Southern Hemisphere, the world has become increasingly polarized between North and South as between 'haves' and 'have-nots', as between those relatively white, wealthy and powerful in terms of knowledge and possessions in the Northern Hemisphere and those relatively black, ignorant, poverty-stricken and powerless in environmental hells mainly to the south of them. The world has also become increasingly polarized between East and West, the Eastern nations under their various Communist and Muslim Suns and the Western nations under their various Christian Suns, each assured of its high moral purpose. Pierre Teilhard de Chardin[15] confirmed many Christians in their belief that they were a chosen people evolving along a phylum separate from the remainder of humankind, as specifically distinct as are sheep and goats.† He argued that they were ascending and converging towards an Omega Point, the Ultimate God of White Light, Legitimacy and Goodness of agricultural-industrial peoples, while the remainder of humankind, and in particular the Communists, would be cast into outer Darkness. This was a most sophisticated expression of Hope for the chosen people. Whether they were or not on such a phylum was entirely immaterial. What was most potently material was that many have seriously believed and behaved as though they were.

Following on, there is the third of the four principal aspects of a

---

*The prevention and prohibition of intermarriage and miscegenation, both within nations and as between nations, confirms that they behave as though they were different species. Furthermore, I argued in Part I, Chapter 5, that although most biologists use the terms parasite and parasitic to describe interactions between, not within, species, such terms may be used to describe the relationship of

Homo sapiens sapiens
Homo sapiens non sapiens

members of composite animals. But such terms may also be used as stated above, to describe interactions between species. It can be argued that those so parasitized – whether *Homo degener* individuals or entire nations – have been treated as though they were different species precisely because of the parasitical relationship between them.

†This is a logical extension of the aspirations to perfection amongst Roman Catholics, as evinced in the celibacy of the Roman Catholic priesthood, who have been wedded to a mythical Christ alone, and in the attempt in earlier times to prevent mixed marriages and the insistence on the children of mixed marriages that did occur being brought up Catholic, so preserving the purity and legitimacy of the Catholic stock within any one nation against actual or ideological interbreeding.

perverted memetic selection enumerated earlier: it is that the dominants and sub-dominants not only deliberately sacrifice those below them *en masse* in wars, but habitually oppress and cause immense suffering amongst them, often actively treating those below them and other nations and races as though they were different species of animal, including experimenting on, and sacrificing, humans regarded as rodents and vermin.

For thousands of years individual lives have counted for nothing in the pursuit by dominants and sub-dominants of personal wealth, status and power, using any and every means to those ends, no matter how cruel – as when some 12 million Africans were transported, over the 150 years between 1660 and 1810, to the New World to work on cotton and sugar plantations as slaves. They were regarded and treated as less than human, as virtually a new form of domestic animal.* Today there are, according to the UN, an estimated 100 million adult and child slaves. Kevin Bales[16], in his book *Disposable People*, has given a more conservative estimate of 27 million, of whom some 15–20 million are represented by bonded labour (or debt bondage) in India, Pakistan, Bangladesh and Nepal.† Bales defines a slave as 'a person held by violence or the threat of violence for economic exploitation'; while he likens the world of the slave to that of a concentration camp, where there are only those with total power and those with none. Slaves are treated variously as subhuman, as livestock to be used and abused and finally dumped when no longer of use. Bales argues that rapid population expansion and economic and technological change are reducing ever more people to poverty and destitution, and that companies and businesses across the world are taking advantage of this often anarchical situation to enslave more and more adults and children, for profit. For instance, in Brazil slavery was abolished 100 years ago. Today, according to the UN, some 7 million Brazilian children work as prostitutes or as slaves on plantations

---

*In 1822 some freed slaves were shipped back to West Africa, to Liberia which, in 1821, had been purchased by the philanthropic American Colonization Society and turned into a settlement for liberated black slaves from southern USA. It is profoundly ironical – though thoroughly in keeping with the collective memetic inheritance of the settlers – that these ex-slaves began to imitate the lifestyle of their erstwhile masters, building houses like those of the plantation owners they had once worked for, dressing their womenfolk in fashions similar to those of the Southern gentry, and enslaving the indigenous population. In other words, those who had been conquered imitated their conqueror in his main characteristics, and in their turn became masters over enslaved peoples.

† As well as the estimated 27 million enslaved people referred to above, there are about 1,000 forced labour camps and approximately 10 million forced labourers in China – described as 'the biggest slavery enterprises this century', producing more wealth for the government than the heavily subsidized state enterprises.

See Part III, Chapter 3, for the importance of slavery in supporting the global economy.

cutting cane which goes to fuel cars. Children also sweat in the fields of Malaysia and Mexico, slave in the factories of Bangladesh and Turkey, and prostitute themselves to foreign tourists in the Philippines. In Thailand 3 million children a year are sold into slavery and prostitution. All are the innocent victims of an economic order in which we in the West rely on their labour for cheap commodities, cheap goods and cheap fun. The UN has branded child slavery and prostitution 'an intolerable evil'. The evil lies in the parasite pyramidal structuring of societies that enables the powerful property and land owners to force, if necessary by violence, the powerless, landless poor and destitute into slavery in pursuit of profit. This process has been imitated at the national and international levels as many developing nations have been reduced by the more powerful developed nations to debt bondage, in turn to force their own destitute citizens into slavery.

Likewise, for thousands of years individual lives have counted for nothing in the pursuit by dominants and sub-dominants of territorial conquest, national status and glory. Sacrificed *en masse* in wars, they have been variously described as 'cattle' or 'sheep' led to the slaughter. When, for instance, the guns of the Great War fell silent in 1918, more than 8 million people had been killed.

> What passing-bells for these who die as cattle?
> Only the monstrous anger of the guns.
> Only the stuttering rifles' rapid rattle
> Can patter out their hasty orisons.[17]

According to President Wilson, the Great War was supposed to have been the 'war to end all wars'. Since then, an estimated 55 million people were killed in the Second World War, the majority of whom were civilians, another 2 million in the Korean War and at least 1 million in the war between Iraq and Iran. In 1996 it was estimated that some 23 million people had died in wars since the Second World War, since then many more millions have died in further major wars.* A new expression, 'ethnic cleansing', has entered the language, arising out of the conflict between the warring factions of the former Yugoslavia. Hatred between rival ethnic groups, combined with hatred arising from their different religions (Christian and Muslim), has caused each to view the others as vermin. All have been the victims of a perverted memetic selection.

---

*It has been estimated that, in recorded history – that is, since c.3500 BC – over 14,500 major wars have killed some four billion people, equivalent to two-thirds of the current world population.

In Germany, in the 1930s and early 1940s, the Nazis, as revealed in their literature and on film, saw the Jews as rodents, and proceeded to concentrate them in camps and eliminate them. The gas they used for that purpose was Zyklon B, a gas used to eradicate vermin. It is noteworthy that the Jews were selected to die in accordance with the viral memeplexes of National Socialism, Germany's state religion. Hitler was the messiah of a 'Church-state' with its own intolerant dogma, preachers and rites. Its radio-propaganda and communal radio-listening may be likened to church worship. Just as Christianity had its demons, those confronting the Nazis were Bolsheviks and Jews. The Germans were Hitler's 'chosen people', chosen to establish a 'thousand year Reich' of pure-blooded Germanic stock untainted by Semitism. As well as exterminating the Jews, they experimented on many of them, and used prisoners of war as slave labour to develop rocket research installations. The results of such experiments and inventions were used after the Second World War by other nations, as were the results of similar experiments undertaken by the Japanese on prisoners of war, whom they regarded as subhuman. During the Second World War the Japanese built Unit 731, a complex of research laboratories in north-east China, where scientists developed deadly microbes such as anthrax, bubonic plague, cholera and typhoid as weapons of mass destruction. These they tested on human guinea-pigs, infecting and killing hundreds of thousands of Chinese civilians and prisoners of war, dissecting the latter while still alive to determine the effects of their experiments. At the end of the war, while generals were executed for war crimes, the Americans struck a deal with the Japanese scientists: they handed over all their test data in exchange for immunity from prosecution for war crimes.

In his book, *The Paperclip Conspiracy*, Tom Bower[18] shows how nations such as America, the Soviet Union, Britain and France granted immunity from prosecution for war crimes to many German scientists recruited for exploitation in their respective national interests. Intent on plundering ideas as well as material, the Allies benefited immeasurably from Nazi experimentation and inventions: a great range of technological fields were affected, including space exploration, communications, aviation, medicine and military development. The relationship between the acceptability of scientific knowledge, the methods by which it is acquired and the ends to which it is applied shows yet again

> ... that there is no pile of corpses so high that it cannot be surmounted in the interests of 'national security.'[19]

Rodents, like insects, can be exterminated without feeling, without thought. With every scientific and technical advance the forest canopies of the developed nations of the world are raised ever higher above the forest floors, making it all the easier to treat those below without feeling, without thought. Originally the ability to destroy people from a distance and from on high was the prerogative of Farmer Gods and priesthoods of nations through their ostensible control of inimical natural phenomena. Today, science, with the invention of the aeroplane and rocket, has made it possible to unleash devastation thousands of miles away, without physical contact with, or feeling for, those destroyed.*

> When you're at the top, a rather successful friend of mine once whispered to me, you don't know how to feel. For when you are at the head of a large firm, or you have your head in Mach 2 clouds, you're completely cocooned.[20]

The residence of the dominant decision-makers in the increasingly rarefied atmosphere of the top canopies of nations, combined with demands of 'national security', has enabled the scientific and industrial dominants to wield an increasingly arbitrary, often secret and extraordinary power of life and death over people and the animal world in their research laboratories and through the products of their industries and technology. For instance, there occurred in Alabama, USA, one of the 'most repugnant episodes in the history of medical research', the Tuskegee Syphilis Study.[21] From 1932 to 1972 American researchers observed 400 poor African Americans with syphilis to follow the progress of their disease. And although penicillin became available in the 1950s, the researchers withheld the cure so that medical science might benefit from the study of untreated syphilis. The victims were not regarded as human beings but as disposable guinea pigs.

Governments and medical researchers in both the USA and Russia have also been involved in calculated experiments to test the effects of their technology on human beings. The United States Government, driven by its conviction that it must stay ahead of Russia in the nuclear arms race, carried out atomic weapons tests in the Nevada Desert, knowingly exposing thousands of its citizens to potentially dangerous doses of

---

*The same effect is now also achieved with the aid of anti-personnel land mines. Made in the UK and other European nations, these have been sold abroad and perform their killing and maiming mission thousands of miles away from their place of origin. According to UN figures, some 100 million mines are laid in some 64 countries. Every week some 500 people have been killed or maimed by land mines – 26,000 a year, mostly civilians. Afghanistan has some 400,000 amputees.

radiation – just as the Russians knowingly exposed thousands of their citizens to their atomic weapons tests.* The US Government also deliberately used its citizens as guinea pigs to test the effects of radiation.

> In an episode that U.S. Secretary of Energy Hazel O'Leary, in 1993, likened to the Nazi experiments of World War II, approximately 250 experiments were conducted in the United States between 1944 and 1973 on an estimated one hundred thousand individuals, including hospital patients who were injected with plutonium and pregnant women who were given radioactive pills. Thousands of American soldiers were ordered to march through the mushroom clouds of atomic test blasts.[22]

Britain conducted atomic tests off Christmas Island in 1958. Some 12,000 soldiers were obliged to witness the tests without any form of protective clothing. Some 60 per cent of these soldiers contracted radiation-related diseases, many dying in their fifties. Classified documents obtained from the Public Records Office at Kew revealed that one purpose of the tests was to discover the effect of radiation on soldiers.

Any person and any animal may suddenly find himself or itself acting as a guinea-pig and becoming a victim of scientific research and technological advance, sacrificed either deliberately or unwittingly on the altar of progress – that is, on the altar of individual and national aggrandizement and security – Minamata in Japan, Bhopal in India, Chernobyl in Russia and Seveso in Italy are notorious examples of the attitude of dominants world-wide. The senior officers of Hoffmann-La Roche knew five days after the Seveso accident in 1976 that their ICMESA factory had spewed out dioxin – one of the deadliest poisons known – over the surrounding countryside and homes. Yet they persistently withheld – from mercenary motives and to protect their own positions – this crucial knowledge from local politicians and the people who were already suffering because of their exposure to the chemical. The name of the poison was not publicly admitted for a fortnight after the accident. Tens of thousands of people were affected by the superpoison.

> The basic ethical problem is that the people who benefit from the making or use of hazardous chemicals of this type are not usually

---

*Recall my observation in Part II, Chapter 1, that a turning point in our anti-evolutionary history was reached when nations, as giant human beings, began to imitate each other, giving rise to the arms race between nations, the most significant example of which was that between the USA and Russia during the Cold War of the 1960s.

those who are at risk from them... The final immorality of ICMESA was that Hoffmann-La Roche had the benefit of a profitable product while the innocent citizens of Seveso unknowingly took the risk. They are now paying with their health for La Roche's profits and for the arrogance of the engineers and managers who set up (ICMESA) Department B...

'Capitalism means progress,' Dr Adolph Jann, President of Hoffmann-La Roche is reported as saying in a television interview about Seveso, 'and progress can lead sometimes to some inconvenience.'[23]

Of course laws have been enacted and safeguards erected, both at the national and international levels, to protect against some of these abuses: International Laws on Human Rights, the US Toxic Substances Control Act and the British Health and Safety at Work Act and Medicines Act of 1968 are just such measures. Nevertheless, such acts and laws have always proved to be too little too late, particularly when great national and multinational companies are involved, as in the case of the victims of thalidomide. The *Sunday Times* Insight Team[24] showed how a number of businessmen wreaked unimaginable harm upon many communities in the pursuit of profit. It also described how the law can erect almost insuperable barriers against the progress of justice and the pursuit of truth. But that is the perennial predicament of those who suffer a perverted memetic selection which is the price of progress and of the preservation of national security.

Torture, whose abolition in the last century in Europe was regarded as a mark of progress, has made such a comeback in the name of 'national security' that it is currently practised by one government in three. Amnesty International points out that torture is 'often less to do with pain than absolute humiliation and domination'. The aim is the destruction of the individual as a person. The torturers themselves are slowly desensitized and brutalized by those in authority, to the extent that they can be induced to see and treat their victims as less than human. This reveals the attitude of those in authority towards those whom they regard as enemies of the State: the latter are viewed as subhuman.

With so many human beings deliberately, or unwittingly, mutilated and sacrificed like guinea pigs, it is understandable that such animals themselves – particularly apes and monkeys living in the true forests of the world – should have received short shrift at the hands of experimental scientists. The justification of the use of experimental animals in research lies in the advancement of human welfare, interpreted not only in terms of material benefits and the conquest of disease, but in the necessity to explore the world around them to enlarge their understanding of nature. Some 20 million animals a year in the USA, and some 5 million a year in Great Britain, have been used in the cause of medical and military research (particularly in the development of antidotes to chemical and biological warfare) and to monitor commercial products such as herbicides and pesticides, food flavourings, cosmetics and fire extinguisher fluids. Changes in the law have indeed taken place here, too, as evinced in Great Britain in the Animals (Scientific Procedures) Act of 1986; the number of animals sacrificed to science in Britain stood at about 2.7 million at the end of 1999. However, such changes in the law not only show that the critics were right, but conceal the fact that such scientific progress as has already been made in the medical, military and commercial fields has been achieved by similar cruel experiments over hundreds of years. Furthermore, this much heralded law is applicable only in this one country in the developed world. The laws in this and every other developed nation are effectively circumvented, both by scientists moving to laboratories in other developed countries where the laws relating to their particular experiments are less stringent or non-existent, and because much animal research has moved away from the public arena, where it was vulnerable to questioning, into industry, where it is protected by commercial secrecy and cannot be questioned.

There is, however, a far more profound aspect of this whole argument, which is that the human beings whose health, well-being and security are so much the concern of science are not in any sense true human beings: their needs, and the way science meets those needs, are both inhuman. No human needs whatsoever can justify experimentation on other species of animal, because *all* our diseases and needs are the end products of our own re-evolutionary, or anti-evolutionary, condition as subhuman beings. Nothing can justify a demand for chimpanzees for biomedical research that requires between 10 and 29 chimpanzees to die to provide a single infant for export to the laboratories of the developed world.[25] The cruelty surrounding their procurement and any use to which such animals may be put by scientific dominants, merely serve to perpetuate and, as I will show in the following chapters, to exacerbate an already profoundly degenerate condition of deranged people.

Just as laws have the unfortunate effect of forcing scientists to move to laboratories in developed countries with less restrictive laws, they also have the unfortunate and unforeseen effect of driving manufacturers' operations underground – they often force companies to move some of their operations to developing countries. Western drug companies and medical researchers have been conducting clinical trials in poor countries, using people like 'laboratory rats' to test whether drugs and vaccines are effective and safe before putting them on sale in Western countries, at the same time withdrawing them from the now otiose 'rats',* while drugs such as thalidomide and dangerous pesticides have been made available in developing countries long after they have been proscribed in Europe or America.†

As in the case of man-made famine, man-made poisons are spreading across, and have spread across, the world in the wake of colonialism and neo-colonialism. The UN has estimated that perhaps 40,000 people are killed each year by pesticides, and a further 2 million injured. Despite denials to the contrary, what we have to face is a continuous and insidious poisoning of the entire environment. In relation to chemicals and their manufacturers we are 'in little better position than the guests of the Borgias'.[26]

A perverted memetic selection works not only to maim and destroy people in the present, but also those of future generations. For as well as imitating and resembling certain natural ecosystems, and as well as creating artificial ecosystems that imitate natural systems – all of which cause *Homo degener* to behave in inhuman ways – nations have developed chemicals used as pesticides which are radio-mimetic, or radiation imitating chemicals, whose effects are as damaging to the genetic make-up of the individual (and so to future generations) as are the effects of radiation. This accords with the observation made earlier in Part II, Chapter 1, that, whereas amongst *Homo sapiens* hunter-gatherers genes and memes reinforced one another, the interests of the memes amongst *Homo degener* peoples have been opposed to those of the genes, to produce behaviour that is memetically adaptive but biologically maladaptive, and therefore altogether evodeviant.

In a multiplicity of ways, down the ages and throughout the world, nations have afforded dominant élites the facilities to treat, to maim and

---

* In 1997, poor people in the Third World had AIDS treatment withdrawn by multinational drug companies after participating in trials which proved the success of the companies' latest drugs for use in the West.

† A similar perverted memetic selection, that places profits before people, concerns the export of asbestos. While exercising strict national asbestos controls, Canada exported 98 per cent of its asbestos production in 2000, mostly to South-East Asia and South America. An article in the *New Scientist* quoted Antti Tossavainen of the Finnish Institute of Occupational Health as saying that 'Developing countries are importing a health time bomb from Canada that is set to explode in around 30 years'. Though known as a killer, 'Canada has been lobbying hard to maintain its exports. In July, the country's Prime Minister Jean Chrétien telephoned Chilean President Ricardo Lagos in a failed attempt to dissuade the country from banning imports.' (James Randerson, 'Canada's killer export', *New Scientist*, Vol. 171, No. 2310, 29 September 2001, p. 16)

to destroy their fellows as though they were different species of animal for the sake of their own aggrandizement, health and security. This brings me to the last and perhaps most important aspect of a perverted memetic selection.

Underlying the three principal ways in which super-dominant Sun and top canopy of dominant élites are the principal agents of a perverted memetic selection, there has been a more profound super-dominant: the atavistic fear of the wilderness, arising from the profound void of the Mesolithic, from which all these other super-dominants and dominants are descended and by which, through the collective memetic inheritance of each nation, they have been nourished and fed. This was earlier described as the negative aspect of the Life-Force of the nation which, unlike the top canopy which may be described as the power plant of white Hope, forms the basis of what may be described as the power plant of humiliating ignorance and black fear, out of which the power plant of hope has grown. Their desire to whiten themselves in the vertical, as an expression of success, is of course underpinned by the fear of failure, of sinking to a lower level within the forest-like society, which in turn is expressive of the original failure of people as hunter-gatherers and their associated fear of the wilderness. The lowest common denominator governing their collective behaviour has been humiliation: humiliating ignorance, fear and hatred of wild nature and of their own true natures.*

Homo degener, by his adoption of agriculture, had declared war on wild nature and its inhabitants. When the English first arrived in Australia they declared they had discovered 'Terra Nullius', or 'empty land', which gave them, in their opinion, total land rights. They classified its Aboriginal inhabitants as sub-human, part of the existing flora and fauna, to be exterminated as necessary.† The Bushmen, regarded as 'wild beasts' by the Boers, were mercilessly gunned down.‡ They, like the Aborigines, fought back, but to no avail. As Laurens van der Post wrote of the Bushman in 1984:

> His culture was dying before our eyes and he, and what was left of it, was about to vanish physically and spiritually into the bastard bloodstream of his unworthy conquerors.[27]

---

* See Part III, Chapter 2, for an amplification of this argument.

† The Aborigines were not seen as citizens of Australia, nor even as human beings at all. They were, as I intimated earlier, legally voted for inclusion in the Flora and Fauna Act.

‡ When Dutch settlers arrived in the Cape in the 1600s, they regarded the Bushman as the South African equivalent of the orang-utan – or 'forest man' – of Indonesia, regarding them as less than human. They continued to shoot them as vermin until early in the 20th century.

A succinct description of the absorption of hunter-gatherer peoples into the illegitimate body of a composite animal.

The settlement of America provides a classic example of invasion and a declaration of war on humans regarded as subhuman. When the Pilgrim Fathers landed in America, they did so as a community, as a rudimentary composite animal, carrying with them viral memeplexes peculiar to the English nation. As important was their preconception of the New World. One of their number recorded,

> The place they had thoughts on was some of those vast & unpeopled countries of America, which are frutfull & fitt for habitation; being devoyd of all civill inhabitants; wher ther are only savage & brutish men, which range up and downe little otherwise then the wild beasts of the same.[28]

So when they met the Native American hunter-gatherers, they could not and did not see them for what they really were: highly developed as hunter-kings of natural food pyramids, who were successfully adapted to the continent they roamed. Instead, what they thought they saw were savages, something brutish and subhuman, a projection of their own fear of the unknown. Viewed as another hostile feature of the wild landscape, the Native Americans, like the forests, had to be cleared away. As was said of their treatment of the Native Americans:

> If any tribe remonstrated against the violation of their natural and treaty rights, members of the tribe were inhumanly shot down and the whole treated as mere dogs.[29]

Homo degener members of nations are governed, not, as anthropologists and others would have us believe, by instincts acquired during the prehistoric struggle for survival of *Homo sapiens* in a world which was in fact their beloved home, but by instincts acquired during the prehistoric struggle for survival of rudimentary nations in a world regarded by them as implacably hostile. Such instincts are those which I have described as the collective memetic inheritance of the composite animal, instincts which are inherently imbued with a collective primary schizophrenia and paranoia. In that their learned behaviour is dominated by that inheritance, it is dominated by the 'memory grown automatic' of the Mesolithic. *Hence the prior super-dominant governing the behaviour of* Homo degener *is the profound void of the Mesolithic, the profoundly humiliating two-fold fall that gave rise to their fears and hatred of the wild world and of their own true natures.* Subsequent contact with the wilderness would continue to give rise to atavistic fears, and to consequent acts of cruelty against its inhabitants. The incredibly cruel treatment of the wolf by *Homo degener* in North America is a case in point.

A lot of people didn't just kill wolves; they tortured them. They set wolves on fire and tore their jaws out and cut their Achilles tendons and turned dogs loose on them. They poisoned them with strychnine, arsenic, and cyanide, on such a scale that *millions* of other animals ... were killed incidentally in the process. In the thick of the wolf fever they even poisoned themselves, and burned down their own property torching the woods to get rid of wolf havens. In the United States in the period between 1865 and 1885 cattlemen killed wolves with almost pathological dedication. In the twentieth century people pulled up alongside wolves in airplanes and snowmobiles and blew them apart with shotguns for sport. In Minnesota in the 1970s people choked Eastern timber wolves to death in snares to show their contempt for the animal's designation as an endangered species.[30]

Such exhibitions of mass cruelty and massacre – a 'savagery almost beyond comprehension' – like those practised upon Tasmanians during the 19th century, were not only government-approved but often government-financed. Fortunes were made by bounty-hunters. The wolf's treatment in Europe and Russia has been similar to that in America. In the former the wolf has been vilified and persecuted ever since the arrival of the first farmers; in Russia it has been poisoned like vermin and machine-gunned from the air. Yet the wolf is a beautiful, 'incredibly intelligent' and benign animal, which does not, except under extreme duress, prey upon humans.

Whether in Europe, in Russia or in America, wolf-killers have believed they were doing something deeply and profoundly right. As instanced by B.H. Lopez, Theodore Roosevelt placed his hand upon the Bible as he vowed to exterminate the wolf, which he called 'the beast of waste and desolation', so destructive to commerce and a threat to progress. After all, as Lopez points out, the aim of the state is a subdued, pastoral and productive countryside. More importantly, this righteous extermination of the wolf shows quite unambiguously the extraordinary change in attitude of mind and in behaviour that has taken place as between world-loving hunter-gatherer and world-fearing farmer.

In a hunter society, like that of the Cheyenne, traits that were universally admired – courage, hunting skill, endurance – placed the wolf in a pantheon of respected animals; but when man turned to agriculture and husbandry, to cities, the very same wolf was hated as cowardly, stupid, and rapacious. The wolf itself remains unchanged but man now speaks of his hated 'animal' nature.[31]

Both Church and Science, the two main branches of knowledge that relate the nation to the natural world, proposed that man is superior and that animals were put on Earth to do his bidding. Man reasons, he is whitened by the Light of civilization, he has a soul; the non-human animal does not reason, it inhabits the outer darkness beyond civilization, it has no soul – it is inferior. Therefore men incurred no moral guilt in grossly abusing animals and killing them. By association, similar treatment has been meted out to Jews, women – especially those accused of witchcraft – *Homo sapiens non sapiens* labouring poor, criminals, dark-skinned peoples and *Homo sapiens* hunter-gatherers. For nigh on two thousand years the Jews have been regarded as the people of the Devil, the embodiment of cosmic evil. In the Middle Ages

> ...the Jews were accused of poisoning wells and causing the Black Death and other horrors; the massacres of the Jews by the Crusaders were a foretaste, hampered by inadequate technology, of the Nazi Holocaust...[32]

while in Germany the criminal was expelled from the company of his fellows and forced into that of the beasts of the forest.

> The Middle Latin *wargus* – i.e. 'expulsus' – is also the name of the wolf; and thus the two conceptions – that of the wild beast to be hunted down, and that of the man to be treated as a wild beast – are intimately associated.[33]

The concepts of cosmic evil, criminal and wild beast to be hunted down were conjoined in the Final Solution, of which the 'Jew hunt' throughout Nazi occupied Poland in 1942 and 1943 was an important and statistically significant phase.

> It was a tenacious, remorseless, ongoing campaign in which the 'hunters' tracked down and killed their 'prey' in direct and personal confrontation.[34]

Like the wolf, like the Jews, all are victims of the atavistic fears underlying the survival and growth of nations. All, at various times, have been seen as other, as alien, as incomprehensible and as frightening as the wilderness, and therefore a threat to the existing social order. All, like the wolf, have been used as scapegoats for the economic and other ills of societies. None more so, however, than the wolf which, as I argued in Part I, Chapter 4, was regarded in the Middle Ages as 'the devil devourer of man's soul', and become the subconscious scapegoat for deranged man's loss of natural inhibitions and consequent bestiality. So not only have dominant élites acquired the right to decide and select who and what shall live and who and what shall be experimented upon, set gravely at risk, or cruelly persecuted in order that the nation shall survive and prosper, but the mass of people themselves, in imitation of the dominant élites of their societies, may act to remove from within their territory human and animal elements considered detrimental to their economic well-being, and therefore variously regarded as dogs, rodents, insects, pests.

The four aspects of a perverted memetic selection enumerated above have tended to reinforce one another, turning the majority of humankind and the fauna of wild nature into victims of a perverted memetic selection. Such a selection constitutes an extraordinary degeneration of the human psyche, physique and behaviour, and concomitant degeneration of the Earth. It is a degeneration that has been intensified and spread abroad with the phenomenal rise and fall of empires and related interregnums of anarchy.

Chapter 7

The Degenerative Effects of the Rise and Fall of Empires

> There is the moral of all human tales;
> Tis but the same rehearsal of the past;
> First Freedom, and the Glory – when that fails
> Wealth, Vice, Corruption – Barbarism at last
> And History, with all her volumes vast,
> Hath but one page.
>
> (Byron)

In the last chapter I showed some of the effects of the forest-like spread of the Spanish culture across Peru. As important as the rise of empire are the long-term effects of their fall. Since the earliest days of Sumeria empires have risen and fallen throughout the world, spreading and intermingling cultures, often submerging and destroying cultures, the Arab Empire being a classic example.

I referred in Part I to the birth, c.570 AD, of the Prophet Muhammad, and the growth and spread of Islam throughout the whole Arabian peninsula. Following the Prophet's death, in 632 AD, Abu Bakr, his chief lieutenant, took over the leadership with the title of khalif or successor. So great was the enthusiasm inspired by the Prophet, who had himself expressed it the duty of his followers to fight against unbelievers, promising that any Muslim killed in battle against infidels would be instantly translated to Paradise, that the Arabs set out, a year after his death, to attack both Byzantium and Persia. Spurred on by their recently acquired Manifest Destiny – their divine mission and right to engulf and control as much of the world as possible, together with the belief that God Himself intended them to win – they drove the Byzantines across the Taurus Mountains into Asia Minor and destroyed the Persian army at

Nehawand. By the middle of the 7th century AD the Arabs had occupied the whole of Persia, spread across part of North Africa and launched a fleet to capture Cyprus.

Such a sudden and dramatic rise from point zero to a pinnacle of power was later to be followed by an equally swift and dramatic fall.

The Abbasid khalifs achieved a glittering peak of wealth, worldly glory and power during the reigns of Harun al-Rashid (786–809 AD) and his son Ma'mun (813–33 AD). Yet only two generations after Ma'mun their successors were being tortured and humiliated, despised even to the extent of appearing unworthy of assassination. So died the prestige of the khalifate, which stemmed from the Prophet Muhammad, the Apostle of the Farmer God, and which, together with the initial humiliations suffered by the Prophet and his followers, formed the Sun and Life-Force to ascent of the imperial stratified structure. The man-made Sun which had shone so brightly upon the Muslim world for some 250 years was virtually extinguished.

The dramatic rise, and equally dramatic fall, of the Arab Empire is a prime example of the rising and setting of an illusory man-made Sun, that perverts the light of the true sun illuminating the glory of all humans as hunter-gatherers, leaving only darkness. The eclipse of the Sun of Islam was, however, only temporary, for in time similar Suns would shine, if intermittently and less brightly, over the many Muslim nations now in being.

There is, according to John Glubb,[1] a marked similarity between the Arab and British Empires in their decline. Both empires (and several others also) lasted for some two hundred and thirty years in their prime. The complete disintegration of each followed within fifty years of its highest pinnacle of glory.

If the Arab Empire can be said to have been established with the elevation of Mu'awiya to the khalifate in 661 AD, the dominion of Spain broke away 94 years later. And if the British Empire can be said to have begun in 1700, the American Colonies broke away 82 years later. In both cases, however, the original empires continued to grow for another hundred or more years. Harun al-Rashid and his son Ma'mun, and Queen Victoria and her son Edward VII, reigned over empires at the height of their wealth, power and glory. In both cases, within fifty years of their ascent to a seemingly unassailable peak of glory, the empires disintegrated and the imperial dependencies were lost. In due course, the Spanish Empire arose out of the ashes of the Arab, and survived for a similar period of time.

To the extraordinary similarity between the lives of the Arab and British

Empires, particularly with regard to their duration and their similarity in decline, may be added that of Spain. Glubb[2] argues that the forces behind this extraordinarily similar and regular rise and fall of empires do not appear to depend on forms of government or political constitution. Rather, empires undergo changes, and have a life span, that is often as regular as those of a person in the transition from infancy to old age.

This growth and decline may be ascribed to the drive on the part of nations, as composite animals, to grow, to become both rich and strong, and thereafter to protect their wealth.

> If they neglect to provide adequate military defences, they may be unable to respond if a rival power takes advantage of them; if they spend too much on armaments – or, more usually, upon maintaining at growing cost the military obligations they had assumed in a previous period – they are likely to overstrain themselves, like an old man attempting to work beyond his natural strength.[3]

For example,

> Like the British Empire three centuries later, the Habsburg bloc was a conglomeration of widely scattered territories, a political-dynastic *tour de force* which required enormous sustained resources of material and ingenuity to keep going. As such, it provides one of the greatest examples of strategical overstretch in history; for the price of possessing so many territories was the existence of numerous foes, a burden also carried by the contemporaneous Ottoman Empire...
>
> The failure of Habsburg Spain's European aims by the mid-seventeenth century was clearly related to its internal problems and relative economic decline; having overstrained itself in all directions, it was now weak at heart.[4]

So, here we see a process of growth and decline, exhibiting changes as regular as those of persons in their transition from infancy to old age; when, as Paul Kennedy points out, 'they are likely to overstrain themselves, like an old man attempting to work beyond his natural strength ... (and) now weak at heart'. This rhythmic rise and fall of empire – a horizontal expansion to vertical growth, and subsequent contraction and decline – is further evidence of the nation behaving as a super-animal, a giant human being. This horizontal expansion to vertical growth, and subsequent contraction and decline, may also be seen as further evidence of the nation behaving as a forest-like super-plant, growing under relatively favourable climatic (i.e. religio-socio-economic) conditions, and contracting under relatively unfavourable conditions.

As the opaque body of the imperial race intercepts the light of the Farmer Suns of the peoples it overlays – or light of the true sun in the case of the hunter-gatherers – it creates an umbral zone of total eclipse under the imperial shadow and a penumbral or partially eclipsed zone of mandated territories that service the imperial race. India, for instance, was a major part of the umbral zone under the Imperial shadow. The penumbral zone may act as a buffer to the umbral, protecting the communications routes to profit and power derived mainly from the umbral – as in the establishment of virtual British rule in Palestine, Transjordan, Egypt, the Sudan, Aden and Iraq, the better to keep open Imperial communications with India. By means of umbral and penumbral imperialism, the imperial race was enabled to rise, layer by layer, higher and higher, eventually achieving an approximate equilibrium with its environment as an empire. (See figure 7.1)

However, unlike the forest, its equilibrium is an illusion and short-lived. Whereas forests may reach a comparatively long-lived and stable climax, forests of deranged people achieve a dangerously unstable and relatively short-lived climax. For the cost of achieving and sustaining the climax often proves too great. It suffers from what has been described as 'imperial overstretch':[5] in the course of repeated and protracted conflicts it tends so to over-extend itself that it becomes militarily top-heavy for its weakening or under-powered economic base.

The Russian Empire, for example, lasted for some 400 years. Having expanded from its Volga heartland in the mid 16th century in response to its felt need for security following centuries of conflict with the Tatars, the Russians conquered a variety of peoples to the east and south, to create an empire, underwritten by Orthodox Christianity, which ultimately crippled Russia – a prime example of imperial overstretch.

A principal outcome of the rise and fall of empires has been the spread of degeneration throughout the world. This includes both a primary degeneration, when hunter-gatherers such as the Native American and Australian Aborigines were forcibly de-ranged and domesticated, and a secondary historical degeneration.

The Native American hunter-gatherers, the Aborigines and Tasmanians were almost all reduced to a primary degeneration – or destroyed – by the spread of the British Empire and its subsequent offspring, the USA and Australia. Their enforced degeneration, and concomitant degeneration of the wilderness, under the cloak of a Manifest Destiny, reveals *Homo degener* as the agent of wrong-doing all the more malign because it is

Part II: fig 7.1

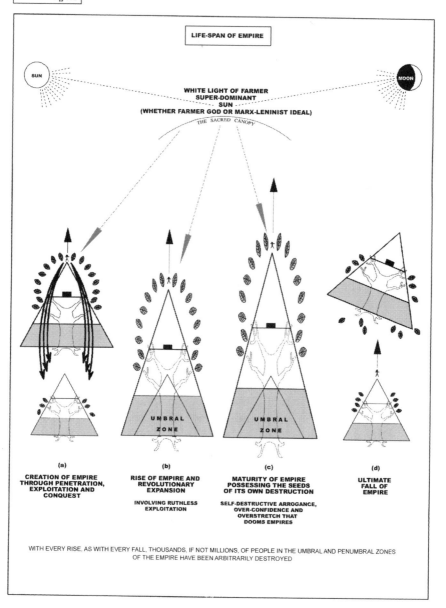

LIFE-SPAN OF EMPIRE

WHITE LIGHT OF FARMER
SUPER-DOMINANT
SUN
(WHETHER FARMER GOD OR MARX-LENINIST IDEAL)

THE SACRED CANOPY

(a)

CREATION OF EMPIRE
THROUGH PENETRATION,
EXPLOITATION AND
CONQUEST

(b)

RISE OF EMPIRE AND
REVOLUTIONARY
EXPANSION

INVOLVING RUTHLESS
EXPLOITATION

(c)

MATURITY OF EMPIRE
POSSESSING THE SEEDS
OF ITS OWN DESTRUCTION

SELF-DESTRUCTIVE ARROGANCE,
OVER-CONFIDENCE AND
OVERSTRETCH THAT
DOOMS EMPIRES

(d)

ULTIMATE
FALL OF
EMPIRE

WITH EVERY RISE, AS WITH EVERY FALL, THOUSANDS, IF NOT MILLIONS, OF PEOPLE IN THE UMBRAL AND PENUMBRAL ZONES
OF THE EMPIRE HAVE BEEN ARBITRARILY DESTROYED

disguised in the garments of the greatest good. The British Empire was both projected and experienced as a religious calling, to take freedom and the rule of law to countries which would never have known them otherwise. The belief that they were the bearers of a burden of responsibility for the betterment of the human race not only masked the greed and arrogance, the voracity and violence which governed relationships both within the homeland and the empire, but in particular masked the loss of the very real freedom and perfection under the natural law by hunter-gatherers forcibly de-ranged and domesticated in the imperial advance. A 'divine right to be there'* implies the existence of a Farmer God and then the delusion that such a God sanctions and sanctifies the ruling few in their possession, governance and exploitation, whether they govern and exploit a nation or an empire. They sanction and sanctify in effect an ongoing primary and secondary historical degeneration; delusion and self-delusion are once again shown to be the most dangerous aspects of that ongoing degeneration.

There are other notable aspects of a secondary historical degeneration. Earlier, in Chapter 6, I argued that the relationship between conqueror and conquered has been a prime factor in the perverted memetic selection of peoples. The spread of empires (whether territorial or commercial) across the world has ensured a degeneration of the cultures of those conquered as they seek to emulate the main characteristics of the conquerors, making for an increasing homogeneity of the peoples and cultures world-wide.† In addition, colonial expropriation and exploitation is the process that not only encouraged the spread of man-made famine over the face of the Earth, but also the spread of diseases such as tuberculosis, typhoid, smallpox and cholera. It is also the process by which prohibitions against miscegenation have built up and spread across the world, and so by which different races have come to be treated as though they were different species, as with the inclusion of the Aborigines in the Australian Flora and Fauna Act.‡ Meanwhile, in the homeland of the empire, there has

---

* 'When I was a child three or four thousand British Civil Servants and sixty or seventy thousand British troops governed several hundred million Indians. It is ridiculous to suppose that this handful ruled so many millions by force; they governed by the hypnotic effect of prestige, because they believed in their divine right to be there...'[6]

† The rise of empires has spread abroad all those aspects of a perverted memetic selection which were outlined in Chapter 6 above.

‡ Ironically, the Aborigines, as wild and true human beings, were rightly so included. The intention of the Australians was, however, to denigrate them, thereby justifying their own subhuman treatment of them as though they were different species; justifying too their theft of the land and subsequent growth of the Sacred Species of composite animal that is Australia.

arisen the demoralizing influence of luxury and wealth, when manufactured material objects become the only reality, and laxity of sexual morals, violence, corruption, effeminacy and the influence of women in public life become commonplace. This, as John Glubb[7] has pointed out, was the case with the Roman and Arab Empires: it is now also the case with Britain.

The introduction of women and machinery into the workplace in Britain has increasingly made men redundant, debasing their identities, sense of belonging and self-esteem. This is in keeping with the ongoing emasculation of the generality of men, which makes for increasing violence against their fellows. Deprived of their hunting identities and then of their farming identities – both based on close identification with the land – they are now being deprived of their industrial identities as they are replaced by women and by machinery. Women are assuming rôles originally created by men for men. At the same time men are forced to assume rôles that were originally the prerogative of women, such as nursing. This, as I argue in the next chapter, accords with the gregarious colony or hive-like situation, that usually favours the sterile female or neutered form in preference to the male. This is in sharp contrast to hunter-gatherer societies, where male and female rôles were entirely different by virtue of their sex, yet of equal importance to the well-being and survival of the group. Women's true equality in their specific rôle precluded any need on their part to assume the male rôle.

With the spread of empires, both territorial and commercial, we thus find not only that the conquered tend to imitate the conquerors, a perverted memetic selection making for an increase in homogeneity of the peoples and cultures world-wide, but that women tend more and more to imitate men, and vice versa, making for the increasing standardization of peoples as integral parts of composite animals – phenomena to which I drew attention earlier – and showing that the members of nations are, one way or another, no more than interchangeable housekeepers in their greater houses.

These degenerative processes have been further intensified and spread abroad by the fathering of new nations by the imperial power, which, in imitation of their erstwhile conquerors, compete in their turn for a place in the sun. They replace the imperial order and euphemistically termed 'peace' – for example, '*Pax Romana*, the peace within the Roman empire; so *pax Britannica*, the peace imposed by British rule' (*OED*) – with an interregnum of anarchy.

At the same time as a colonial power's ability and will to dominate and subdue parts of the world beyond its own realm has waned, freedom movements within its colonies have tended to unite in the struggle for independence, eventually becoming strong enough either to challenge and throw off the authority and yoke of the colonial power, as did the American Colonies, or at least to 'stand on their own two feet' once given their independence. For instance, the British Empire at different times and in different parts of the world united many separate tribes or nations, which had earlier resided under their own Culture Ancestors, Gods and Kings – their own Suns – under one imperial Sun. In Nigeria, for instance, there were over 250 nations that were to become grouped in a colonial entity. The dominant ethnic groups were the Hausa-Fulanis, the Ibos and the Yoruba, each of which held sway over large territories.

As the imperial power waned and control from the centre weakened at the periphery, these new composite animals created by the colonial powers broke away from the parent animals – while yet retaining many of the features of the parent animals* – to form such nations as the USA, India, Pakistan, Kenya, Uganda and Nigeria, each under its own new super-dominant Sun.

Each was now possessed, to a greater or lesser degree, of a displacement drive to vertical self-aggrandizement out of a humiliating colonial experience, competing with others for a place in the sun. Hence an imperial order – one Sun, one 'imperial peace' and law – was replaced, as we see today following the departure of the British Empire, by an anarchy of competing States and associated Suns and laws: a large number of often mutually hostile tribes, that had previously been incorporated under one 'imperial peace' and Sun, became a smaller number of often hostile nations. These possessed an infinitely greater power to anarchy over a far wider area than had the earlier tribes for three main reasons.

Firstly, on account of the incipient paranoia inherent in every nation competing for a place in the sun. Secondly, since ethnic groups and their traditional lands have often been divided by the entirely artificial and arbitrary territorial frontiers bequeathed by European imperialism, they have tended to create, as in the case of the Kurds and Kurdistan, a potential threat to the stability of the states they are forced to inhabit. Thirdly, because their constituent ethnic groups, who may earlier have united in the struggle for independence, tend to fall apart after the colonial power has departed and engage in bitter internecine conflicts rooted in ethnic and religious rivalries. They continually threaten to break

---

*With the approach of independence in the New Hebrides – or Vanuatu – in 1980 the New Hebrideans themselves split into two angry and apparently irreconcilable camps – one loyal to Britain, the other to France. Each mirrored the intolerance that their colonial masters have exhibited towards one another down the centuries, an example of the conquered imitating the conquerors.

up into their constituent ethnic parts. Such threats have important international implications, particularly when the territories concerned are rich in strategically important minerals. When Ibo Biafra, whose territory was rich in oil, tried to secede from Nigeria, the subsequent war of 1967–69 to preserve the unity of Nigeria against Balkanization and to prevent strategic oil supplies and revenues falling into the hands of a breakaway Biafran nation was rapidly internationalized. The British, Russians and Egyptians supplied arms to the Nigerians, while the French, Czechs and Chinese supplied them to Biafra. Over a million people died.

This descent into anarchy represents a major secondary historical degeneration following the rise and fall of empire, when any relative freedom people might have enjoyed under the 'imperial peace' tends to be subverted by a new tyranny, and so many millions of people are either maimed or killed in the ensuing violence.

David Lamb, for instance, wrote in the introduction to his book, *The Africans*, that it was

> …the story of people who won their freedom on battlefields and at negotiating tables, only to discover that their white colonial masters had been replaced by black neocolonial leaders more concerned with personal power and wealth than national consensus or development.

He goes on:

> Many readers will find this an unsettling book because the Africa of the 1980s is neither a happy nor a hopeful place. The colonialists designed the scenario for disaster, and the Africans seem to be trying their best to fulfil it. Calamity waits within arm's reach, oblivious of Africa's potential strength. Across the whole continent, economies are collapsing, cities are deteriorating, food production is declining, populations are growing like weed-seeds turned loose in a garden. Governments fall at the whim of illiterate sergeants and disgruntled despots, prisons are as overcrowded as the farmlands are empty, and at last count the number of refugees in Africa had reached the incredible figure of five million – people driven from their home-lands by wars, tyrants and poverty.

'Africa is dying,' Edem Kodjo, secretary-general of the Organization of African Unity, told a group of African leaders in 1978. 'If things continue as they are, only eight or nine of the present countries will survive the next few years. All other things being equal, absolute poverty, instead of declining, is likely to gain ground. It is clear that the economy of our continent is lying in ruins.'[8]

In Africa generally, in the words of Harry Oppenheimer,

> The fact is that in the majority of the new African states a new tyranny has limited individual freedom, wrecked the economy and over large areas has produced a state of endemic violence and sometimes starvation.[9]

This was still the situation in 1999,* as violence flared up once more in Angola, Ethiopia and Eritrea, Rwanda, Burundi and Sierra Leone. Violence continues in Sudan, while the war in the Democratic Republic of Congo drew in several other nations. Between 1999 and 2005 more than 3 million people have been killed in the Congo. Many of the wars are about control of natural resources – in Sierra Leone these include diamonds and bauxite, and in the Congo tantalum, diamonds and copper. But there are also those fighting to preserve the old order against democratization.† There is, in consequence, a proliferation of weapons, and millions of children are growing up in a culture of violence. Meanwhile declining commodity prices – whether for Zambian copper or Ghanaian cocoa beans – looting, corruption and AIDS help further ravage the continent. And the poor are even poorer.

In the Indian sub-continent the story has been similar: the separation of India and Pakistan caused the loss of some 500,000 lives, and the subsequent secession of Bangladesh from Pakistan caused further appalling loss of life. New extremes of wealth and poverty, religious fanaticism and violence have flourished. Despite this, India has remained remarkably stable, though the issue of a divided Kashmir remains so serious a bone of contention between India and Pakistan that it could destabilize the whole sub-continent.

A sustained period of anarchy has normally followed the fall of empire.

---

*In 1999 President Mbeki of South Africa persuaded the Organization of African Development (OAU) and Southern African Development Community (SADC) to signal that they will no longer tolerate military coups and corruption. Though an end to conflicts and corruption in southern and central Africa is a thoroughly commendable aspiration, it cannot, however, disguise the fact that this anarchical and chaotic state of affairs has arisen directly out of the rise and fall of the European empires. Like their teeming populations the African states themselves are also the victims of a perverted memetic selection.

†In addition, the severe inequality of landownership bequeathed by colonialism has persisted not only in African countries such as Zimbabwe and Kenya, but also throughout South America and in other nations, giving rise to considerable violence.

Not only do empires appear to have risen and fallen with peculiar regularity, as regularly as night follows day, but the interval between one so-called 'imperial peace' and the next has also tended to follow a pattern, that of a period of anarchy lasting several hundred years. The fall of the Roman Empire was followed by six centuries of barbarism. After the fall of the Arab Empire, 'imperial peace' was not reconstituted over the area for six centuries, when the Ottoman Turks imposed their rule. The fall of the British Empire (together with that of other dominant West European colonial powers) has so far followed lines similar to those of the Arab Empire, namely fragmentation into small states which, as argued above, are often mutually hostile and possess a much greater power to anarchy than was the case prior to their colonization and subsequent creation as nation-states bounded by internationally recognized frontiers. For they are governed by a perverted memetic selection that causes most of them to imitate the offensive-defensive vertically orientated structure-building behaviour of their erstwhile masters, at the cost of *Homo sapiens*, wildlife and wilderness. Botswana, where the San (Bushmen) have been deprived of their land in favour of its exploitation for diamonds, is an outstanding example. The domination of parts of the world under an 'imperial peace', that has been followed by a long interregnum of anarchy, has in fact been conducive to the evolution, not of *Homo sapiens*, but of more and more, and increasingly powerful,

$$\frac{Homo\ sapiens\ sapiens}{Homo\ sapiens\ non\ sapiens}$$

nation-states overlaying the kingdom of nature – and so to the regressive evolution of *Homo degener* at the cost of that of *Homo sapiens*.*

The natural environment in which our earliest ancestors evolved was generally one of long-sustained order and peace, interspersed with relatively short periods of natural catastrophe and chaos, the whole contributing to the overall harmony and balance, as in a symphony, of nature. Such a natural flux and succession of innumerable natural food pyramids favoured the evolution and perfection of *Homo sapiens* hunter-gatherers. The man-made environment of

$$\frac{Homo\ sapiens\ sapiens}{Homo\ sapiens\ non\ sapiens}$$

farmer-industrialists, on the other hand, has generally been one of disorder and anarchy, interspersed with occasional periods of what are euphemistically

---

* To these oppressive nations has been added a new layer of oppression over the wild world – the multinationals. These are modern commercial and industrial empires that transcend political boundaries and operate outside the sway of national governments. They are, as I pointed out in Part I, Chapter 8, the neo-colonial successors of the West European nations.

termed 'imperial order' and 'peace'. Yet the distinction between 'imperial order' and anarchy is largely illusory, simply because each nation that aspires to empire creates anarchy in its expansion over other peoples, and anarchy in decline. Because of their parasitical or predatory nature, all 'order' or 'peace' *imposed* by stratified societies is conducive to anarchy.

> The international system, whether it is dominated for a time by six Great Powers or only two, remains anarchical – that is, there is no greater authority than the sovereign, egoistical nation-state ... this is an anarchic world in which 'dissatisfied' powers jostle alongside 'satisfied' ones...[10]*

That is so, even when the greater authority is that of a nation-state temporarily fulfilling the rôle of empire. As the direct result of the spread of nation-states throughout the world, and their consequent enclosure of all the land-surface of the world, the authority of some 200 sovereign, egoistical nation-states, each under its own black Sun – whether Muslim, Christian, Hindu, Communist or secular ideology – has replaced the world-wide authority of the Great Spirit over all humans as hunter-gatherers moving freely under the one true sun, thus replacing a world-wide order and harmony with a world-wide anarchy and disharmony.

Hence a perverted flux between imperial 'order' and its apparent antithesis, the long interregnum of anarchy between the rise and fall of successively larger and more widespread imperial powers (or parasite pyramids of power, both territorial and commercial), has increasingly overlaid and replaced the natural flux and succession of innumerable natural food pyramids and the royal beings at their summits, the whole contributing to an overall disharmony and imbalance of the world. Forest-like empires are fundamentally unstable not only for all the reasons I have adduced in this chapter, but also for all the reasons I have instanced in earlier chapters, of which I now recall four as being most important from the evolutionary standpoint of nature and its laws.

First, because each is a stratified structure that is a grossly unnatural biome of degenerate plants, animals and men – a composite half-plant/half-animal structure – whose human members in particular suffer a multi-layered suppression and perversion of their true selves, the suppressed genetic and memetic inheritance that tries to reassert itself in every generation through violence and disease. Secondly, because the suppressed

---

*I discussed the origins of anarchy in Part I, Chapter 7, while depicting in Fig 7.5 the replacement of an overall natural order by an overall anarchy and chaos.

forces of nature tend to reassert themselves – through environmental catastrophe and disease – against the alien farming bases of stratified societies which block the selection and succession of true life forms. Thirdly, because the superposition of parasite pyramid on parasite pyramid, building empires ever higher against the natural flux, violates the basic rule of a harmonious environment with its primacy of horizontality. Fourthly, because of the primacy of the verticality of their stratified structures: the larger and more elaborate the creations at the top (e.g. the more sophisticated and greater the Princes and the more elaborate the Palaces at the top) the more complex and expensive they become to maintain, both in economic terms and in terms of the consumption of lives and natural resources.

For all these reasons, the laws that govern these forest-like composite animals are the reverse of those that govern their natural counterparts. For unlike the selective processes underlying the growth of natural food pyramids and structures, we are witnessing here the perverted memetic selection to the growth of parasite pyramidal structures: the parasitization of the *Homo sapiens non sapiens* many by the *Homo sapiens sapiens* few and their parasitical relationship with the enslaved Earth and its plant and animal inhabitants. Parasitism is the predominant relationship between members of nations and between them and nature. Inevitably nature is operating at every moment to undermine and destroy such alien structures and behaviour, particularly when they achieve the size, and involve the degree of parasitism necessary, to constitute empires.

> Seven years ago, in lectures delivered at Clark University in the US, William McNeill reflected upon what he called 'The Human Condition'. He focused attention upon his theme by use of a striking metaphor: that communities change and survive under perpetual pressure from two hostile influences; one he called 'microparasitism', the invasion of human beings and their crops and domestic animals by disease; the other he called 'macroparasitism', the exploitation of human beings by tyrannies, governments or organisations which impose taxes, curtail liberty and enforce ideologies. Ground between these two 'millstones', civilizations rise and fall, empires spread and shrink.[11]

Every century has had its fair share of anarchy as composite animals have been ground between the millstones referred to above, but none more so than the 20th century. That century was indeed, in Byron's terms, one of Barbarism. This will undoubtedly carry over into this century as national sovereignty and economies are eroded by the growing power of modern commercial and industrial empires, that is, by the power of the multinationals to parasitize, unify and homogenize the world to their own advantage. Before, however, proceeding to examine the effects of globalization in greater detail, it is necessary to examine several other processes at work on *Homo degener*, including the 'perfecting' of *Homo degener*.

The net result of the regular rise and fall of empires and related interregnums of anarchy has been to hasten and intensify the spread both of the primary degeneration amongst surviving hunter-gatherers and the secondary historical degeneration of *Homo degener*. Thus the life-enhancing and perfecting natural environment and flux, conducive to the evolution and perfection of *Homo sapiens*, have given way to life-degenerating and destroying artificial environments and flux, conducive to the evolution and 'perfection' of *Homo degener* as component parts of composite animals, and the concomitant degeneration of the Earth.

Chapter 8

The Perfecting of Homo Degener

Indeed, is a man as he now exists the end point of an evolutionary development? One might claim, or at least hope, that we are still in the midst of an evolution toward a more nearly perfect stage of that which is now represented by *Homo sapiens* with all his glaring imperfections. (Ernst Mayr)[1]

Amongst the 'glaring imperfections' to which Ernst Mayr refers are all those which I have shown to be principal characteristics of *Homo degener* populations that stemmed from the two-fold fall. They were denatured by degrading captivity – turned into subhumans whose domestication is a special kind of regressive evolution. As William Hazlitt wrote,

> ...men do not become what by nature they are meant to be but what society makes them. The generous feelings, and higher propensities of the soul are, as it were, shrunk up, seared, violently wrenched, and amputated, to fit us for our intercourse with the world, something in the manner that beggars maim and mutilate their children, to make them fit for their future situation in life.[2]

Their imperfections persist because *Homo degener* peoples are not yet fully adapted to the termitary-like conditions to which their regressive evolution has reduced them. In order to reveal more fully their 'evolution towards a more nearly perfect stage', it will be useful, as the argument proceeds, to summarize and compare certain salient physical, physiological, psychical and behavioural characteristics making for the perfection in degeneration of *Homo degener* in national termitaries with those that made for the relative perfection of *Homo sapiens* to show how increasingly at variance they are. For *Homo degener* is undergoing a process of development similar to that which occurred amongst termites.

391

Eugene Marais[3] has argued that in a termitary the wingless and blind worker and soldier termites would appear to be degenerate descendents of a perfect flying individual insect. Similarly the soldier and worker members of nations are the result of a degenerative change in a relatively perfect hunter-gatherer. However, whereas in a termitary all the inhabitants are now, after millions of years of evolution, relatively perfect and perfectly adapted to their rôles, as is the termitary itself in its rôle in the natural environment, such is not yet the case with members of nations. In their case, the degenerative process, and so the perfecting process, is still in train.

An actual change in the physique as between Stone Age hunter and civilized man may be observed. In fact, recent scientific studies have indicated that the physique of the civilized male has, over the past 10,000 years, more and more nearly approached that of the female.

A well-tried index for sex determination, developed by Acsadi and Nemeskeri, is based on 22 characteristics of the skeleton, especially the skull and pelvis. Each of these characteristics can be scored on a five-point scale, ranging from 'supermale' to 'superfemale'. The scores on all 22 characteristics are totted up, with some given more weight than others, and averaged to give a composite measure of maleness or femaleness. Between the Stone Age and the Middle Ages changes took place in both the male and female skeleton. The difference between the sexes remained as great as ever, but both sexes moved in the female direction: a modern man is not very different in skeletal structure from a Stone Age woman, whereas a Stone Age man was a 'supermale' and a modern woman is a 'superfemale'. A systematic long-term change of this kind suggests the actions of natural selection and indicates that female skeletal characteristics confer greater fitness...[4]

In the Stone Age the hunting of animals was a major source of food, so a hunting economy would favour 'male' human types – types adapted to the sudden bursts of physical and mental energy required in pursuing and dispatching animals. By the Middle Ages the predominant source of food was agriculture, an occupation demanding, not sudden spurts of energy and decisive action, but rather the long periods of sustained and nearly mindless hard physical work to which the 'female' type of body is best adapted. In addition, as pointed out earlier, the principles governing horticulture and agriculture are feminine. Combine this factor with their gregarious colony or hive-like situation, which usually favours the sterile female or neutered form over the male,* and it will be appreciated why female skeletal characteristics confer greater fitness. After all, all the members of a nation are, one way or another, no more than housekeepers of their colony or greater house. The unthinking 'feeling' *Homo sapiens non sapiens* masses have been treated, and have behaved, as though they were female, obeying, and doing the physical 'housework' for, the ruling classes of societies. Even though one nation might conquer another, and however manly and virile an imperial race might appear in its hey-day, eventually it is reduced to effeminacy and the growing influence and importance of women in society, conditions that have spread with the spread of empires across the world.

There is now an increasing 'feminization' of the workforce world-wide. In Britain in the years since the Second World War, the female percentage of the workforce has risen to more than 50 per cent. As fast as men have been losing their jobs, women have been moving into the workplace – for brawn is now largely redundant, replaced by machinery. In the export-processing zones in Asia, more than 90 per cent of the workforce is female. This process has been further advanced by the need of contemporary societies for human atoms, each one of whichever sex the same, functioning smoothly in a mass aggregation: a social process of the standardization of people that matches the standardization of mass produced commodities. It is a process that has been assisted by television, which has helped blur the distinction between men and women as rôles, dress and so on increasingly unite the sexes in a unisex world.

This degenerative trend may be accentuated by chemicals and detergents. In order to obtain the maximum artificial growth rate, animals have been fed chemical hormones. However, scientists have repeatedly expressed concern that residues of synthetic oestrogens could remain in carcasses, creating a risk of feminization and development of cancer. Chemicals and detergents are estimated to have lowered sperm counts by 2 per cent a year in Europe, together with a lowering of quality, while in America over the past thirty years some 22 million women were prescribed barbiturates to soothe them during pregnancy, possibly resulting in the relative feminization of some 12 million males. All these poisons tend to feminize foetuses. Scientists estimate that sperm counts amongst Europeans have fallen by half over the last 50 years. By the year 2030 Western men could all be sterile.

---

*In this connection it is noteworthy that the relationship of Yahweh with Israel was that of husband and bride/wife/harlot; Christ is the Bridegroom, and the body corporate of the Church is the Bride of Christ. Roman Catholic priests, monks and nuns have ostensibly been celibate – that is to say, sterile from a reproductive point of view.

The overall effect is that the sexes are recognizably becoming more like each other, converging towards some physical median. Natural selection – together with a perverted memetic selection – is thus perverted to act, not upon people moving freely as hunter-gatherers, but held captive as the members of static stratified societies, to perfect them as neutered components of termitary-like composite animals.

As well as an anti-evolutionary development of the degenerate physique, it can be argued that a change has taken place in the physiology, psyches and behaviour of these degenerate members of composite animals. Their individual bodies and brains have remained subordinate to the collective bodies and brains of their composite animals, developing in accordance with the individual's status within, and with the requirements of, those composite animals. This has largely been achieved by the manipulation of the behaviour of the people by playing upon their experiences.

Once people can be persuaded to experience a situation in a similar way, they are likely to respond with similar behaviour. So if a Government wishes to influence a society, it induces the members of that society to want, hate, feel the same things, and thereby make captive their behaviour. Induce in people, generation by generation, the belief that their protected hierarchically ordered environment is God-given unto eternity, and the wilderness is a place of evil, the home of dragons and devils, and the necessity to preserve and extend the existing system of collective security becomes self-evident and self-perpetuating, or second nature.* The threat of bankruptcy and a dark annihilation barely held at bay was so constantly paraded before the eyes and the imagination in ritual and myth – just as it is in relation to terrorism on national radio and television networks in many States today – as to amount to an obsession with the security of society which persists to this day.

I argued earlier that the divorce of the brain from its full utilization in conjunction with the sensory apparatus ranging through the wilderness, combined with the 10,000 year experience of people as degenerate members of composite animals, will have been recorded as a change in brain organization. Their experience and their behaviour are indeed so vastly different at every level from those of their *Homo sapiens* hunter ancestors as to warrant such a hypothesis.

---

*That second nature is obedience to the collective memetic inheritance of the nation. The difference between *Homo sapiens'* true nature and *Homo degener's* second nature is the difference between *Homo sapiens'* obedience to their combined genetic and memetic inheritance and *Homo degener's* obedience to the collective memetic inheritance of the nation and denial of their combined genetic and memetic inheritance.

The cultural environment in which we grew up is totally different from the one in which children grew up 500 years ago, or indeed 10,000 or 100,000 years ago. And because of this, our brains are wired differently. As a result, the adult human being of modern Europe is a biologically different animal from the adult human of medieval times, not in any observable way, but because he or she has a brain that is different in its wiring and its chemistry, and is therefore different in the way that it operates.

In particular, medieval people grew up with the basic notion that the world is innately mysterious, and that we may understand only what is told to us by God, through the revelation of prophets. We moderns grow up with the idea that the world is innately explicable, and that insight can be formally acquired, by observation and experiment... We are different from them not simply because we know more (which is cultural evolution) but because our brains, as infants, were formed and shaped in a different way, and now operate according to different parameters.[5]

If that is so, how vastly different must have been the brains of our hunter-gatherer forbears. As insiders, the world was 'innately explicable' to them; while we, as outsiders removed from that world by several hundred generations of anti-evolutionary development, observe and explain the world to ourselves while actively destroying it. Furthermore, in contrast with the peripatetic hunter-gatherers, vibrant with continually renewed challenges, and in contrast too with *Homo sapiens sapiens* intellectuals, the work in which the greater part of the *Homo sapiens non sapiens* cultivating population has been employed, like that of industrial populations today, has been of a repetitive kind which rapidly becomes automatic. This means that the tasks are taken over almost entirely by the motor centres of the brain, and the worker forfeits the exercise of brain and nervous system that once worked superlatively as one unit perfected in a freedom of vivifying movement within nature. *Homo sapiens'* brains were more properly and fully exercised than those of *Home degener* just because they functioned within the natural setting for which, in conjunction with all the senses, they were designed. They possessed phylogenetic and ontogenetic abilities relating to ecological understanding, language, healing, telepathy, trance, music-making and dance which I only hinted at in Part I, abilities shared by all and denied to none. Even the stunted abilities of the *Homo sapiens sapiens* intellectual or scientist are beyond the reach of the majority of *Homo sapiens non sapiens* workers forced over many generations to indulge in repetitive work processes *ad nauseam*.

Such a change in brain organization and use, which has favoured the growth and prosperity of *Homo sapiens sapiens* élites on the backs of *Homo sapiens non sapiens* majorities, at the cost of a wilderness destroyed, must be registered at the very least as a progressive degeneration of the physiology of those concerned, particularly of the *Homo sapiens non sapiens* majorities, resulting in near total phylogenetic evodeviation on the part of the majority of humankind.

There is an important corollary, and it concerns the relationship between people's genetic natures and natural selection. Julian Huxley pointed out that it is probable that

> ... man's genetic nature has degenerated and is still doing so. In general, the more elaborate social life is, the more it tends to shield individuals from the action of natural selection; and when this occurs ... harmful mutations accumulate instead of being weeded out. As a result of this process, there can be no reasonable doubt that the human species today is burdened with many more deleterious mutant genes than can possibly exist in any species of wild creature.[6]

Homo degener peoples, with the aid of food production, food storage, clothing, housing and heating, have made themselves independent of the fluctuations of the environment; they have isolated themselves, to a great extent, from the natural flux and selective pressures of the physical environment, forces which had earlier helped shape and perfect *Homo sapiens'* physique, psyche and behaviour. Termitary-like nations indeed grow, prosper and progress, but only at the cost of the continuing degeneration of their members and of the natural environment – which is what the perfection in degeneration of *Homo degener* is all about.

The change in physiology, and especially in brain organization, is arguably the most important single outcome of the change from *Homo sapiens* to *Homo degener*, particularly because the brain controls behaviour, while the brains of the nation control the behaviour of that nation. And if our brains operate 'according to different parameters', and those parameters are anti-evolutionary, such degenerative physical and physiological changes as I have recorded must inevitably have had a similarly degenerative effect upon the psyches, and so on the morality and behaviour, of successive generations of *Homo degener*.

Each nation has seen history and other nations through its own eyes, its own world view. A nation's concept of right and wrong has been built up solely in relation to itself, each one certain of its own rectitude and of the moral turpitude of the others. For, as I argued earlier, the moral backbone of the entire pyramid of power originated in the identification of those at the summit with goodness and of those regarded as threatening their survival as evil. To a great extent the moral values of each depend upon the Farmer God religion (or ideology) each espouses. In the West a variety of Christian Churches pretend to moralities that are absolute, as do the various Islamic sects throughout the world. Any variations are seen by their members as merely short-term distortions. In the light of these absolute moralities, each country tends to regard itself in relation to others as righteous and good, especially in the event of a nation being threatened by another, as were the European nations by Japan during the Second World War. When Japan invaded European held territories in South-East Asia and Australasia, her actions were regarded as immoral. Yet she was attacking European empires in the Orient which had themselves been won by force or threats during the 19th century, and were subsequently held by force or threats. 19th century European statesmen such as Cavour and Bismarck were in fact exponents of *Realpolitik* – the view that government and state policy should be dictated only by the requirements of power and judged solely by success, not by any moral considerations. Before them Hegel had already elevated the process of world history above the confines of morality.

In a course of lectures on the philosophy of history at Berlin University in the mid 19th century, Hegel argued that those whom he described as 'World-historical individuals', or Heroes – men such as Alexander the Great, Caesar and Napoleon – were the agents by which 'the Will of the World Spirit', the plan of Providence, is carried out. Such agents cannot be bound or judged by the standards of ordinary morality, even if their activities involve great sufferings for others.

> World history occupies a higher ground than that on which morality has properly its position, which is personal character and the conscience of individuals... Moral claims which are irrelevant must not be brought into collision with world-historical deeds and their accomplishment. The litany of private virtues – modesty, humility, philanthropy, and forbearance – must not be raised against them... So mighty a form must trample down many an innocent flower – crush to pieces many an object in its path.[7]

Hegel might here be describing the beliefs of Hitler and Stalin, as well as the collective beliefs surrounding what has been described as a nation's Manifest Destiny. All these bear out Machiavelli's account of human nature and the struggle for power in *The Prince*, according to which rulers should always be prepared to do evil if they consider good will come of it, implying that morality is irrelevant in political affairs and any means is justified in the pursuit and maintenance of power. In effect, morality amongst *Homo degener* peoples is not only the product of a multitude of culturally and racially prejudiced communities and nations, but within them it is subject to the sway of consensus, depending largely upon the degree to which it can be used to further the self-interests of the community concerned. Society's ethics change to accommodate new technologies whose development is primarily because of their usefulness to *Homo degener* peoples in their ongoing search for wealth, well-being and security; at the national level 'Reasons of state' continue to justify any means, provided they yield the intended results.

There is only one arena in which morality is stable, universal and absolute, one standpoint from which to view morality for all times and everywhere: from the evolutionary standpoint of *Homo sapiens*. Their morality was absolute because they belonged to the land and obeyed the laws of the land, the laws of nature. This is not special-pleading. There cannot be a more profound basis of morality – or, come to that, a more profound basis of anything that might be described as human – than that constituted by the law-enforcing and law-abiding conditions under which humankind evolved as hunter-gatherers. They evolved as world-loving, law-abiding citizens of the world. In their loyal obedience to the Great Spirit, they were highly responsible and morally good. As I argued in Part I, their moral principles were based in universality, that is, in their view of the wilderness as sacred and in their preservation of the stability of biotic communities world-wide. With the voiding loss of the hunter-gatherer culture *Homo degener* peoples lost the evolutionary basis, the foundations, of their entire value system and morality. New codes of ethics grew with the growth of each new stratified society, each code based on the *immoral theft, enclosure and exploitation of no man's land,* each the justification of a perverted memetic selection in all its many guises, thus rendering all such codes and associated behaviour immoral.

The Puritans, for instance, evinced a high moral purpose, combined with hopes of wealth and fears of failure, when they arrived in the New World to set up their cities of God. The essence of their system was the idea that every community was a government in itself, a congregation of God's elect, run by God's laws. 'Blessed is the man that feareth the Lord... His seed shall be mighty upon earth... Wealth and riches shall be in his house...' A further text, taken from the Book of Deuteronomy, was used to motivate the Puritan elect. 'But thou shalt remember the Lord thy God: for it is he that giveth thee power to get wealth...'

It was the Great Spirit and Earthmother that originally gave the true elect – the whole of hunter-gatherer humankind – the power unpossessively to pursue and enjoy the incomparable beauty and wealth of the wilderness. That elect was now destroyed by those who sought to acquire wealth through possession, enclosure and exploitation, often pleading to that end the highest moral intent as the elect of their Farmer God. For in their alienation from a true value system, shared wealth and stability of all people moving unpossessively as hunter-gatherers, and in their static vertically oriented unstable condition, *Homo degener* élites sought to possess something of a fixed value, something stable and lasting, as exemplified in their rapacious search for gold and God – two of the principal physical and psychical pillars of their static Stable States. They exploited their fellows to dig down for gold to raise up wealthy élites and Kings towards their Farmer Gods of Providence.* Dee Brown highlights two of the principal motives – elemental greed and hatred of the wilderness – underlying the exploitation of the American West, an exploitation later attributed to Manifest Destiny, to the Providence of their Farmer God, and therefore morally right and good.

> In the beginning it was a search for the Western Sea and seven mythical cities of gold. Most of those who ventured there were driven by elemental greed...
>
> The West was there to be exploited and in the accomplishment of this, in their march to the Western Sea, they and many of the thousands who followed them destroyed a native civilization and obliterated innumerable species of animals and birds. They ripped apart the delicate balance of Plains grassland, they gutted mountains for metals and poisoned the earth, they leveled forests and created wastelands. They raped, stripped, and plundered the land as if they hated the Garden of the West with a violent passion. They built large cities in waterless places where even the most primitive tribes knew that cities should never be built. Upon their city lawns the exterminators of wild animals placed iron effigies of deer and buffalo, and on the gables of killers of eagles rose gold-plated images of the great birds.[8]†

---

* In the first weeks after making contact with the Indians of the New World, the word 'Gold' recurs some seventy-five times in Columbus' journal.

† In addition, nations themselves have adopted wild animals as their national symbols. England has adopted the lion, China the panda, New Zealand the kiwi, South Africa the springbok, USA the bald eagle, etc.

At the core of *Homo degener* morality world-wide there is a gross immorality which must ever undermine and negate *Homo degener* claims to a moral status.

Because of their witness to the true, evolutionary morality and behaviour of humankind, I make no apology for quoting the words of two Native Americans out of thousands whose wisdom so far exceeds our own. First, Crazy Horse, an Oglala Sioux, whose view of white encroachments upon his people's land is summed up in the following statement:

> We did not ask you white men to come here. The Great Spirit gave us this country as a home. You had yours. We did not interfere with you. The Great Spirit gave us plenty of land to live on, and buffalo, deer, antelope and other game. But you have come here; you are taking my land from me; you are killing off our game, so it is hard for us to live. Now, you tell us to work for a living, but the Great Spirit did not make us to work, but to live by hunting. You white men can work if you want to. We do not interfere with you, and again you say, why do you not become civilized? We do not want your civilization! We would live as our fathers did, and their fathers before them.[9]

Meditate on those few words: '...the Great Spirit did not make us to work, but to live by hunting'.* That is *the* most profound observation on the true being and purpose of humankind. A further penetrating judgement on the proper relationship of humankind with the Earth was passed by Heinmot Tooyalaket (Chief Joseph) of the Nez Percés:

> The earth was created by the assistance of the sun, and it should be left as it was... The country was made without lines of demarcation, and it is no man's business to divide it... I see whites all over the country gaining wealth, and see their desire to give us lands which are worthless... The earth and myself are of one mind. The measure of the land and the measure of our bodies are the same. Say to us if you can say it, that you were sent by the Creative Power to talk to us. Perhaps you think the Creator sent you here to dispose of

---

* 'Work is of two kinds: first, altering the position of matter at or near the earth's surface relative to other such matter; second, telling other people to do so. The first kind is unpleasant and ill-paid; the second is pleasant and highly paid.'[10]

    Work for the majority of *Homo degener* humankind down the millennia – for the legs, hands and feet of composite animals – has fallen into the first category. Work is a characteristic of worker termites and suchlike insects – it is not a characteristic of *Homo sapiens*.

us as you see fit. If I thought you were sent by the Creator I might be induced to think you had a right to dispose of me. Do not misunderstand me, but understand me fully with reference to my affection for the land. I never said the land was mine to do with it as I chose. The one who has the right to dispose of it is the one who has created it. I claim a right to live on my land, and accord you the privilege to live on yours.[11]

Heinmot Tooyalaket here reveals the vast gulf that exists between the thinking and behaviour of hunter-gatherers and the deranged members of nations. He shows that *Homo sapiens* is attuned to the Creative Power of the world, a free land, a limitless wilderness – while citizens of nations are attuned to mythical Creator Gods of domesticated farming worlds that delimit and destroy the wilderness and, by implication, its Creator and Governor, the Great Spirit. The New World was made with the assistance of the Farmer God of a perverted memetic selection, whose followers treated the original inhabitants as an altogether different and subhuman species of animal, and disposed of them as they saw fit.

Columbus commented upon the amazing beauty and friendliness of the Indians, before the Spaniards set about enslaving them. Other Indians rescued the original white settlers in Virginia from starvation, only to have their friendliness and trust turned against them, to destroy them. With the Bible in one hand and a Winchester repeater in the other, the white Americans won the West. So it was that the evolutionary elect of the Great Spirit were conquered by the anti-evolutionary elect of a Farmer God. This tragedy – which is representative of many similar tragedies down the millennia and throughout the world – together with the associated immorality of *Homo degener* that made it inevitable, by comparison with the morality of *Homo sapiens* obedient to the fundamental of environmental ethics outlined above, reveals that *Homo degener* is not only in the wrong, but wrong in the scheme of things, evil. He has destroyed the real world, and reverence for what is the real world, for the sake of imagined new and better worlds both here on Earth and hereafter in space or beyond the grave.

To deranged Christians, for instance, death is the end of suffering and heartbreak on Earth. It is the beginning of life in Heaven with God. Yet the Christian European has been a principal agent of suffering and heartbreak throughout the world, particularly amongst hunter-gatherers and a paradisial wildlife, in the name of that self-same Farmer God! The continuing struggle within civilizations for a higher sense of values has always been undergirded and surpassed by a perverted predatory voraciousness and ferocity as mindless as that exhibited by a colony of army ants. Such absurd beliefs, hopes and psychopathically possessive and destructive behaviour are surely evidence of an extraordinarily degenerate morality, understanding and behaviour. It might, however, be argued in defence that one of the most profoundly moral acts of the Church, for instance, is to pray for and minister to the sick, while Science has made possible organ transplants for those who would otherwise die. But this is entirely contrary to the laws of nature and of our own true natures. We only survive as degenerate beings because such interference with the operation of natural selection permits forms of maladjustment to persist almost indefinitely. Seemingly moral acts on the part of the Church and Science are, therefore, fundamentally immoral acts, in that they are, like agriculture, acts of war against nature. They deepen and perpetuate the original disobedience and contempt of the natural law, further alienating us and exacerbating our relationship with the real world.

Morality does not exist independently of social and economic relations, nor independently of relations with the biotic community. Furthermore, no moral principle can claim to be moral unless it is based in universality, that is, based on the preservation of biotic communities world-wide. The moral systems subscribed to by *Homo degener* élites compete for a universal status which must forever elude them. (The fact that there are many religions, each laying claim to, and proclaiming, the truth, is a principal reason for not believing in any of them.) The world of *Homo degener* provides incompatible goals and withholds any single scale of value by which to measure right behaviour and the goodness or validity of ideas. Because of the incompatible goals of the variety of disparate visions of the world – whether philosophical, religious or scientific, all pretend to convey a complete and comprehensive view of life – they give rise to exclusive moral systems which clash irreconcilably in unbridgeable confrontation. All issue from within stratified societies, themselves founded in irreconcilable conflict with the wilderness and responsive to subsequent suspected threats to their hierarchies. Virtually all stratified societies down the ages reveal a gross inequality between rich élites and poor workers who do not share a common freedom nor subscribe to a common morality, whose societies have achieved their present sacred national status through the world-wide destruction of biotic communities originally held sacred by *Homo sapiens*, and whose moral principles are not universal but are entirely relative to their own national wealth and survival as separate Sacred Species of composite animal. Each national élite claims the moral high ground in relation to all others. *Universality, including universal freedom and equality of social and economic relations, and the universal preservation of biotic communities, can only pertain amongst hunter-gatherers as the ground of a true religion, true morality and perfection for human kind.*

The secondary historical changes arising as a result of the primary degeneration of deranged men, that are reflected in their physiques, physiology, psyches and behaviour, are also reflected in their susceptibility to debilitating diseases – infectious, occupational and nutritional. *Homo degener* peoples are prone to diseases that were almost entirely unknown to their hunter-gatherer forbears. The disease ecology of small groups of *Homo sapiens* hunters was quite different from that of a population of half a million plant-like men. The social organization of hunter-gatherers was very fluid. They were grouped into bands of a few families, each of which operated as an independent subsistence unit. Mobility was high, both spatially and as between groups: fission and fusion of the bands was frequent. Such small, mobile, isolated populations were incapable of the continuous transmission of disease, and outbreaks of endemic infectious disease, where they did occur, were likely to be sporadic. In effect, both cultural and genetic responses combined to make them extremely mobile and responsive, so that they might renew themselves and keep themselves 'without blemish' in unpossessive adaptive change of habitat.

A dramatic change came 12,000 years ago, with the emergence of agriculture, when, as I argued in Part I, diseases began to flourish. The accompanying shifts in population size, population density, settlement pattern and the associated alterations in the environment, including extensive land clearance, brought about considerable changes in the disease ecology of human populations. Large and sedentary populations not only increased the possibility of the transmission of infectious diseases, but many infectious diseases, such as measles and influenza, actually require a static interacting population of some 300,000 people for their sustenance. In particular, the sedentary agricultural lifestyle eventually led to the spread of what became the two biggest single causes of death in human populations: malaria and schistosomiasis. One World Health Organization study suggested that 80 per cent of all the world's sickness and disease was attributable to contaminated water:

The estimated numbers of people involved are immense: 400 million cases a year of gastro-enteritis, 250 million of elephantiasis, 200 million of bilharzia, 160 million of malaria, 30 million of river blindness. The figures mean little as abstract millions. But how about the entire population of non-communist Europe with gastro-enteritis;

every Soviet Citizen with the fat, swollen legs of elephantiasis; the whole of the US urinating blood from bilharzia; everyone in Japan and Malaysia and the Philippines sweating and shivering with malaria; the total population of Iran sightless from river blindness? That, repeated year after weary, painful year, is the reality of inadequate and unsafe water.[12]

Although these figures relate to 1977, and although modern health measures and medicine may be finding ways of eliminating these diseases (a new drug, mectizan, has been developed to control river blindness, and insecticides have been targeted against the blackflies that transmit onchocerciasis, the disease which causes river blindness) they are nevertheless an indication of the extent and depth of individual suffering world-wide because of *Homo degener*'s evodeviant life conditions. Their blindness to the reality of their ecological condition may now be compounded with actual blindness.

If the situation at the periphery of civilizations is most often perilously debilitating, that in the crowded centres of civilizations, if much more complex, has been equally debilitating. In the developing world, crowds of deranged humans provide environments which encourage airborne diseases such as tuberculosis, waterborne diseases such as cholera, and diseases such as malaria, to thrive; in the developed world, *Homo degener* humans are subject to such stresses and strains as to make them prone to a wide range of mental and degenerative diseases. Where once plague and then smallpox were the principal killers, today, as the result of both civilized environment and inheritance, it is the degenerative diseases that tend to kill us. An epidemic increase of chronic degenerative diseases now ravages Western societies, including heart disease, cancer, hypertension and diabetes.* With regard to mental illness and crime rates in cities,

A classic study was carried out in Chicago in the thirties by Faris and Dunham. The city was divided into 11 types of area comprising 120 sub-communities, and rates established for each. In every case, the rates were high at the centre and declined steadily as one moved further away from it. Thus there were 362 cases per thousand of schizophrenia in the centre, grading down to 55.4 on the periphery. There were 240 cases of alcoholic psychosis per thousand in the

---

*In February 1999, the World Health Organization predicted that, by 2020, depression, more than either heart disease or cancer, will have become the most pervasive serious illness world-wide.

centre, grading down to 60 at the periphery. Crime, suicide, drug-taking all showed a similar pattern...

The question was at once raised whether city-existence caused these high rates, or were the insane, suicidal and alcoholic drawn to the centre of cities just because they were round the bend? The smooth grading from the centre outward made this look unlikely, and closer study showed that the rates were linked with the level of social organization.[13]

Increasing cruelty to children, crime, and divorce rates, whilst filling the Sunday newspapers, are not signs of merely individual wickedness (or, at any rate, it is not profitable to think of them as such). They are symptoms of a diseased society.[14]

A combination of crowded conditions, absence of meaningful work, poverty, boredom, drug taking and alcohol abuse adversely affect not only bodily and mental health but social health as well, favouring a loss of social cohesion and responsibility. According to a report in January 1999 by the Mental Health Foundation, one child in five in Britain was suffering mental health problems due in part to family breakdown. In the world today, there are an estimated 250 million overtly 'insane' people, who, abused or rejected, become a shameful and growing pool of city beggars and bums.

Yet not only is the world's population inescapably rising, but a growing proportion will live in cities. In the developing world, about 50 per cent of the populations are now living in urban areas, rising to around 60 per cent in 2025.

Now 1.4 billion people are living in the urban areas of developing countries; there will be a crushing 4.1 billion in 2025. By that time Latin America will be the most urbanized region of the world, with nearly 85 percent of its population living in cities; in Africa the figure will be around 58 percent and in Asia about 53 percent.[15]

As Lord Ritchie-Calder so rightly observed in 1969, by the year 2025 there might be cities many times bigger than the 'horror city of Calcutta, where three-quarters of the population live in shacks without tap water or proper sewage and, in the monsoon, wade through their own floating excrement'.[16] As it is, the UN Population Division has estimated that, by 2015, 27 cities will have more than 10 million inhabitants, and that 7 of those will have populations of over 20 million.

In general, the more the environment changes as a result of *Homo degener*'s activities, the less does it resemble that in which he evolved, and the less efficiently can his normal behavioural mechanisms enable him to adapt to it. With every year that passes, the increasing numbers of such degenerate people reduces still further what little mobility and ability to improvement or escape remain, particularly because of the associated deterioration of the environment.

This began with the arrival of the first farmers and can be seen in all developed and developing countries throughout the world, where settlers have come from elsewhere bringing their exploitative way of life, domestic animals, diseases and detritus with them. Who but a physically and morally degenerate people *without an ecological niche* could have turned a world-wide paradise into what is fast becoming a world-wide purgatory. As Grand Chief Andrew Rickard (of Canada) has said of the behaviour of the white people who invaded North America:

> My people welcomed the visitors with sincerity, trust, and open arms. We helped them discover our land. We helped them survive the harsh environment that was strange to them. That is the Indian way. Can you not see what has happened? Visitors were welcomed to a paradise. But within 300 years, they've turned it into a living hell and garbage dump.* They destroyed and destroyed until there is little left to destroy. And now white eyes look to the last frontier – as they call it – and plan to destroy the only part of the land left in a natural state as created by the great spirit. But, if it should die, my people will die.[17]†

Not only does the behaviour of *Homo degener* adversely affect the natural environment, but the consequent degradation of that environment further assists in the physical, psychical and behavioural degeneration of present and future generations of *Homo degener*. The one interacts with the others. Instead of the daily education and stimulation of the senses being conducted by the wonder, majesty and grandeur of nature, the education of a captive majority is now undertaken under the all-pervading influence

---

*In America, this has been shown to be literally true. Toxic wastes have been dumped almost indiscriminately at thousands of sites, many as yet undiscovered, all over the US. This is quite apart from the already long-standing pollution of North American rivers and the Great Lakes with industrial wastes, and the poisoning of the land, rivers and lakes with pesticides and insecticides.

See Appendix xiv for a diagrammatic representation of the cumulative effects of agriculture and industry on the environment.

† Grand Chief Rickard was referring here to northern Canada, and in particular northwestern Ontario and the havoc caused by logging, and mercury flowing from paper mills.

of a squalid, noisy and depressing urban environment, or in surroundings that are both mutilated and noxious.*

As important as the quality of the environment is the quality of the food. It is often said that you are what you eat. *Homo sapiens* hunter-gatherers had a choice from a quite extraordinary range of (free-ranging) fresh meat, fish and fruit. They ate a balanced diet and kept fit finding their food. By comparison with their diets based on biochemical variety, modern agricultural peoples are what Colin Tudge describes as 'pharmacologically impoverished'[18], deprived of that host of quasi-vitamins that our physiology has evolved to make use of and which kept disease at bay. Furthermore, many harmful foods and food substitutes such as cheap biscuits, potato crisps, inferior ice-cream and confectionery, that now constitute the staple diet of many of the uneducated and poor, actively encourage disease. As pointed out by the Politics of Health Group (BSSRS) in their booklet *Food and Profit: It Makes You Sick*, junk foods rich in sugar, saturated fats and additives are not only the easiest and most profitable to produce on an industrial scale, but they are the components of modern diets most seriously implicated in a whole range of degenerative diseases, diseases that were unknown to *Homo sapiens* hunters. Here again, evodeviation and degeneration are all too apparent.

One of the most dangerous aspects of their degeneration, however, is their inability to realize that they are profoundly degenerate, even the virtual impossibility of their understanding of the extent of their degeneration in relation to *Homo sapiens*. This is because their development of powers to dominate and subdue their fellows and the natural environment have been accompanied by equivalent powers to deceive themselves, and others, as to their humanity and to the propriety of their behaviour.

Deception and self-deception are such an important aspect of the immorality of *Homo degener* that they merit separate treatment. For it is, as I argued in Chapter 4 above, as much by deception as by violence that *Homo degener* has conquered the world, when the cruelty and ruthless dispossession involved have been concealed behind a beautiful mask. Modern commercial and industrial enterprises are built with the same disregard of social and environmental cost, and behind similar facades of beneficence, being heralded as necessary to the well-being and progress of the countries concerned. A report published in 2000 by the World Commission on Dams[19] stated that the construction of dams has seldom

---

*The fortunate one-fifth of the world's population who do live in a stimulating environment that makes them think more are thus enabled and persuaded to seek yet more stimulation, enhancing the activity of the brain and increasing intelligence. It is, however, an intelligence increasingly alienated from its true arena of integration and operation – the wilderness.

been studied to see if the benefits outweigh the costs. Benefits include the provision of irrigation to fields that provide up to a sixth of world food production, while hydroelectric dams power many homes and factories. The costs, however, have been enormous. Described as the biggest drain on aid budgets for the past 50 years, costing $4 billion a year in the 1980s, they have driven some 80 million people from their homes, made flooding worse, caused ecological havoc and social conflict, and in general have been of benefit only to the urban and well-off and not at all to the rural poor.

In every case, one side of the picture, as presented by the élite or experts concerned, has been missing: the cost in terms of environmental degradation and the sacrifice of cultures and of life. What Brian Inglis points out in relation to the hidden effects of chemo-therapy may be applied to the whole spectrum of behaviour under discussion. He has shown that we have been suffering from what Professor Edmond Cahn described, at the 1963 Johns Hopkins Conference on 'Drugs in Our Society', as today's two great hypocritical disorders: the Pharaoh syndrome, and the Pompey syndrome.

> When Pharaoh built a pyramid, he presumably considered the … thousands of human lives lost as part of the over-all expense; they were expendible. We, too, have allowed ourselves to be lulled by such phrases as 'the social cost of progress' into accepting the side-effects and hazards of chemo-therapy as 'natural and inevitable' forgetting that the personal cost in lives, in deformities, in pain and in distress may actually outweigh the benefits. When Pompey's lieutenant came to suggest that they should murder his guests, Antony and Caesar, he replied:

> > 'Ah, this thou should'st have done
> > And not have spoken on't! In me 'tis villainy:
> > In thee't had been good service.'

Here, Cahn argued

> 'we have the most pervasive of moral syndromes, the most characteristic of so-called respectable men in a civilized society. To possess the end and yet not be responsible for the means, to grasp the fruit while still disavowing the tree, to escape being told the cost until somebody else has paid it irrevocably; this is the Pompey syndrome, and the chief hypocrisy of our time…'[20]

The acceptance of the social and environmental cost of progress, and the hypocritical concealment of that cost behind a facade or myth of legitimacy and beneficence, are common to every level – the individual, the company and the national.* Equally evil is the other side of the coin: the criminalization and punishment of behaviour by governments and establishment bodies whose own behaviour is even more questionable and criminal, and who are often themselves directly responsible for the behaviour they describe as criminal. European governments, for example, talk about peace and human rights, but engage in the business of arms. They get high minded over 'the dregs of humanity' who trade in heroin, yet support the sale of arms to cruelly repressive regimes in countries like Indonesia, where, since 1965, the prosecution of state terrorism has accounted for the lives of hundreds of thousands of Indonesians and 200,000 of those of the people of East Timor, which the Indonesians invaded in 1975. In addition, governments and establishment élites in countries such as Great Britain, who have themselves become wealthy and powerful through the theft and enclosure of land, have created much crime, both by tolerating gross inequality of wealth and opportunity and by arbitrarily labelling certain forms of behaviour as criminal.

The double standards, the high moral tone which conceals the criminal behaviour of élites, compound the immorality of nations exemplified earlier. Their histories, that speak of great men and of national greatness, are myths of deception and self-deception.

> Even the most factual historian can scarcely help being a myth-maker himself, what with the selective, biased and arbitrary nature of the sources he gets hold of, and his equally selective and biased interpretation of them. Conversely, myths *are* history, because they are the beliefs of the people of the time, and Lévi-Strauss is quite right to stress that in their consequent impact on the course of events they have quite as much validity as history has.[21]

The Public Relations machines devised and operated by the priestly and scientific experts and historians of civilizations, and the illusory images they have impressed (above all that of a caring Farmer God) have been imposed upon posterity for some 7,000 years. It is science which now makes the situation of *Homo degener* more acceptable at the intellectual level, and more comfortable at the material level. Science is the new

---

* Recall the hidden environmental costs behind the building of civilization that required the blood-letting of millions of whales in the cause of pure profit.

religion and its practitioners the new priesthood. However, in making their captive condition more comfortable and acceptable to many – that is, in breeding each captive generation for captivity – *Homo degener* peoples have become increasingly blind to their true condition. It is their power of deception and self-deception, as evinced today in their belief that they are evolving and progressing as human beings, that is perhaps the most dangerous aspect of their deranged and degenerate condition. It is this delusion, perhaps more than any other aspect of their cultures, which most makes for the perfection in degeneration of *Homo degener* as a termite-like animal. For it is a delusion which empowers Governments and the scientific community to manipulate and control the growing populations of mindless consumer/producer peoples to increasingly mechanistic, termitary-like ends.

All the degenerative effects of the two-fold fall of humankind, as summarized above, have since been exacerbated by the increase in the numbers experiencing them. With the increase in the number of nations and in their size and power, a few members at the summits have become more and more powerful on the world stage,* while the majority have become increasingly powerless and irrelevant. This can be seen even at the level of mere numbers. If there were 20 million inhabitants 100 years ago within a given territory, each inhabitant was 1/20,000,000 part of the whole. If there are now 40 million inhabitants within the same area, each one is now reduced to being 1/40,000,000 part of the increasingly complex composite animal, each a very small cog in a very large machine – or replaceable cell in a composite animal. For just as money loses its value 'when it has become too much multiplied,' the general value of *Homo degener* peoples is lowered in proportion as they become abundant or plenty. Each plays a more highly specialized part within the whole, adapting within smaller and smaller niches – if unemployed or a refugee, he has no niche at all. Even if the relative deprivation as between groups remained unchanged, the numbers experiencing such deprivation would have doubled. More important, the absolute deprivation of freedom and alienation from a real evolutionary path and relative perfection as hunter-gatherers is increased both by the accretion of agricultural/industrial revolutions on the original re-evolution, and by the related increase in populations, which together submerge and destroy more and more of the wilderness.

Given that the nation is a single entity whose members combine to perform such different functions as the eyes and ears, the brain, the

---

*The most powerful person on Earth is the President of the United States.

nervous system, the fetching and fighting arms, and the productive hands and feet of the composite animal, its members have, in a sense, regressed to that spineless part of creation that represents 95 per cent of the species of the Earth. Each person has become a cell – a 20 millionth, 50 millionth, 100 millionth or 600 millionth part – of a cold-blooded composite animal. They have become, as it were, invertebrates. It is the nation itself that now possesses what may be described as the backbone and intricate nervous system centred upon it, controlling through the governing brain the movements of the body of the people, particularly in times of crisis and of war. In Britain, for instance, Cabinet Committees, and not even the full Cabinet, took the decisions to build the atomic bomb (1947) and to invade Suez (1956). And arrangements made to meet crises tend to remain in being long after the crises have passed, just as they did after the crisis of the Mesolithic.

With the growth of successively larger nations and empires – particularly in relation to size of population – the communal brain has grown steadily smaller in relation to the increasing size of the body mass. In Stalin's Russia, where many major decisions lay with Stalin alone, the ratio of brain size to body mass may be said to have been $1:200,000,000$. Following the German invasion of Russia in 1941, and during the war that followed, Stalin alone made all major (and many minor) decisions. He literally conducted the war on every front himself. Stalin's situation at the centre of the termitary-like Russian nation was made similar to that of the queen termite of a termitary.

Because their adaptations within nations are as yet still very imperfect, *Homo degener* scientists are actively searching for the optimum human development. The development of more and more sophisticated methods of persuasion and of psychosurgery, and also that of genetic engineering, will make it possible to breed and select people to fit their rôles within the wholly urban and domesticated rural environments. The dream of every leader is to control the behaviour of his people, which, as I argued above, is largely achieved by playing on their experiences. Because the brain is the organ of behaviour, leaders attempt to discipline brains and mould opinions, particularly with the aid of the mass media. Their seductive influence forms and changes opinions and creates 'mindsets' which may often bring the brains of millions of people to work as one. At his trial after the Second World War, Albert Speer said this of Hitler's dictatorship:

Through technical devices like the radio and the loud-speaker, eighty million people were deprived of independent thought. It was thereby

possible to subject them to the will of one man... The nightmare
of many a man that one day nations could be dominated by technical
means was all but realized in Hitler's totalitarian system.[22]

Few people have the strength of mind to resist ideas with which they
are continually bombarded by the media. Irrespective of the type of
government, the controllers of information technology may soon be the
unacknowledged leaders of the nation. Viewed in terms of memes, this
is already the case. For although those in positions of power down the
millennia have been the principle spreaders of memes, the fact that the
members of nations now imitate one another in their collective commitment
to information technology, and that such technology is the principal
medium for the spreading of memes, the controllers of information
technology already possess illimitable power over the minds of the
population through their ability to disseminate memes most beneficial
to themselves, enabling them to operate a perverted memetic selection
to their own advantage and to that of the power structures they serve –
and in particular the scientific community.

Mind-altering drugs, too, are, to a certain degree, already being
prescribed. Most industrial nations, through their drug companies,
neuropharmacologists and doctors, are systematically engaged in the
chemical manipulation of the minds of their populations, in the name
of therapy. Already many intelligent, energetic, inquisitive non-conforming
children are being diagnosed as hyperactive and drugged into conformity.
Tens of millions of prescriptions a year are made out in Britain alone,
supplying chemical agents for the tranquillizing and sedation of the minds
of people passing through doctors' consulting rooms, hospitals and prisons.
All help prevent people acting to improve their environments. A leading
neuropharmacologist[23] actually looks forward to an increasingly rational
psychotropic drug therapy, when drugs will more and more be able to
offer a more complete mind adjustment to the actuality of a polluted
and unjust world.

Because people's natural adjustments can occur only within the narrow
limits set by their evolution as hunter-gatherers, and because 'progress'
as we have known it has nearly reached its physical and psychological
limits, science will surely rise to the challenge and attempt, with the aid
not only of brain-control mechanisms and psychosurgery but also of
genetic engineering, to ensure that the powers of adjustment of modern
humans become as unlimited as the technological inventiveness of scientists.

As regards genetic engineering, recombinant DNA technology has
opened up the possibility of dissecting and understanding the genetic

blueprint of all Earth's organisms, including humans. Such understanding has brought with it the potential to manipulate the gene pool of the planet to our own ends, reordering and reassembling it as we see fit. This has opened the way to creating pest-resistant crops, manufacturing drugs that will eliminate diseases such as malaria and HIV/Aids, and repairing human genetic diseases. It has even opened up the possibility of 'improving' the genetic stock of *Homo degener.*

There are two aspects to genetic intervention: negative genetic intervention (to eliminate defects) and positive intervention (to bring about improvements in normal people, including the wherewithal for people to 'design' their own children).

As regards the former, scientists are developing 'germ-line' gene therapies to tackle not only diseases inherited at birth, such as cystic fibrosis and Tay-Sachs disease, which damages the brain in early life, but also diseases arising later on in life, such as cancer and cardiovascular disease, which, in Western societies, now account for some 25 per cent and 50 per cent of deaths respectively. MIT molecular biologist Jonathan King argues, however, that expensive recombinant DNA research is not the way to try to solve medical problems, such as cancer, but rather that

> ... it is much more responsible to identify the environmental causes of cancer than to attempt to make people less biologically susceptible to those causes.[24]

Four-fifths of cancers are believed to be due to environmental poisons.

One of the dreams of modern surgery is putting genetically-engineered animal organs, such as hearts, kidneys and livers, into humans, adding years to their lives, thereby fulfilling the age-old dream of combating the ageing process. There are already human organ donation schemes and organ banks, but they are insufficient to meet the growing demand from the growing numbers of elderly people in Western societies. There is also a trade in human organs: poorer people in Eastern Europe and India sell their kidneys for cash, and there is a trade in the organs of executed prisoners in China and Taiwan. Mechanical hearts are increasingly being used to replace the diseased hearts of those who cannot get a transplant. It is hoped, however, that the increasing shortfall will be met by genetically-engineered organs from animals such as baboons and pigs. The increase in the number of such human-animal composites is entirely in keeping with our status as members of composite animals. In addition, scientists are planning to make test tube bodies and body organs, and grow human organs such as livers in laboratories. Thereafter, it is hoped that genetic manipulation will ultimately render organ transplantation redundant. Because each organ in the body has the genetic and metabolic equipment to reproduce itself it is hoped that within a few generations it will be possible to activate the genetic switches to make this happen within the individual, thereby cloning a new heart, liver or kidney as required, as well as regenerating new limbs. This will make possible a cure for every known disease or disability that afflicts humankind.

Positive genetic intervention amongst normal people implies a commitment to eugenics – that society should try to upgrade the gene pool as a whole. That would enable people to design children to suit their needs, enhancing characteristics such as height or intelligence, while at the same time enabling them to escape the genetic effects of exposure to environmental pollution, particularly low level radiation. Chinese society, which is most noticeably focused on the good of society rather than that of the individual, is contemplating the widespread use of eugenics both to eliminate disabilities and deleterious genes, and generally to improve the health of their nation while reducing population growth, thus combining both the negative and positive aspects of genetic intervention at the national level. It will, however, be appreciated that the normal – i.e. what society regards as 'good' genes – in this case would be a standard established amongst people who are already abnormal anti-evolutionary degenerates, by scientists who are the same. Together they can pursue only the anti-evolutionary path already established for the safety and well-being of *Homo degener*. Scientists have merely replaced God and priest as the principal agents of a delusive healing and social improvement, the agents of a perverted memetic selection. Such selection would once again benefit the wealthy at the expense of the remainder, and of wild nature. Most importantly, germline gene therapy would harden the heritable inequity of society which is already well established by caste, class, education, entailment and so on. The beneficiaries would qualify as a genetic elect, a caste above the genetically unimproved – or even divide employers and workers into separate species, the gene-rich and gene-poor, unable to interbreed, a point to which I shall return at the end of the chapter.

Scientists now have the ability to influence and to alter the physical course of evolution to suit *Homo degeners*' own parasite pyramidal needs and assist our ascent. All of us are now subject to the technological imperative which, in the absence of scientific accountability and public debate, rules science: *if it can be done, it will be done*. No laws, nor pronouncements of committees nor joint statements to the effect that 'attempts to enhance general human characteristics should not be contemplated',[25] will stop the process. For we are not dealing with truly human characteristics at all, but with those of *Homo degener*, whose anti-evolutionary essence is to become as 'company or nation-minded' as possible. At present this means adapting our identities to the requirements of companies and nations in their promotion of the capitalist dream through education, training, television and the Press, promoting a continuous flow of new consumer needs, together with new jobs, for the sake of rapid economic growth. If our ability to manipulate DNA develops at the same pace as our ability to intervene in the processes of procreation, we shall be able, in the future, to grow humans to specification, as Aldous Huxley's *Brave New World* predicts. Furthermore, such standardization of humans would be entirely in keeping with other aspects of scientific advance, within our increasingly 'precise prisons'.

A model that has governed the thinking of *Homo degener* societies is that of the efficient machine. Whereas earlier élites gained their wealth from human megamachines comprising hundreds of thousands of workers, industrialized societies gain theirs from the growing mechanization of the megamachine. To the images of nature as a machine, images which have inspired science for centuries, must now be added the image of human beings seen in similar fashion, thus fostering the mechanization of human nature, together with the complementary characteristics of precision, standardization and repeatability. Science uses standardization and repeatability as its core element of engineering systems and scientific experiment. Weights and measures, time, etc., are all standardized and repeatable throughout the world. Standardization of machine parts and machines, their repeatability and their mass production proceeded apace with the advent of the First and Second World Wars, as did that of the human constituents of the megamachines within nations. Stalin pointed this neatly when he referred to

> ... 'the tens of millions of simple, ordinary modest people' as '*vintiki*', literally 'little screws', translated as 'cogs in the great state machine', a phrase he repeated: 'the *vintiki* who keep our great state machine in motion ... the people who maintain us as the base maintains the summit'.[26]

The social process increasingly requires the standardization of people. In the near future, the development of robots will likewise be standardized and repeatable, and they will become so human in their abilities and behaviour that they will make possible what has been described as a 'humanoid robot economy'; the human genome project, which uses electronic technology to help cure diseases, can extend repeatability to humans, a kind of standardization which has proved so successful with machines that it is most likely to be used to perfect the human members of megamachines, making them increasingly like robots or cogs. In the USA, for example, work is highly organized. All processes are analysed and people are trained to be efficient cogs, producing the most units necessary for a given increment of time and motion. Such uniformity in the physical apparatus of life is matched by the growing uniformity in matters of thought and opinion, through the power of radio, television, schools, computers and the Press. Furthermore, a symbiosis of humans and machines is in progress: more than eleven million Americans have some kind of artificial implant to improve and prolong their lives, showing how increasingly dependent *Homo degener* is becoming on the products of materials science, not only for his wealth but also for his health and survival. According to Ian Sample[27], nano-engineers are developing machines on the scale of living cells to insert inside cells to repair bodies from the inside out. The use of nanotechnology to provide nanomedicines could spell the end of ageing and, ultimately, even defeat death.* Meanwhile, programmes for machines such as computers are being designed loosely to follow the biological rules of natural selection, sexual reproduction and mutation, a process called genetic algorithms.

By the humanization of machines, and by the deliberate bending and changing of minds and alteration of the genetic endowment of the individual human ovum by laboratory intervention, tampering with and selecting the most suitable genes, it will be possible to make machines and the minds and genetic inheritance of individuals conform to the memetic code of their composite animals. Thereafter, it will become possible to develop self-replicating machines and to produce biological replicas of people by the process of nuclear transplantation, or cloning, in which a cell is made to produce an exact genetic duplicate of the donor of the nucleus, male or female. Thus to create one's own clone would be to carry the narcissism inherent in *Homo degener* societies to its ultimate limits.† Furthermore, with the aid of cloning, scientists will be able to create brain-dead copies of humans as sources of perfectly

---

* 'Ultimately, we will merge with our technology. This will begin with nanobots (blood-cell sized robots) in our bodies and brains. The nanobots will keep us healthy, provide full-immersion virtual reality from within the nervous system, provide direct brain-to-brain communication over the internet and greatly expand human intelligence.' (Ray Kurzweil, *Human 2.0*, New Scientist, Vol. 187, No. 2518, 24 September 2005).

† Two types of cloning are under consideration: therapeutic cloning, which is acceptable to the scientific community, and reproductive cloning, which is at present considered a crime against humanity, given that any survivors of such a process face the prospect of living with a potential life-threatening abnormality.

matched organ transplants. By manipulative processes such as those outlined above, combined with the symbiosis of humans and machines, members of nations – like termites that have become perfectly adapted in a caste-like division of labour within the internal protected environments of their termitaries – would be brought to a perfection of adaptation in equally caste-like divisions of labour within the internal protected environments of nations.

Scientists are likewise increasingly concerning themselves with standards of living and economic well-being. Earlier ascribed to Providence, to the beneficence of God and nature, they too have become the prerogative of science, and in particular the concern of biotechnology. Food is now being genetically modified, as are plants to make them disease resistant and able to collaborate with the environmental changes wrought by *Homo degener*. At the same time scientists are developing more and more laboratory-based products. The idea behind the biotechnical approach to living organisms is basically to engineer biological resources to convert them into living products at a rate far exceeding that of nature's own production process, and create an economic cornucopia.

At the same time as perfecting individuals to conform to the memetic code of their composite animals and accelerating the conversion of domestic animal and plant material, scientists will attempt to perfect the internal protected environments of each nation to make our unnatural social conditions more bearable, thus advancing on three fronts – the human, the domestic animal and plant, and the environmental – to make for a greater stability of nations.

This will include the development and perfection of measures to recognize, and then counteract, environmental change in order to maintain a constant internal environment akin to that pertaining in a termitary. However, Earth environments will prove far more intractable to manipulation than will human beings, and scientists will probably have to postpone the making of perfect internal environments until they can create them in space-stations or on the moon. Once in limitless space, they will be able to reproduce internal protected environments to their own specification as requisite.

By eliminating, by all the processes outlined above, many of the stresses and strains within and between members of nations, and between them and their environment – stresses which in fact reveal the inherent falseness of their

$$\frac{Homo\ sapiens\ sapiens}{Homo\ sapiens\ non\ sapiens}$$

condition – they would make their fundamentally unstable systems more stable and controlled. Instead of having to rely on threats from without to ensure effective co-operation within, recourse to such methods of scientific control – which might include ethnic cleansing of the nation by means of genetic engineering – would circumvent race and class wars and violence, together with disease and other signs of stress. The inmates would be as perfectly predictable as termites in a termitary, while yet being persuaded of their humanity.

There is one further major reason why societies are likely to move in this direction: the growing international competition between nations to enhance their status, wealth and power. There is already a model for the structural organization and social behaviour necessary to achieve those aims in the future: Japan, which, at least until it entered a period of severe recession in 2002, had perhaps the highest standard of living on Earth. It is one of the most termitary-like of all nations. In order to meet the challenge, other nations may feel obliged to improve and perfect their social organizations and efficiency along the lines of Japan and the termitary.

Paul Kennedy[28] listed five structural factors underlying the economic performance and strength of Japan, including the very high quality of the Japanese work force, to which should be added its docility and conformity. There was a further factor, arguably the most important of all, underlying that strength, which was education. Following the Second World War Japanese society was turned into 'a robotized machine, with the Japanese as the component parts'. This was achieved through the systematic application of intelligence by an élite of civil servants, bankers, managers and engineers. But undergirding this system was 'the finest centralized mass system of education in the world'.* It was in school that the peer group pressures in the enforcement of shared goals moulded young Japanese to fit into the national hierarchy with its own peer group pressures in the enforcement of the shared goals of the economic growth to Super-Power status of Japan Inc.

Given Japan's earlier achievements through imitation and improvement, the possible need to imitate much of the Japanese social system in pursuit of wealth creation is indeed an ironic comment on the forces of convergence at work upon nations throughout the world. Even more ironic is the fact that a country conquered only sixty years ago by military means has

---

*Although Japan's system of education has been accused of stifling creativity through its heavy reliance on rote learning and conformity – its share of Nobel Prizes in 2002 in the main science spheres of physics, chemistry and physiology was only 6, whereas that of Britain was 70 – Britain at the beginning of 2002 had, according to its Education Minister, a 'shocking' record for literacy and numeracy. Some 7 million people had difficulty reading and writing. The majority of them were 'functionally illiterate', meaning they had a reading age of the average 11-year-old or worse, which forced them into low paid, boring, unproductive jobs.

spread abroad its memes through commercial conquest right across the globe – profoundly affecting the collective memetic inheritance of nations, making increasingly for a memetic homogeneity world-wide. This is the direction in which the competitive challenge is most likely to impel nations, whose social systems and behaviour have been likened to those of a termitary. All the evidence points to nations becoming more and more termitary-like in order to survive and to prosper in tomorrow's high technology world. In the last four decades of the 20th century Hong Kong, Singapore, South Korea and Taiwan – the 'four tigers' of S.E. Asia – followed Japan's lead by raising themselves to economic and industrial supremacy by dint of iron discipline and collective will. (China is all set to follow their example.) Though their economies may have faltered along the way, as they follow Japan into the era of high technology they will be as arrogantly assured of the rightness of their behaviour, and of their moral superiority, as are the Japanese.

Those at the summits of nations are certain that they are jewels in the crown of human evolution. Such powers of deception and self-deception originally lay with the priest-scientists and scholars of the early civilizations, who justified and controlled their social structures and artificial environments with the aid of myth and ritual. Today, as I argued above, those powers lie increasingly with the scientists and their ability actually to mould people and shape their environments to accord with the anti-evolutionary myths and paths they are already committed to and pursuing, so justifying their commitment as evolutionary and necessary to the Ascent of Man. And they will be believed.

The ultimate power will be the ability to design the blueprint of a human being, an animal or a plant, whose instructions they will then execute biologically. Scientists are concerned to engineer a change in the genetic make-up of *Homo degener* populations, enabling them to conform more closely to the requirements of their meme pools through the intimate merger between people and the information technology which nations are creating. Genes and memes will then once again reinforce one another – a perverted genetic selection will be married to a perverted memetic selection as *Homo degener* peoples become perfectly adapted to their

Homo sapiens sapiens
Homo sapiens non sapiens

rôles. It is at this point that the evolutionary trend towards speciation becomes most apparent, when what may be described as cultural speciation – that is, speciation through memetic isolation into separate Sacred Species – becomes true biological speciation through the reproductive isolation of *Homo degener* populations (perhaps as a super-rich genetic elect unable to interbreed with the gene-poor, or in new niches in space) but also because of the destruction by *Homo degener* of the original evolutionary line of *Homo sapiens*. Power will lie increasingly with those scientists who develop and manipulate the gene therapy and information technology that will enable them to perfect, and eventually prolong, their own lives and those of other *Homo sapiens sapiens* dominants indefinitely as a genetic elect. This power to grant or withhold immortality in this and other worlds in space is a prerogative that had previously belonged, so it was believed, to God alone, and then only in a life after death. Thus they would acquire the power to govern life on Earth to their own perceived ends, *ad infinitum*, giving them superhuman, even god-like, status. As James Watson, co-discoverer of DNA's double-helix, observed: 'If biologists don't play God, who will?'

Devoid of their original humanity, self-regulating and self-reliant behaviour and ecological understanding, cast in the mythopoeic-cum-mathematical image created by the priestly and scientific experts, *Homo degener* peoples will become their own artefacts, moulded and perfected within their composite animals. Like Narcissus, they will have become trapped by their own reflection.* Their perfection will be like that achieved by the blind worker termite in a termitary, a perfection as different from that of the free-ranging hunter-gatherer as is that of the blind worker termite from the free-flying termite. It will not be a perfection of true human beings integrated in a freedom of unpossessive movement within the real world, but of subhuman beings – many man-machine composites – integrated and perfected, imprisoned in hierarchies in machine-dominated environments alienated from, and forever at war with, the real world.

In this way, a universality of a very different and opposite kind to the one discussed earlier is steadily coming into being. From the standpoint of wild nature, the perfection in degeneration towards which *Homo degener* is inexorably moving will include a universal immorality – which undermines and negates any morality to which *Homo degener* might aspire – a universal unfreedom and inequality of social relations, and the universal degradation and destruction of biotic communities, all of which will near completion with the imposition of World Government.†

---

*They might become so trapped both metaphorically and actually. For the possible development of national identity cards and biometric passports would ensure that personal details would be held on National Identity Registers, stored on government databases, enabling governments to exercise maximum control over people to their own ends. For many purposes a digital identity would become more important than an actual physical identity, reinforcing all the genetic and technological factors making for the perfection of *Homo degener* societies.

† In this connection see Part III, Chapter 3.

The Falangist motto, 'Long live death', threatens to become the secret principle of a society in which the conquest of nature by the machine constitutes the very meaning of progress, and where the living person becomes an appendix to the machine.[29]

What we are witnessing and experiencing is the perfecting of *Homo degener* as the component part of a composite animal that is fundamentally at war with the world. This is a most profound consequence of the two-fold fall of humankind. As members of composite animals they are in direct and world-wide competition with all other similar structures – both artificial and natural – which they resemble by convergent evolution.

Chapter 9

The Convergent Evolution of Nations and Nature

When two elephants fight, it is the grass which is crushed.
(African proverb)

Founded in similar physical and psychical adaptations for survival, the early settlements and cities were separated geographically – in the Old World in Egypt, Mesopotamia, the Indus Valley and China; in the New World in Mexico, Yucatan and Peru – developing along parallel or convergent lines as composite animals of collective security against the wilderness. Each was marked by most, if not all, the following characteristics: the cult of Divine Kingship; imposing monumental structures such as palaces, pyramids, temples and walled cities; astronomical measurement of time; written records; a vertically oriented division and specialization of labour; organized agriculture, granaries, canal and irrigation systems; organized war. All present parallel, or convergent, pictures of disciplined, even regimented, civilizations; while differentiations in customs, in laws, in script, in metalwork, in pottery, in dress, in agricultural practices, in domesticated animals and in environment indicate a divergent development within each as each grew as an independent composite animal with its own individual features. Each composite animal, in the obedience of its members to a Life-Force and laws ostensibly stemming from its own peculiar God on its own sacred land, was a Sacred Species entirely different from the others. Their differences and similarities were such that, when they met, it was inevitable they should compete.

The dawn of history is notable for the picture it presents of groups of priest-scientists of the various city-states of Sumeria fighting each other, fighting for possession of the other's Farmer God in their struggles to gain hegemonic control, ascending towards the sun the better to enrich,

422

to dominate and to stabilize their environment. Inevitably as nations have grown in size and landed wealth, and the city has become the heart and brain of an empire, armies too have grown, together with ever more refined weapons of offence-defence. Moscow when it was the powerful capital of the USSR, once said that it could send missiles to any part of the world, and that it was fighting for peace. 'A capital crying like some primeval mastodon over the great political swamp to what it thinks may be its own species in Washington or Peking.'[1] But appearances lie, just as protestations of peace often deceive. In fact, as I argued in Chapter 1, these composite animals are no more nearly related than are the ostrich, emu and cassowary. They are separate Sacred Species only made similar by convergent evolution. Their protestations of peace mask not only their true origins but also the fact that they *must*, by reason of their convergent evolution, compete for the same scarce resources in their efforts to acquire (or to retain) status, wealth and power relative to other nations – and that all *must* compete with the kingdom of nature to that end, driving the *Homo sapiens* inhabitants to the margins of the world (see figure 9.1).

I shall first of all examine and provide examples of the ideological, technological, territorial and resource competition between nations, and then that between nations and the kingdom of nature. Before doing so, however, it is necessary to emphasize that all such aspects of competition may be reduced to one main objective – power. Such power may be gained either by peaceful means or by war.

> One generalisation about war aims can be offered with confidence. The aims are simply varieties of power. The vanity of nationalism, the will to spread an ideology, the protection of kinsmen in an adjacent land, the desire for more territory or commerce, the avenging of a defeat or insult, the craving for greater national strength or independence, the wish to impress or cement alliances – all these represent power in different wrappings. The conflicting aims of rival nations are always conflicts of power. Not only is power the issue at stake, but the decision to resolve that issue by peaceful or warlike methods is largely determined by assessments of relative power.[2]

In addition, the behaviour of those in power has had much in common down the millennia because they have all been specialists in power within their stratified societies. It is the struggles for power within and between nations – whether ideological, economic or military – and the preservation of power once gained, that would seemingly make for the convergent

Part II: fig 9.1

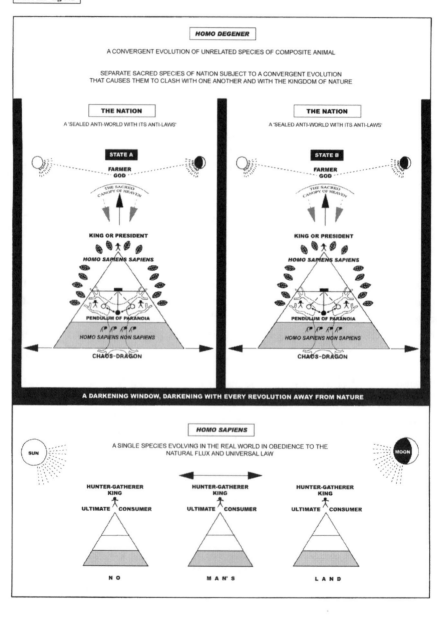

evolution of nations. However, the issue of power should be seen as the direct product of humiliation. The trappings of power, like the pyramids of power themselves, originated in the humiliating loss of status and powerlessness attendant upon the two-fold fall of man. Such power has in its turn been the cause of continual humiliation and consequent revenge down the millennia. It is the underlying humiliation, or avoidance of humiliation, which is the fundamental driving force behind the convergent evolution of nations.*

Examples of the ideological, technological, territorial and resource competition that help fuel the struggles for power in the ascent of nations to the sun are many.

In the last chapter I referred to the competitive challenge posed by Japan in the race to acquire wealth and power, inclining nations to follow her example. Earlier instances of such convergence may be found in eighteenth and nineteenth century Europe. First there was the organizational and technological competition engendered by the France of Louis XIV (1661–1715), whose ministers sought to heighten the powers of the Sun King at home and to enhance his glories abroad. A French war ministry was established to help build up and sustain the Sun King's army, while a large fleet was established at sea. This military build-up drove the other powers to emulate France for fear of being eclipsed.

Then there was the competitive drive for territorial expansion in the late nineteenth century.

As the twentieth century approached ... the pace of technological change and uneven growth rates made the international system much more unstable and complex than it had been fifty years earlier. This was manifested in the frantic post-1880 jostling by the Great Powers for additional colonial territories in Africa, Asia, and the Pacific, partly for gain, partly out of a fear of being eclipsed. It also manifested itself in the increasing number of arms races, both on land and at sea, and in the creation of fixed military alliances, even in peacetime, as the various governments sought out partners for a possible future war.[3]

Following the First World War, and prior to the Second, some of the Great Powers possessed empires or protected zones from which they could derive enhanced prestige and adequate resources. This was the case with the United States: the greater part of the American continent was the

---

* See Part III, Chapter 2, for an amplification of this argument.

United States' sphere of interest.* Such was also the case with the British and French Empires. Three of the great industrial countries of the world – Japan, Germany and Russia – however, did not possess such zones, and they were lacking in prestige; the two former, were also short of resources. Quite apart from other things – their national feeling, their ideology (e.g. German Nazism) – they were discontented with their lot and were seeking to break into the monopoly of the other great powers. They were

... 'dissatisfied' powers that jostle alongside 'satisfied ones'.[4]

The dissatisfaction of Germany led to the rise of Hitler and the Nazi Party, at the same time as a similar phenomenon was occurring in Russia after the Revolution, with the rise of Stalin and the Communist Party. The convergence between these two heads of state and their ideologies has been vividly portrayed by Alan Bullock in his book *Hitler and Stalin: Parallel Lives*. Both were outsiders, born on the margins of their respective countries. Both were filled with the compelling urge to avenge past humiliations. Both sought power, setting out to win the support of the masses with at least the appearance of legality, seeing them as incapable of organizing themselves and as a resource to be mobilized rather than a membership to be represented. They were mobilized to the ends of National Socialism and Communism respectively, each an ideology or set of beliefs which everyone was obliged to accept.

> To the believer in either the Nazi or the Communist ideology, the opposition between them was absolute: if one was a Nazi, by definition one was anti-Marxist; if a Communist, anti-Fascist. No compromise was possible.[5]

Though in direct conflict, their function was similar: to provide a vision which could inspire and galvanize the masses into action.

> Looked at from the point of view of function rather than content, there are clear parallels between the Communist and Nazi ideologies. 'Race', 'class', 'the bourgeoisie', 'the Jew', play the rôle of mythical symbols rather than sociological categories, symbols with which the

---

*US influence over the American continents was laid down by the Monroe Doctrine of 1823, when it established the principle that non-American powers should not intervene in affairs in either of the American continents. This has since been taken as God-given law.

masses can identify positively, as with 'Volk' or 'prôletariat', or which they can reject, as with 'capitalists' or 'kulaks'. In a time of upheaval, (collectivization in Russia) or anxiety (the renewal of crisis in Germany with the Depression) these were symbols of great potency, particularly in providing a focus for fears and hatreds. Hitler and Stalin alike depicted history as struggle, the first as a struggle between races, with 'the Jew' doubling in the rôles of both capitalist and communist, the second as a struggle between classes, or between 'the Revolution' and the 'enemies of Soviet power', 'agents of foreign powers', 'imperialists' who sought to overthrow its achievements and restore the old order.[6*]

Hitler's power was greatly enhanced by the Hitler myth, the Führer cult of the Nazi Party. He was presented and seen by Germans as the embodiment of national unity. His sense of mission was at the heart of the Hitler myth ('I go the way that Providence dictates with the assurance of a sleep-walker'); it was his 'world-historical' rôle to defend the Aryan race against racial pollution, and European civilization against Bolshevism. The cult of Stalin was the Russian counterpart to that of the Führer. It identified Stalin as 'Our Beloved Leader', successor to the Tsars and heir of Lenin. Stalin exalted 'the Party' and 'the Revolution', identifying himself with both, and called for their defence against class enemies at home, and Fascist and capitalist enemies abroad. With the outbreak of war between them, Hitler and Stalin became the focus for a welling up of national patriotism in their respective countries, miracle-workers in whose names millions fought and died.

> This later development led to a convergence between the Stalin cult and the Hitler myth, in both of which there was present the same yearning for a substitute religion, for a messiah in the guise of a leader, salvation rather than solutions... The Hitler myth and the Stalin cult of personality played a central part in their exercise of power, and anything that might disturb the official, carefully constructed version was liable to suppression.[7]

Both created youth organizations – the Nazi Party the Hitler Youth and the Russians the Communist League of Youth (Komsomol). And both took over their systems of education, reworking the textbooks to accord with the German racist and Russian Marxist-Leninist interpretations of history. In addition, both countries instituted compulsory labour service

---

[*]In Part I, Chapter 4, I argued that cults originated in periods of crisis and mass disorientation.

and conscription for military service. In sum, all their efforts to brainwash, command the loyalties of and control their youth enabled each country to use the same expression – the 'New Man' – to describe the younger generation they had moulded.

As well as finding further parallels in both the attitudes and the experiences of Germany and Russia in relation to the Spanish Civil War, Alan Bullock cites their convergence during the invasion and occupation of Poland between 1939 and 1941.[8]

It was at the end of 1941 and the beginning of 1942 that the parallel between the rôles of Stalin and Hitler became most apparent. It was then that the leadership of both men was put to the most severe test: Stalin as Supreme Commander moved to halt and reverse the German advance on Moscow, and Hitler tried to prevent his troops falling back from Moscow. As Stalin counterattacked, Hitler ordered his generals to stand their ground, sacking those who retreated or advocated retreat. In the end, Hitler, declaring he knew of no general capable of instilling the National Socialist spirit in the army, took over as Commander in Chief of the army as well as Supreme Commander of the Wehrmacht. The retreat was halted by his intervention. 'Both Hitler and Stalin thus combined in their single persons the highest offices in the state, party and the armed forces',[9] and were pitted against each other in personal command of operations. Finally, each one, living in his own fantasy world, defended his power to the death.

Here, then, is evidence of the convergent evolution of two composite animals growing up under totally different and opposed ideologies, and their consequent clash in competition over ideology, territory and resources.

Following the Second World War the predominant ideological, technological and resource competition, convergence of interests and fears of conspiracy was between China, the Soviet Union and the USA. China, like the Soviet Union, wanted to expand its influence and become a great power; the Soviet Union was the main obstacle to such Chinese expansion. The Russians were much more obsessive about the Chinese 'peril' than they were about a possible Western attack. They were afraid of China, not only because its overcrowded billion people – as against their 250 million or so – threatened their long and extremely vulnerable frontier, but also as an up-and-coming super-Power. The fear of what they regarded as 'Peking's world hegemonist ambitions' largely dictated their African and Asian policies. They saw the Chinese increase of influence in east and south-east Africa as a threat to their own world-wide strategic interests, and they intervened in Angola in 1975 more to pre-empt the Chinese than to injure Western interests.

The USA, on the other hand, was obsessive about Soviet world hegemonist ambitions, and as a result was caught up in a constantly escalating arms race with the USSR. The sense of competition between them was primarily the outcome of an irreconcilable conflict between their opposing ideological, economic and political systems, capitalism and communism. But each was also driven by an arms competition. Each country, because of the weapons it invented and acquired, forced the other to do likewise if it was not to be humiliatingly eclipsed. This is an excellent example of technological advance through imitation, initiated and driven by the fear of humiliation.

We are, in fact, observing an example of the evolution of nations as the survival of the fittest, or best adapted, in terms of its measures of offence-defence. It has been pointed out that evolution may be seen as an arms race, in which each side has at least to match the abilities of the other if it is to succeed. Organisms must avoid being eaten, and mechanisms that solve this problem will be selected. Other organisms must, perforce, eat, and will evolve mechanisms to overcome the defences of their food. The food will in turn evolve better defences, and the two sides in the struggle for survival will egg each other on to ever better performances. This argument also applies to the struggle between nations. During the Second World War the German U-boats were hidden predators which would lie in wait for, or steal up on, their prey, the British merchant ships carrying vital supplies of food and raw materials to Britain. As the German Navy developed improved systems of offence, such as U-boat wolf packs and acoustic torpedoes, the convoys and their escorts developed better tactics and improved Asdic (sonar) for their mutual defence.

So it can be said that the arms race between nations has been a principal agent in their evolution as composite animals – though, as I argued above, *the* principal agent underlying that race has been the fear of humiliating eclipse. All are competing for the same limited resources in their concern for ideological and economic growth to ensure survival. If genes may be said to 'play war games', the same may be said of the collective memes of nations.

This model of an arms race accords with the argument that the eternal duel between the hunters and the hunted is one of the driving forces of evolution, and that that duel was now perverted as a duel between stratified societies, becoming one of the main driving forces of their re-evolutionary progression, or convergent evolution, as composite animals. In every case, with the passing of evolutionary time, the one that is most competitive in religio-socio-economic and military terms will survive

better, to describe the whole process as progress or the Ascent of Man. They – and we – are the victims, not simply of evolution, but of convergent evolution: the convergent evolution of nations, each assured of the righteousness of its cause to dominate as much of the world as possible – ideologically, commercially, technically – each persuaded that the other is overtaking it in the pursuit of that cause.

During the Cold War between the USSR and the Western powers following the Second World War, the USSR and the USA achieved an arms 'balance of terror' known as MAD, or Mutually Assured Destruction to which I referred in Part I. During the Cuban missile crisis of 1962, President Kennedy of the USA and Nikita Khrushchev of the USSR held the fate of the world in their hands as they negotiated a settlement under the threat of MAD.

The fact that armaments breed armaments, and always will, is a prime factor in this convergent evolution. More recently, other, increasingly sinister, arms races have loomed over the horizon – the development of chemical and biological weapons. Their use may be overt or covert. In the olden days, the Farmer God of country A could be blamed for natural disasters occurring in country B, providing good reasons for a pre-emptive strike by country B against country A. Technology has now made such (seemingly natural) catastrophes possible. With the aid of biological agents, a country can now cripple another's agriculture or economy without engaging in overt conflict or even raising suspicions of deliberate sabotage.

This is also the case with the use of weather modification as a weapon. G. Breuer[10] argues that cloud seeding was used by the United States armed forces against the Vietcong between 1967 and 1972 in the Vietnam War. Its aim was to increase rainfall over the Ho Chi Minh trail to reduce traffic through the jungle, creating landslides and washing away river crossings. As great a threat as the actual use of the weather weapon, however, is the *fear* on the part of country B that its adverse weather and climatic changes bringing drought or flooding is due to weather modification by country A. This is another technology with the potential to further destabilize relationships between nations, inclining them to imitate one another in the development of more and more deadly weather weapons.

Just as chemical weapons have been described as 'the poor man's atom bomb', so covert activities with biological agents and weather weapons are available to all, making their use increasingly likely as nations struggle desperately, like trees in a forest, to grow towards the sun, or just to survive, in an increasingly unstable world of high technology, rising populations and dwindling resources. For even without arms competition, there remains the convergence of interests that underlies arms competition, such as that which led to Pearl Harbor, and which more recently led to the war between America (and its allies) and Iraq. Many more nations within the forest of nations are going to fight for a place in the sun in the coming decades. For given both the relativity of the economic and military strength of nations, and the anarchic and competitive nature of rivalries between nations, the international balance of power is always changing. An unequal growth of nations poses a constant threat of humiliating eclipse to some, and so the likelihood of war between them – or if not overt war between nations, then covert war waged by terrorist organizations.

As in the days of the European empires, it is the short-term interest of each nation to control and exploit as much of the world as it conveniently can to its own ends, and the devil take the hindmost. As Queen Victoria is said to have remarked to Disraeli:

Have we no permanent friends?

to which Disraeli replied:

Madam, we have no permanent friends and no permanent enemies. We only have permanent interests.

In short, each composite animal is motivated by ideological, technological and resource competition, convergence of interests – particularly commercial interests – and, above all, by the fear of being humiliated, of being eclipsed, to make for a convergent evolution of nations.

Nature's command to diversify and divide, particularly as to environment and food, ensuring a minimum competition and maximum co-operation, as amongst the hunter-gatherers, has been negated and reversed by the compression of herds of gregarious uncomprehending subhumans into similar pyramidal shapes, which also resemble giant human beings.

The superpowers often behave like two heavily armed blind men feeling their way around a room, each believing himself in mortal peril from the other, whom he assumes to have perfect vision... Each tends to ascribe to the other side a consistency, foresight and coherence that its own experience belies. Of course, over time even two blind men can do enormous damage to each other, not to speak of the room.[11]

Homo degener peoples are the victims of a convergent evolution of unrelated composite animals which inevitably compete for physical and psychical food and root space and for mineral resources to promote growth and guarantee security. For it is an indisputable fact that struggles between Great Powers throughout history have turned as much around the control of natural resources as around ideologies or national prestige. Many wars in the 20th century were about oil. Today large resources are being channelled into the struggle for control of the Caspian oil fields.[12] Wars in the area are not only being waged over the ownership of the oil, but also for control of the territory over which proposed pipelines may pass.

One of the most important issues facing the United Nations at the end of the 20th century was that of shared water resources: rivers, lakes and groundwaters. As the demand for water continues to rise, and the supply remains constant or (through pollution or other mismanagement) even declines, and as more and more governments intercept or divert for economic purposes the rivers which pass through their countries, present water conflicts are likely to become more acute: between India and Pakistan over the Indus, and India and Bangladesh over the Ganges; Israel and Jordan over the Jordan; Turkey, Syria and Iraq over the Tigris-Euphrates; Ethiopia, Eritrea, Sudan and Egypt over the Nile; the USA and Mexico over the Colorado. Wars in this century are as likely to be about water as they are about oil. The potential for conflict will grow if global warming causes dry areas to become wet and wet areas dry.

Today one of the major arenas of present and future friction is the sea. Failure to agree on the constitution of a law of the sea could lead to war between nations seeking space and resources. For history shows that the law of the sea, or lack of it, contains the seeds of many conflicts.*

Fish are the only source of animal protein for many people. They are a vital yet increasingly scarce resource because the world fisheries are evincing the usual political patterns of conquest and colonialism that lead to outright conflict. The three 'Cod Wars' (1958–76) between Great Britain and Iceland, and the more recent battles with the Spanish fishing fleet, were examples of conflict over rights to the wealth of the sea. Yet all the while, behind the scenes, lurk the elemental forces of nature, that are still the principal and common enemy

---

* Even where an international law has been established, as with the Antarctic Treaty, it has been shown to be impossible to enforce. One rule of that Treaty was to ban any nation from enhancing any territorial claims. Already, two signatories – Chile and Argentina – have violated this rule by establishing 'permanent' communities and claiming large sections of the continent as national territory.

of *Homo degener.** as when one 'Cod War' between Britain and Iceland was brought to a standstill by gale force winds and mountainous seas.

It is still a principal concern of nations to conquer and control the natural forces of the world, just as it is a principal 'concern' of those self-same forces to overwhelm and destroy such alien forms as nations. In fact, we are witnessing not only the convergent evolution of nations, but the convergent evolution of anti-evolutionary nations and evolutionary nature, to the increasing disadvantage of both. This is the other major arena of competition to which I referred earlier.

Parasite pyramids of primary producers and ultimate consumers strike at the very base of the ecological pyramid – by rearranging habitats, and destroying the primary producers at the base of natural food pyramids. When, for instance, the Native American hunter-gatherer was replaced by the European farmer, and the grassland by fields of wheat and corn, the life-cycle of the Great Plains was changed for ever. The indigenous wildlife, including the Native Americans, are now mainly to be found in national parks, reservations, zoos and museums. Thus we have come full circle, from being enclosed in enclaves by wild animals and wilderness 10,000 years ago to enclosing a remnant of wildlife and wilderness in national enclaves, or exterminating them. Almost all that now remains of a lost heritage and real paradise of flora and fauna for each new generation to explore is a domesticated farming landscape that is itself being rapidly eroded by the products of industry and by urban expansion, a caged wildlife, and books that recall that lost heritage. Any remaining wildlife which competes with us for food or space, or interferes with the profitable and efficient running of our lives, is ruthlessly eliminated. According to a report in 1990 from the Royal Society for the Protection of Birds, the managers of grouse moors have been deliberately killing one of Britain's rarest birds of prey, the hen harrier, because it was seen as a competitor. Similarly, because the structures of nations as composite animals and the behaviour of their members also resemble those of the forest and its inhabitants, they also compete with and destroy the forests of the world in their growing need for the space and resources presently occupied and utilized respectively by the remaining forests and their inhabitants. For example, the demand for tantalum – which has been

---

*The following remark, made by a captured German officer to the young Scots intelligence officer who was interrogating him during the desert war in North Africa in 1943, is relevant:

Africa changes everything. In reality we are allies, and the desert is our common enemy.[13]

In Antarctica co-operation between members of otherwise antagonistic nations is enforced by the hostility of nature.

fuelling the civil war in the Democratic Republic of Congo – has led to the near extinction of the eastern lowland gorilla.

World Wide Fund For Nature (WWF)[14] has estimated that by the year 2025 few large tracts of tropical forest will remain, except in a few remote parts of Amazonia, the Democratic Republic of Congo and Papua New Guinea. WWF argued that the greatest single cause of tropical forest destruction was the relentless pressure of poor people hungry for land, accounting for 60 per cent of the loss of the rainforests. This situation was exacerbated because Third World debtor nations cut down their forests and opened up new land to earn money to try to pay the interest on their crippling debt burden. As they slid yet further into debt, their poorest suffered most, driving them to destroy the forests for land and fuel.

As well as the unofficial migration of encroaching cultivators into the forest, a number of countries with rapidly rising populations are organizing large scale clearance of jungle for the purpose of resettlement. These include Malaysia, Indonesia and Brazil. But the people placed on these cleared areas often find the conditions too difficult. They suffer from insects and unfamiliar diseases, and the soil is often thin and quickly farmed out.

The other major cause behind the destruction of the tropical forests is greed amongst the wealthy nations. In Latin America, for instance, which contains more than half the world's tropical moist forests, cattle farming, sponsored by both local and international concerns, has also eliminated forests. Most of the beef went to the United States and other developed countries to make hamburgers. The life-style of the developed countries is definitely 'a substantive factor' in the disappearance of the tropical moist forests. Working alongside the farmers are the timber companies, mostly multinationals based in the industrialized West. Their presence once again reveals the vast disparity between the hundreds of millions of rural poor who are forced to destroy the forests in the daily struggle for food, and those who exploit the forests to maintain a highly developed life-style, as expressed in the uses to which the felled timber is put, ranging from survival at one end of the scale to parquet floors and yachts at the other. In contrast to a preoccupation with oil shortages in the developed world, many of our fellow human beings depend overwhelmingly on firewood – woodfuel is the main source of domestic energy for half the world's population. In short, greed amongst the wealthy for personal enrichment, coupled with landlessness and economic necessity amongst the poorest, are the driving forces of ecological destruction. However, there is in addition an even more profound force affecting rich and poor alike.

Behind this convergent evolution of forest-like structures there lies the underlying suspicion and fear of the incomprehensible and hostile forest that evokes the desire to push back the frontiers of wilderness and expand those of comforting civilization.

> Panama's military rulers have made *La conquista de la selva* (the conquest of the forest) their slogan. The phrase has psychological and political appeal; it unites a macho assertion of power over the unknown with the naming of a new frontier where displaced peasants can, without threat to the owners of large estates, find new land.[15]

Yet land hunger is not even the prime motivation in many government-sponsored settlement schemes. Some of the largest ones, as in Indonesia and Brazil, are mainly intended to secure national sovereignty by establishing a civilian presence in the frontier regions. In the words of one member of the Brazilian junta,

> 'When we are certain that every corner of the Amazon is inhabited by genuine Brazilians and not by Indians, only then will we be able to say that the Amazon is ours.'[16]

At the same time such settlement and associated economic development of the border areas in Brazil serves the interests of national security by stamping out what is seen as 'a demographic void' that is vulnerable to infiltration by Marxism from neighbouring states. Altogether, therefore, a number of positive (or hopeful) and negative (or fearful) forces, constituting aspects of the Life-Force of each composite animal, combine to contribute to the destruction of the forests and their aboriginal inhabitants. Nations compete with and destroy their forests because their own societies, in striving upwards for a higher place in the sun by extending and securing their bases laterally, resemble those of rain forests by convergent evolution. In relation to the sea they have been similarly destructive.

The spread of nations across the world has brought them into increasing competition with the sea for space and resources. Civilization, as well as being built on the backs of slaves and wage-slaves, has been described as being built on the back of the whale, as shore-stations near whaling grounds grew into cities – in the Americas, in Europe, in Russia and in the Far East. A dramatic decline in whales has been accompanied by decline in fish stocks caused by over-fishing, and 'collateral damage' caused by trawling and dredging. Trawlers from a variety of nations have been dragging large nets or scoops to gather prawns, scallops and fish such as cod and haddock from the shallow waters of continental shelves, devastating natural habitats on the seabed in the process. Such forms of fishing have been described by marine ecologists as 'the marine equivalent of forest clear-felling'.[17] Furthermore, because they compete with fishermen for fish, seals are regularly hunted by Norwegians and Russians off Greenland and the Barents Sea.

In addition to the maximum exploitation of animal life to sustain cities and nations, the sea is increasingly used for the essential ingredients – sand and gravel – for making concrete for the construction and reconstruction of cities as sources of these materials on land are depleted. The extraction of oil and gas, and mining for mineral wealth, are other forms of exploitation of the seas that are proceeding apace. As a result of this increased industrialization, the poisoning of the seas is also proceeding apace, despite legal agreements at regional and international levels to control the situation. Oil, heavy metals such as mercury, pesticides, hazardous chemicals from industrial waste, radionuclides and sewage all reach the seas, from the air, from rivers, from deliberate or accidental discharge from ships and from dumping. Tens of thousands of tonnes of radioactive waste have, for instance, been dumped in the North Atlantic by European nations.

If the examples I have given tend to concentrate on the behaviour of the Western nations, it is important to understand that the attitude and behaviour of the Communist Eastern nations towards nature has been fundamentally the same. For while Genesis I: 26–28* enshrines the attitude of the Christian Western nations, hostility towards the natural environment appears to be endemic in Marxist psychology generally:

> The belief that it is not only in the power of the human race to change Nature, but that this is its historical calling, was shared and emphatically asserted by Lenin.[18]

As V. Zazubrin, a delegate to the First Congress of Soviet Writers in 1926, declared:

---

* '26 Then God said, "Let us make man in our image, after our likeness; and let them have dominion over the fish of the sea, and over the birds of the air, and over the cattle, and over all the earth, and over every creeping thing that creeps upon the earth." 27 So God created man in his own image, in the image of God he created him; male and female he created them. 28 And God blessed them, and God said to them, "Be fruitful and multiply, and fill the earth and subdue it; and have dominion over the fish of the sea and over the birds of the air and over every living thing that moves upon the earth."' (RSV)

Let the fragile green breast of Siberia be dressed in the cement armour of cities, armed with the stone muzzles of factory chimneys, and girded with iron belts of railroads. Let the taiga be burned and felled, let the steppes be trampled... Only in cement and iron can the fraternal union of all peoples, the iron brotherhood of all mankind, be forged.[19]

This psychotic declaration against nature was accepted wisdom in its day, driving 'the Stalinist industrial machine in its assault on nature'.[20] It was not until the 1970s that any indication of the extent of the ecological damage wrought in the Soviet Union leaked out, with the publication of a book by Ze'ev Vol'fson, writing under the pseudonym Boris Komarov. His book was a damning indictment of the Soviet authorities for permitting the despoliation of the country's air, land, water and wildlife, while claiming that serious environmental damage is a capitalist phenomenon. In a seeming contradiction of the Marx-Leninist philosophy, environmental protection, like human rights, was guaranteed by the Soviet constitution. However, in reality the leading Soviet planning agencies connived at the widespread destruction of nature, and sought to cover up the disastrous effects of their policies. Komarov asserted that mining, logging, dumping, reservoirs and erosion had made sterile and laid waste about 10 per cent of the habitable land – an area the size of Western Europe – while oil pollution was destroying the small Sea of Azov, adjoining the Black Sea. Another example of despoliation concerned the unique eco-system of Lake Baikal in central Siberia – the largest volume of freshwater and deepest lake in the world. Baikal is 25 million years old, but Komarov claimed that chemical wastes had brought it to 'the brink of irreversible change' in a single decade.

Major ecological problems in the Soviet Union began with Baikal, but unfortunately they will not end with the lake. During these years 'the blue orb of Siberia' has become a symbol of hundreds of Russian lakes and rivers being ruined by pollution, a symbol of the smoke-filled sky suffocating forests and people, a symbol of perishing nature.[21]

After 1988 the situation changed for the better, and a specific programme for preserving Lake Baikal was developed, though some scientists and federal ministries interested in industrial operations still believed the lake could survive any damaging effects of intensive development.

More recently, western Siberia has seen the realization of V. Zazubrin's dream of Siberia being 'dressed in the cement armour of cities' as engineers have constructed cities like Surgut and Noyabr'sk, built to house and sustain large populations of oil workers and their families. These were brought in to develop the region's hydrocarbon reserves, at the cost of burning and felling the forests and polluting the underground waters. Russia hopes that western Siberia could be the world's largest source of hydrocarbons in 15 years' time. Meanwhile Japanese and South Korean companies are felling trees in the taiga of east Russia at an increasing rate for export.

WWF reported in 1992[22] that the biggest threat to temperate forests is logging for the pulp industry, whether in Russia, in South America or elsewhere. On the other hand, Russia, over the past 25 years – like the USA, Canada and Scandinavia – has been planting trees sufficient to cover an area three times the size of Britain. But these new plantations bear no relation to the 'old-growth' forests they replace. Whereas the latter were complex ecosystems comprising a variety of trees and a wealth of wildlife, the new second-growth plantations comprise regimented stands of a few species at most: they are likely to be much less genetically diverse, and therefore more vulnerable to threats such as disease and climate change.

The Chinese have also been ardent exponents of the Marxist philosophy of hostility towards nature. In the last half of the 20th century government policies veered from one extreme to the other, but always at the cost of nature. In the 1950s economic and population growth were encouraged. Peasants were persuaded to smelt iron in their backyards, felling millions of trees to feed their furnaces, while neglecting grain production. In consequence, famine killed some 20 million people and drove others to destroy much of the wildlife of the western regions in order to survive. In the 1960s grain production assumed importance, leading to the ploughing up of pasturelands and further felling of forests. Then birds were designated as farm pests by the central directorate in China. The whole population was enlisted to wage war on birds, particularly sparrows, throughout the country. The Chinese then became involved in eliminating their insect populations. The almost total elimination of the common fly, for instance, was achieved by a mass campaign in which every member of the community was expected to deliver a minimum number of corpses. Similar mass involvement in other pest campaigns, like that against moths and beetles, and their conversion into animal food, together with the return of all manner of organic waste to the land as fertilizer, has turned Chinese society into a vast recycling super-plant.

Chinese society has gone further than most in transforming itself into a forest or termitary of a billion obedient subhumans. Inevitably, convergent evolution operates to ensure the elimination of anything competing with the Chinese termitary for space and resources. It is possible that China, by the end of 2006, will have lost more than a quarter of its scarce forests, while grasslands, farmlands, fisheries and water are suffering degradation from the spread of rural industry, housing developments and highways. According to government figures, China's 1.5 million square kilometres of desert, a sixth of the total land, has been expanding at the rate of 2500 square kilometres a year, a process which may in time be reversed as China undertakes what has been described as the world's largest ever reforestation programme. However, vulnerability of these new forests to disease and climate change will depend upon their genetic diversity.

Whether East or West, North or South, the attitude and behaviour of nations generally towards nature are such that it could be said that their members are the unwitting victims of a global death wish. World-wide there is a convergent evolution of nations and nature, which includes massive urban growth and intensification of both industrial and farming practices, resulting in progressive defertilization of formerly productive farmland, widespread pollution of the land and associated food chains and water supplies, widespread pollution and poisoning of the seas, and so rapid a deterioration of nature and the ecosphere in general as to threaten the extinction of all life on the planet, with the exception perhaps of bacteria. All this is done for the sake of national development and growth, which is described as progress.

> In virtually every arena, public concerns about ethical and environmental issues have been overridden by the imperative of scientific progress on the one hand and larger economic or military goals on the other.[23]

The progress thus aspired to is nothing less than the ascent of *Homo degener*, the progression of composite animals to the moon and beyond, competing with one another to that end, and with the kingdom of nature – a convergent evolution and clash of nations and the kingdom of nature. It is, in terms of a competition for energy and space, a convergent evolution and clash between parasite pyramids of energy and power, and between them and the natural pyramids of energy, on land and in the sea. Multinational companies and nations are myopic opportunists, seeking whatever is most immediately advantageous and profitable to themselves.

... every nation puts its own interests first and the devil take the hindmost.[24]*

No matter which nation the devil may take, the kingdom of nature is 'the hindmost' of them all.

So the relationship between nations and wild nature is also that of convergence, of an arms race, a duel between nations and nature, with nations arming themselves with more and more advanced technology and virulent insecticides and pesticides, and nature replying with more and more virulent, pesticide-resistant pests and diseases. For parasitism, like predation, is also an arms race between competitors.

We are no longer witnessing the expanding evolution and long-term survival of the fittest of humans as hunter-gatherers, but the convergent evolution and short-term survival of the largest and most powerful of anti-evolutionary composite animals, as the world is squeezed more and more tightly by a tyrannous technology of competing nations into a vertically oriented global uniculture. Evolutionary technology brought *Homo sapiens* ever-increasing freedom in adaptive understanding as kings of natural food pyramids, whereas the anti-evolutionary technology of *Homo sapiens sapiens* scientists binds more and more *Homo sapiens non sapiens* millions ever more closely in parasite pyramidal prisons. It is a world being made by and for the ruling few, and looked at helplessly by the many. In Part III I examine the underlying forces that are causing these presently unstable pioneer species of composite animal to converge towards a 'climax' condition.

---

* Hsiao Ch'ien, who witnessed the first meeting of the United Nations and the struggle for supremacy it uncovered, learnt from that conference '... that whereas such a thing as altruism might occasionally appear in relations between individuals, there was only the most naked self-interest in relations between nations.'[25]

PART III

THE HISTORICAL IMPERATIVE

'... and they shall reap the whirlwind'
(Hosea 8:7)

Chapter 1

An Infinitely Disadvantageous Mutation

It is a rule in paleontology that ornamentation and complication precede extinction. And our mutation, of which the assembly line, the collective farm, the mechanized army, and the mass-production of food are evidences or even symptoms, might well correspond to the thickening armor of the great reptiles – a tendency that can end only in extinction. If this should happen to be true, nothing stemming from thought can interfere with it or bend it.[1]

(John Steinbeck)

As a direct outcome of their two-fold fall, the genetic and cultural characteristics of *Homo degener* peoples became divorced from their evolutionary setting and were perverted to the growth of composite animals. During their isolation they gradually built up cultural mechanisms specific to their own societies, which were transmitted down the generations by what have been described as memes. The memes of *Homo degener* built survival machines for themselves, giant human beings now called nations. Each has been governed by a collective memetic inheritance fixedly attuned to the wilderness – and so to the world in general – as an environment hostile to its members, an environment to be changed and exploited rather than lived in and enjoyed.

It may therefore be said that a mutation has taken place, resulting in the re-evolutionary change from free-ranging hunter-gatherer to sedentary farmer: not a mutation in the biological sense of a change in one or more genes that provides part of the raw material on which natural selection acts to produce evolutionary change, but a cultural mutation in terms of memes. The change in memes as between free-ranging hunter-gatherer and sedentary farmer imprisoned in a composite animal, that provided part of the raw material on which a perverted memetic selection has acted to produce re-evolutionary change, may be described as a memetic mutation.

443

Such memetic mutations into separate Sacred Species of composite animal were of a religio-economic and psycho-social nature. For cultural evolution works chiefly, not by natural selection operating on genetic innovations, but by religio-socio-economic selection operating on cultural and practical innovations. Their re-evolution as *Homo degener* has in fact placed them in the power of an accelerating cultural evolution, a Lamarckian rather than Darwinian evolution.

> Cultural evolution has progressed at rates that Darwinian processes cannot begin to approach. Darwinian evolution continues in *Homo sapiens*, but at rates so slow that it no longer has much impact on our history. This crux in the Earth's history has been reached because Lamarckian processes have finally been unleashed upon it. Human cultural evolution, in strong opposition to our biological history, is Lamarckian in character. What we learn in one generation, we transmit directly by teaching and writing. Acquired characters are inherited in technology and culture. Lamarckian evolution is rapid and accumulative. It explains the cardinal difference between our past, purely biological mode of change, and our current, maddening acceleration toward something new and liberating – or toward the abyss.[2]

It is Lamarckian also to the extent that most of the acquired characteristics are injuries, not improvements as in the case of Darwinian evolution. All the characteristics of *Homo degener* are degenerative or deteriorations from those of the original hunter-gatherer stock, thus making for widespread degenerative genetic mutations in *Homo degener* populations.

As component parts or cells of composite animals, the members of a nation are themselves the 'chemical factories' within which the memes of the nation operate. As nations have developed, their members have proliferated as component cells and have become, in accordance with a perverted memetic selection, more and more highly specialized as parts of the head, nervous system or hands and feet of nations, while natural selection now acts in a modified or perverted fashion upon the inmates, making, for instance, for the degeneration of the genetic nature of *Homo degener*, due not only to the deleterious effects of pathogens such as bacteria and viruses on our genome, and of man-made agents such as chemicals and radiation, but also to the shielding of individuals from the action of natural selection on unfavourable, or disadvantageous, characteristics.

I argued in Part II that, as Julian Huxley[3] has pointed out, it is probable that human genetic nature has degenerated and is still doing so. For *Homo degener* peoples have, to a great extent, isolated themselves from the natural flux and selective pressures of the physical environment, forces which had earlier helped shape and perfect *Homo sapiens'* physique, psyche and behaviour. Thus shielded from the action of natural selection, nations enlarge the advantages of variation: varieties not immediately favourable, varieties even unfavourable to the individual are given a chance of survival. This interference with the operation of natural selection permits forms of maladjustment to persist, seemingly indefinitely, allowing harmful mutations to accumulate instead of being eliminated. Yet in spite of *Homo degener's* attempts to prevent it, natural selection will continually work to destroy these populations of degenerate peoples. For unlike the varieties of hunter-gatherers which were true varieties in a wild world, the varieties within nations are degenerate varieties in artificial worlds, whose convergent evolution and competition to survive is not only a competition between nations but also between them and wild nature. It is this change, from functioning co-operatively as a sovereign hunter-gatherer within the wilderness to functioning as one amongst thousands, and now as one amongst millions, of other workers or cells within composite animals struggling for survival in world-wide competition with one another and with wild nature, which may be described as a degenerative mutation, and as presaging a change in the hereditary material of the individual. With the development of the science of genetic engineering it will be possible to select individuals to fit and more successfully fulfil their rôles within the wholly urban environment, attuned to the unlimited expansion and growth of nations. So initial cultural innovations over 12,000 years will slowly be changed to genetic innovations, to the same ends: the genetic structure of *Homo degener* will be altered to accord with the memetic requirements of their composite animals, as will that of certain flora and fauna. This will be particularly the case amongst those perfected as a genetic elect.

Hence the re-evolution from *Homo sapiens* to

<u>*Homo sapiens sapiens*</u>
Homo sapiens non sapiens

is both a change in learned behaviour and ultimately a change in the hereditary material, as the environments and behaviour of *Homo degener* come more and more to resemble those of monkeys and termites. If they also become the subject of genetic engineering, then *Homo degener* will actually become genetically different from *Homo sapiens*. The great danger is that their habitual obedience to the collective memetic inheritance of nations to grow increasingly thick armour against the wilderness by further urbanization of the environment will increasingly affect their learned behaviour, making the behaviour of *Homo degener* more and more inhuman by comparison with the true humanity of *Homo sapiens*, while at the same time making it appear to them to be human and natural, blinding them to their true condition. When combined with their blind submission to the historical progression of anti-evolutionary nations, which takes place at the expense of the evolutionary kingdom of nature, such blindness turns a generally inimical mutation into an *infinitely disadvantageous mutation*, and demands their destruction by nature.

Homo degener is the degenerate descendant of ecologically aware free-ranging animals in command of their own individual destinies who has deteriorated into an uncomprehending captive animal at the mercy not only of the flux and forces of nature but of the man-made flux and forces as well – and of the flux and forces of nature as these are unpredictably affected by the man-made flux and forces ... and so on *ad infinitum*. The combined effect of these is not additive but exponential, as exemplified below.

Homo sapiens evolved in a natural environment which, in obedience to the natural flux, was generally one of long-sustained order and peace interspersed with shorter periods of chaos, the whole contributing to the overall balance of nature. To *Homo degener*, however, the whole natural world was a hostile environment. Both the orderly and peaceful periods, and the shorter periods of confusion and chaos, were inimical to them, turning their erstwhile home into an irremediably inhospitable place of disorderliness and darkness. Furthermore, the man-made environment of *Homo degener* has generally been one of disorder, interspersed with occasional periods of 'imperial order' and 'peace'. Such a perverted flux and succession of pyramids of power, mythologized as evolutionary and progressive, has overlaid the natural flux and succession of innumerable natural food pyramids and true evolutionary progress of the royal beings at their summits, the whole contributing to a secondary historical degeneration and an overall disharmony and imbalance of the world, in which more and more degenerate subhumans compete for less and less space and increasingly scarce resources.

Globally it appears catastrophic that a world population of some six billion subhuman beings are continuing to increase in the face of declining reserves of energy and minerals, and world food reserves that can be wiped out by the vagaries of weather, climate, disease or pollution from radioactive fall-out in the event of accidental nuclear catastrophe or nuclear war. By comparison, had the Mesolithic not occurred, or had *Homo degener* readapted to his original evolutionary path, we can estimate that the human population of the world would now have been no more than 10 million entirely healthy people evolving in relative harmony in ecological understanding within the natural environment, hunting and gathering for no more than three days in any seven in a generally abundant and paradisial land. As it is, over one billion people – the 70 or 80 per cent of the populations of the Third World who exist either by subsistence farming, as landless labourers or as slum-dwellers in the cities – now live under conditions of absolute poverty, resulting in protein-calorie malnutrition, squalor, illiteracy and disease. Amongst these are some 320 million children who are undernourished to the point where they will probably never grow to realize even a subhuman potential; 100 million of them are homeless, scavenging and scrounging for a living.

> The income disparity between these people and the richest billion in the world is 150 times.[4]

In terms of the numbers and quality of life of those occupying the different levels as between poverty and wealth Kirkpatrick Sale argues that

> Today, of the approximately 6 billion people in the world, it is estimated that at least a billion live in abject poverty, lives cruel, empty, and mercifully short. Another 2 billion eke out life on a bare subsistence level, usually sustained only by one or another starch, the majority without potable drinking water. More than 2 billion more live at the bottom edges of the money economy but with income less than $5,000 a year and no property or savings, no net worth to pass on to their children. That leaves less than a billion people who even come close to struggling for lives of comfort, with jobs and salaries of some regularity, and a quite small minority at the top of that scale who could really be said to have achieved comfortable lives; in the world, some 350 people can be considered (US dollar) billionaires (with slightly more than 3 million millionaires), and their total net worth is estimated to exceed that of forty-five per cent of the world's population.[5]

At the present rate of increase, the planet's population will have risen to around 8 billion by 2050, of whom some 90 per cent will be living in the underdeveloped nations of Africa, Asia and Latin America.* The

---

*UN demographers predicted in 2005 that the world population would peak at around 9.2 billion by 2075, and then go into long-term decline.

population of Nigeria, for example, has been projected to rise to 191 million by 2015 and to 338 million by 2050. Ethiopia has been projected to rise to 213 million by 2050.[6]

> How can our global environment, our atmosphere, our soils, our water supplies, support the economic aspirations of these people, together with the ever increasing demands of the developed world?[7]

The dilemma of India is a case in point. The population of India was already some 982 million at the end of 1998, and at the highest estimate could rise to 1.5 billion by 2050, equalling that of China, also projected at 1.5 billion in 2050.[8] The growing subhuman population, the aspirations of everyone to be better off, the increased need for, and supply of, energy, and the 1000 million livestock in India, are all arrayed against the remaining fragments of the country's natural heritage. Everywhere the story is the same: the remaining wild places, from Alaska to Antarctica, are directly threatened or are already being defiled.

Nature is hitting back harder and harder with flood, drought, disease and other disasters. As just one example of many possible inimical effects of the man-made flux and forces on the natural environment, as the direct outcome of the immense sum total of energy already required and consumed to sustain the phrenetic world-wide activities to raise standards of living and assure the collective security of nations, we may be threatened with an overall rise in global temperatures sufficient to melt the polar icecaps over the next century. This is because gases entering the atmosphere from human activity – in particular carbon dioxide arising from the burning of forests, grasslands and fossil fuels – could, through what is described as the 'greenhouse effect', raise the Earth's mean temperature by between 1.4°C and 5.8°C by the year 2100, with a concomitant rise in sea level.[9]

Such a rise in temperature would enable agriculture to spread further north, but at the same time it would reduce much cultivated land in the south to desert, severely upsetting the world economy and endangering the existence of whole nations. Already lands to the south are suffering desertification owing to overcropping by farmers, over-grazing and deforestation. Many researchers, however, argue that such aridification occurs not because of human activity, but because of climatic oscillations which may equally bring about a recovery. Nevertheless, it is indisputable that prime agricultural land is being lost to urbanization. At present, about one-third of the land area of the Earth is forests and savannah, one-third is cropland and pasture and one-third is paved cities, towns and deserts. The last one-third is now growing fast at the expense of the other two-thirds. For instance, according to the Campaign for the Protection of Rural England (2000), every year in England an area the size of Bristol – some 70 square miles – is lost to urban development and road building. Such urbanization on a world-wide scale will undoubtedly exacerbate global warming.

By reducing the ability of the oceans to absorb carbon dioxide, rising temperatures could also affect the sea. By means of convection currents and marine organisms, the oceans remove CO_2 from the surface layers of water and cause it to be deposited on the ocean floor. As reported in the *New Scientist*,[10] warmer oceans, resulting from global warming, could become more stratified and their populations of CO_2 absorbing plankton considerably reduced, thus slowing down the ocean circulating system, reducing the ability of the oceans to absorb CO_2 by anything up to 50 per cent, and leaving that much more greenhouse gas in the atmosphere to amplify the heating of Earth. This in turn could generate a greater rise in sea level.

The existence of whole nations could be endangered by a rise in sea level, as a result both of an expansion in the existing amounts of sea water, and an increase in the amount of sea water from the possible melting of the polar icecaps. It is worth noting, given the uncertainty surrounding any scientific prediction, that in the event of a rise of only 2 metres, six island nations in the Pacific and Indian Oceans could well disappear, forcing up to 300,000 islanders to become refugees. More than one-third of Bangladesh could be covered by the sea. A rise of 1 metre would put at risk some 70 million people in China. Elsewhere low-lying cities such as Venice and Alexandria could be flooded – much of Alexandria is less than a metre above sea-level. People would be driven to seek higher ground, just as they were so driven 10,000 years ago. In other words, the combined effect of *Homo degener's* ritualized conflict behaviour down the millennia now threatens to bring him around full circle, face to face with those self-same waters, whose rise would now be a man-made disaster.

For the same reasons, *Homo degener* is also threatened with a desiccation of the land. Glaciers world-wide are receding, affecting the rivers they feed. Were the glaciers to disappear, the rivers would dry up. The effect in some countries would be devastating. Mark Lynas[11] has observed that in Peru the tens of millions inhabiting the parched coastal strip in the shadow of the Andes would be left without water. In India, in the event of the disappearance of the Himalayan glaciers, half the population, some 500 million people, would be similarly affected.

WWF has argued that the changing climate is likely to kill forests, causing them to release more carbon dioxide, thus accelerating the disaster. In a poll at the end of 1991, a third of the world's leading scientists said that 'they feared this could lead to the so-called "runaway greenhouse" where global warming becomes unstoppable, ultimately making the Earth uninhabitable'.[12] On the other hand, recent studies suggest global cooling may present a more immediate threat than global warming! Because low cloud and layers of dust and pollution are spreading across the Northern Hemisphere, Earth is becoming hazier, leading to an overall cooling effect that may offset global warming. Global warming itself, by affecting the Atlantic Ocean currents, could plunge most of Europe into freezing conditions lasting many hundreds of years. Thus affected by several opposing challenges to its basic physics and chemistry – so constituting a man-made flux – the atmosphere, climatologists suggest, will show increasing signs of unpredictability and stress.* Furthermore, as a result of *Homo degener*'s anti-evolutionary activities, the concentration of ozone in the stratosphere may decrease, with possible devastating effects on life forms world-wide.

In the event of natural catastrophe and immutable natural selection, it is the most flexible, self-reliant and adaptable of the species that survive. Hunter-gatherers were unpossessive, adaptable animals who, when faced with difficult situations, could immediately go elsewhere. They so evolved to respond to immediate threats to their survival. As bad weather animals, they were fully in command of their existential situation, whereas the nation is fundamentally a deep-rooted super-plant designed primarily to shelter its members against the weather and wilderness without, making it deeply vulnerable to drastic changes in the environment. In the past, while there were still virgin lands, members of nations were able to migrate *en masse* in order to escape persecution and disaster. During the great famine in Ireland in the 1840s, though many died, some were able to escape to North America. This is the great difference between those who starved in the 1840s and those who face starvation today. There is virtually no remaining virgin continent to which they can migrate. In fact, the very urge and ability of earlier generations to escape persecution, poverty and starvation by migration has guaranteed the filling

---

* Other factors unpredictably affecting the atmosphere are small changes in solar radiation caused by wobbles in Earth's orbit, known as the Milankovitch cycles, and the creation and decomposition of peat bogs, which might play a major rôle in the changes in the concentration of carbon dioxide in the atmosphere.

As pointed out by Fred Pearce (*New Scientist*, Vol. 187, No. 2512, 13 August 2005), the world's largest frozen peat bog, in western Siberia – comprising an area the size of France and Germany combined – is melting. This could release billions of tonnes of methane, a greenhouse gas 20 times as potent as carbon dioxide, into the atmosphere.

up of the remaining empty spaces. Many now end up without a homeland, anywhere.

> The UN calculates that, throughout the world today, there exists a
> huge and frightening society of *twelve million* rootless people – a
> wholly new international factor of life that the world has never seen
> before and, for that reason, tries to forget.
>   In every sense 'refugee' is an ugly word, without redemption. It
> means fugitives, people dispossessed by the bitter quarrels of other
> people, not seeking a better world but escaping from a worse one,
> and almost always through no fault of their own. It means twelve
> million homeless of the earth, the lost, the hungry, inevitably the
> poor and, too often, the dying. A community of three million more
> than the whole population of Belgium, a nationless nation with no
> homeland, no flag, no common language, for ever on the move or
> rooted somewhere now only in despair.[13]

This figure, according to the UN High Commissioner for Refugees
(UNHCR), had already swelled to 17 million by 2004.* To the hunter-
gatherers, the whole world was their home. Now 17 million refugees, a
nationless nation, have no home anywhere in the world. In effect, 10
million or so *Homo sapiens* hunter-gatherers at home in the world, a
natural wilderness, have been replaced by

Homo sapiens sapiens
Homo sapiens non sapiens

nations (whose 6,000 million members are alienated from wild nature
in national homelands), and by 17 million *Homo degener* homeless of
the Earth, itself become a man-made wilderness.

There is, in addition, a growing trade in illegal immigrants fleeing
from Third World poverty towards First World wealth. Thousands of
people a year are paying to be transported under, and into, conditions
which have caused the trade to be described as 'a new international slave
trade'. This migration may in turn be fuelled by waves of migration on
a massive scale during this century – to the USA from Mexico and
Central America, and to Western Europe both from Eastern Europe and
Russia, and from the states of North Africa – as a result of imbalances
in demographic growth between adjacent 'have' and 'have-not' societies,
environmental damage, and social and economic catastrophe. As pointed
out by Sir Crispin Tickell,[14] when Britain's ambassador to the United

---

*This figure includes refugees, internally displaced people, asylum seekers and stateless persons.

Nations, global warming alone could prompt mass migrations of some 300 million 'eco-refugees' during the 21st century.

A flood of ecological refugees could soon create ecological wars.[15]

Re-evolutionary *Homo degener* originated in a 'Gulag Archipelago' of enclaves surrounded by a hostile wilderness – the first doubly deprived 'eco-refugees' in the first arks of survival. Projects designed to cure symptoms – including mass migration – have only the now all too familiar effect of worsening the overall problem in the long term. Once an imbalance begins, as it did with the arrival of *Homo degener*, only a remedy for the cause of the imbalance can produce any real improvement. Escaping or patching up the effects of the imbalance – which is what the scientific community is doing – ignores the real problem completely and makes it worse. Civilizations such as that of the Maya collapsed because their people, rooted to the ground like plants, were unable to counteract the local environmental changes that were often brought about by their own destructive activities, particularly deforestation. But now subhuman influences on the environment are increasingly global. What fantastic inflexible national termitary of 50–500 million inhabitants can adapt in the event of sudden catastrophic environmental change or destruc-tion today? Most members of nations can no longer escape *en masse* to virgin lands, nor can they dismantle and remove their stratified structures elsewhere, but must stay rooted to the ground, developing more and more sophisticated measures to resolve their multitudinous problems *in situ*. Yet the growing sophistication and complexity of everything world-wide makes everything more vulnerable not only to the man-made flux and forces but to the natural flux and forces as well. Belated efforts are being made by governments to reduce ozone depletion by banning CFCs, and to reduce the greenhouse gases that threaten to warm us up;* geoengineers are devising means to counteract the global effects of our activities with technical fixes that will preclude the need for any drastic change in our behaviour. Further efforts are being made to bring population increases under control with the aid of family planning, health care and education. Governments may also succeed in halting, even closing, the growing gap between rich and poor which is creating a vicious circle of poverty, conflict and environmental degradation. But all economic

---

*In 1997 the United Nations Framework Convention on Climate Change met in Kyoto, Japan, to set national targets for the reduction of greenhouse gas emissions. The Kyoto climate control accords – or Kyoto Protocol – have since been the subject of many reviews and adjustments.

development and growth will inevitably be at the cost of a steady deterioration in environmental quality. As with every age since the Mesolithic, this is 'an age of compounded crises and patch-it-up perspectives' which does not take account of the fact that *Homo degener* peoples are not real human beings and are unwittingly pursuing an anti-evolutionary path to perdition. They are facing the unbalancing of the planet's entire ecological system, and every act of theirs to stabilize the situation can only make matters worse.

The remorseless threats of population explosion, famine, resource shortage, growing arsenals of nuclear, chemical, biological and electromagnetic weapons, and environmental disruption and degradation are occurring in a profoundly unstable world arena, being as it is the arena of the convergent evolution of nations, and of nations and the kingdom of nature, which all together constitute what may be described as a multiplicity of convergent threats. We can only substantially moderate the impact of these threats through the most drastic action. Yet such collective action is unlikely, to say the least. Because the greatest of all dangers lies in our individual blindness and the certainty that we can act, with the aid of science and technology, to combat the challenges that threaten us. For this leaves out of account the fact that corporate science is bound up with the sheer weight and inertia of the global economy, and so with the economic inflexibility and associated search of people around the planet to imitate Western lifestyles that is hastening ecological deterioration. It is precisely these characteristics of blindness and self-deception that have helped bring us to our present parlous condition, a collective insanity. This blindness, this self-deception and this insanity are, in reality, inherent properties of anti-evolutionary composite animals comprising hollow, failed people, whose understanding and behaviour are more akin to those of termites in territaries than to those of true human beings.

Hence the danger is even more profound than we may suppose. Both *Homo sapiens* and *Homo degener* are the unwitting victims of manifold convergent threats set in train by the growth of cities and states, a growth that was, ironically, meant to protect *Homo degener* from external threats and climate stress, yet whose deleterious effects, particularly in relation to the natural flux, are exponential. In the words of Brian Fagan,

> In our efforts to cushion ourselves against smaller, more frequent climate stresses, we have consistently made ourselves more vulnerable to rarer but larger catastrophes. The whole course of civilization (while it is many other things, too, of course) may be seen as a

process of trading up on the scale of vulnerability... The times require us to learn the vagaries of the global climate, to study its moods, and to keep our skies relatively clear of excessive greenhouse gases with the same diligence, and for the same reasons, that Mesopotamian farmers five millennia ago had to learn the moods of the Euphrates and keep their irrigation canals reasonably free of silt. If they didn't, the gods grew angry. Or, to put it in more modern terms, sooner or later they got unlucky, and their silted-up ditches brought crop failure, humiliation, or disaster.

In fact, sooner or later, they got unlucky anyway, and were forced to adapt yet again.[16]

Fagan's book tells the story of those adaptations, 'one built upon another, in a spiral of climate change and human response that continues today'.[17] It was the two-fold fall which began the whole spiral and which has perpetuated it. This is the essence of the mutation that took place 12,000 years ago, which can only be described as infinitely disadvantageous to the survival of the species *Homo sapiens*. The driving force throughout has been the oft-repeated challenge of the humiliating threat to status and survival, that originated in the profound void of the Mesolithic.

Chapter 2

The Historical Imperative

I felt as if I had been crushed by the horrible fatalism of history. I find in human nature a frightful sameness, in human relationships a force which can't be averted, given to all and to none. The individual just foam on the wave, greatness a mere accident, the sovereignty of genius a puppet-play, a ridiculous struggle against an iron law. To recognise this law is our highest achievement, to control it impossible. (Georg Büchner)

Earlier, I made the point that members of nations are governed by instincts acquired during the prehistoric struggle for survival of rudimentary nations in a world regarded by them as implacably hostile. Such instincts are those which I have described as the collective memetic inheritance of the composite animal. In that their learned behaviour is dominated by that inheritance, it is dominated by the 'memory grown automatic' of the Mesolithic. Hence the prior super-dominant governing the behaviour of *Homo degener* is the profound void of the Mesolithic: the humiliating void within of a loss of a natural status and identity, and without of an unknown, frighteningly incomprehensible wilderness.

Humiliation and hatred of the wilderness, combined with humiliation and self-hatred, formed what has been described as a dark veil between *Homo degener* peoples and their hunter-gatherer past and wild home. Their abysmal loss of status, identity and security in relation to the wilderness was exacerbated by poverty, disease and starvation. Their manifold humiliations instilled in *Homo degener* an all-pervasive sense of powerlessness, of uncertainty and insecurity – just as they did in the case of Native American and Aborigine hunter-gatherers following their forcible de-rangement and abysmal degeneration into disease-ridden poverty during the 18th and 19th centuries. Stratified societies of dehumanized élites elevated on the backs of dehumanized cultivators grew out of the abyss in an assertion of power over the unknown. Their pyramids of power over their environment were further empowered by the creation of Farmer God religions promising status, wealth and security. These re-evolutionary developments out of failure and the abyss reinforced the initial failure and dark veil by further concealing them behind a veil of myth, such as the myth of a Flood, and thereafter beneath layers of religio-socio-economic artefacts expressive of narcissism and self-glorification. But the abyss has remained, ensuring that composite animals would thereafter be subconsciously governed by a fear of humiliating failure, of falling back into the abyss and losing that veneer of civilization. That fear, dark veils and veneer formed the foundations of the collective memetic inheritance of each composite animal as it struggled to solve its problems and survive in a now alien environment. To that end, *Homo degener* élites of composite animals have humiliated one another, and humiliated and oppressed both the *Homo degener* workers and wild nature. Situations reminiscent of the humiliating, identity-eroding, survival-threatening circumstances surrounding the origins of *Homo degener* people have challenged them to respond in ways similar to their original response, and so on down the millennia.

There are several principal levels of challenge and response: a primary level in relation to the wilderness and natural world; a secondary historical level relating to the subjugation of people within stratified societies and to subsequent humiliating threats against them; and a third historical level which concerns threats to nations themselves, both from within and from nature and other nations. Altogether these constitute what may be described as *the historical imperative of reaction to humiliation*, to the threat to survival, as I shall now explain. Before so doing, however, it will help to repeat that I am using the word 'humiliation' in its most profound sense. The principal humiliation to which every *Homo degener* generation is condemned is the mortification or destruction of their evolutionary status and autonomy as independent hunter-gatherers and as true human beings. All subsequent, or secondary and tertiary, historical humiliations arise from that original and ever present humiliation, which includes theriophobia, or ignorance and fear of one's own wild nature and of wild nature itself, and the projection of those fears onto the hunter-gatherers and other wildlife.

The primary level of response in relation to the changing climate and wilderness arose from the humiliating loss of a natural hunter-gathering status and security, a challenge that gave rise to a new artificial

Homo sapiens sapiens
Homo sapiens non sapiens

identity and security.* The secondary historical level of humiliation arose both from the humiliating subjugation of the *Homo sapiens non sapiens* workers by the *Homo sapiens sapiens* agents and from potentially humiliating threats to the new artificial status and security of persons within stratified societies, threats both natural and institutional. In the case of the individual, the threat to status and security may come about in any one of a number of ways. These include loss through natural or religio-socio-economic causes, as with illness such as paralysis, loss of a limb or a birth defect, illegitimacy and impoverishment, deprivation of love and rejection in childhood.† One and all may affect the victim as a humiliating threat to identity and security, a void – 'He cannot bear the void'. He fills it with religion, with art, with science, which provide status, wealth and power, and therefore meaning. Furthermore, examples of the reactions of individuals to threats to identity and security not only reflect the response to the primary level of challenge, but often epitomize the reactions to similar threats by nations regarded as giant human beings, for they too 'cannot bear the void' and react in similar fashion.

A classic example of a man driven by humiliating childhood traumas and the deprivation of love to climb on the backs of his fellows to claim the status of King was the first Zulu King, Shaka, who has been described as epitomizing

> ... the formula of the great man produced by a scarred cradle. The child of an unhappy union, a bastard and an outcast who was bullied in his youth, he turned tormented energy first to military and then to political achievement. Here, in a father's rejection and a domineering mother, in childhood traumas and adolescent yearnings for status, lie the forces that have shaped revolutionary leaders across cultures and down the ages.[1]

Composite animals likewise originated in scarred cradles. They have provided innumerable pathways to positions of status and power to which humiliated individuals might aspire, and from which they might also subsequently revenge themselves and so perpetuate humiliation.

In China in the second half of the 20th century, there was a woman, Jiang Qing, whose humiliations drove her to seek power and instigate a reign of terror, known as the Cultural Revolution. Jiang Qing, having

---

*See Appendix xv for an amplification of the drive to unity and associated hope surrounding the building of new physical and psychical structures.

†See Appendix v for a further study of the effects of physical and psychical trauma.

grown up poor and fatherless, sought and acquired status and power as
Mao Zedong's fourth wife. She was, however, prevented from playing
any public rôle. It was this humiliation, combined with the earlier
childhood deprivations and her battle to claw her way up the Shanghai
film ladder, which turned Jiang Qing into a monster when she acquired
power in the mid 1960s as a leader of what came to be known as the
Gang of Four.

As another actress, Tsai Chin, said of Madame Mao:

> She was always a victim, of humiliation, that thing all megalomaniacs
> suffered early in their lives. Her poverty, the sexual demands made
> on her as an actress, the humiliation, that's what made her a monster
> ... her faults got worse and worse, like a cancer. But her revenge
> was her way of surviving... Imagine, 40 years of humiliation. For
> her, survival was everything.

She instigated the Cultural Revolution in China, 1966–1976,

> ...commonly considered in China to be the worst period of the
> past 5,000 years. According to the official indictment, 34,800 State
> and Party leaders were 'persecuted to death', together with hundreds
> of thousands of others. One hundred million Chinese, party leaders
> say, a tenth of the entire population, became targets of the internecine
> rage unleashed by Madame Mao and the rest of the Gang.[2]

Those unable to escape humiliating oppression often become, as I argued
in Part II, the victims of self-abuse. People in authority in society – in
offices, in factories, in schools, in the armed forces – can so play with
the self-respect of subordinates that they help create any one of a variety
of stress disorders.

As well as the secondary historical level of humiliation there was a
third level arising from humiliating threats to the new artificial

<u>Homo sapiens sapiens</u>
Homo sapiens non sapiens

identity and security. These were threats to nations themselves from nature
and from other nations. They were humiliating threats to national survival,
including threats to national ideological, cultural, economic or territorial
status and security, leading in turn to the search for means of acquiring
control over the situation, and so the development of religio-socio-
economic offensive-defensive measures.

Concerning the threat to nations from nature, their stratified structures were religiously and scientifically – that is, mythopoeically and mathematically – organized to combat the fundamental threat of collective annihilation by the humiliating forces of nature, and in particular catastrophic climate change. The fear of extinction through natural calamity lay heavily, for instance, upon the Mesoamerican peoples, challenging them to develop ever more sophisticated measures of control and security. More recently, as pointed out in Part I, the challenging threat to national survival from natural forces of chaos gave rise to a demographic response when, in 1988 in Armenia, an earthquake killed 25,000 people – 16,000 of them in the city of Leninakan – and rendered thousands homeless, a third of those who died being children.

The threat of extinction from natural calamity has since been augmented by the threat to nations from within – from heresy, terrorism, treason, insurrection or revolution – and from other nations. In 1989 the Chinese authorities put down, notably in Peking's Tiananman Square, what they described as a counter-revolutionary rabble out to destroy socialism and to establish a capitalist state. The Chinese Communist Party then charged an astrophysicist, Fang Lizhi, with challenging its leading rôle, attacking Marxism and advocating 'bourgeois democracy and freedom'. According to the Party, his purpose was to instigate *luan*, or chaos, the condition most feared by Chinese rulers for 2000 years. Like the rulers of Imperial China, the Party leaders regarded internal threats to security as far more dangerous than external ones.

As to humiliating invasion, defeat and the threat of extinction at the hands of other nations, this is a challenge that may also act as a trigger to internal revolution. Russia is a case in point. Born, to all intents and purposes, around Kiev 1,000 years ago, Russia was humiliated by the Golden Horde, a Tatar tyranny that lasted two centuries, and then by a succession of despotic Tsars and invasions by the Swedes and the French. These were followed by defeats in the Crimea and in the Russo-Japanese War of 1904. If humiliating defeat in the Russo-Japanese War drove Russia towards revolution, the war with Germany was the disaster which brought down the régime, leaving a vacuum which was filled by the Revolution. In 1922 Stalin became General Secretary of the Party Central Committee. In 1928 he launched the first five-year plan for the forced industrialization of the economy, which he claimed would save Russia from further humiliating defeats arising from the country's backwardness. Yet there remained the fear that Russia would once again be submerged as it was in 1918. Following the Second World War such fears of humiliating eclipse led to a purge of dissidents and preparations against invasion. This entailed the spread of Russian influence across Eastern

Europe, and gave rise to the Cold War. But Russia quickly overstretched herself and was forced to withdraw into the homeland.

Perhaps the most outstanding example of challenge and response at both the secondary and tertiary historical levels was the rise of Adolf Hitler and the Nazi Party in Germany. This was a response to the challenge of humiliation at the combined individual and national levels.

The first 30 years of Hitler's life were characterized by failure. His early life consisted of a dismal succession of losses and failures and by the age of 20 he was subsisting as a down-and-out in Vienna. Joachim Fest, his biographer, said that he appeared to have spent his youth in 'a great hollow space'. That void was so filled with resentment as to suggest that out of it grew an overwhelming urge to revenge himself on a world which had humiliated and rejected him. Humiliated as a failure at school, a failed artist, a down-and-out and a defeated German soldier, Hitler rose to power after the humiliating defeat of Germany in the First World War and the additional humiliations of the Treaty of Versailles, inflation and the Depression.

It is important to note that Germany, as well as eventually being led by a man – Hitler – who was profoundly humiliated and defeated in his youth, was itself a young nation profoundly humiliated by defeat in the First World War and by the Treaty of Versailles, by which Germany lost much land and suffered punitive reparations. Like Hitler, many Germans also had a feeling of having been treated unfairly, of having been cheated. It was felt that the Government had betrayed the Army. Then came inflation and the Depression. In 1914 there were 4.2 marks to the dollar; in 1923 there were 4.2 million marks to the dollar. Because it destroyed money and property, and faith in money and property, inflation on such a scale undermined the foundations of German society to a greater extent even than the war or the Treaty of Versailles. Hitler's bitter attacks on that Treaty and his violent denunciations of the corrupt, Jew-ridden system that had brought about inflation, were echoed in the misery and despair of many levels of German society.

The 1923 inflation in Germany was followed by the Great Depression. By 1932 there were some 6 million unemployed in Germany. With the framework of their society crumbling all around them, arguments of reason succumbed to grotesque fears, and extravagant hatreds and hopes, which found expression in the demagogy of Hitler and for the first time assured him of a mass following. As the very spirit of hatred, Hitler's vitriolic words found an audience of frustrated and profoundly humiliated and downtrodden people, only too ready to hate.

Hitler filled the void in himself and in Germany with the Nazi Party and ideology, raising himself to the top canopy and crown. With the aid of the Nazi Party, Hitler set out to revenge himself on those he held responsible for his own humiliation and that of Germany, and to seek *lebensraum* for the German people. To those ends, Germany rearmed and invaded Austria, Czechoslovakia, Poland and France. Alan Bullock wrote of Hitler at the signing of the armistice between France and Germany in July 1940:

> The one-time agitator, who told the Munich crowds in 1920 that he would never rest until he had torn up the Treaty of Versailles, had reached the peak of his career. He had kept his promise: the humiliation of 1918 was avenged.[3]

Hitler's personal response to humiliating deprivation struck a chord in an equally humiliated and deprived Germany. He epitomized the common man. (In this connection, the writer Jakov Lind made a most penetrating comment when he said there were no Nazis: given the appropriate humiliating social conditions, a similar aberration is likely to break out at any time anywhere.) Hitler's early subsistence as a down-and-out, his existence in a 'great hollow space', the shared sense of humiliation in the defeat of 1918 and subsequent economic collapse, his ascent to the top canopy and subsequent laying waste of Europe reflect the original doubly deprived, insecure condition and delinquent ascent of *Homo degener* peoples, and their subsequent vengeful laying waste of the wilderness. Most importantly, he epitomized the evil inherent in *Homo degener*, the evil growing out of humiliation and consequent corruption of people to behave in an inhuman way that had its roots in the profound void of the Mesolithic, the evil that issues in humiliating parasitism, predatory behaviour, destructiveness, and so on *ad infinitum*.

In short, whether in relation to other nations or the kingdom of nature, humiliation and revulsion against humiliation, and subsequent revenge, are prime motives of a degenerate delinquent humankind. Even in the world where the pen is regarded as mightier than the sword, revenge is a principal motive. When asked what was the impetus behind his writing, S.J. Perelman replied:

> Chiefly, it's commercial, to be very frank about it. And secondly it's the desire to get one's own back. George Orwell listed four principal reasons why people write, the fourth of which was 'revenge'.[4]

James Baldwin craved and used his success as a writer 'as a means of wreaking vengeance on the merciless republic (America)'.[5]

Even death, which to *Homo sapiens* is the natural end to a life naturally and unpossessively fulfilled in obedience to the Great Spirit, is often meaningless, a humiliating void to *Homo degener*; it is also seen hopefully as the gateway to everlasting life and eternal revenge. Most religions have attempted imaginatively to overcome and negate death with illusions of an after-life in the Heavens above. Now scientists are seeking ways actually to conquer death, so to give élites everlasting life, that will also enable them to explore worlds beyond worlds in space. In addition, scientists seek immortality through Nobel Prizes and similar recognition. Death and an after-life in Heaven are seen by many of the humiliated poor and deprived not only as the promise of future reward, but also the means by which they may eventually be avenged for their exploitation and suffering on Earth. Expectation of a Judgment Day – 'Vengeance is mine, I will repay, says the Lord'* – is widespread. At such a time the Chosen of God will be rewarded with eternal life, while the remainder of humankind will be cast into outer darkness.

It is this ongoing historical process of challenge and response – at primary, secondary and tertiary levels – which I describe as the historical imperative. I have discussed the operation of the historical imperative at the level of the humiliated individual and that of the humiliated nation, but it is even more important to examine its operation at the international level, involving as it does the continual search for economic and military security, and humiliating threats to that security, on the part of some 200 nations in an anarchic world. It is anarchic primarily because of the manifold threats from climate change, a powerful catalyst throughout history, as evinced in the world-wide effects of El Niño down the millennia; and secondly because of the manifold threats to security arising from the phrenetic economic and military activities of nations in their efforts to achieve a permanent security, which inevitably eludes them. For their search for economic security, as represented by an enhanced national status, prosperity and power, tends to be vitiated by their simultaneous search for strategic security and excessive expenditure on armaments. The key word throughout is 'security' – that is, the avoidance of humiliation. Nations compete with one another, jostle together, driven partly to gain glory and riches, partly out of a fear of being eclipsed. But the drive to gain glory and riches is only the other side of the same coin, which is humiliation: it is the drive to avoid or to escape humiliating insecurity, poverty, powerlessness, deprivation, defeat or eclipse, which has been the common inheritance of the majority of *Homo degener* peoples. These two

---

* St Paul's Epistle to the Romans, Ch. 12, v. 19. (RSV)

sides of the same coin may also be viewed as the two poles of the Life-Force or dynamic to growth of each nation, Life-Forces which themselves stemmed from the original humiliation or eclipse of *Homo sapiens* humankind. Hence,

Social status is the escape from, avoidance of, humiliating social oblivion.

To be somebody is to escape, avoid, being a humiliated nobody.

Wealth is the escape from, avoidance of, humiliating poverty.

Power is the escape from, avoidance of, humiliating powerlessness.

Victory is the escape from, avoidance of, humiliating defeat.

Success is the escape from, avoidance of, humiliating failure.

To be a winner is to escape, avoid, being a humiliated loser.

To rival, outshine, eclipse is to escape, avoid, being humiliated, eclipsed.

Security is the escape from, avoidance of, humiliating insecurity.

To progress is to escape from, avoid, humiliating regression.

To hope is to escape from, avoid, humiliating hopelessness, fear and despair.*

All the above have their origins in fear – that is, the fear of humiliation and humiliating fear. Such fear – at the individual, national and international levels – constitutes *the* psychological core of the historical imperative, driving individuals and nations to compete.† Economic and technological advances consequent upon competition to avoid humiliation or eclipse constitute a dynamic to growth: this then impacts upon political systems, military power and the relative position of individual states and empires, in that it forces rivals to converge in a similar dynamic to growth by imitating, or striking at, a rival, or by pre-empting territory or resources, still in order to avoid being eclipsed.

It was this urge which caused the manifold rivalries of the European states eventually to break out onto the world stage, culminating at the end of the 19th century in the Scramble for Africa‡ – ever an anarchic

---

*A Life-Force apparently founded in hope is really based on the avoidance of, or escape from, humiliation. In this connection, see also Appendix xvi.

† Boris Becker, the German tennis star, once said of himself: 'I draw my strength from fear. Fear of losing. I don't remember the games I won, only the ones I lost.'

‡ In his book *The Scramble for Africa* (Weidenfeld and Nicolson, 1991), Thomas Pakenham uses the words 'humiliate(d)', 'humiliating' and 'humble(d)' 97 times as a principal cause or effect of actions in the scramble for territory by the European powers. Companies behave in similar fashion, for similar reasons. Merger mania, like the Scramble for Africa, is infectious. In an atmosphere of takeover bids and mergers, boardrooms fear being humiliated, left out in the cold.

world in which 'dissatisfied' powers compete with 'satisfied' ones. Japan was one such 'dissatisfied' nation. Between 1853 and 1865 Japan was forced, by the threat posed by American, British, French and Dutch warships, to abandon two centuries of isolation and to sign treaties of trade with the outside world.

> The humiliation of the Japanese by these events was intense, and it would seem that the salvation of peoples lies largely in such humiliations. With astonishing energy and intelligence they set themselves to bring their culture and organization up to the level of the European powers. Never in all the history of mankind did a nation make such a stride as Japan then did. In 1866 she was a mediaeval people, a fantastic caricature of the extremist romantic feudalism: in 1899 hers was a completely Westernized people, on a level with the most advanced European powers, and well in advance of Russia. She completely dispelled the persuasion that Asia was in some irrevocable way hopelessly behind Europe. She made all European progress seem sluggish and tentative by comparison.[6]

Japan attempted at this time to expand into 'Greater East Asia'. Her ambitions were, however, thwarted by France, Germany and Russia. Deeply embittered, Japan planned for the day of revenge. This dawned ten years later when her ambitions in Korea and Manchuria clashed with those of tsarist Russia, and in the ensuing struggle a Russian Fleet was decisively destroyed at Tsushima.

International anarchy inevitably gives rise to 'dissatisfied' nations, whose consequent humiliation in turn may force them, as in the case of Japan, to undergo rapid economic and technological development. For the Japanese the nationalist impulse in the 19th century was the forced 'opening' and threat of being swallowed up by Western imperialist powers. Since the Second World War it has been recovery and revenge for the humiliations heaped upon Japan by the American victors. The worst humiliation was being forced by the Americans to accept, in 1946, their English-drafted 'Constitution' which, amongst other restrictions, reduced the Emperor to a 'symbol' and denied Japan the right to belligerency. Many Japanese, including at least one Prime Minister, Yasuhiro Nakasone, have been fired by a need for revenge on the US. Much of the spiritual energy and undirected loyalty of postwar Japanese has found a home in the new empire of commerce. Japan is now an economic giant striving for world domination. The retreat of both superpowers (the USA and erstwhile USSR) in Asia created a vacuum and Japan's growing sense of national assertiveness will play a still unpredictable part in filling it.

The historical imperative is the driving force behind a perverted memetic evolution, and so behind the convergent evolution of nations and the infinitely disadvantageous mutation of *Homo degener*. It is the moving force behind the inexorable and inevitable rise and fall of empires: inevitable, 'an iron law' (Georg Büchner), 'as irresistible as a natural law' (Admiral Tirpitz), if only because we do not learn from history, which increases the tendency of history to repeat itself, since similar events are the more likely to produce similar responses.* Ignorant of our origins in humiliating degeneration, and so of the origins of history itself, we remain not only in ignorance of the past, but that unrecognized, unacknowledged past will and must govern our behaviour in the present and in the future. Not only do we not learn from history, but we *cannot* learn from history: for the collective memetic inheritance of each composite animal, attuned to the humiliating void of the Mesolithic and therefore primarily attuned to humiliation and the avoidance of humiliation, continues to predominate. The humiliation or humiliating defeat of one people by another can even evoke a vengeful response hundreds of years later: in 1389, at Kosovo, the Turks destroyed the medieval Serbian Kingdom – 500 years later, the Serbs revenged themselves for their previous humiliation and defeat when they rose with other Balkan nationalities and beat the Turks, in October 1912, at Kumanovo. Further afield, the campaigns of Mahmud of Ghazni in India in 1026 were to engender among Hindus a similar revengeful hate. As Sir George Dunbar said of him, '...by his desecration and ruin of Hindu temples he sowed the seeds of hatred and religious bitterness between Hindus and Moslems. The communal feuds of today have their origin in the acts of Mahmud of Ghazni.'[8]

If the moral effects of humiliating defeat can last for hundreds of years, it is important to understand that the moral effects of the humiliating double deprivation and defeat of *Homo degener* following the Mesolithic have lasted down to this day, as the mainspring of all delinquent acts of conquest and revenge against other people and against nature. By the uniformity of nature, whereby the same antecedents tend to lead to the same results, humiliation or threatened humiliation, whether actual or imagined, and whether threatening the individual or the collective identity

---

* 'Many young people are firmly turned away from the study of the accumulated experience of their predecessors by the mountain of facts that they are presented with. Naval officers are no exception. But those who are ignorant of the past are merely condemned to repeat it, horrors and all.'[7]

As the philosopher George Santayana wrote: 'Those who do not remember the past are condemned to relive it.'

and security, poses a challenge that often evokes a response compounded of resentment, anti-evolutionary revulsion* and revenge; such humiliating anarchy and chaos also pose a challenge that may encourage a population explosion.

The loss of natural controls over *Homo degener* populations following the Mesolithic caused those populations to explode across the world. This accords with the demographic effects of natural chaos, as in the case of the 1988 Armenian earthquake. A population explosion may also occur as a form of revenge following colonization: a population rise is occurring among the colonized peoples of the old USSR, in a kind of revenge against Russian colonialism.

> What is happening at present and is projected to continue into the future is a sort of 'demographic revenge' by the colonized peoples, especially in the southern Muslim republics, whose birth rates are similar to those in the Middle East. The average annual population growth rates of those republics range from 2.5 to 3.5 percent, which is *three to five times larger* than the 0.7 percent average annual increases in the Russian population. Already, according to one calculation, Russians represent less than half of the total population, for the first time since the establishment of Bolshevik rule.[9]

Such challenges and responses have deepened and extended the original mutation and anti-evolutionary response that took place 12,000 years ago. There are always individuals and nations waiting in the wings, waiting for the right moment to wreak vengeance for past humiliations. At present these include the Balkan States, where memories of humiliation and revenge go back centuries, and where every victory or defeat presents further reasons for bloodshed in future generations; China's publication of an *Atlas of Shame* charting the 400 year march of Chinese humiliation, a memorial that may be a harbinger of acts of righteous revenge; and America's declaration of war against terrorists world-wide following the humiliating destruction of the World Trade Center in New York on 11 September 2001, an attack itself arising directly out of past and present humiliations suffered by the Palestinians and others at the hands of America and American-backed governments such as that of Israel. 'The past lives and will take its revenge.'[10]

War in particular tends to be experienced by *Homo degener* as a deluge engulfing them and their way of life, accelerating the anti-evolutionary

---

*When hopes are most powerfully redirected or renewed. See Appendix xvi.

response. When, in the late 17th and early 18th centuries, the Swedes swept across Europe, the Poles recalled the wars as 'The Deluge'. The First World War, which devastated a generation and washed away an earlier aristocratic order, was seen by some as a Flood. Winston Churchill wrote of the upheavals in Northern Ireland which followed the First World War:

> The whole map of Europe has been changed ... but as the deluge subsides and the waters fall short, we see the dreary steeples of Fermanagh and Tyrone emerging once again. The integrity of their quarrel is one of the few institutions that has been unaltered in the cataclysm which has swept the world.[11]

The Second World War had a similar profound effect throughout Europe and Russia. 'Barbarossa', the German invasion of Russia in 1941, constituted 'another deluge'. In each case a humiliating void is created, which is then filled with a new assemblage of power structures, institutions and technologies, which again create conditions conducive to a new deluge and humiliating void. Today we are seemingly driven by a world-wide competition for control of the future by means of science and technology – including information technology, biotechnology and military technology – a process that might be described (to use J.K. Galbraith's term) as the 'technological imperative'. That imperative insists that unless we do it first, unless we develop the next generation of whatever product first – in the 19th century it was unless we annexe whatever territory first – our competitors will beat us to it and eclipse us. But it is that fear of failure, of eclipse, that gives impetus to the technology – behind the 'technological imperative' lies the historical imperative.

Continually repeated cycles, down the ages and throughout the world, of humiliation, revulsion and revenge – the historical imperative of reaction to humiliation, that causes humiliation – became the main driving force behind what *Homo degener* likes to describe as 'progress'. *The historical imperative is in fact the dynamic to the development and growth of nations as giant human beings, negating and replacing the dynamic of the natural flux that underlay the evolution of* Homo sapiens, *or true human beings.*

The operation of the historical imperative in relation to the natural flux and wild nature is its most important aspect. For if the history of nations down the millennia has all too frequently been a history of warfare, it has also been a history of continuous warfare waged by farmer-industrial communities on wild nature for the sake of economic growth and national power, causing the natural flux – particularly climate change – to have increasingly inimical effects world-wide.

The historical imperative is the key to the comprehension of the whole tragic history of the human race over the last 12,000 years. If this is the key to history, the keynote of history has been people's inhumanity to people and to nature. Dominated and humiliated by the wilderness for thousands of years, *Homo degener* began to create a man-made wilderness of composite animals dominating, humiliating and exterminating each other and the true wilderness, in obedience to the historical imperative. We are indeed prisoners of the historical imperative. The whole process may be seen as one of humiliation piled on humiliation down the millennia, accelerating the competitive anti-evolutionary ascent of nations on the backs of those weaker than themselves; accelerating too the exploitation of the last of the wilderness to that end, and increasing the magnitude of the clashes between nation and nation and between them and wild nature to such an extent that the world is now a man-made wilderness of companies and nations in competitive conflict with one another, and with wild nature. (Recall, for instance, President Kennedy's declaration of war on the weather; or these words of Sting:* 'If I was a Brazilian without land or money or means to feed my children, I would be burning the rain forest too. And, believe me, so would you.'[12]) Under the circumstances, these presently unstable pioneer species of composite animal are converging, in obedience to the historical imperative, towards a 'climax' condition, turning the world into a single artificial vertically oriented Stable State in stasis, which is in direct contravention of a true climax: the world a natural horizontally oriented stable state in flux.

---

*Gordon Sumner, singer and song-writer.

Chapter 3

Convergence to the Stars

Behind the threat of world destruction, there is still the shadow of
a world state, perhaps benevolent, or probably repressive, as it might
turn out to be. (Hugh Thomas)[1]

I argued in Part I that *Homo degener* had turned a slow evolutionary
development of all people as hunter-gatherers into an accelerating anti-
evolutionary development of stratified societies ascending to the stars. I
have now shown that that process may also be viewed as the convergent
evolution and ascent of *Homo degener* composite animals to the stars in
obedience to the historical imperative.

Such an ascent has been greatly accelerated by *Homo degener's* increasing
conquest of the skies. The convergence of technology, and related artificial
environments, has assisted not only the world-wide dissemination of
information originating from national élites, but also their ascent, world-
wide transportation and eventual transportation into space. For instance,
there is a prodigious effort to raise astronauts to the moon – not to
mention 'high flying' executives residing at the tops of high-rise office
blocks, scientists working high up in mountains such as the Alps, and
aircraft filled with luxury passengers and luxury food, all enjoying
figuratively and literally the highest standards of living in perfected artificial
environments that resemble one another to a remarkable degree. 'Airlines,
airports and international hotels all conspire to make every place look
like every other place, and they are greatly assisted by the spread of air
conditioning, which provides the same atmosphere everywhere.'[2]* There
are too the combined efforts of nations to put communications satellites
in orbit around the Earth. As scientists develop the capability to send

---

* See Appendix xvii for an example of the social effects of establishing air-conditioned staging posts
across the world.

unmanned spacecraft deeper into space, and to move people further out into space, there to search for extra-terrestrial intelligence, for new sources of energy and for new worlds to inhabit, parasite pyramids will tend to become more alike as they become more extended in the vertical, competing for energy and wealth to sustain and protect their ascent.

At present nuclear power is being shown to be essential to meet our insatiable demand for inexhaustible supplies of energy. In the future, in order to meet the global energy requirements for the continued ascent of nations, scientists are investigating several main energy technologies: 'fusion power', the source of the sun's energy, hydrogen and wind and solar energy. However, the construction of successively larger and larger fusion research machines and then of fusion power stations, the harnessing and development of solar energy and the ascent of scientists towards the sun will likewise necessitate and effect the concentration of more and more of the wealth of the world – for reaching to the skies has become the most expensive business on Earth – towards the northern hemisphere, which accords with the inherent nature of the parasite pyramidal structuring of the world as between First and Third World countries.* Already the richest one-fifth of the Earth's population enjoys a disproportionate four-fifths of its wealth. The progression from an original Industrial Revolution through further revolutions is certain to continue, absorbing more and more of the world into the industrial system, and creating a 'hyper-industrial' world society. For in history, as in politics, it is usually the short term that counts, and in the short term the power lies with the Great Powers and the multinational corporations, who wish only to keep on growing. That growth has given rise in the developed nations of the world to the revolution into biotechnology, robotics and electronics technology. This implies a world-wide movement from a material-based to a knowledge-based production, which Alvin Toffler has described as the transition 'from a brute-force to a brain-force economy', which does not provide employment for uneducated people – nor for many of the educated. Changes taking place in the economic structure of Britain, as a result of the introduction of microprocessors and the inexorable rationalization of the advance in information processing, already threaten millions with underemployment and unemployment.

---

*The USA is planning to build space colonies, with the aid of metals from the moon, which will in turn build power satellites to beam back solar energy to Earth. Thereby, the USA would become the supplier of an inexhaustible energy source to the nations of the world. As T.A. Heppenheimer argued in his book *Colonies in Space* (Stackpole Books, 1977), the nation that builds the first space colonies, delivering cheap plentiful solar energy to Earth by power satellites, would wield immense power in an energy-hungry world, like the Arab oil cartel of recent times.

...the despair and hopelessness of permanent unemployment will breed its own violence and disconcern, sometimes politically directed, sometimes not, as the contrast sharpens between those with personal computers and plug-in information links in their own homes, and the surplus population outside.[3]

In short, as everything that can be automated is being automated, what remains are highly paid managerial and professional jobs which involve the control of computers, and lower-paid jobs (and the unemployed) which involve being controlled by computers. In accordance with the pyramidal structure of society, information (providing food for the mind and the imagination) is being enclosed and concentrated in the vertical in the hands of fewer and larger knowledge-owners and computers, just as in the past land (providing food for the body) was enclosed and concentrated in the hands of fewer and larger land-owners. Like land, some fields of knowledge will be rented out, others will not. Just as huge tracts of land are barred to the public – 'Trespassers will be prosecuted' – huge areas of knowledge will be sealed off by Government edicts and by the need to protect commercial secrets.

With the development of global electronic communication, the global division between the rich and the poor will widen dramatically. This is because more than half the world's population has no access to a phone network nor to a computer network, the basis of the new information networks, and because some information is now published exclusively in electronic form, available only through the Internet. It is also because most software is developed in English, which is increasingly the principal language for the exchange of scientific and academic information. Hence the global division between the rich and the poor within nations, and between rich and poor nations themselves, is going to be greatly exacerbated by the added division between 'information-rich' and 'information-poor', because information is not only power but also profit. Already global telecommunications and computers have helped concentrate global power in the financial quarters of several large cities, including London, Frankfurt, Tokyo and New York. This concentration of global power is furthermore both a consequence and a cause of the dispersal of global manufacturing. Global telecommunications and computers have made possible what is described as a 'global production line', enabling companies to shift work processes in the direction not only of the lowest bidder but also of the country with the least interest in human rights and the weakest laws. At the same time, new specialisms are growing up at the international level to service this process – international lawyers, accountants and consultants skilled in the law and business procedures of many countries. Thus power and profit are increasingly accruing to multinational companies outside the control of any one nation. Already some 80 per cent of world trade is in the hands of just 500 such companies. Money and business do not recognize frontiers, while international money in turn tends more and more to influence the internal policies of nations.

The new global commercial, financial and communication trends will inevitably be of greatest advantage to the developed nations responsible for this new global infrastructure, and in particular to the upper one-fifth of each nation who are the agents and beneficiaries of the new revolution. The lower four-fifths of each nation will be increasingly at the mercy of multinational companies moving production into and out of regions in search of competitive advantage. The prospect is, therefore, of the upper one-fifth of the world's wealthy nations growing yet richer, while four-fifths of the Earth's population, unable to take advantage of the new commercial and financial trends, becomes yet further marginalized. In the 1999 Reith Lectures, entitled 'Runaway World', Anthony Giddens, director of the London School of Economics, argued that, while the share of global income of the richest fifth of the world's population had risen over the past 10 years, that of the poorest fifth had declined from 2.3 per cent to 1.4 per cent.

This process of the increasing globalization of world markets may be shown to have its most important and profound effects on food production and distribution, which form the ground upon which the other aspects of globalization specified above are enabled to thrive, and also the ground of the convergence and combination of nations into trading blocs. Agribusinesses, for example, are gaining control of more and more of the land world-wide, consolidating small-holdings into large, managed and mechanized farms, forcing millions of small farmers and peasants – in India, in South America – off the land and into urban slums: a double deprivation similar to that following the Enclosures in the 18th and 19th centuries in Britain. Control of the parasite pyramidal food chain is thus being concentrated into ever fewer hands. Globalization, which is grounded in a convergent evolution of a homogeneity of parasite food pyramids, is forcing the world into a single stratified structure of nations. At the same time, however, there are centrifugal forces making for fragmentation.

The tendency will be for two sharply polarized classes to develop within super-industrialized countries – responsible technocratic élites in charge of every important sphere of life, and the irresponsible under- and unemployed masses – and thereafter to develop on a world scale as between nations, as between super-industrialized First World countries and industrialized and non-industrialized countries in the Second and Third Worlds, to make for an international division of labour and consequent stratification of nations themselves. Relative deprivation within nations, and of whole nations, in relation to the richer few, together with the erosion of the last remnants of humanity by technology, will increase the tensions not only within societies but throughout the world, leading to increasing fragmentation and conflict, to violence and terrorism on a world-wide scale. There is, in accordance with the generally anarchical condition of nations, a present tendency towards fragmentation, not only amongst minorities claiming self-determination within nations and empires – the Scots in the United Kingdom, the Quebecois in Canada, the Kashmiris in fissiparous India, the Catalans in Spain, the Kurds in Turkey and Iraq, and the various nations in the erstwhile Soviet Empire. Africa's condition is even more unstable, partly because of the European 'carve-up' of Africa, when boundaries were drawn without regard for tribal affiliations and ethnic groups. Ethnic tensions have produced countless civil wars – in Angola, in the struggle between Hutu and Tutsi in Rwanda and Burundi, in Nigeria following the attempted secession of Biafra. In 1945 there were 51 members of the United Nations; today there are some 200, a figure that is expected steadily to rise. A similar tendency to fragmentation is occurring at the individual level.

During the modern era, man's impulse to wholeness has been steadily transferred from organised religious beliefs to organised beliefs in secular progress toward unity, order and harmony through science, technology, political and ideological structures etc (all of which are supposed to be based on rational thought). In recent years it has become evident that such a notion of progress is a dream that is extremely unlikely ever to be realised.

Indeed, what is actually to be observed is an ever-increasing fragmentation, not only on a worldwide scale between different nations, religions and ideologies, but also within each nation, each religion, each ideology, as well as within most smaller social units going down to the size of the family, and indeed, even to each individual, whose psyche, divided against itself, inevitably reflects the pervasive fragmentation in the society in which all human beings live. The world as a whole is now, in fact, a seething mass of conflicts between these various fragments, many of which threaten to develop into catastrophes that endanger the very existence of civilization and perhaps that of mankind itself.[4]

The impulse towards wholeness is fundamental to the human psyche. However, the only person who can possibly be, or be described as, whole is the hunter-gatherer, for the only possible ground of human wholeness is the wilderness. The above quotation could well represent a summary of all that has happened to humankind as a direct outcome of its fragmentation into *Homo sapiens* hunter-gatherers and *Homo degener* farmers, when, as I argued earlier, the genetic and memetic inheritance of *Homo degener* were directly opposed to one another. This opposition has the potential to tear the individual apart, while the conflict between farmers and wilderness, which has torn wild nature apart, is fundamental to all other conflict behaviour and conflict.

The early farmers found the wilderness a frightening and threatening place against which they fortified themselves. A frightening and threatening man-made wilderness has now arisen out of the ashes of the natural wilderness destroyed, in which, as for instance in Los Angeles, affluent individuals and groups are enclosing themselves in fortresses of wealth, protected by security guards and electronic gates, against ghettos of poor outside where police and criminals wage perpetual war. Similarly, at the national level wealthy nations such as the USA and its allies are preparing to defend their wealth by force against the threat of the ghetto poor nations of the Third World, developing tactics for a potential North-South confrontation.

A global market combined with technological imperialism, national and individual fragmentation, relative and absolute deprivation – whether in First World city ghettos, or in ghettos, slums and shanty towns of Third World cities, where the poor savage each other and their environment like laboratory rats in overcrowded cages – now inspire acts of violence and terrorism on an increasingly world-wide scale, in turn to be further fuelled by ethnic or religious aspirations, such as those of fundamentalist Islam. Their aim is to mobilize the masses, to radicalize the world by sacrifice.

So, to the multiplicity of convergent threats to *Homo sapiens* and *Homo degener* which I revealed earlier, we must add the threat of intense ethnic nationalism and religious turmoil, the growth of international crime syndicates and spread of drug-related violence, together with the parallel growth in international terrorist co-operation. A most recent threat is that of cyber terrorism, the use of the Internet by computer hackers to break into, and wreak havoc in, communication, power, financial and Government institutions of any country they choose, with potentially devastating consequences world-wide. The permutations and combinations to sudden individual and mass destruction are in fact growing, like populations, to astronomic proportions, crying out for the world to be controlled at the international level, calling for draconian measures of national and global management and environmental control. But such management of societies brings its own considerable problems, and vicious circles are already emerging:

– dissent, repression, more dissent, more repression...
– complexity breakdown, engineered solution, more complexity breakdown, more engineered solutions...
– fear, surveillance, more fear, more surveillance...[5]

As long ago as 1941 George Orwell was warning of the probable world-wide extension of totalitarian government. The more likely scenario is, I believe, a mixture of Orwell's vision of the future and that envisaged by Kafka and Aldous Huxley. More and more towns in Britain are investing in video security systems, with a blanket covering of a network of cameras. Not only will people sitting in control rooms looking out for lawbreakers soon be replaced by computers, but it will soon be possible to link every town in the country to a central computer. Yet those same computers will be available for the entertainment of the populace in their well-protected homes. For if escalating wealth and technology in the West have done nothing else, they have led people to believe that the universe exists for their entertainment. Thus video security, controlled by computer, merges with Huxley's vision of a caste society where thought and responsibility are voluntarily surrendered for pleasure, with small power élites running the country. So the outlook is more in keeping with Arthur C. Clarke's vision of the future, consisting of 'nations of village idiots' tuned in to virtual reality – Aldous Huxley's Epsilons in *Brave New World* – with small groups of experts running the real world, now become a playground for the rich. It is because of the power accruing to the experts and their technology as they grapple with the problems of the world – 'The deterioration of the environment produced by technology is a technological problem for which technology has found, is finding, and will continue to find solutions'[6] – and because the irresponsible masses are more and more dependent on, and therefore deferential towards, experts of every kind, whose decisions turn on matters most people do not understand, that they will be powerless to challenge the experts in their ivory towers. Nor, for that matter, will they be able to challenge the records held centrally on computer by an electronic bureaucracy. Electronic inviolability will make such a quest as vain as that of Kafka's K in his attempts to search the inaccessible castle for the overwhelming force that oppressed him.

The humiliating oppression of the new technological imperialism and the stifling uniformity of the technological age both give rise to national and individual fragmentation and conflict as people seek status in ethnic and religious separateness, and to enormous pressures forcing people into more and more of a single mass. Centrifugal forces are opposed by enormous centripetal forces. We are fragmenting and being drawn into a global uniculture at the same time. In the event, the nations of the world will, I believe, tend to converge towards a single world government, the managed planet. And because the brave new world is likely to be one over which individual members of nations have no control, it is also likely to be more totalitarian than otherwise.

The rapid growth of surveillance devices and national computer systems – the modern equivalents of the all-seeing eye of the Sun God and all-knowingness of the Oracle – and the development, procurement and deployment of other new technologies for police, paramilitary and internal security forces immeasurably increases the totalitarian potential of the authorities of nations not yet under totalitarian control. As in the earliest civilizations, there is, too, a tendency to the convergence of architecture as an expression of state power. Robert Hughes has given some examples of the world-wide similarity and humiliating grandiosity of the architecture of state power:

> The scariest example we have of it is the seat of government for New York State, Albany Mall. As Nelson Rockefeller's monument, it has a Roman coarseness and a more than Roman size: a stone plateau, modelled on the ceremonial buildings of Brasilia and, if possible, even uglier than they. It is designed for one purpose and achieves it perfectly: it expresses the centralisation of power... What speaks from these stones is not the difference between American free enterprise and, say, Russian socialism, but the similarities between the corporate and the bureaucratic states of mind, irrespective of country or ideology. One could see any building at Albany Mall with an eagle on top, or a swastika, or a hammer and sickle; it makes no difference to the building. For if one considers what is actually built (rather than what was said about what is built), there can be no doubt that modernist culture has its own language of political power. It is not linked to any particular ideology. It is value-free and can mean anything the patron wants. It is, in essence, an architecture of coercion.[7]

This vertical convergence, concentration and contraction of bureaucratic power at the national level is also happening at the international level. The European Community was established by the Treaty of Rome in 1957 to create a common customs union as the basis for greater European unity. Europe now possesses a European Commission that acts as a central planning executive, a European Parliament and European Court of Justice, which together provide the constitutional framework for a federal state. The 'nervous systems' of the separate European nations are also being merged in the single 'nervous system' of a super composite animal, Europe. This will link all the electronic networks of Europe into a single supra-national structure – the European Nervous System (ENS) – which will permit the unrestricted movement of information throughout the body of Europe.

Other nations are merging into larger entities without dismantling their national borders – in eastern Asia, in the Americas – to form free trade areas. Together with the European Union, this trend towards greater economic integration may be replicated elsewhere in the world – in Southern Africa, for example – and may be sufficiently powerful to overcome the trend towards ethnic separatism and strife. If not, the international community may increasingly be called upon to use force to separate warring parties and to police potential trouble spots. A permanent international force may have to be established to that end.

At the same time, international organizations of scientific experts, representing every imaginable specialist function – including organizations to monitor Earth's processes, such as the Intergovernmental Panel on Climate Change (IPCC), the World Meteorological Organization (WMO), the International Whaling Commission (IWC), and the International Union for Conservation of Nature and Natural Resources (IUCN) – have come into existence to develop measures that will ultimately enable them to predict, to conquer and control all the inimical forces – both natural and man-made – mentioned in this and earlier chapters.

For example, by making continual, small changes to the atmosphere, meteorologists are hoping that they may one day be able to control the weather. Other scientists have been monitoring the ocean's behaviour, using the ocean as a laboratory in order to explore the possibilities of reducing global warming. Altogether, therefore, scientists are combining in joint ventures that will amount to planetary engineering. As one might expect, this means that just as all the problems are converging so too are efforts to solve those problems. The inevitability of some form of world-wide steady state, or world order, is gaining wider acceptance, to bring into being the managed society at the supra-national level.

For instance, the need for a world weather authority to regulate climate modification and weather control throughout the world is seen by G. Breuer[8] as a step towards world government. Millions of people world-wide live in fear of violent weather, weather which may be getting more violent as a direct result of global warming making the climate more unstable. People are turning to scientists to control the weather, to reduce the power of hurricanes, typhoons and tornadoes, while increasing the rainfall over drought-stricken areas and reducing rainfall over areas susceptible to flooding. Yet such weather modification could, as I argued in Part II, adversely affect the weather in other areas. It could have undesirable side effects – particularly if those effects cross national boundaries – and give rise to diverging national weather interests, even to weather wars. A world weather authority, under the entirely independent authority of a World Government, is therefore seen as essential.

The world's statesmen and scientific community will be under increasing pressure to bring the world under the control of a single World Government as the only solution to their multitudinous problems. Such a government would need to develop a planetary policy and planetary unity, a unity which transcends the merely selfish concerns of nation states. (The United Nations was born in 1945 out of a similar idealistic desire for a one-state world and world peace.) Such a policy would include instruments for the supra-national control of nuclear, biological and chemical weapons, the restructuring of the global economy in order to reduce the gap between the overconsuming rich and the burgeoning poor and to ensure an environmentally sustainable future, and major changes in human reproductive behaviour, in values and lifestyles. If global economic growth is to continue, it will need global energy planning. At the same time control over Earth's environment will need to be tightened. The principal force involved in propelling the nations in the direction of a world-wide steady state under a Supra-National Authority is *the convergent evolution of nations in obedience to the historical imperative.* The accumulating threats, and in particular threats from an increasingly disturbed and unpredictable nature, amount to an unprecedented degree of threat and humiliation impelling *Homo degener* towards World Government.

A rudimentary form of World Government is already taking shape in the form of the World Trade Organization (WTO) – a global organization which regulates free trade on behalf of nations and transnational corporations – in association with the World Bank and International Monetary Fund. These possess the ideology, organization, technology and money to manage the Earth as an integrated economic unit. Yet implicit in such management is the globalization of the economy in conjunction with free trade, which together have been shown to be a new kind of corporate colonialism –

a parasite pyramidal structure – and which, given the inherent parasite pyramidal structuring of nations and of world markets, ensures that the poor in rich countries, and the poorer countries themselves, remain poor and that the environment remains degraded. For free trade operates in favour of the 500 powerful multinational corporations which, as I argued above, control some 80 per cent of world trade. Globalization gives ever greater freedom to corporations while further diminishing that of poorer peoples, bringing increasing poverty and environmental destruction in its train.

> Surveys conducted last year found that the rules and conditions laid down by the International Monetary Fund, World Trade Organization and others make the poorest nations poorer. Even a study of western-style patent rules, which WTO members must adopt, found that they benefit rich nations at the expense of the poor.[9]

Global trade rules, established by the WTO, actively prevent the development of poor nations, which

> ... are locked into their position as the suppliers of cheap labour and raw materials to the rich world's companies.[10]

A World Government, founded in conjunction with the WTO and IMF, would, in the name of an environmentally sustainable future, perpetuate the already existing inequalities within and between nations which in turn inevitably fosters the anti-evolutionary degradation of the environment. The international community of scientists would be principal agents in the management of the globe and so in the perpetuation of its parasite pyramidal structure and consequent environmental degradation.

It is scientists amongst the intellectuals who already form an international community. This includes groups specializing in chemical, biological and nuclear weapons, a Scientific Committee on Problems of the Environment, and the International Geosphere and Biosphere Programme that is linked with the Human Dimensions of Global Change. They formed part of the 1992 United Nations Conference on Environment and Development (The Earth Summit), subscribing to an Earth Charter of environmental and economic principles and Agenda 21, a blueprint for planetary survival in the 21st century. It is scientists who are already engaged in planetary engineering. It is scientists whom the head of the 1992 Earth Summit, Maurice Strong, called upon to help form an 'Earth Council', to act 'like an Amnesty International for the environment, pointing a credible finger at environmental wrongdoers and offering alternatives'[11] – in other words, to act as *guardians of the globe*. It is scientists who believe they have it within their power to unite the world, to solve its problems and to perfect humankind and their environment.

Such has been the promise, and such the expectations of the people, ever since the days of the early priestly-scientific experts of Egypt and Sumeria. And therein lies the evil that is of the essence of the parasite pyramidal structure: the gross deception and self-deception practised by those in authority, the self-delusive expectations of the people, and the related divisions and degeneration which science perpetuates. One is the division of people into *Homo sapiens sapiens* and *Homo sapiens non sapiens*, the one promising, manipulating and holding in thrall the other, who expectantly await the millennium that never comes. This division applies not only within nations, but as between (information) rich developed nations and (information) poor developing nations. It is estimated that four-fifths of the world's scientists and technologists work in Europe, Russia and North America. Roughly four-fifths of the world's population lives elsewhere. According to the Science Policy Research Unit at Sussex University, less than 1 per cent of research carried out in the developed countries has any significance for the developing world, and half that research effort is devoted to military and related activities. It is scientists who have played a major rôle in the development and spread of multinational corporations. Scientists are employed by the multinationals to further their interests and increase their profits – they are not employed to question the ethics of those they serve. In every field scientists are contemptuous of the public ignorance, giving the public a simplified, often entirely distorted, version of the truth. These strictures are borne out by Greenpeace, when it condemned an official report from the International Atomic Energy Authority into the effects of the Chernobyl nuclear accident in Ukraine in 1986.

> There has been a massive attempt to deny and cover up the true costs of the accident. The Agency has thrown in its lot with the people manipulating the truth…With this report, the IAEA has made its allegiance clear, and that allegiance is 100% on the side of government and against the victims.[12]

The second major division which science contemptuously perpetuates is that between *Homo degener* and nature, which has been twisted and tortured out of all recognition. Science and industry, and in particular the multinational companies – 'the agents of rain forest destruction, the generators of greenhouse gases, the plunderers'[13] – have played a key rôle in the accelerating destruction of the natural environment. Scientists invented the CFCs that are threatening the ozone layer. They helped develop nuclear power, which has brought persistent environmental problems in its train. They developed the pesticides which have both contaminated our food and the wild environment. Some environmentalists thus see scientists as active collaborators in our society's ecological destructiveness. When Rachel Carson[14] discovered that certain outstanding entomologists were among the leading advocates of the chemical control of insects, she investigated the background of some of these men and found that their whole research project was sustained by the chemical industry. Their professional prestige, sometimes even their jobs, relied on the continuing application of chemicals. Given their bias, she asked how much we could believe their claims that insecticides are harmless.

It would appear that there are now few truly independent academic scientists whose views can be trusted. This was made most apparent during the BSE crisis and after the potentially disastrous introduction of Genetically Modified Organisms (GMO). The majority of scientists are entirely creatures of the establishment, who are engaged, wittingly or unwittingly, in an elaborate series of cover-ups to prevent the general public from learning how natural resources are being pillaged and the Earth poisoned in the interests of profit. The integrity of scientists is compromised by vested interests.

> Scientists are increasingly dependent on their paymasters for opportunities and appointments, and to be published. What is more, the proprietors of science – governments, health authorities, commercial interests and the military – end up owning the knowledge they acquire, through intellectual property rights and patenting. The ownership principle is the most insidious feature of the corruption of science, and has been increasingly dominating science since the end of the second world war... The silence and indifference of scientists have enabled their paymasters to undermine the integrity of science with impunity.[15]

With every scientific and technological advance the divisions – between *Homo sapiens sapiens* and *Homo sapiens non sapiens* peoples, and between them and nature – are made more profound, and the methods of manipulation and torture more refined, carrying the *Homo sapiens sapiens* head ever higher into the heavens above, while at the same time destroying the wild environment, ground of the true science of true human beings.

The ultimate revolution, into world government, would make these deceptions and divisions absolute.

In obedience to the historical imperative all the anti-evolutionary forces set in motion with the arrival of *Homo degener* 12,000 years ago are tending towards the moulding of the world into a single parasite pyramid of maximum energy and power to ascent, and collective security and control: a superorganism resembling any one nation, but comprising an integrated hierarchy of all the nations, representing a climax state following 12,000 years of anti-evolutionary convergence of composite animals. Such a superorganism would consist of a global nervous system, comprising nerve nets of information linking all the peoples, together with a world-wide health or immune system based on the global vaccination programmes already run by the World Health Organization. It would also include an interdependent division of labour – a global division of labour similar to that within any one nation – leading up from mainly *Homo sapiens non sapiens* primary and secondary producer nations suffering the lowest standards of living in the Southern Hemisphere and Third World, through predominantly *Homo sapiens sapiens* primary and secondary consumer nations in the Northern Hemisphere, to ultimate *Homo sapiens super sapiens* bureaucratic and scientific guardian consumers enjoying the highest possible status and standard of living established at physical and intellectual energy centres on Earth and circling the heavens in satellite suns and on the moon, whence they could dominate and control all the peoples, lands and seas of the world, the whole under a single World Government (see figure 3.1).

Such a World Authority and scientific guardians (the new priesthood) would be the guardians of the globe and of the heavenly highway to the stars, to new worlds without end. They would control a Global Protection System, both military and environmental. They would thus be the guardians and defenders of law and order against the threat of world-wide pollution and annihilation by the inadvertant escape of radioactive waste from international repositories in geologically stable areas in countries such as Russia and Australia, where waste will nonetheless constitute a danger for tens of thousands of years*; and against the threat of chemical, biological or nuclear war. They would also be the regulators of solar energy; the regulators of world food supplies, natural resources and land use; and the repository of all the secret knowledge necessary to the

---

*Physicists in America and Europe are, however, hoping to build what one described as transmutation reactors which will destroy plutonium, reduce the amount of radioactive waste and minimize the threat of nuclear terrorism.

Part III: fig 3.1

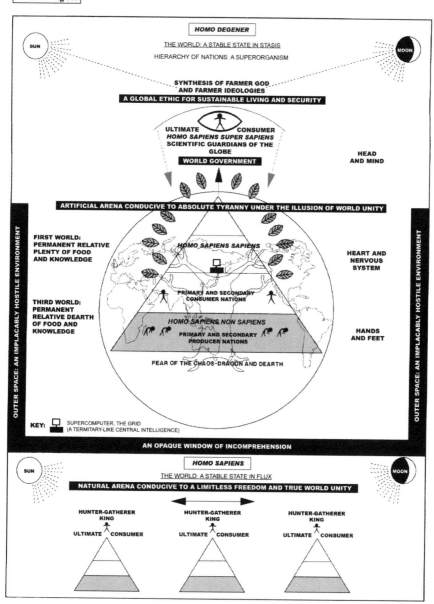

monitoring and manipulation of the forces of nature and the natures of people, ostensibly to the ultimate benefit of both.

It is, however, as guardians of the heavenly highway to the stars, and in their exploitation, development and control of certain celestial bodies, that scientists' greatest energies will be concentrated. The ascent of humankind away from Earth towards the heavens is most likely to be driven by a combination of scientific exploration and commercial exploitation. The largest new space project is the International Space Station, launched from Earth as a trial for people living and working together in space. Thereafter, scientists are looking forward to the colonization and development of space, particularly as a means of exporting surplus populations from Earth to man-made space colonies or to Mars and beyond. It is further hoped to use space as a dumping ground for all our radioactive waste. The fulfilment of such scientific goals would give scientists a god-like power as absolute as any enjoyed by the earlier priest-scientists of Egypt and Mesopotamia, where priestly-scientific fiction prevailed as fact. But now science fiction *is* becoming fact. Space-orientated scientists, engineers and other specialists are visualizing islands in the sky, self-supporting human habitations capable of housing thousands, and ultimately millions, of people in conditions free from the pollution, overcrowding, food shortages and energy crises that threaten our future on Earth – somewhere, in fact, where humankind might be able to make a new start.

> If we go on to two centuries from now, it is my guess that space will have then moved to a point where, with fusion power having been unlocked, and the ability that will give us to propel large, self-sustaining space-colonies completely out of our solar system, the first few colonies will have decided to leave the sun and throw in their lot as an orbiting system of another star. Perhaps the other star would have planets that would be hospitable to man, but, even if they did not, it would be perfectly possible, with the kind of life-systems that we will have developed two centuries from now, for mankind to use the solar energy from other stars to found colonies of mankind many light years away from Earth.[16]

It will be appreciated that such colonies would be the direct descendants and inheritors of the first primitive farmers who, separated by the abyss of the Mesolithic from their original evolutionary path, forsook a true freedom of movement under the sun and developed as separate colonies each under its own Sun, each a stratified society of people imprisoned in a hostile environment, each an ark of survival in the midst of chaos. These colonies would be, in Paine's words, 'under control', and that control would inevitably be that of the scientific community, a scientific hegemony. A principal motive behind the establishment of space colonies is still survival in face of the threat of extinction. As argued by Ian Ridpath:

> In addition to the charm of space colonies and their provision of low-cost clean energy to Earth, there is a pressing reason why they should be established. If some catastrophe overtook the Earth and wiped out civilization on our planet, the colonies could survive on their own. They are lifeboats for mankind that effectively make him immortal from natural or man-made disasters.[17]

The irony is that the hunter-gatherers were already virtually immortal from natural or man-made disasters. A further tragic irony is that it is not a *Homo sapiens* remnant that would be saved, but *Homo degener*, who carries with him the collective memetic inheritance of his origins in the first lifeboats of a de-ranged humankind, as mythologized in Noah's Ark. Twelve thousand years of ritualized conflict behaviour in face of a world become a hostile environment has been a fundamental training ground for those persons privileged to travel in the hostile environment of space. It is outer space and the varieties of life that might inhabit it, together with the hope of establishing unfettered, stable and pollution-free working conditions beyond the threat of anarchy and increasingly restrictive conditions and laws on Earth, that fascinates scientists. Yet it was this world, their true and truly spacious home, and the infinite varieties of life that inhabited it, that fascinated the hunter-gatherers and maintained them in a true stability in ecological understanding, and which civilized people destroy in their phrenetic search for the knowledge and the means for the fulfilment of their dreams. The first space programmes and the first men to arrive, as it were, in space were the Pharaohs of Egypt, who imaginatively broke out beyond the biosphere of Earth, to seek immortality as Sons of the Sun God, circling the heavens in the Chariot of the Sun. Ever since, *Homo degener* peoples, alienated from their true home on Earth, have imaginatively sought a home amongst the stars. Still in pursuit of that dream, modern subhumans have developed the technology *actually* to break out beyond the biosphere of Earth.* Yet they will be no more at home amongst the

---

*This refers to the actual colonization of space. There is, however, still an imaginative aspect to this colonization – the belief of the Chosen Few that they will be raised up and transported to Heaven on the Last Day. In the USA, for example, a fundamentalist religious movement, Christian Coalition, teaches creationism – the belief that the world was created by God – as against the theory of evolution, and the belief that we are in what they call the 'end time' of biblical prophecy, when the holy are taken up to Heaven and the Antichrist takes over Earth under a malignant one-world government.

stars than they are on Earth. Encapsulated in space colonies they will be as alien and as vulnerable in a hostile universe as they have been on a hostile Earth. However, just as genetic engineers may soon be able to make the genetic inheritance of individuals conform to the 'memetic code' of their composite animals, they may soon be able to make them conform to the requirements of travel and life in space.

Already genetic engineers are experimenting with re-designed life forms to enable them to flourish in space. Not only will they be re-designed to live on other planets but, perhaps, around other suns. This expansion of life from Earth into the solar system and beyond has been described as the creation of the 'supercosm'. Because *Homo degener* peoples in association with machines already have a decisive, though perverted, selective advantage over those not so associated, the future evolution of the supercosm will almost certainly involve the actual physical integration of people with machines. The inhabitants of the supercosm will be as different from us as we are from bacteria; they will usher in a future as non-human as our Prephanerozoic past.

It is this ascent of degenerate subhumans since the fall, 12,000 years ago, that was portrayed diagrammatically in Part I. Human life is coming round full circle: from highly evolved human as hunter-gatherer, through subhuman anti-evolutionary farmer-industrialist to anti-evolutionary subhuman forms and conditions akin to the primitive life-forms and conditions from which our hunter-gatherer ancestors evolved.*

If science fiction becomes fact with the arrival of colonies of *Homo degener* in the sky, the Space Wars of science fiction could likewise become fact. Just as the existence of separate Sacred Species of *Homo degener* nations under their own Suns on Earth gave rise to wars between them, thus increasing the abyss between them and between them and nature – and so between them and their own true natures – the existence of separate colonies of *Homo degener* orbiting each around its own star in space† would logically cause each to become specifically different from the others, giving rise to the possibility of wars between worlds, such as envisaged by H.G. Wells. They could add a new dimension to human conflict – the war in space – to make the abyss between them and their own true natures and true evolutionary path of cosmic or infinite proportions. They would also most powerfully reinforce the trend towards One World on Earth. Even as the threat of invasion by alien nations

---

* See below Part III, Figure 4.1, for a diagrammatic representation of the regressive re-evolution of *Homo degener* into space.

† They would form biotic islands in space, with all that that implies from the standpoint of speciation.

replaced that by an alien wilderness as the principal threat binding the peoples together in nations of collective security, the actual or manufactured threat of invasion from alien outer space could replace that of alien nations as the principal threat, to bind the nations together under one World Government.* However, at present it is natural objects in outer space which are seen as presenting the greatest potential danger to civilization. NASA and the Institute of Theoretical Astronomy in St Petersburg are seeking to instigate an international programme to counter the threat of asteroids striking, and perhaps even destroying, the Earth, seeking in asteroids a 'common enemy in the sky', and thus encouraging international co-operation in furthering the exploration and conquest of space.

In meeting this threat, the Earth itself would closely resemble one huge termitary. Within a termitary the queen acts as the nerve centre, operating a defence system that enables her to identify a source of threat to the integrity of the termitary and to despatch soldiers to intercept the invader. Similarly, as reported in the *New Scientist*,[18] an Earth-based control centre would operate a defence system comprising a set of orbital telescopes (called Sentry) which would identify and track objects threatening Earth, and deploy space-craft (called Soldier craft) to intercept the incoming body.

I suggest, for all the reasons given in this and earlier chapters, that the convergence towards World Government is a likely model of the future because it is a logical outcome of the initial re-evolution and subsequent ascent of *Homo degener* peoples. They will thereby achieve the termitary-like perfection – a perfection in degeneration – argued in Part II, and which is the direct opposite of the relative perfection achieved as hunter-gatherers. However, an equally logical outcome, because of their profoundly degenerate natures, would be their destruction by nature, a point to which I return in the next chapter.

The inflexible movement towards one vertically oriented uniculture and world has gained added momentum from several other sources. One such concerns the nature of science and the type of person who practises science, and who will be involved in any scheme of global management,

---

*Another common concern of scientists has been the search for extra-terrestrial intelligence (SETI), and for Earthlike planets rather than aliens. The assumption is that they, like *Homo degener*, will also be listening out and probing for life-forms elsewhere in the universe. But if my hypothesis regarding the two-fold fall is correct, it is highly unlikely that any other planet inhabited by humans or any other kind of intelligent beings has undergone a similar evodeviation that necessitates their breaking out and invading the universe. Their whole beings, like those of *Homo sapiens*, would be totally and meaningfully absorbed in whatever natural environment they occupied. It is *Homo degener* who is and always will be alien on Earth and in the universe.

488 THE HUMAN REALITY

space exploration and settlement. Scientific research is firmly rooted in a tradition whose origins are re-evolutionary and not evolutionary. Whether by accident or design they cause revolutions which, if they break with contemporary tradition, nonetheless reinforce the overall anti-evolutionary change of direction of humankind out of the horizontal into the vertical. Scientists tend to be 'convergers' – those who tend to rule out all possibilities (of action and invention) except those most in keeping with conventional knowledge and technology. Their research is a highly convergent activity based firmly upon a settled concensus before ever it is revolutionary, when it again becomes a highly convergent activity.* They obey the technological imperative that rules science – 'if it can be done, it will be done' – which has overlaid, if not replaced, the religious imperative – 'Thy will be done' – and provided technological ladders to assist a heavenward ascent of *Homo degener* that was pioneered by religious ladders of myth.

Scientists have replaced the Church as the custodians of revealed truth. As in the days of the ascendancy of the Church and the subservience of the citizenry to its interpretation of 'the will of God', the oft repeated question directed at scientists today – 'Where are you taking us?' – reflects their increasingly god-like dominance and the continuing absence of control of the average citizen over his own destiny. Yet it would be more precise to say that science is reinforcing rather than replacing religion and its belief in God. For not only have scientists down the centuries believed in God – Kepler saw astronomers as 'the priests of God, called to interpret the Book of Nature'; Newton saw the solar system as the work of 'an intelligent and powerful Being' – but certain scientists are now talking about the laws of physics as evidence of the existence of God. Religion and science are converging, as the propositions in the Book of Genesis merge with those of the big bang theory of cosmologists – 'In the beginning was the big bang' – or as physicists discover a complete theory of the universe, enabling us to discuss, and discover, why it is that we and the universe exist. The answer to that would be 'the ultimate triumph of human reason – for then we would know the mind of God.'[19] Such convergences bestow an infinitude of power on those who present them as the ultimate truth of the past: for those who control the past control the future. Add to that Nietzsche's dictum, that 'Men believe in the truth of all that is seen to be strongly believed in',

---

*An example of convergent research is that undertaken by Werner Heisenberg, Paul Dirac and Erwin Schrödinger in the years 1925–26. They started from three widely different assumptions, converging upon a single mathematical structure – now called 'quantum theory' – which solved the major physical problem of the day: the interaction of light with matter.

and the position of those in power becomes well-nigh impregnable. So whether by reinforcing tradition built up on the original re-evolution or by initiating further revolutions, both the priestly and the scientific hopes and intentions are powerful forces making for the convergent evolution of the world.

In this connection, it is noteworthy that the priest-scientist, Pierre Teilhard de Chardin,[20] envisaged a world of individuals merging as one mind, minds merging in a collective consciousness he called the 'noösphere', or thinking envelope of the Earth, converging towards one central or Omega Point, which he equated with God. Such a global consciousness would envelop the world in a psychic, as well as a physical, domination of humankind over nature. Technology would provide the global linkage which would make a collective consciousness possible. Already many peoples, with the aid of global telecommunications, are experiencing the same events, such as the Apollo moon landings and the 1999 total eclipse, at the same time. Ultra-intelligent machines, connected to a world-wide network of data stations and computer banks, could eventually convert the world into a single thinking entity: the domination by a single world picture – a single world view – of science and technology. This is already being made possible by the development of what is known as the Grid, the connection of hundreds of thousands of the most powerful computers to form a global supercomputer, possessing what has been described as 'unprecedented processing power and data handling capabilities'.[21]* Such a collective consciousness would comprise not only what may be regarded as a collective global intelligence but also a collective social nervous system for managing millions of our problems. A man-made global intelligence and global nervous system would thus combine to replace the global 'intelligence' and global 'nervous system' of wild nature that has governed the evolution of Earth for 4.6 billion years, and which governed the behaviour of *Homo sapiens* but was lost to *Homo degener* 12,000 years ago.

As well as the convergence of computing, telecommunications and semiconductor technology into the powerful force called informatics, or information technology, that might eventually make for a global intelligence and global nervous system, there is the growing uniformity of the two principal languages – mathematics and English – in which information is both collated and disseminated, to the detriment of those who neither speak nor understand such languages. Firstly, because information is

---

* See Appendix xviii, which includes a *résumé* of Geoff Simons' book *Eco-Computer* (Wiley, 1987). Simons speculates on the evolution of the eco-computer, a world-wide electronic matrix which will enable the world's scientists and managers to govern the world as a 'global village'.

increasingly mathematics based; secondly, because English is increasingly becoming the *lingua franca* for the dissemination of information.

Mathematics, the language of scientific élites that not only cuts across national boundaries but unites national scientific élites, leaves the majority of citizens outside the walls, so to speak.

> As electronic data-processing and coding pervade more and more of the economics and social order of our lives, the mathematical illiterate will find himself cut off. A new hierarchy of menial service and stunted opportunity may develop among those whose resources continue to be purely verbal. There may be 'word-helots'.[22]

The language in which information is disseminated grows ever more uniform. Each person is joined to more and more millions of other people by products such as television, which turn the world into a global village with a uniformly passive audience, a convergent process which is encouraged by the increasingly widespread use of English to disseminate information – in particular that deriving from the principal actors, the scientific experts.

The inexorable movement towards a vertically orientated uniculture and world has gained added momentum through the adoption of English as an international language. As George Steiner has argued, English has an increasingly firm grip on international communication for a wide range of purposes. It is the chief language of the United Nations and its agencies such as the World Health Organization. Above all, English is the language of modern science and of the Internet.

English, or American-English, is increasingly becoming the *lingua franca* throughout large parts of the planet, to the detriment of hundreds of local languages. With the spread of media and communication technologies, increasing numbers of speakers of local languages are likely to abandon their mother tongues in preference for a dominant language associated with status, wealth and political power.

The most powerful and pervasive language in the world is, metaphorically speaking, money. Money (and in particular the US dollar) talks; it speaks louder than words. 'Money speaks sense in a language all nations understand'.* So too does American-English. Together they are tending to unite the world in a single parasite pyramid of status, wealth and power while at the same time destroying the true languages and wealth of the wilderness. The loss of those languages which spoke of a true

---

*Aphra Behn, *The Rover*, Part III, Act 1.

wealth and status within the wilderness are the most serious. It is estimated that about 80 per cent of North American Indian languages, and 90 per cent of Australian Aborigine languages, are spoken by adults only, and are therefore likely to become extinct when those adults die. This means that their ways of understanding the world will have died as well.

In previous centuries the Latin language bound together the ruling castes of the Christian West. Now it is the turn of the English of scientists to bind the world in one whole: English underpins the concept of globalization. A uniform pyramidal intellectual, technical, economic and linguistic superiority of technocratic élites and inferiority of the great mass of humankind bears the hallmarks, not of freedom and mutual understanding, but of tyranny.

We are already well on the road to Francis Bacon's hierarchical utopia *New Atlantis*. In Bacon's utopian community both human society and the kingdom of nature were being dominated and dictated by a priesthood of scientists. The remainder of humanity and nature were reduced to the rôle of submissive and obedient servants. The average layman's present relationship with scientists is similar to that which exists between the primitive tribesman and his witch doctor. Ignorance and fear of the wild environment on the part of doubly deprived people led to the tyranny of the witch-doctor and priest-scientist over them. Similarly the uninformed layman's incomprehension of modern science and technology as surely invites a new tyranny. Perhaps the answer would be for everyone to be imbued with the ABC of science, but that is even less likely than universal literacy.

Not only does the logic of our anti-evolutionary path point in the direction of tyranny, but so do all the indicators discussed above, and particularly the growth of slavery. Out of sight at the bottom of the parasite pyramidal superorganism will be the inarticulate slaves, for slavery is playing a major rôle in the globalization of the market place. Slaves constitute a considerable workforce supporting the global economy, and slavery, as I argued in Part II, is on the increase world-wide. As rapid population expansion and economic and technical change reduce ever more people to poverty and destitution, companies and businesses across the world are taking advantage of this often anarchic situation to enslave more and more adults and children, for profit.

From being an expanding world conducive to the limitless freedom in ecological understanding of hunter-gatherers developing languages, cultures, artefacts and arts as diverse as the landscape, flora and fauna around them, the world is shrinking to one of homogeneity, contracting into banks of computers conducive to a tyranny of:

well-fed knowledgeable governing	*Homo sapiens super sapiens*
well-fed knowledgeable mediating	*Homo sapiens sapiens*
ill-fed uncomprehending governed	*Homo sapiens non sapiens*
inarticulate domesticated	kingdom of nature.

This whole process may be summed up as the inevitable outcome of the re-evolutionary adaptation of deranged people into pioneer species of composite animal. For it is of the essence of the pioneer stage to be unbalanced and relatively unstable. It is only when such composite animals achieve a 'climax' condition that they can maintain a complex and stable equilibrium, however temporary. After a historical succession as pioneer composite animals, nations are now converging towards a climax condition of civilization itself. For civilization can only maintain a complex and stable equilibrium world-wide when it has achieved a climax under one World Government. Such a man-made Central Authority would, however, be a gross perversion of, and would absolutely contravene, the true and universal authority and government of the Great Spirit.

Because a true order of humankind and of the Earth may only be found amongst hunter-gatherers and wildlife obedient to the command of the Great Spirit, *Homo degener*'s attempts increasingly to dominate and control the environment by arrogating to themselves the ultimate powers of arbitrary life and death over their own kind and over the natural world will only exacerbate an already parlous situation, inviting nemesis. The historical imperative is propelling *Homo degener* towards both World Government and ultimate self-destruction. The combined effects of the black Suns of nations on the true sun are such as to threaten all life on Earth. Retribution, in whatever shape or form, must surely overtake such evolutionary misfits.

Chapter 4

Nemesis

And as the smart ship grew
In stature, grace, and hue,
In shadowy silent distance grew the Iceberg too.

Alien they seemed to be:
No mortal eye could see
The intimate welding of their later history,

Or sign that they were bent
By paths coincident
On being anon twin halves of one august event.

Till the Spinner of the Years
Said 'Now!' And each one hears,
And consummation comes, and jars two hemispheres.

(Thomas Hardy – *The Convergence of the Twain*.)[1]*

The most important consequence arising from the perversion of the true processes of natural selection, out of an evolutionary succession of a diversity of wild forms and into an anti-evolutionary succession of an increasing homogeneity of degenerate domesticated forms, concerns the convergent evolution and clash of nations and the kingdom of nature, and so the convergent evolution and clash of the man-made processes of evolution with those of a true evolution. As the whole world converges and contracts into a hierarchy of nations, into a single parasite pyramid of power or superorganism comprising

---

*Hardy is describing the convergence and clash of a man-made structure – the *Titanic* – with a natural structure – an iceberg.

governing	*Homo sapiens super sapiens*
mediating	*Homo sapiens sapiens*
governed	*Homo sapiens non sapiens*
domesticated	kingdom of nature

the world that was made relatively perfect in evolutionary change and renewal and whose imperfection has become more and more advanced with the growth and expansion of nations will reach the zenith of imperfection (or perfection in degeneration) as it contracts into a single world-wide Stable State in stasis. In the event, the world will be moving towards a direct confrontation between a man-made world ordered primarily as a vertically oriented superorganism and the biosphere ordered primarily as a horizontally oriented superorganism.

It is important to see why this should be, because even if *Homo degener* people, by unifying the world under one government, stop the warring between nations and avoid destroying themselves with their own devilish devices, they cannot escape the ultimate fate that is reserved for those who not only hold in contempt and disobey the laws of nature and of their own true natures, but actually pervert those laws to their own anti-evolutionary ends. By making absolute the vertical integration of the world, they would be making absolute their suppression and perversion of nature and of their own true natures, thereby intensifying the war between themselves and the kingdom of nature, a war which they cannot hope to win.

The biosphere is an immense, integrated living system, a superorganism, of which human beings as hunter-gatherers formed a small, if important, part. They learnt and understood the secrets and laws of nature the better to survive in the wild environment. They evolved as the near-perfect, self-controlled, problem-solving animals *par excellence. Homo degener*, divorced from the wild environment, forcibly wrests the secrets of nature from her the better to exploit the Earth. In addition, because *Homo degener* communities were also devoted to the perpetual exclusion of the wilderness, they actively blocked the bloodstream of the kingdom of nature. Their own life-forces and those of nature were thus prevented from fulfilling their true potential in a freedom of lateral movement and succession of forms and were instead perverted to serve the ascent of nations. As a result, not only are *Homo degener* peoples – in their derangement, pyramidal posturing and exclusive ownership of territory – deeply hostile both to their own kind and to wild nature, but each nation is a structure that slowly destroys its host. So, as well as actively blocking nature's bloodstream, nations began to dismember its body and drain dry its bloodstream.

Diversity has been described as the linchpin of biology. The diversity of wildlife is not only vital to the well-being, but also to the understanding, of the world; to lose even a little woodland to build a factory is to destroy that diversity. Yet economic development and growth, together with the pollution that accompanies them, still invariably take precedence over the health of the environment, while modern agricultural techniques continue to destroy natural habitats, replacing a diversity of species with vast tracts of monocultured land. Furthermore, as alien invaders themselves of the wilderness, *Homo degener* communities are introducing alien species into the remaining wild habitats of the world, an invasion which is irreversibly homogenizing the biodiversity of the planet. Also, with the aid of genetic engineering, entirely contrived species of animals and plants can be created and sustained in environments which, though highly productive, will be largely artificial and greatly simplified. At the same time *Homo degener* peoples are becoming increasingly uniform as their world is standardized and contracted by communication and tele-communication networks to the size of a global village. So as well as the erosion of a diversity of wildlife, the diversity of domesticated life – subhuman, animal and plant – is being reduced by standardization and increasing uniformity. Such uniformity goes against the grain of nature. It effectively reverses natural evolution, which favours diversity, particularly because only diverse populations can respond effectively to all the unknown stresses environmental change might impose upon them.

In addition, not only has every source of energy *Homo degener* might exploit the potential to damage the environment in some way, but all their own personal energies – soon to be 7 billion personal energies – cannot but increase that environmental damage as they pursue their daily tasks and upwardly mobile aspirations to a better life and a better world. Theodore Roszak, for instance, tells of the effect that tourism – one of the major consumers of energy – is having on the remaining wilderness:

> It represents the final, most humiliating stage of human domination. It is the domestication of the once proudly untamed for no better purpose than amusement. Is there something worse than rendering the tigers extinct in their native habitat? Yes. Turning them into playthings in a theme park...
>
> Let it not go unnoted: with our generation, the urban-industrial dominance of the Earth has reached saturation point. There is nothing left that is authentically remote, autonomous, unblemished. The globe as a whole has become an artefact of our civilization. Where the primitive and wild linger on, it is only as national parks,

game preserves, reservations organised by megalopolis for its diversion or instruction. Nothing non-industrial survives outside industrial society, but only inside and on sufferance, as a licensed enclave.[2]

As Roszak said of the wilderness, following a visit to Yellowstone National Park (USA):

The sight was too much like that of a great king conquered and exhibited in chains.[3]

We are subhuman peoples fouling our evolutionary nest, enslaving and laying waste our erstwhile home. At the American Association for the Advancement of Science in 1995, Professor E.O. Wilson estimated that there were approximately ten million species then in existence, and that the number of species being destroyed each year was around 27,000. The extinction rate is 100 to 1000 times faster than would be predicted from past extinction trends. More than exterminating species, we are threatening the evolution of new species. Our anti-evolutionary degeneration, our humiliating enslavement and degeneration of the Earth – for comfort, for power, for profit, for amusement, for survival – demands our eventual annihilation, if not at our own hands then at those of nature.

The conclusions I have arrived at in this book show an ascent, not of true humankind, but of *Homo degener* at the cost of true humankind, an anti-evolutionary process which is rapidly overlaying and destroying the original evolutionary processes, so as to endanger the very existence of life on this planet. Viewed in this wider context, the ascent of *Homo degener* peoples must be seen as an upward and regressive process, the turning back of a curve upon itself. Their termitaries, extending outwards and upwards to the skies, are devoted to the replication of unnatural domesticated life at the cost of all true mammalian life. They are an affirmation of, and return to, the insect way of life. In evolutionary terms, *Homo degener* is regressing to a time long before the arrival of the mammals on Earth (see figure 4.1).

As I have argued throughout, parasitism and a perverted predatoriness are the predominant relationships between members of nations and between them and nature. Inevitably, nature and *Homo degener*'s own real nature are operating at every moment to undermine and destroy such alien structures and behaviour. *Homo degener*'s real nature has, until recently, been represented by hunter-gatherers in America, Africa, Asia and Australia. The Government Resident of the Northern Territory of Australia said in 1889 of the Aborigines:

Part III: fig 4.1

THE RELATIONSHIP BETWEEN THE ORIGINAL EVOLUTIONARY PATH OF ALL LIFE ON EARTH
AND THE ANTI-EVOLUTIONARY PATH OF *HOMO DEGENER* MAY BE REPRESENTED AS FOLLOWS:

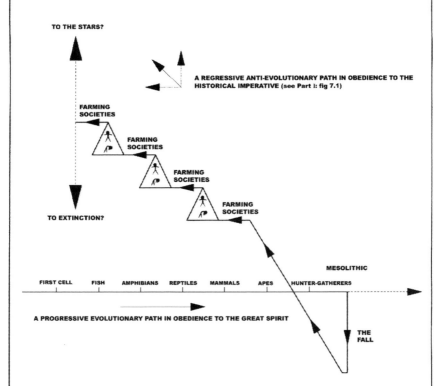

TO THE STARS?

A REGRESSIVE ANTI-EVOLUTIONARY PATH IN OBEDIENCE TO THE
HISTORICAL IMPERATIVE (see Part I: fig 7.1)

FARMING
SOCIETIES

FARMING
SOCIETIES

FARMING
SOCIETIES

FARMING
SOCIETIES

TO EXTINCTION?

MESOLITHIC

FIRST CELL   FISH   AMPHIBIANS   REPTILES   MAMMALS   APES   HUNTER-GATHERERS

A PROGRESSIVE EVOLUTIONARY PATH IN OBEDIENCE TO THE GREAT SPIRIT

THE
FALL

WE ARE THREATENED BY AN ENVIRONMENTAL HOLOCAUST THAT STARTED 12,000 YEARS AGO AND IS ACCELERATING.
IN A FRACTION OF THE TIME THAT IT HAS TAKEN FOR LIFE TO EVOLVE OVER 4000 MILLION YEARS, THE ANTI-EVOLUTIONARY
PATH OF *HOMO DEGENER* IS OVERLAYING, SMOTHERING AND DESTROYING THE TRUE EVOLUTIONARY PATH OF
HOMO SAPIENS AND OF ALL TRUE LIFE ON EARTH.

Entrance into their country is an act of invasion. It is a declaration of war, and they will halt at no opportunity of attacking the white invaders.[4]

Such too was the attitude of the San, the Native Americans and many others long since destroyed. As humans integrated within nature, and as representatives of humankind's real nature, their attitude surely expresses that of wild nature which likewise will halt at no opportunity of attacking the *Homo degener* invaders. In conquering and clearing the forests, and in replacing them with forest-like structures based on polluting cities, agricultural holdings and industrial plants, *Homo degener* peoples have raised up new forces against themselves.* Nature has begun to strike back in a variety of ways. I have already argued that, as the original alien invaders of Earth, we are the victims of an infinitely disadvantageous mutation, and that nature is hitting back harder and harder with flood, drought, disease and other disasters.

One major avenue of conflict is through epidemics being converted into global pandemics. This is happening first because more and more millions of poor people are concentrated in foul slums with polluted water and poor sanitation. Secondly, because of the adaptability of disease-carrying organisms such as mosquitoes, which exhibit a growing resistance to standard insecticides, while the adaptability of bacteria and viruses is such that they often develop resistance to vaccines and antibiotics. As in the case of crop pests that develop a resistance to pesticides, biotechnologists will have to invent improved varieties of chemical agent, thus producing a 'treadmill' effect in their efforts to subdue nature. Thirdly, because tourists and refugees from conflicts and wars increasingly move diseases around, creating new environments in which epidemics can flourish and become pandemics. This is happening with tuberculosis, yellow fever, cholera, malaria, and AIDS. In 2004 it was estimated that 38 million people world-wide were infected by HIV/AIDS, a factor seriously undermining the economic future of more than one nation. Bacteria and viruses indeed have the power to overturn the social order, being no respecter of borders nor even of the fortresses of the rich world.

Pandemics are a fitting judgement on animals that believe themselves to be human while yet behaving in grossly inhuman ways.

---

*Note how a true plant-life, as the energy base of natural food pyramids leading up to hunter-gatherer kings, was first replaced by plant-like cultivators, then by industrial plants and now also by radioactive nuclear plants, as the energy bases of forest-like stratified structures supporting at their canopies Kings, Presidents and Prime Ministers.

Because of the destruction he is capable of wreaking on his host – the Earth – man can be viewed as an evolutionary cancer.

It could be said that, by gaining the incredible power that science has placed in our hands, we inevitably sow the seeds of our own destruction; that any species dominating the Earth to the extent that it endangers the survival of its co-inhabitants is bound to self-destruct, therein lying nature's safety valve. Just as a cancer destroys itself in killing its host, so man endangers himself through despoliation of the very resources he himself needs in order to survive.[5]

A cancer is the result of one of the body's cells being so damaged that it replicates abnormally. In the body the behaviour of a cell, including its replication, is controlled by the genes. Damage to these may give rise to abnormal, malignant behaviour including uncontrolled proliferation. The cell 'forgets' it is a part of the body and divides rapidly to produce huge numbers of similarly damaged cells. It begins to pursue its own unlimited growth without regard to the consequences for the whole body, depriving the healthy cells of nourishment and ultimately killing both the body and itself.

Similarly, *Homo degener* peoples, like damaged cells, 'forgot' they were a part of the body of wild nature and divided rapidly to produce huge numbers of similarly damaged cells. In their case, as cells within composite animals they not only sustained damage to their psyches and physiques but also to their memes as these related to the wilderness. The result was abnormal, malignant behaviour, including uncontrolled proliferation regardless of the consequences for the whole body of wild nature. Anti-evolutionary nations at war with the world, like an army, like cancer, must move and grow to conquer, thus creating an infinite enormity of pain world-wide.

Having lost the natural checks on their aggressive and reproductive behaviour as hunter-gatherers, *Homo degener* peoples are most likely to destroy themselves with their own weaponry (whether directed against their own kind or against wild nature), or by climatic and environmental degradation arising from increasing degeneration and population pressures. Natural selection is continually working to destroy the populations of *Homo degener* peoples, by further advancing and accelerating their degeneration and degenerative behaviour. In every case their destruction would be self-destruction that might be described as a natural phenomenon – examples of nature operating 'within itself a built-in safety valve', through a process that the biologist A. Meredith has described as 'devolution'.

As Charles Darwin realized, organisms adapt to their environment because of constant checks on their tendency toward unlimited growth. If they are not adapted they may decline in numbers and become extinct. But, according to Meredith, they may also become *too* adapted, multiply, deplete their resources, and *then* become extinct.

A microcosmic example of devolution would be microbes growing on a Petri plate. (Petri plates are round dishes with clear, transparent food permitting the investigator to see microbial colonies as spots even with the naked eye.) Fed on nutrient agar – bacterial food hardened with a gelatinous substance extracted from seaweed – microbes are often most prolific in the generations immediately preceding their collapse. Depleting all the nutrients in the agar and reaching the edges of the small laboratory dish, the multibillions of bacteria suddenly stop growing and die for lack of food and living space. For us, the world may be just such a Petri plate. Indeed, computer-enhanced satellite images of Spokane, Washington, show urban growth patterns similar to the growth of colonies of microbes. From the standpoint of Meredith's theory of devolution, it is easy to see that the implications of human population growth are not necessarily synonymous with progress.[6]

The sudden appearance of separate Sacred Species of *Homo degener* composite animals in the historical record some 6,000 years ago, and their expansion and proliferation are expressive, not of human population growth, but of that of anti-evolutionary subhuman beings. Whether such growth is regarded as analogous to a cancerous growth, to the growth of colonies of microbes on a Petri dish or to a mammal plague, the implications are that *Homo degener* should self-destruct in the not too distant future.

The problem which now faces *Homo degener* peoples is how to prevent their self-destruction and produce new order out of their own disorder. This has been their perennial problem ever since they adapted to agriculture. Everything they do to establish order and stability must create further disorder and instability, precisely because they are a cancer within the body of nature – and also because, as already argued, nations are governed by the historical imperative.

It was the rhythmic successional rise and fall of a diversity of mountain, forest, savannah and sea, and of an accompanying diversity of wildlife, which led to the emergence of the ultimate in perfected wildlife on land, the hunter-gatherers. As such, they were challenged by, and responded to, the natural flux. The natural flux was the main catalyst not only to the balanced and harmonious evolution of the innumerable species of flora and fauna but also to the single species of *Homo sapiens*. It is quite otherwise with *Homo degener*. As Kings, exploiting consumers and slave producers of stratified societies, they have been challenged by, and have responded to, the historical imperative. The historical imperative has overlaid and replaced the natural flux as the main catalyst, but now to the imbalanced and inharmonious evolution of nations. *Homo degener* peoples are governed by rules and patterns of disorder, fundamentally because they are permanently at war with wild nature, and because nature throughout history has struck back. This encourages more and more sophisticated, draconian and large scale measures of control, as mankind relies particularly on technology to save it from impending environmental crisis. If such measures do not lead to the destruction of humanity and its world, they will yet lead to the establishment of a single World Authority. Such a parasite pyramidal steady state would be in direct contravention of the true stability of the world in which *Homo sapiens* evolved.

If the separate States merge into one Stable State in stasis (a vertically oriented superorganism), they will increasingly come into direct conflict with the world itself, which is in a stable state in flux (a horizontally oriented superorganism). These two antithetical states respectively reflect the sharply opposed processes of anti-evolution, oriented primarily to a uniformity and contraction of degenerate life in the vertical in a protected environment (as in a termitary), and those of evolution, oriented primarily to diversification and expansion of perfected life in the horizontal in the wild environment. *Homo degener* scientists will be increasingly concerned to take over, alter and control the processes of evolution.

> In broad terms, the destiny of man on earth has been made clear by evolutionary biology. It is to be the agent of the world process of evolution, the sole agent capable of leading it to new heights, and enabling it to realize new possibilities.[7]

This will include interfering with the activity of the sun, control of the weather and wildlife, and the manipulation of the human biological and bacterial heritage by means of biotechnology, the better to raise *Homo degener*'s standard of living, to improve and perfect the imperfect degenerate human stock and to safeguard and extend the world-wide artificial environment into the Solar System. All their efforts, however, will merely serve to deepen both *Homo degener*'s own degeneration and that of the environment. A universal immorality of *Homo degener* will have replaced a universal morality of *Homo sapiens*. In terms of energy, as the world begins to resemble a single parasite pyramid, *Homo degener*'s perversion of both 'fossil sunshine', present solar energy and the bacterial microcosm to the ascent of their kind will become total: the true processes of evolution and true energy flow of the world will have been totally perverted to serve the anti-evolutionary ascent of *Homo degener*. Under the circumstances, the order and stability they would achieve would be, from an evolutionary standpoint, a total disorder and instability; the perfection they would achieve would be the perfection achieved by the blind worker termite in a termitary. It would be the perfection of the degenerate individual in the service of a composite animal, which, in the case of *Homo degener*, is the nation. Such perfection as the component part of a composite animal, itself vertically integrated in a hierarchy of such animals, would be the very antithesis of a true human perfection, bringing *Homo degener* into direct conflict with the forces and flux that earlier made for the evolution of *Homo sapiens*.

It is at this point that the final outcome of the whitening effects of the Suns of nations and the concomitant blackening of the true sun may be seen. As the world begins to resemble a single superorganism reaching up to the heavens, energized by a Sun that is a synthesis of a Farmer God and Farmer Ideologies, that anti-evolutionary black Sun will have totally eclipsed the evolutionary activity of the real sun on Earth, to create, as it were, *a black sun which will be totally inimical to all life on Earth*.* These inimical effects include global warming and a possible increase of ultra-violet radiation from the sun, resulting from the depletion of the Earth's protective ozone layer. In addition,

> Airborne pollution from burning fossil fuels and vegetation is plunging vast regions of the planet into a chilly darkness... Studies of sunlight in China show vast polluted regions that have experienced a steady decline in sunshine alongside steadily dropping temperatures. Meanwhile, in Zambia and the Brazilian Amazon, pollution blots out around a fifth of the Sun's radiation at certain times of year.[8]

Such interference with the life-giving activity of the sun will necessitate endless technical fixes to stabilize the climate to accord, not with nature's evolutionary processes, but with the requirements of *Homo degener*. We

---

* See Appendix xix for a poet's vision of 'a black sun'.

are in fact dealing not only with the re-evolution of *Homo sapiens* as *Homo degener*, not only with the convergent evolution of unrelated species of composite animal, but with that of something much more profound: *the convergent evolution and clash of the man-made processes of evolution and those of a true evolution*. For even if, in order to prevent the world tearing itself apart in strife or perishing through the perversion of our natural support systems, we turn the world into a single Stable State, we surely cannot hope to survive as anti-evolutionary degenerates. Nature, and the universe at large, has no place for damaged and injured animals such as *Homo degener*, who must on that account alone eventually be destroyed. If history can be seen as one continual power struggle, with a tendency for existing power structures to lead to the raising up of opposing forces, as the world merges into one immense power structure, so it will tend to raise up an equal and opposite force in nature. As in the case of the rise and fall of empires, and as one reading of history suggests,

> ...all conquerors are in the end conquered, by forces accumulating beneath them which will never cease to be replenished.[9]

Nature *cannot* permanently accept the rôle 'of a great king conquered and exhibited in chains'. Though the power of science and technology might appear to obliterate our weakness as *Homo degener*, in the compulsive addiction to the cruel power we have over nature, we are in reality powerless. The real powers of the world must reassert their usurped authority to pull down that which has been so vaingloriously built up, in which event the agents of natural selection will destroy the degenerate agents of a perverted memetic selection (see figure 4.2).

To summarize, I use some words whose author is unknown to me:

> The combined power of nations is now so out of proportion to the natural world as to appear as a *creative* force, changing geography, landscapes and lives irrespective of the cost. The whole machinery of progress is saying to the world, never mind the cost. It is inconceivable that nature might not hold some frightful revenge for these powers, the foreign invaders of the land, the sea and the air.

The man-made processes of anti-evolutionary creation and those of a true evolution are converging, and must so converge, towards a point of ultimate conflict – a *Titanic*-like clash and consummation – in obedience to the historical imperative. The historical imperative is inexorable, but

Part III: fig 4.2

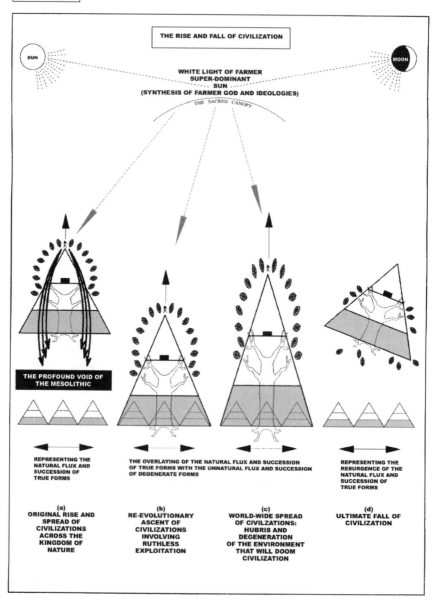

THE RISE AND FALL OF CIVILIZATION

WHITE LIGHT OF FARMER
SUPER-DOMINANT
SUN
(SYNTHESIS OF FARMER GOD AND IDEOLOGIES)

THE SACRED CANOPY

THE PROFOUND VOID OF
THE MESOLITHIC

REPRESENTING THE
NATURAL FLUX AND
SUCCESSION OF
TRUE FORMS

THE OVERLAYING OF THE NATURAL FLUX AND SUCCESSION
OF TRUE FORMS WITH THE UNNATURAL FLUX AND SUCCESSION
OF DEGENERATE FORMS

REPRESENTING THE
RESURGENCE OF THE
NATURAL FLUX AND
SUCCESSION OF
TRUE FORMS

(a)
ORIGINAL RISE AND
SPREAD OF
CIVILIZATIONS
ACROSS THE
KINGDOM OF
NATURE

(b)
RE-EVOLUTIONARY
ASCENT OF
CIVILIZATIONS
INVOLVING
RUTHLESS
EXPLOITATION

(c)
WORLD-WIDE SPREAD
OF CIVILZATIONS:
HUBRIS AND
DEGENERATION
OF THE ENVIRONMENT
THAT WILL DOOM
CIVILIZATION

(d)
ULTIMATE FALL OF
CIVILIZATION

it is only inevitable to the extent that we do not understand the root cause of our parlous condition which is, quite simply, the fact that we are subhuman members of composite animals born out of a two-fold fall of humankind that caused them both to enslave and to destroy wild nature.

The relationship between *Homo degener* peoples and the wilderness they have domesticated is similar to that between lord and slave, a relationship which binds both inextricably together. Just as slavery debases both master and slave, just as the warder is imprisoned by his own jail, *Homo degener* is never free from the operation of the repression and confinement of wild nature. In their urban jungles it is now almost impossible for *Homo degener* peoples to recognize the pain they are inflicting upon wild nature. Yet just as the rapist shares the humiliation and the violation of the dignity of the victim, so the *Homo degener* rapists of *Homo sapiens* and the wilderness share the humiliation and violation of true human and natural dignity. The irony is that it is their own true natures they have turned against in fear and hatred. At the same time they are profoundly in love with their self-image as civilized beings – witness all the distinctions, artefacts and arts devoted to the glorification of *Homo degener* élites. While hatred never fails to destroy those who hate, those who are totally absorbed in the love of themselves are equally at risk. The commitment of *Homo degener* élites to socio-economic growth and the pursuit of perfection through the exploitation and repression of their fellows and of wild nature will carry them inexorably from murder to suicide.

Inevitably nature, and *Homo degener's* own real nature, are operating at every moment to undermine and destroy *Homo degener* nations. As nature strikes back, our confidence in our expertise and entrenched modes of adapting to change will, I believe, as surely assist our downfall. For the idea that technology can provide unlimited 'fixes' for all our ills is surely evidence of overweening confidence and pride. Scientists in particular would find great difficulty in admitting to the reality of civilization and of themselves as the end products of a two-fold fall of humankind, of a titanic failure as degenerate subhuman beings. Such an admission would be the ultimate humiliation, which the historical imperative persuades us to avoid at all costs. More than any other intellectual community, scientists are committed to the Ascent of *Homo degener* – witness the celebrations surrounding the award of Nobel Prizes for scientific advances, or the prestige attaching to the initials FRS after the name. However, such celebrations and evidence of heroic achievements are an illusion, and a product of the greatest delusion of all: that they are true human beings, heroes at the forefront of the proper evolutionary progress of humankind into the next century and beyond.*

The Captain of the *Titanic* was well warned of icebergs ahead as he steamed his 'unsinkable' ship across the Atlantic (1912) while his passengers danced through the night. We still celebrate the heroic and romantic aspects of its sinking rather than highlighting the denial of reality it represents. Similarly, despite the warnings of icebergs ahead, we cheerfully celebrate the progress of our monster Ship of State, called civilization, into the year 2000 and beyond – but how far beyond? In the absence of knowledge and understanding of the two-fold fall that our forbears sustained following the Mesolithic, in the denial of reality that that represents, we whose ancestors sowed the wind in the early Neolithic shall surely reap the whirlwind.

---

* See Appendix xx.

Chapter 5

Born to Be Wild

Without the hunter-gatherers, humanity is diminished and cursed; with them, we can achieve a more complete version of ourselves.

(Hugh Brody)[1]

As I pointed out in the Prologue, Arthur Koestler, seeking to explain man's apparently irresistible drift towards self-destruction, rightly intimates that the first step towards a possible therapy is a correct diagnosis of what went wrong with our species, and that the only really satisfactory diagnosis of the human situation is one which finds a basic cause operating throughout life, from the remote past to the present. This I have attempted, showing that *Homo sapiens* is not, as Koestler suggests, an aberrant biological species, an evolutionary misfit, but rather that, in their true colours as hunter-gatherer kings of natural food pyramids, they are evolutionary marvels. *Homo degener*, on the other hand, is an anti-evolutionary misfit.

In the hunter-gatherer life, seen on the verge of extinction today among the Bushmen and other remnants in the most marginal lands of the world, we observe 'the original affluent society': communities typified by minimal aggression, an ethic of resource-sharing, well balanced economic interdependence of the sexes that precludes male dominance, a physical and social intimacy that is unparalleled in more complex societies, an absence of hierarchy, and a lifestyle in which hours expended for a livelihood are far below averages for farming and industrial communities, leaving much of the time for socialisation and play. With the worldwide shift since the last Ice Age to a more intensive food-producing or farming economy, populations rise, and the new fixed investment, sown land, is the object of territorial defence and a focus for individual possessiveness,

507

together with the growing material possessions that a sedentary lifestyle permits. In the denser populated regions, competition for dwindling resources encourages social differentiation, and finally whole classes of rulers, entrepreneurs and exploited. Competition between communities for resources, and between élites for prestige and dominance over peasant populations, gives rise to mass warfare, and the abuse of prisoners and dissidents.[2]

Richard Leakey argues that these transformations are not illustrative of an innate tendency to aggression and selfishness, but cultural reactions to the potential of the farming economy and to population stresses.

As such, cultural not innate, they are, he maintains, within our power to reprogramme – we have a choice.[3]

If only *Homo degener* peoples could have readapted and reprogrammed their cultures and behaviour to that of hunter-gatherers while they were still in close contact with wild nature, what an enormity of pain the world would have been spared. Now the 'power to reprogramme' will necessitate firstly an acknowledgement of our subhuman status as component parts of anti-evolutionary composite animals driven by the historical imperative to overrun and exploit the wilderness, and secondly a fundamental, re-evolutionary, change in behaviour, including a return of the land to the hunter-gatherer peoples. For, as argued by Nelson Mandela,

An oppressive system cannot be reformed; it must be entirely cast aside.[4]

Homo degener's oppression of *Homo sapiens* and wild nature demands nothing less.

The Church and Science have been principal actors in the drive to dominate and exploit the wilderness. Our hunter-gatherer ancestors revered the Great Spirit of the wilderness and used their truly scientific knowledge to supply all their needs with the minimum of disturbance to the environment. We, on the other hand, built temples and cathedrals out of materials torn from the wilderness, and worshipped illusory Farmer Gods therein. Then, in the name of God, and with the aid of Science and technology, we issued forth from our national territaries to conquer and denude the wilderness of anything that might add to the status, wealth and well-being of our territaries. Science, with its cathedral-like nuclear power plants, missiles and moon-rockets, has now replaced the

Church as the provider and guarantor of our well-being and safety, and a principal force behind our ascent to the skies. Ours is the ascent of subhuman beings far removed from our original evolutionary path. Hence our Religions, Philosophies, Sciences and Laws are false, bearing no relation to the real world. We have destroyed the original world-wide reality and replaced it with the new 'realities' of our separate artificial domesticated homelands, wherein a pseudo-religion and pseudo-science are pursued by the intellectual élites of each nation, their cumulative assertions and inventions blindly accepted by the ignorant masses.

Universities have replaced the medieval church as the guardians of delivered truth. The fact that we take most information on trust, presented to us as truths by churchmen, historians, scientists, politicians and the Press, and accept it as an approximately accurate account of the world, makes no less false the basic premises upon which the whole edifice of civilization is raised up. They are indeed blind leaders of the blind. They are driven and drawn, not to truths but merely to shared delusions and fictions to which they tenaciously cling.

What Professor George Pilleri, of the University of Berne, Switzerland, said of captive dolphins and their study may equally be applied to captive *Homo degener* and the study of human behaviour:

> Whatever efforts are deployed, the keeping of cetaceans in captivity will always pose problems because of the inherent contradiction on which it is based: the keeping in cramped conditions of creatures which are accustomed to vast open spaces.
>
> For – even when the only purpose is scientific study – the animals are so physically and psychologically deformed in the process that any discoveries made are distorted and give a thoroughly inadequate picture of true behaviour in the wild.[5]

Similarly separated from vast open spaces, we are likewise physically and psychologically deformed, to make all scientific discoveries, and particularly those relating to human behaviour, equally distorted. Enclosed in their artificial make-believe worlds, scientists operate from false premises and therefore arrive at the wrong conclusions. Even if the scientist were to use the right means to solve our problems, he is nonetheless the wrong man. The truth of the matter is expressed in the old Chinese saying: 'If the wrong man uses the right means, the right means work in the wrong way!'

The solutions of scientists to any problem can only create other and more intractable problems.

The dreadful truth is that science has played a crucial rôle, often unwittingly, in the *creation* of our problems. This is glaringly obvious in the case of the nuclear arms race. But it is true of our other problems as well. Scientific and technological research make industrial development possible, which in turn creates pollution, depletes natural resources, destroys natural habitats and creates vast differences in wealth and power between different regions...[6]

The overall effect of the scientist's view of the world is well brought out in the following accusation by those forced to dwell on the forest floor, as it were. It is an accusation that is as relevant today as when it was first made.

The 1979 UN Conference on Science and Technology for Development was a court, at which science and technology (S & T) were on trial. The deprived and under-privileged section of humanity was the accuser. There were three main charges:

(1) S & T has ignored the basic needs of the majority of the world's population, and concentrated instead on luxury goods and services for the affluent few, and on military hardware and software to protect this affluence, thereby accentuating the inequalities between and within nations.

(2) S & T has created a skewed demand for skills requiring a few experts with sophisticated expertise for the planning and control of production, and a vast army of workers with the barest minimum of intelligence to execute plans, thereby concentrating power in the hands of experts, and undermining participation and control.

(3) S & T has produced environmental perturbations on a scale and in ways to which nature is totally unaccustomed, so that delicate ecological balances are threatened irreversibly, and perhaps, irremediably and catastrophically in the future.[7]

Within most developing countries, science and technology have consolidated and perpetuated dual societies by widening the gap between élites and masses; internationally science and technology has strengthened the old parasite pyramidal order by widening the gap between developed and developing nations, and between them and the kingdom of nature. A perverted memetic selection, that concentrates a wealth of knowledge, possessions and power at the top, causing a skewed demand for skills, indifference to the needs of the majority and accentuated inequalities within and between nations, is of the essence of pyramids of power.

For millennia small élite groups within nations lived very comfortably at the cost of those brutalized beneath them. Following the spread of European empires across the world, a small élite group of nations is now living very comfortably at the cost of millions of brutalized people in Third World nations living at starvation level, and at the cost of a ravaged wildlife and wilderness.

Far from being set free by their intelligence, as some scientists claim, people are more and more tightly bound in parasite pyramids by the intelligence of *Homo sapiens sapiens* élites at their summits. If the fundamental order of *Homo degener* societies has remained unchanged since the beginning, the pace of what is ironically described as the Ascent of Man has quickened, the inequalities grown more profound and the ecological balances of the world irreversibly threatened with the spread of stratified societies in the Northern Hemisphere across the world. For if the ascent of *Homo degener* is fundamentally an ascent out of the profound void of the Mesolithic and towards an ultimate tyranny or crisis, it is also an ascent away from the only true ground of the equality and freedom in ecological understanding of humankind, and a laying waste and tyrannous control of that self-same ground, to make people's blindness total.

> Man is conquering the diseases that once kept his population in check, and he is spreading his sway, exterminating other animals and exhausting the soil. With the same mentality that once enabled him to vanquish the lion and the bear, he is trying to subdue nature, sacrificing the eternal for the expedient. The destruction of the earth lies at his whim and cunning, yet he does not realise, does not feel, that he is not separate from but one with the plants and animals, rock and water. He is as dependent on them as the protozoan, the tsetse, and the gorilla. By setting himself apart from the ecological community man has become a tyrant of the earth, but a tyrant who surely will fall if he succeeds in winning the struggle for existence.[8]

The Supreme Judge of the world is not, as *Homo degener* might imagine, the Farmer God or Great Architect of nations that have subdued and destroyed the wilderness, but the Great Spirit, the natural flux and law. The Great Spirit is the architect, advocate and judge of the supreme good of the world. In their disobedience to and contempt of that Spirit, and destruction of the wilderness, there is no true good in civilizations whatsoever.

There is both a moral aspect to this disobedience to the Great Spirit and destruction of the wilderness, and an evolutionary aspect. From the moral standpoint, the nearest analogy of our destructive behaviour that comes to mind is that of the man who inherits a great country mansion, full of priceless furniture and works of art, and with many of its rooms occupied by members of his own family and relations, which he then proceeds relentlessly to raze to the ground, destroying his family and relations in the process. He would be adjudged evil, even criminally insane. Are we not similarly evil and insane? To steal the land, to destroy its aboriginal inhabitants, to raze the forests, to indulge in ruthless property development and to rape the Earth are acts of criminal folly. Nothing can wipe out 'the dark stain' surrounding the origins of the USA and of every other nation. We are both inherently conditioned by, and largely indifferent to, our past history of degenerate and delinquent behaviour – a conditioning and indifference which may be described as complicit evil. This is particularly the case in America, South Africa and Australia, where an endless, brutalizing occupation continues and where the reality of what has happened to the native hunter-gatherer peoples, and the related guilt, has long since been suppressed in white and black minds. All *Homo degener* peoples and cultures, together with their Farmer Gods and ideologies are, from the evolutionary standpoint of wild nature and the laws of nature, profoundly unlawful and malign. Furthermore, any attempts to rectify our parlous situation are inevitably nullified by our failure to understand that it is not as *Homo sapiens* that we seek to rectify our situation but as *Homo degener*.

The dilemma facing those who would do good is exemplified by the effects of the activities of Amnesty International. On the eve of its 30th birthday (1991) Amnesty was rightly praised for its 30 years record of success in obtaining freedom for prisoners of conscience, and for the fact that in the field of human rights Amnesty was taken far more seriously than the UN. Yet, as Amnesty itself has reported, methods of torture have become increasingly sophisticated and cruel, while extra-judicial killings and disappearances are increasing. Amnesty estimates that two-thirds of the world's population live in countries that torture and kill their citizens and half the world's countries imprison political opponents. Ironically, some of this brutality and barbarism may be due in part to the effectiveness of Amnesty's campaigns.

As in an arms race, Amnesty's very success may challenge governments to respond in increasingly devious and deadly ways. The spotlight on human rights has also meant some governments no longer arrest people – dissidents simply 'disappear'. Sadly, the choice for *Homo degener* is not between good and evil, right and wrong, but between degrees of evil.

Because all *Homo degener* peoples are the inheritors of the two-fold fall of humankind, of anti-evolutionary evil that has destroyed evolutionary good, all their supposedly good and right actions, hopes and ideals are fatally flawed: they are, to a greater or lesser extent, bad, evil and wrong, at all times and everywhere. The only true good of humanity lies with *Homo sapiens* hunter-gatherers, loyal and obedient to the Great Spirit. As I argued in Part II, Chapter 8, obedience to the natural flux and laws of nature, which thereby preserves the stability of biotic communities world-wide, constitutes the single supreme moral principle for humankind, an obedience attainable only by *Homo sapiens.*

As well as the moral aspect of the disobedience to the Great Spirit and destruction of the wilderness there is the evolutionary aspect. For *Homo degener* peoples are fast becoming the victims of their own machinations, of the accumulated revenge of their own real natures and of nature itself, which, as might be expected, is the proper outcome of a regressive re-evolutionary path. The present relationship of *Homo degener* to a ravished and despoiled nature is, in fact, very like that of the white hunter to the buffalo he has wounded.

> Like most other grazing animals, a wounded buffalo immediately rushes off in headlong flight, but unlike all the others, he almost invariably runs in a narrow circle, so that after a relatively short space of time he is back close to the point at which he was first wounded. This fact seems all too little known and, in most cases where a hunter has been killed following a wounded buffalo, the reports show that the hunter became the hunted, that he was attacked *from the rear* while his full attention was riveted on following a blood spoor in front of him.[9]

This is analogous to the plight of *Homo degener,* personified in the frighteningly optimistic priestly and scientific experts as they lead inexorably along a present aberrant anti-evolutionary path in pursuit of the prize of world stability and prosperity, by the slow bleeding to death of *Homo sapiens,* wildlife and wilderness. No society can survive which turns its back on its own evolutionary history. Not only did *Homo degener* peoples turn their backs upon the traditional hunter-gatherer cultures and societies, but they proceeded grievously to wound and destroy surviving members of that tradition and the traditional natural setting too. Like the buffalo, a retributive nature is surely even now in pursuit of *Homo degener* peoples, to destroy them. The reaction of nature in the long-term will be similar to that of natural humans – as when hunter-gatherers, such as the Indians of the North American Plains and the Aborigines, were provoked into attacking the alien European invaders of their paradisial lands. But whereas they failed, nature will succeed, for nature holds all the trumps. *Homo degener* peoples are fast becoming the victims of the accumulated revenge of their own real natures and of nature itself; this is the proper outcome of a regressive re-evolutionary path. All are the inheritors of anti-evolutionary evil that has destroyed evolutionary good. All must on that account be destroyed.

It is my contention that the only true, meaningful and good human life is that lived by the hunter-gatherers. They are human, whereas narcissistic so-called 'civilized' peoples, consumed as they are with a morbid self-admiration that persuades them to pursue superhuman status amongst the stars, are in reality subhuman oppressors of the world. Truth and time are on the side of the oppressed kingdom of nature and against the oppressor. Nature will triumph, for the natural world has fixed and immutable laws and is unforgiving of those who are contemptuous of, or break, those laws. Even if we do not succeed in destroying ourselves in internecine strife – which may also be seen as nature's revenge by way of our own degenerate natures* – nature will surely devise other means of retribution, such as the world-wide spread of a pathogen or a number of pandemics like AIDS. However, as earlier civilizations were destroyed by their over-exploitation and pollution of land once sacred to the hunter-gatherers, a more likely end of present civilization is a global degeneration to desert of the land and the poisoning of ourselves – a logical outcome of our degenerate behaviour, and our just deserts. For each nation, in seeking power and security through growth in wealth, must, like King Midas, turn everything it touches into gold, to make a desert of the world.

> Only after the last tree has been cut down
> Only after the last river has been poisoned
> Only after the last fish has been caught
> Only then will you find that money cannot be eaten.
>
> (Cree Indian Prophecy)

---

* It was said in October 2001 that we may now be involved in a war without end against terrorism. Terrorists, like the earlier hunter-gatherers who were provoked into attacking the alien European invaders of their paradisial lands, may be seen as the latterday instruments of nature operating to destroy *Homo degener* through internecine strife. Such strife arises principally, not because of poverty or lack of education, but – as pointed out in a *New Scientist* editorial (Vol. 182, No. 2447, 15 May 2004, p. 3) – because their territory has been invaded by an alien power. Such too is the basis of the war without end being waged by wild nature on *Homo degener*.

As for you and me in the immediate present, we can reveal to others the human reality as I have attempted to expound it in this book; support organizations such as Survival International, Greenpeace and Friends of the Earth in their efforts to stem the tide of degradation and destruction; drastically limit our families; and help persuade relevant governments to provide safe havens for the remnant of hunter-gatherers and other wildlife (in Canada, in the Democratic Republic of Congo, in Botswana, in Australia and elsewhere) whence they might one day emerge to regenerate the land. Furthermore, *Homo sapiens hunter-gatherers should be placed at the top of the Red List of endangered species.*

However, although our fundamentally exploitative and hostile relationship with wild nature can certainly be alleviated by the efforts of environmental pressure groups such as Greenpeace and Friends of the Earth, it will be no more than that. For *Homo degener* peoples are doomed by their inherent and self-defeating contradictions. For example, what remains of wilderness – whether as game reserves, national parks or reservations – has become a playground of the wealthy tourist, whose wilderness experience is undergirded by an immense logistical support system and consumption of energy, which is only made possible by an expanding industrial society, and which constitute a rapidly growing threat to the survival of the remaining wilderness. In addition, all such visitors – including scientific observers and exploiters of the wealth of the wilderness, and photographers whose images encourage tourism – are outsiders looking in on wildlife become commodities or playthings in a theme park. Such parks, together with zoos, are the ultimate degradation. Yet, sadly, game reserves provide the only refuges for a fast vanishing wildlife. They could, however, be made to serve a more honourable purpose if they were returned to the loving care of *Homo sapiens.* For it seems to be little understood that, as well as being degraded by *Homo degener,* the wilderness is deprived of much of its true significance in the absence of its wild human inhabitants – who were 'a highly significant variable' in the wild environment. Without them, the wildlife lacks the evolutionary pressures that helped make them what they are; without them, *'wildness',* which Henry Thoreau saw as the essential basis for 'the preservation of the world', is impossible.

So to suggest, as many do, that we should care for the future of our children and grandchildren by protecting the natural environment would be to miss the point entirely. As alien beings they should have no present and no future, no existence at all.

> Man hands on misery to man.
> It deepens like a coastal shelf.

Get out as early as you can,
And don't have any kids yourself.[10]

Only by refusing to bring more of our own subhuman kind into the
world can future generations be spared lives of increasing suffering and
of increasing degeneration as termite-like people.* Desmond Morris rightly
argues that

> We already know that if our populations go on increasing at their
> present terrifying rate, uncontrollable aggressiveness will become
> dramatically increased. This has been proved conclusively with
> laboratory experiments. Gross overcrowding will produce social stresses
> and tensions that will shatter our community organisations long
> before it starves us to death. It will work directly against improvements
> in intellectual control and will savagely heighten the likelihood of
> emotional explosion. Such a development can be prevented only by
> a marked drop in the breeding rate... To sum up then, the best
> solution for ensuring world peace is the widespread promotion of
> contraception or abortion...[11]

Whether or not we succeed in curbing population growth, the degenerative
anti-evolutionary process, an infinitely disadvantageous mutation, that
was set in train with the arrival of farming and domestication following
the Mesolithic, must soon end in the total annihilation of *Homo degener*
and perhaps of the world – unless we can learn in time to return the
land to hunter-gatherer peoples, and to offer ourselves to them as humble
pupils rather than arrogant destroyers. For the only redemption of
humankind is through a total love of, and return to, the wilderness.

In a Foreword to Sandy Gall's book *The Bushmen of Southern Africa,*
Prince Charles asks

> Who knows ... what ancient, traditional knowledge we may need
> to turn back to in the future for our very survival in a world sorely
> damaged by our own carelessness and folly? Will we not then curse
> the day we let slip the great store of Bushman wisdom and abandoned
> such a people to their destruction?[12]

It is my hope that governments, in the light of my hypothesis, may be

---

* See *The Machine Stops*, E.M. Forster's vision of humankind forced to live underground. The more
perfect the degeneration, the more closely *Homo degener* societies will resemble termitaries.

persuaded to protect the remnants of hunter-gatherer peoples, such as the San of the Kalahari, and the wildlife necessary to their survival, so that together they may form nuclei of evolutionary wildlife that may eventually expand throughout the world to replace *Homo degener*. For it is my belief that only those who tread lawfully and lightly upon the Earth as hunter-gatherers may inherit, for they alone can offer an optimum life-style, dignity, freedom and equality for all humankind. More importantly, they alone are true friends of the Earth. Only with their help and example may we develop a new understanding of the true purpose of our existence on this Earth.

Epilogue

Waiting at the Margin of the World

Daring to think the unthinkable is a necessary prelude to doing the impossible.

(Germaine Greer)[1]

Charles Darwin developed the theory of evolution, but he was unaware that he, and we, have stepped outside that process following a two-fold fall out of a highly developed hunter-gatherer way of life – revealed as a model of what it is to be human – into an anti-evolutionary path leading out of a primitive subsistence agriculture. The first farmers were the original alien invaders of planet Earth. Their subsequent advance over the last 12,000 years has so devastated the land as to threaten not only the survival of the original inhabitants of Earth but of themselves as well.

In 1966 some 75 scholars, social anthropologists, human biologists, archaeologists and ecologists participated in the *Conference on Man the Hunter*, held at the University of Chicago. The results are embodied in *Man the Hunter*. Part of the opening paragraphs of the introduction reads as follows:

Cultural Man has been on earth for some 2,000,000 years; for over 99 per cent of this period he has lived as a hunter-gatherer. Only in the last 10,000 years has man begun to domesticate plants and animals, to use metals, and to harness energy sources other than the human body...

To date, the hunting way of life has been the most successful and persistent adaptation man has ever achieved. Nor does this evaluation exclude the present precarious existence under the threat of nuclear annihilation and the population explosion. It is still an open question whether man will be able to survive the exceedingly

518

complex and unstable ecological conditions he has created for himself. If he fails in this task, interplanetary archaeologists of the future will classify our planet as one in which a very long and stable period of small-scale hunting and gathering was followed by an apparently instantaneous efflorescence of technology and society leading rapidly to extinction. 'Stratigraphically', the origin of agriculture and thermo-nuclear destruction will appear as essentially simultaneous.[2]

Fewer and fewer true hunter-gatherers remain. They have largely disappeared in India and Australia, though there are a few beleaguered enclaves of them in Canada, South America, Africa and the Far East. This process is seen as an inevitable progression from a mode of subsistence which is too primitive to be viable in the modern world, a stage of evolution which must eventually disappear. It is a notion shared by decision-makers in both national governments and industry, many of whose members stand to gain from the incorporation of hunter-gatherers into local and national economies. In places, such as North America, hunter-gatherers are struggling to retain the essentials of their culture. For example, the Dene of the Northwest Territories of Canada have been struggling for independence and self-determination as a nation of hunter-gatherers within the country of Canada, encouraging within the Dene nation government by the people rather than representative government. The James Bay Cree have instigated a similar programme 'to avoid extinction or assimilation and to create new, viable and relatively autonomous forms of hunting societies'.[3]

Sol Tax, the Chairman of the *Conference on Man the Hunter*, referred to the still extant groups of hunter-gatherers in his final words:

> ...we should study the reasons for the persistence of these peoples all over the world in the light of all the conditions militating against their persistence. I think that the case of the North American Indians is especially significant. They seem to be waiting for us to go away...[4]

Germaine Greer has made some particularly trenchant observations concerning the future of Australia which are relevant. She does not wish to purge the taint of European conquest by giving back the country to the Aborigines because it isn't theirs to give, but rather to admit that it has been an Aboriginal country all along.

> As a hunter-gatherer nation, Australia could play a further rôle in world affairs by making common cause with other hunter-gatherer

peoples, all of whom are taking a terrible hammering. Most are isolated from the mainstream, as presently Aborigines are; the emergence on the world stage of a hunter-gatherer nation, with policy aims and initiatives that are consonant with hunter-gatherer values, could be a lifeline for such peoples, and provide useful precedents in their struggle to protect country, heritage and habitat from annihilation.[5]

People are only truly stable, truly efficient and truly human ranging freely as hunter-gatherers in a world treated lovingly and unpossessively as no man's land in obedience to the Great Spirit – therein lies the true immortality of the species.

Understand what the world is waiting for. It is waiting for those who love it enough, who care enough for wild nature, to release it from bondage.

I do not want your laughter,
I want your tears.
So weep and water the Earth with your tears
that together we may wash
the mountains of people and their polluting ways
into the sea.

Then will be the time for laughter,
When the deep imprints of our passage are wilderness once more,
And people hear again the call of the Great Spirit
To tread lightly through the land.
Then may we laugh
And sing the songs of the Earth.

(Peter Prew)

APPENDICES

Appendix i

The Loss of Environmental Sensitivity

The dog is the first animal to have been tamed, if not domesticated, in the service of humankind. According to Helmut Hemmer,[1] it is most likely descended from the most primitive and small brained of wolves, the southern wolves from the Arabian Peninsula and South Asia, and spread throughout North Asia, North America and Europe with our hunter-gatherer ancestors. All other domestic animals originated within sedentary farming communities, and, with the exception of cattle descended from the aurochs, are descended from the most primitive and particularly small brained of their species. This is apparently the case for the cat, the pig, the sheep, the horse and the goat. Furthermore, in every case the brain sizes of the domesticated animal were even smaller than those of their wild progenitors, and in every case there has been a loss of what Helmut Hemmer describes as 'environmental appreciation',[2] and which I have described in the case of de-ranged people as the loss of environmental sensitivity and ecological understanding.

Environmental appreciation includes an animal's perception through the use of all its sensory organs and brain of all the features of its environment, while also evaluating what it perceives in the light of its memory. From this standpoint, Hemmer argues that the environmental appreciation of domestic animals appears to be characteristically reduced by comparison with that of their wild ancestors. Broadly speaking, domestic animals live less intensely than wild ones. Hemmer explains the basis of their decline in environmental appreciation as follows:

> ... domestication of mammals as a general rule involved a fairly considerable reduction in the brain size. That the neocortex would have to be affected most due to its general relation to the whole brain has been directly confirmed in all species on which quantitative studies of individual brain areas have been carried out. The reduction

in storage capacity and complexity of interconnections must without doubt affect information processing in this system. Changes in information processing in turn correspond to a change in environmental appreciation that is fed with all kinds of stimulus... So the structural alterations to the brain and sensory organs during domestication can be interpreted as the morphological results of a selection for decline in environmental appreciation, attenuation of behaviour, and lower reactivity.[3]

Hemmer's studies are concerned with the brain sizes of the various species of domestic animals relative to those of their wild ancestors. They show not only that, in species with distinct differences in brain size between geographically separate populations, domestication began in each case with just that population having the smallest brain size within its species, but also that the phenomenon of brain size reduction occurred as a general rule during domestication. By analogy, the domestication of people most likely took place amongst the comparatively less progressive, smaller-brained of the species. Furthermore, in the light of Hemmer's conclusions in relation to domestic animals generally, it is likely that domesticated people also suffered not only a decline in environmental sensitivity but too in brain size. The subsequent cultivation of *Homo sapiens sapiens* as thinking head on the backs of *Homo sapiens non sapiens** would slowly have reversed the process of brain reduction, as in the case of domestic animals bred for special performance.

> Dogs highly bred for special performance, such as watchdogs or sheepdogs, have distinctly larger brains than primitive breeds. The same seems to be the case for European thoroughbred horses. In such cases, where learning ability or memory acquired positive selection value, the original process of brain reduction during domestication has been reversed.[4]

In both the case of *Homo sapiens sapiens* and of animals bred for special performance, the selection process involved is an artificial or perverted cultural selection.

---

*See Part I, Chapter 5 (and figures 5.1a, 5.1b) in which I differentiate between *Homo sapiens*, meaning true human being evolved as hunter-gatherer; *Homo sapiens sapiens*, meaning degenerate, cultivated, knowledgeable human being (high grade intellectual or landowning status) imprisoned within an agricultural/industrial social pyramid; and *Homo sapiens non sapiens*, meaning degenerate cultivator or labourer without knowledge (low grade manual work status) imprisoned at the base of the social pyramid.

Appendix ii

The Loss of a Primary Memory

In human beings there appear to be at least two 'layers' of memory which are used in different contexts. There is a short-term memory that is used for the temporary retention of small items of information, such as a telephone number which is looked up in a directory and retained until the number is dialled. If, however, the number is used often enough, or there is a strong motive for retaining it, it will be transferred into the long-term or primary memory. It would appear from studies of ordinary memory that what is ordered, interesting, meaningful and often repeated is more easily remembered. Random sequences of numbers and letters are much harder to retain. Most important, memory that is disorientated is liable to be destroyed.

Homo sapiens hunter-gatherers evolved in an ordered, harmonious and meaningful setting, inheriting a long-term memory and ecological understanding attuned to millions of years of infinitely slow evolution in obedience to the natural flux. When climate change de-ranged so many, that primary memory, and the mode and setting in which that memory was handed down and inherited, was destroyed. How catastrophic can be a decline in memorization was shown by George Steiner:

Scriptural and, in a wider sense, religious literacy (during the 17th, 18th and 19th centuries) ran strong, particularly in Protestant lands. The Authorised Version and Luther's Bible carried in their wake a rich tradition of symbolic, allusive and syntactic awareness. Absorbed in childhood, the Book of Common Prayer, the Lutheran Hymnal and Psalmody, cannot but have marked a broad compass of mental life with their exact, stylised articulateness and music of thought. Habits of communication and schooling, moreover, sprang directly from the concentration of memory. So much was learned and known *by heart* – a term beautifully apposite to the organic, inward presentness of meaning and spoken being within the individual spirit. The catastrophic decline of memorization in our own modern education and adult resources is one of the crucial, though as yet little understood, symptoms of an after-culture...

Concentric to these spheres of 'book-knowledge' lies a personal, unforced intimacy with the names and shapes of the natural world, with flower and tree, with the measure of the seasons and the rising and setting of the stars. The principal energies of our literature draw constantly on this set of recognitions. But to our housed, metallic sensibilities they have become largely artificial and decorative. Do not, today, inquire of the reader next to you whether he can identify, from personal encounter, even a part of the flora, of the astronomy, which served Ovid and Shakespeare, Spenser and Goethe, as a current alphabet.[1]

What then of the current alphabet of all the elements, flora and fauna of the kingdom of nature that served the hunter-gatherers? How much more catastrophic was the decline in memorization when these people lost their common secret language of nature, ecological understanding and identities as hunter-gatherers? For our memories, as the amnesiac discovers all too painfully, are deeply linked with our sense of identity and with every meaningful relationship to the surrounding world. Continuity of memory, beliefs and attitudes is crucial to personal identity.

The whole existence of *Homo sapiens* was a concentration of memory in movement as kings of natural food pyramids. *All* was learned and known *by heart*. Their memories, that thrived on natural imagery and associations, were deeply linked with a sense of identity integrated within the greater family of the kingdom of nature, and with every meaningful relationship to that surrounding world, so giving the hunter-gatherers a very definite and exciting place in the universe. When that world collapsed for some into a meaningless chaos of waters, forest and sand, obliteration of a primary memory would have been accompanied by a painful loss of identity. Once this had been replaced by a de-ranged agricultural identity, such as that of dominant priest-scientist or lowly cultivator, and by myths of a new Creation, truth became what was told by those in control of the organs of information feeding the new 'after-cultures'. The new de-ranged identity, together with the earlier loss of a hunter-gatherer identity, combined to destroy utterly the peoples' memory of the past, obliterating dreams and expectations that came from a time when people could control their own destinies as hunter-gatherers. To borrow an apt phrase of George Steiner, who applied it to the rebuilding of Europe after the cataclysm of the Second World War: 'It is as if a violent instinct of effacement and renewal had prevailed, a creative amnesia'.[2]

A primary memory common to all hunter-gatherers began to be replaced by the long-term memories of the separate nations, in particular by myths that served as the birth certificate or foundation charter of the societies in which they were told, when 'the real journey to the cave sanctuary becomes the journey to Hades, the Land of No Return'.[3] In other words, an individual evolutionary memory as *Homo sapiens* was replaced by the collective long-term memory – the 'memory grown automatic', based on myths such as those of a Fall and new Creation – of the nation, binding each generation of members to the nation. Thereafter, what was learned and known by heart related to 'book-knowledge' and to the seasons and natural world as these were experienced and celebrated by people imprisoned within the confines of national hierarchies. The increasing mechanization, and artificiality, of national environments has been accompanied by an erosion of 'book-knowledge' and of the natural world, and a degradation of memorization down the millennia, arising directly from the loss of a primary memory, and related divorce from, and destruction of, wild nature. Their literature, however beautiful and great, has unwittingly celebrated that divorce. From an evolutionary standpoint, literature, together with other artefacts and arts of de-ranged societies, have formed the grounds of a false memorization and of regression. True literature, memorization and progress obtain within the evolutionary setting of wild nature. As pointed out so poignantly by a Stoney Indian, Tatanga Mani:

> Civilized people depend too much on man-made printed pages. I turn to the Great Spirit's book which is the whole of his creation. You can read a big part of that book if you study nature. You know, if you take all your books, lay them out under the sun, and let the snow and rain and insects work on them for a while, there will be nothing left. But the Great Spirit has provided you and me with an opportunity for study in nature's university, the forests, the rivers, the mountains, and the animals which include us.[4]

Appendix iii

A Cognitive Barrier

Steven Mithen[1] has argued that when a modern child is born its mind is already hard-wired with information about the structures of the real world, together with separate content-rich mental modules containing a multitude of rules for solving problems. These include modules that come into action immediately at birth, such as modules for eye contact with the mother. Young children would appear to have intuitive knowledge in at least four domains of behaviour, all evolved during the hunter-gatherer way of life: language, psychology, physics and biology. For example, research in child development has shown that children appear to be born with an intuitive awareness that living things and inanimate objects are fundamentally different.

Children are thus born with what Mithen describes as a 'blueprint' for the structures of the living world hard-wired into their minds. He suggests that, in the evolutionary environment of hunter-gatherers, those individuals born with content-rich mental modules to facilitate the acquisition of natural history knowledge would have had a substantial selective advantage. The same may be said of the other aspects of intuitive knowledge. With the advent of agriculture, however, all such knowledge, as it applied to evolution in movement within the wild environment, was effectively nullified amongst sedentary farmers.

Given that their brains and their sensory apparatus were dis-integrated from their original evolutionary integration and function as hunter-gatherers, the sensory apparatus of de-ranged farmers fell into desuetude. A cognitive barrier rose up between the social and natural worlds, fundamentally changing their interaction with the wilderness and with other humans. Because of the plasticity of early brain development, and because the cultural context in which a child develops affects the type of mental and behavioural domains that arise, children who had lost contact with the evolutionary outlets of their innate knowledge (as hunter-gatherers) were forced to develop

528

cognitive domains related to knowledge necessary to survive and prosper within the new agricultural/industrial settings. Given what Mithen describes as 'the cognitive fluidity' of the modern mind,

> ... the hard-wired intuitive knowledge within the minds of growing infants may have 'kick-started' new types of specialized cognitive domains. For instance, a young child growing up in an industrial setting may no longer have developed a 'natural history intelligence'. Instead, in some contexts, a specialized domain for mathematics may have developed, kick-started by certain features of 'intuitive physics', even though no prehistoric hunter-gatherer had ever developed such a domain.[2]

In such ways the adaptation to agriculture opened the way to the purely intellectual pursuits so common to de-ranged élites, enabling and encouraging the ascent of those I describe as knowledgeable *Homo sapiens sapiens* cultivated on the backs of *Homo sapiens non sapiens*, the cultivators without knowledge, in pursuit of wealth and power at the summits of stratified societies.* *Homo sapiens sapiens* minds, singly or combined, at the summits sought to regulate and control members of stratified societies and the natural world. As societies developed, these systems of regulation and control gave rise to a variety of branches of knowledge and associated institutions – such as those concerned with astronomy and astrology.

So minds that had earlier evolved integrated in equality in movement within the wilderness now erected cognitive barriers between themselves and that world and proceeded to select – often through hereditary descent, and later through the medium of schools and universities – for the kind of highly specialized intellectual élites that are met with in universities today. The mass of men and women who have not been so selected have fulfilled minor intellectual rôles, or have been employed in physical rôles, as in the mining and agricultural industries. Such a polarization between psyche and physique, between those involved in primarily intellectual activities and those involved in primarily physical activities, has helped make for an extraordinary inequality amongst members of stratified societies.

In evolutionary terms, the effect of such selection has been profound. Natural selection – which, under the overall governance of the natural flux, was the most important architect of the minds and bodies of *Homo sapiens* – has been overruled by knowledgeable *Homo sapiens sapiens* élites of stratified societies, arbiters of what may be described as a perverted cultural selection that functions in direct opposition to the earlier

---

* See Part I, Chapter 5 (and figures 5.1a, 5.1b) and Appendix i.

evolutionary processes through which the minds of *Homo sapiens* had originally evolved.* The inevitable outcome of such a perverted cultural selection has been the intellectual stimulation of the minds of the *Homo sapiens sapiens* few, while those of the *Homo sapiens non sapiens* mass of mankind have, like their sensory apparatus, atrophied, making them mindless, emasculated men susceptible to manipulation and control.

As well as the dichotomy between farmer and hunter-gatherer, and the dualism between those involved in primarily intellectual activities and those involved in primarily physical activities, there also occurred a dualism in the minds of the governing Homo sapiens sapiens *élites of societies.*

A further profound effect of the dis-integration of the brain and sensory apparatus from their evolutionary integration and function as hunter-gatherers, and the subsequent hierarchical polarization between psyche and physique, between dominant *Homo sapiens sapiens* agents and subservient *Homo sapiens non sapiens* workers, has been the effect on the brain itself and consequently between men, women and the wilderness. Leonard Shlain[3] has argued that, generally speaking, the two hemispheres of the brain are opposite and complementary in their function: the left hemisphere is more concerned with speech, with action, with doing, and its agent, the right hand, fashions and operates tools; while the right hemisphere is concerned with being in space, imagery, dreams, metaphor and music. These correspond to a hunter/killer and gatherer/nurturer strategy respectively. However, each man also has a gatherer/nurturer aspect to his psyche, just as each woman has a hunter/killer aspect to hers. The demands of the environment accentuate one or the other of these two ways of interacting with the world.

When all humankind lived in the wild environment, the brains of both men and women were in harmony with the demands of their respective hunting and gathering occupations – they obeyed and fulfilled the evolutionary demands of the Great Spirit and Earthmother. There was no dualism, no duality in the brains of either sex. With their adaptation to agriculture they lost most of their hunter-gatherer characteristics and a cognitive barrier rose up between the social and natural worlds. Their brains now functioned in the new sedentary agricultural situation which, as Shlain has pointed out, is governed by principles which are feminine. For the process of planting seeds, tending their germination and growth and eventually harvesting the products of the Earth symbolized impregnation and gestation. The imagery of the female as life-giver was strengthened with the need to encourage herds

---

* See Part II, Chapters 1 and 2, for a development of this argument in terms of a perverted cultural selection seen as a perverted memetic selection.

of domestic animals to be fertile. As fecundity and fertility became farming society's most valued attributes, so societies developed religious symbols that expressed these, their profoundest concerns. Images of a Great Goddess appeared c.7000 BC in the Fertile Crescent and spread, with the spread of agriculture, around the Mediterranean and into Europe and Siberia. She was venerated for some 5,000 years. However, as I argued in Part I, in contradistinction to the Earthmother symbolizing a wealth of natural food pyramids, the Great Goddess symbolized the fertility of the farmer's domestic animals and fields. Even though she reigned at first over the relatively harmonious, egalitarian, agricultural societies, they were not of course in harmony with the wild world, but rather continuously at war with that world as they expanded their settlements over the land. It was a war waged primarily by the male members of these societies.

Deprived of the hunter/killer strategy originally involving the left hemisphere of the brain and associated with hunting, imprisoned in a primarily feminine setting, the hunter/killer urge was frustrated and underwent a 'drastic psychological reprogramming'.[4] Needing to protect his home, his harvest, his animals and his land from the depradations of wild animals and of men, and needing to expand his settlement to provide for a growing population, the farmer became a hunter/killer of animals and of men that threatened the survival of his settlement or stood in the way of its expansion. With the growth of settlements, the frustrated and redirected hunter/killer traits of the male – arising mainly in the left brain of doing, of action – were devoted to the building of walls, architecture, irrigation schemes, the deployment of armed men and the development of administrative functions necessary to the growth and government of their rudimentary stratified societies.

The fundamental dualism in the minds of farmers as between their settlements regarded as friendly and good, and the wilderness as hostile and evil, was now reinforced in the minds of the ruling classes risen upon the backs of the cultivators. For with the accretion of possessions and power on the one hand, and on the other the growth in the number and variety of potential humiliating threats to their possessions and power, both from within their societies and from without, the dualism between order and chaos, good and evil took on a new dimension and became the subject of religious sanctions.

Slowly, with the aid of the revolutionary invention of literacy, the patriarchal warrior-dominator rose up. At the same time, the male Farmer God – or a male dominated religion – was installed, over a 2,000 year period, in place of the Goddess. This occurred in both the West and the East. It occurred because of the reinforced or two-fold dualism in the brains of the ruling classes, whereby the males at the summits of stratified societies used their left hunter/killer hemispheres to secure and strengthen their elevated positions against perceived threats to humiliate and eclipse them, using their Farmer God and writing to enhance and secure their status as sacred. The two-fold dualism in the minds of the ruling class was one between knowledge of their settlements, and now also of themselves, as sacred and good, and of the threatening 'other' – the masses, women sub-consciously equated with wild nature, other stratified societies and the wilderness – as potentially or outright evil. This led to a diminution on the part of the ruling classes in the use of their right gatherer/nurturer hemispheres. It profoundly affected the status and treatment of women, who comprise some 50 per cent of the world's population.

However, with the advent on the stage of history of the invisible monotheistic male Farmer God of the Israelites (whose Commandments were communicated by means of alphabet writing in the Bible), the effects of the reinforced dualism in the brains of the ruling classes believing in Him increased dramatically, being nothing short of revolutionary and catastrophic. For, as Shlain points out, monotheism, divorced from any concrete image, is an extremely abstract concept. Such an abstract God, whose presence and words have been revealed through the left-brain masculine activity of alphabet writing in a variety of books, like the Bible and the Quran, has given rise to a great number of different interpretations of His being and His message by different peoples down the millennia. Each nation that has officially embraced the male monotheistic Farmer God has tended to interpret His words in ways that have self-righteously served its own interests, in effect making for as many different monotheistic Farmer Gods as there are nations that have embraced Him! Religious and ideological differences, and the associated self-righteousness of each protagonist, added new dimensions to a dualism, already millennia old, following that arising between farmer and wilderness, and to ever more devastating wars between them.

If the skulls of the people who have been killed in the name of God, Jesus, and Allah in religious wars and persecutions could be piled in one place, they would form an immense mountain.[5]*

---

*It is ironical that the truly sacred and holy land – the wild world of *Homo sapiens* hunter-gatherers – was seldom if ever fought over by *Homo sapiens*, whereas that which is described as the Holy Land – which is holy to the three great monotheistic religions, Judaism, Christianity and Islam – is arguably the most fought over region in the world. The wars that have raged across the Holy Land following the Israelite conquest of Canaan have included the Babylonian, Macedonian and Roman conquests, the Muslim Arab and Crusader conquests, the Muslim reconquest and six subsequent Crusades that failed to dislodge them, the Turkish and British conquests, the Israeli War of Independence and the subsequent Arab-Israeli Wars.

Appendix iv

Prisoners in Conflict

The behaviour of farmers imprisoned in an alien wilderness may be compared with that of monkeys imprisoned in a zoo. The behaviour of monkeys in the wild is vastly different from that of monkeys incarcerated in zoos. In the wild, every monkey forages for itself, and such competition as there is takes place within an overall co-operation, harmony and balance. The place of a monkey in its group, the relationship between one group and another, and between groups and the environment, are normally in equilibrium. If the overall balance both within and without the group is drastically and unnaturally altered by man, the resulting uncertainty and redirection of responses may be extreme.

Solly Zuckerman has argued that

Feeding is a field of behaviour in which the effects of artificial conditioning are obvious... It is conceivable that an assured and constant supply of food has important effects upon the behaviour of captive animals, since it provides leisure that would otherwise have been expended in foraging over a large tract of country. An excess of energy may therefore be liberated for expression in other channels, and sexual behaviour may perhaps be intensified...

It is also possible that captive conditions modify fighting behaviour. Confined to a small area animals cannot separate from one another as they would in a natural environment. A baboon worsted in a fight is unable to escape from his aggressors. An animal not dominant enough to maintain himself and his harem in a large herd cannot succeed in retaining his females by avoiding contact with his fellows, as he might in a wild state. These considerations suggest that fights may often be carried much farther in captivity that they would in nature. This, however, adds to their interest. From the point of view of the observer, confinement concentrates a normal response both temporally and spatially.[1]

Confinement may also cause such responses to be radically displaced and redirected, as when frustrated aggression turns into aggression against infants and against the self – into attacks of self-mutilation.

Zuckerman has shown what happened to a troop of 100 hamadryas baboons forcibly removed from their natural habitat in Africa in 1925 and enclosed in the London Zoo. Overcrowded, with many more males than females, there was no chance to form their regular groups, which in the case of baboons usually consist of one male with several females and their young. Naturally aggressive, the males were bound to fight over the females and over which should dominate. Stronger males also threatened, and seized food from, the weaker, both male and female; females behaved selfishly towards their young, even snatching food from their very hands. These were animals which lacked space (a band of monkeys in the wild normally roams an area of several square miles, whereas the London Zoo baboons had to make do with an area of 660 square metres), whose principal drives were frustrated and who, unable to attack their captors and unable to escape, were forced to redirect their responses against their own kind. Within two years the original population of 100 had been reduced, through fights and disease, to 56. In 1927 the population was augmented by a new batch of 30 adult females and five immature males. Within a month 15 females were killed as the males fought over them. By 1930 eight males and 30 females had died from fight related injuries. Of the 15 baboons born to the colony, all but one died, many from injuries received, and mostly within six months of birth. And though, as Zuckerman observed, the colony settled down in a state of balance following serious fights which ended in the death of the female round which it raged, it was a balance which, as revealed by subsequent events, contained all the seeds of further disruption.

Baboons seldom behave in the wild with the ferocity these animals showed in the abnormal conditions of their captivity. The extent to which their behaviour differs from that of free-ranging monkeys may be gauged from observations by Claire and W.M.S. Russell,[2] who collated accounts of some 15 species in the wild and of approximately half that number of the same species in various forms of confinement such as zoos. Amongst monkeys living relaxed and contented lives in the wild quarrelling is seldom seen and violence is virtually unknown. In the stress of captivity the reverse is the case, with violence sometimes leading to serious injury and even death. These differences between behaviour in the wild and in the zoo, which amount to a complete reversal of all social life and behaviour, are common to all the species observed.

Similarly, the behaviour of people forcibly de-ranged as farmers and imprisoned in enclaves was atypically competitive and savage by comparison with the co-operative altruistic behaviour of the generality of people as *Homo sapiens* hunter-gatherers. Compare their situation with that of the Ika people of Uganda, who were forcibly amputated from their hunting grounds by Government edict. The Ika are a mountain people whose habitat lies in that part of Africa where Uganda, Kenya and the Sudan converge and border each other. They are farmers who also hunted – that is, until 1962, when the Ugandan Government designated their main hunting area as a National Park, forcing them to settle as subsistence farmers in one corner of their former territory. The subsequent life of the Ika, like that of other peoples in the Karamoja province of Uganda, was completely dominated by the search for food and the avoidance of starvation during the periods of serious droughts which strike the area every five years or so.

Colin Turnbull[3] has shown what happens when people such as the Ika are forcibly de-ranged – i.e. prevented from ranging freely as hunter-gatherers – and divorced from their earthly paradise. Denied their traditional hunting economy under circumstances of drought, the Ika were forced to adjust to a primitive subsistence agriculture as their sole source of survival in the stony uplands of northeastern Uganda. They starved. All altruistic and humanitarian behaviour disappeared in the fight to be the one to survive. They lost their traditional structure of relationships. Turnbull describes a living purgatory where hunger, greed and callousness completely replaced love, goodness, altruism and co-operation. The Ika were reduced to a primitive and ignoble savagery as subsistence farmers. They were old at twenty. Only the cleverest of predators upon their fellows survived. Their behaviour had in fact become similar to the famine behaviour common in other people living in the Karamoja province. Amongst these parents are often forced by severe famine either to abandon their young children or exchange them for money or food.

Turnbull shows that the enforced loss of a sovereign identity and freedom in movement as hunter-gatherers, followed by extreme poverty and starvation where basic human values are abandoned and nothing counts but survival, corrupts absolutely. As he points out, the nearest analogy to the Ika society experienced today by Western man is the culture of the concentration camp. In the case of the Ika, as in the case of a concentration camp, it will be appreciated that the principal agent frustrating freedom of movement and causing a crisis or loss of identity is the imprisoning force at the boundary of their prison, be it the Ugandan Government in the case of the Ika or Nazi guards and barbed wire in the case of a German concentration camp. Caught between fight and flight, unable either to attack or to flee, wild animals herded under similar circumstances are liable to engage both in conflict behaviour and in outright conflict against their fellows. It is likely in the case of the early Neolithic farmers imprisoned by wilderness that food and sex, then status and property, became major sources of conflict. Small groups of inmates may have begun to acquire power over their fellows, thereby acquiring new identities or status over them. They began to climb, as it were, on the backs of their fellows the better to keep their heads above water, moving away in the vertical from cultural and economic poverty and from the now frightening unknown without; under such circumstances only the cleverest of predators upon their fellows survived to attain even a short-lived prime. Others may in addition have turned to head-hunting, human and animal sacrifice and cannibalism. Homicide became the norm in Europe, while in the East Indies primitive subsistence farmers have customarily made good their deficiencies of identity and diet with head-hunting and cannibalism. Yet others, like the Indians of North America when they were forcibly de-ranged and imprisoned on reservations in the 19th century, probably sought to insulate themselves from their present personal and environmental hells in alcohol and drugs. All such in-fighting and predatory behaviour, alcohol addiction and drug-taking are further evidence of mixed displacement activities and redirected responses on the part of people whose principal drives were frustrated by their enforced de-rangement, dehumanization and transformation of the outside world into a hostile environment. In every case, the lives of these primitive, ignorant and ignoble savages born in captivity, as compared with those of hunter-gatherers born free, were nasty, brutish and short.

Perhaps the apogee of the redirected responses of de-ranged men was the arrival of one man at the top of the heap as dictator. Amongst monkeys made captive in a zoo, under sufficient crowding stress, dictatorship of the many by one powerful individual is a commonplace observation. By contrast, the form never found in relaxed wild conditions is arbitrary dictatorship by a single individual. Similarly, tyranny of the one over the many would now become a predominant feature amongst people made captive in (overcrowded) hierarchically ordered farming communities, a condition unheard of amongst small bands of free-ranging hunter-gatherers. Fear in crowded, prison-like, conditions brings tyrants into power. Rendered helpless, powerless in a powerful, threatening land, de-ranged people were the victims of a collective, contagious fear, throwing up tyrants who could play on that fear – and thereafter also on fears of neighbours, of upheavals, of other tribes and so on – thus permitting them to exercise extraordinary power over their fellows and over nature and to take extreme measures which then became part of the culture. The dictatorship and tyranny of Saddam Hussein of Iraq is only one example of a system of government that has been the general rule down history throughout the world. The tyrants of the 20th century alone were responsible for the deaths of more than one hundred million people.

When de-ranged people did eventually acquire the collective strength and technology to spread across the world, they did so by cutting down the forests ahead of them. They advanced by pushing outwards the walls or frontiers of their prison-like enclaves, to make them less like prisons and more like 'home'. But they have always remained prisons to the oppressed majorities of stratified societies.

In more recent times, artists and writers, like Hogarth, Swift and Dickens, have made us aware of the extent to which the structure of society constitutes, at both physical and psychical levels, a prison which we may accept – particularly if we are comfortably placed as warders – or attempt to escape. But in the latter case it is an attempt that never succeeds. We carry the seeds of our imprisonment around with us always, ready to germinate in a new environment, as happened with the white invaders of North America and Australia. Within our prison-like societies we can everywhere observe those forced to the bottom of the heap savaging one another, just as do baboons and macaques in the abnormal, overcrowded conditions of captivity.

In the USA, for instance, young American blacks in many cities are at violent odds with a prosperous, white American establishment. In Los Angeles black youths live in abject poverty and naked filth, while a few miles away are palm trees and houses built like Spanish farmhouses with neat lawns. Inextricably stuck with their lives of incurable poverty, they savage one another rather than the common enemy, the whites, and are possessed of a barely restrained desire to burn something down. When they do and are caught, they do not care whether they are in jail or outside, for it is all the same to them.

Violence, riot, theft and other forms of crime all provide varying degrees of status and excitement to those who, in their prison-like predicament in cities throughout the world, are without jobs, without money or prospects, and are powerless, hopeless, desperate and deeply vulnerable – as powerless, desperate and deeply vulnerable as were their subsistence farmer forbears.

It will be appreciated that we have come full circle: in destroying the wilderness, true home of humankind, we have created an urban jungle, a man-made wilderness as frightening as was its natural counterpart. The threat of the urban jungle – and in particular the threat from terrorists

– has replaced that of the earlier wilderness in which de-ranged men were imprisoned as primitive subsistence farmers, and again as colonists when Europeans settled in North America and felt themselves threatened by the Native American inhabitants, against whom they erected a string of forts. Today it is the rich upper and middle classes who are incarcerating themselves behind gates and high walls against the threat of the (criminal) poor outside, just as the rich nations in the North are raising barriers against immigrants from the poorer South. In America alone, some eight million Americans now live behind gates and walls in what are described as 'gated communities', while a further 50 million Americans live in security zones known as common-interest developments (CIDs). Meanwhile, some two million American criminals are in custody, just as earlier the Native Americans were incarcerated on reservations. In short, growing numbers of American citizens are imprisoned – and self-imprisoned – in what has been described as Fortress America, evincing a conflict behaviour that is inherent in the de-ranged condition.

Appendix v

The Deprivation of Love

As well as the analogies of the prison and the zoo,* there are other analogies which may be used to reveal the condition of de-ranged men in relation to the wilderness. For in addition to being physically and psychically imprisoned in a situation of stalemate, a situation of frustrated fight and flight, these were also forcibly de-ranged peoples who were, as it were, not only orphaned, the victims of multiple deprivation, including deprivation of the love of the Great Spirit and Earthmother,† but also illegitimate and physically and psychically deformed. The effect on their minds and imaginations, and so on their behaviour, may be likened to that of children deprived of parental love, and/or imprisoned through illness or physical deformity and/or born bastards. In every case those involved have been isolated from the mainstream of their fellow human beings and suffered a crisis of identity, at which point a few have begun to fantasize, seeking larger worlds through myth-making, technical innovations and ascent on the backs of their fellows to the stars, while the majority have stoically accepted their fate.

Lucille Iremonger[1] has drawn attention to the relationship between the deprivation of love in childhood and the subsequent drive to ascend to the summit of their society. In her researches into the lives of Britain's Prime Ministers, she discovered that many had suffered from some sort of emotional deprivation in childhood which had set up compensatory drives in them.

Out of 24 of the more recent Prime Ministers she chose to study –

---

* This Appendix should be read in conjunction with Appendix iv.

† The love was that bestowed by the Great Spirit, the natural flux and law, and Earthmother, the providential succession of natural food pyramids and enchanting earth. They were the host and hostess in whose prodigal company *Homo sapiens* realized himself and was fulfilled. It was they who inspired his affection and trust; or, as in the case of the pygmies, it was the total wild environment itself which they inhabited which inspired their affection and to which they sang 'a lusty chorus of praise'. With their alienation from the wilderness, de-ranged people were also alienated from the foundations of their affection and understanding.

from Spencer Perceval to Neville Chamberlain – 16 had been bereaved in childhood. They had been deprived of parental love by the death of one or both parents, or by the physical absence through illegitimacy of a parent, or through rejection by one or both parents, or by a combination of deprivation through death of a parent and rejection. When Mrs Iremonger looked more closely at the early lives of the Prime Ministers outside her period of study, from Walpole to Spencer Perceval, she discovered that of those 16, nine had been bereaved in childhood. (She took the extreme age of 'childhood', during which parental bereavement might have a decisive effect on a developing personality, as 15.) So from Walpole up to and including Neville Chamberlain, some 25 out of 40 Prime Ministers, including one acknowledged bastard suffered deprivation of parental love. (Winston Churchill once wrote, 'It is said that famous men are usually the product of an unhappy childhood', referring to the Duke of Marlborough, but doubtless mindful of his own experience.) Furthermore, not only had many of these men suffered the traumatic and unusual experience of deprivation of love in childhood, but many were abnormally sensitive, reserved and isolated. Many exhibited a 'hysterical search for love', recklessness in that pursuit, excessive devotion to their own children coupled with extreme reaction to bereavement, extreme religious concern, and an intuitive, superstitious faith in personal destiny. These were men virtually helpless before their own over-riding personal emotional needs. They were driven upwards, impelled towards the summit of society by those needs. Early de-ranged people were similarly so driven.

Lucille Iremonger has linked this characteristic behaviour pattern with a similar pattern first described by Dr Maryse Choisy, relating to bastard children. This is known as the Phaeton complex. Phaeton was son of the sun god, Apollo. Growing conceited, Phaeton acquired a habit of boasting of his divine parentage. He was accused of arrogance, and insinuations were made about his birth. Angry and resentful, Phaeton begged his mother, the nymph Clymene, to direct him to his father, so that he might obtain proof that he was indeed Apollo's son. Following her directions, Phaeton approached Apollo in his Palace of the Sun, and begged for undeniable proofs that he was his father and that he loved him. Apollo swore on the river Styx he would grant him what he asked. So Phaeton, to Apollo's horror, asked to drive the sun chariot that very day, stating that all the world would be certain to watch his passage across the sky and know that he was indeed Apollo's son. Eventually acceding to Phaeton's presumptuous request, Apollo showed him how to guide the four fiery steeds which drew the golden-wheeled sun-car through the heavens. But soon after Phaeton had taken the reins he lost his way, first approaching so close to Earth that the plants shrivelled up, then driving so far away that the remaining vegetation perished in the intense cold. So loudly did the mortals complain that they roused Zeus from a profound slumber. Angry at the sight of the devastated Earth and youthful charioteer, Zeus vowed he would make the rash mortal pay for his presumption. He thereupon struck him to Earth with a thunderbolt. As Mrs Iremonger points out, the message of this myth is clear and eternal:

> Phaeton's lack of a father, his seeking one in the god, his desire to be acknowledged by him in the sight of all the world, to the extent of even being allowed to exercise his godlike functions, and his own overweening and suicidal determination to display himself to all men carrying out a superhuman task, could lead only to disaster for himself, and possibly for others.[2]

The pattern of behaviour discovered by Mrs Iremonger amongst Prime Ministers, and that discovered by Maryse Choisy amongst bastards, both correspond to the Phaeton pattern of behaviour. The common denominator, according to Mrs Iremonger, is the deprivation of parental love.

> It was, to my mind, that parental deprivation, whether caused by bereavement, bastardy, rejection, illness, or mere absence (e.g. at war, or even because of the pressures of gay or demanding social lives and careers), which set up all the stresses, and created the kind of person we now know so well, forever seeking to compensate by rising to the top.[3]

Of course, not every deprived person attempts to ascend to the summit of his society to become Prime Minister. There are many fields in which such deprived men may distinguish themselves – in industry, in the professions of medicine, the armed services, the Church, in the arts and sciences and so on.* However, it is only those with exceptional qualities – and a measure of luck – who, dominated by an almost manic drive for power and a compulsive need to be loved and to prove themselves, fulfil their desires. (Amongst others mentioned by Mrs Iremonger are

---

* Oliver James[4] has observed that one third of all American Presidents lost a parent before the age of 14. Similar losses have been sustained by many well-known scientists and artists, perhaps half our best poets having lost a parent in childhood. The potential leaders are driven to control their destinies rather than be at the mercy of fate; the scientists become obsessed with explaining and controlling a hostile Universe by means of theories and experiments; the artists desperately seek an outlet for their melancholy.

Julius Caesar, William the Conqueror, Nelson, Wordsworth, Isaac Newton, T.E. Lawrence and Hitler.)* Like Phaetons, they push harder than the rest, and often plunge to their doom. The many millions of deprived children without such qualities to rise in the vertical are for ever fated to lead lives of constant frustration, chronic delinquency and perennial disappointment in their hopes.

In addition to the conflict behaviour and redirected responses of deranged people explored in Part I, Chapter 4 and Appendix iv, which led to the growth of stratified societies, people also began to ascend to the summit of their societies for precisely the same reasons as people ascend to those summits today: the deprivation of parental love and security. But their deprivation was more profound, being a combined physical, intellectual and emotional deprivation. As well as being deprived of the love of the Great Spirit and Earthmother, they were imprisoned by their physical and psychical degeneration, and made illegitimate by their coherence in stratified societies which were not only born out of wedlock with the wilderness, but have since grown by the illegal or criminal suppression of that wilderness. It is aspects of the individual bastard's status and behaviour in relation to society, as revealed by Maryse Choisy, which most clearly exemplify the status and behaviour of these stratified societies in relation to the wilderness and to one another.

Because of their 'birth blow' nothing (bastards) do succeeds. Guilt-ridden and ashamed at being alive, they merely exist, barely integrated, never properly belonging to family, group or community, strangers on the face of the earth. They cannot mix except uneasily, so fundamentally ill-adapted are they to ordinary life. The anguish of living never leaves them. They have no place in the accepted order of things; do not belong; do not even accept themselves, since they are not accepted.[5]†

---

*Moses was an orphan. The Buddha's mother died in childbirth. Confucius' mother may have died in childbirth, while his father died when he was a child. The Prophet Muhammad was an orphan. Martin Luther, on his own testimony, was severely abused as a child by both parents, while John Calvin's mother died when he was an infant.

† In 1987 the concept of bastardy in the United Kingdom was removed from the statute books. But this in no way changes the situation of women who bear children outside marriage. They pose a serious threat in a society which makes it almost impossible for most of them to support themselves and their children alone. Over a million women and their million and a half children have become dependants on the state. The social stigma may have gone but the social problem they pose is increasingly serious, and the children remain misfits. A father is a vital necessity for a child's emotional health. Lacking a father a child, particularly a boy, is liable to fantasize about his father and fatherhood and to take a negative view of women. Furthermore, lone parent [*Continued over*]

The same may be said of the de-ranged members of stratified societies in relation to the wilderness. Ill-adapted to ordinary life – which in their case is that of *Homo sapiens* – they too are strangers on the face of the Earth, though at a much more fundamental level. The myths of a Fall show them to have suffered a similar 'birth-blow'. Bastards fantasize throughout their lives. One of their main, predominant fantasies is that of a marvellous birth. The bastard often creates a god for a father, seeing his own conception by remote impregnation and his birth of a virgin, perhaps in the midst of a storm, the heavens riven and rent by thunder and lightning. Similarly, de-ranged members of stratified societies created, as evinced in their myths of Creation, new fathers and mothers, Gods and Goddesses, out of, and in the midst of, Chaos. As in the case of Phaeton and Apollo, these Gods would not only legitimize their societies but make them better and supply them with the universal love they craved. But, in both the case of the illegitimate child and illegitimate stratified society, these are only man-made artifices, illusions of legitimation and love which conceal a fundamental illegitimacy and hatred of the world:

> To an illegitimate child who has not known love the only other possible relationship with the world is hate... What happens to all this hatred? It shows itself in two distinctive ways, against the world and against itself. It takes the form of rebellion and refusal of the social pact in the first instance, often creating delinquents, and in the second of a determined seeking of self-destruction in one way or another.[6]

Similarly, the hatred of these stratified societies has shown itself in their refusal of the social pact with the wild world, in their delinquent destruction of that world and in wars amongst themselves. The paradox is that, though

---

[*Continued from previous page*] children are more likely to be poor, do badly at school, have a drug or drink problem, and to drift into lives of homelessness, drug abuse, crime, failed relationships, despair and suicide. The key to all these problems is deprivation and multiple deprivation. And while multiply deprived boys often turn to the excitement of crime in a search for power in a world that rejects them, girls turn to pregnancy – for giving birth is the most creative and exciting event in their lives. Their own inadequacy breeds further inadequacy.

'You bastard' is an expletive that well expresses society's attitude to bastards; on the other hand, 'the poor bastard' might express a degree of sympathy with someone suffering the indignity of deprivation.

As well as the rise in single parent families in the United Kingdom, the number of abandoned children is increasing world-wide. In Brazil alone, for instance, some 12 million abandoned children roam the streets of the major cities; in South America as a whole there are an estimated 40 million abandoned children living in an environment of desolation and despair, a figure which is expected to rise dramatically in the next decade.

they might pretend to Gods of hope and love, and protest a love of the world, their underlying drives are fear and hatred of the world. This paradox is well brought out in the life of Alfred Nobel. His obsession with explosives and subsequent involvement with the Nobel Peace Prize neatly points the paradox facing both science and civilized people as a whole.

Born in Stockholm in 1833 into a family concerned in military manufacture, Nobel was not only subject to a severe physical disability – he suffered from a spinal complaint and was often bedridden – but he was also subject to his father's derision over his efforts to prove himself, and later suffered persecution and expulsion from France after 18 years residence there. He grew up, on his own admission, withdrawn and self-centred, and probably obsessional. As a young man he wrote:

> For torture in the shape of illness threw
> A gloom around me from the dawn of life.
> My cradle looked a death-bed.[7]

There is evidence that the pain, suffering and loneliness of his childhood stimulated him – as it did Leonardo da Vinci and Isaac Newton – to an intense intellectual curiosity and drive for power over nature. He invented the detonation principle, dynamite and cordite, making him the progenitor of virtually all modern 'conventional' weapons. This scientific-technological achievement of Nobel crowned a bitter childhood, just as the original technological innovations of the early civilizations crowned their bitter birth and childhood as stratified societies. Despite the fact that his early experiments with nitroglycerine destroyed his younger brother and four other people, Nobel was apparently driven to spend his life manufacturing and improving violent and destructive materials by an obsession formed in his miserable childhood and reinforced by a highly unsatisfactory private life and by public abuse. Like civilized people in their debasement as farmers and extraordinary feeling of inferiority in relation to wild nature, Nobel felt stupid and lost among people, and his whole life was likewise embittered by feelings of debasement.

Looking back at his achievements, Nobel once commented:

> A miserable half-life, which ought to have been choked to death by a philanthropic physician as, with a howl, it entered life.

This could be said of a majority of suffering humankind. Nobel directly contributed to that suffering by his inventions. He became known as 'The Merchant of Death'.

David Wilson wrote of Alfred Nobel:

No other single scientist has made so many 'successful' military inventions, to no other single brain can so many deaths be directly attributed. Nobel Prizes are science's highest awards, the Nobel Peace Prize brings honour among men of every nation, yet these prizes are paid for by the profits Nobel made from selling munitions.[8]*

Likewise they are given to men who, if individually outwardly peace-loving and creative, are nevertheless members of stratified societies whose explosive re-evolutionary growth and behaviour have been aided by, and been as destructive as, the products of Nobel. As Nobel once commented: 'It cannot be expected that an explosive substance should come into general use without some waste of life.'[9] Chief Anthony Enaharo of Nigeria made a similar under-statement on the loss of life to be expected in the creation of a Nigerian nation, during its war with Biafra: 'People appear to me to be concerned only with loss of life,' said Chief Enaharo, who led the Nigerian delegation to the peace talks in June, 1968. 'We are trying to create a nation... Whatever sacrifice we have to make, we count it well worth it if at the end we emerge with a Nigerian nation.'[10] Explosives and the explosive growth of nations at the expense of the individual life are inseparably linked, as in the classic example of the American Civil War of 1861–65 – the first 'modern' war according to historians of military technique. Wars between 'brothers' have replaced the relative peace and potential brotherhood of man as hunter-gatherer.

The irreparable loss of that potential in the wilderness and its replacement with stratified societies of exploitation and oppression has fuelled both the wars between 'brothers' and wars against the wilderness. It is this that underlies the paradox of de-ranged peoples. Search as they might for peace through the weapons of war, true peace must be eternally denied degenerates born into hatred of, and war against, the wilderness. It is precisely those who in every generation are isolated by their various infirmities and deprived of love in childhood – the future Prime Ministers,

---

* Nobel's paradoxical legacy – that Nobel prizes (for literature, physics, chemistry, economics, medicine and particularly peace) were paid for by the profits Nobel made from selling munitions – lives on in the duplicity of the Nobel Foundation which has been funding its awards by investing in arms companies with dubious human rights records. For example, the Foundation awarded the 1996 Peace Prize to Bishop Carlos Belo and José Ramos-Horta for their fight against the Indonesian régime in East Timor, then invested in a company selling arms to the Indonesian Government.

the Newtons, the Nobels, the illegitimate children and children of the ghetto – who add most fuel to the flames that threaten to ignite the world.

Appendix vi

Law and Order

If the words of the 18th century Utilitarian philosopher Jeremy Bentham – that 'The greatest happiness of the greatest number is the foundation of morals and legislation' – may be taken as a good rule of thumb for what government and administration should be about, that condition most surely pertained amongst *Homo sapiens* hunter-gatherers, whose greatest joy and well-being lay in their faithful obedience to the authority of the Great Spirit. By a two-stage process certain people became divorced from the natural law that had governed the evolution of their species. They first of all lost touch with the natural law; then altogether renounced that law by establishing re-evolutionary man-made laws which, though peculiar to each separate enclave of sedentary farmers, had in common their rejection of the wilderness and natural law.

The first stage in the divorce of de-ranged people from the natural law was simply a case of losing touch with the natural law and its requirements.

> You get out of touch very quickly if you don't actually wet your feet in the waters of the law.[1]

Equally, you get out of touch very quickly if you do not actually wet your feet and walk in the waters of the natural law that bound all people as hunter-gatherer kings in a cosmic unity within nature. This is what happened to those forcibly de-ranged as primitive subsistence farmers.

The second stage in the divorce of de-ranged people from the natural law arose as a direct result of disorientation consequent upon the loss of that law, and of the consequences flowing from the rejection of natural authority. (For any man-made law arising from the loss of the natural law implies a rejection of the latter.)

Once external authority has been renounced, we find ... a new bondage. For we become the victims of our unconscious impulses, masquerading as reason or faith.[2]

The instinct of self-protection and self-preservation, coupled with the search for a new identity and self-justification, brought into being a plethora of re-evolutionary creeds and laws oriented in the vertical, laws ostensibly handed down by their Farmer Gods. Their descendants, such as the Gods of Judaism, Roman Catholicism, Islam, Protestantism, Hinduism and Communism and their related laws, are the inheritance and justification of nations today. These represent the penultimate betrayal of the unity of their sovereign nature with that of their fellows within the one indivisible kingdom of nature.* (In modern parlance, each enclave of de-ranged people was a 'no-go' area for the laws of the others, and for the laws of nature.)† The principal cause of their divorce from the natural law and their betrayal of unity lay in the dramatic change that occurred in their relationship to the land, in the division of the (until then) indivisible kingdom of nature between farming groups that was sanctioned and sanctified by their Farmer Gods, and is now sanctioned by international law.

Their relationship to the land changed drastically from being one of hunter-gatherer peoples *who belonged to the land* to being sedentary farming peoples *to whom the land belonged*, turning the land into a commodity to be exploited, fought over, bought or sold. Hunter-gatherers such as the San have no concept of land ownership – rather, people are owned by the land. It is the law of the land as wilderness that governs the people, whereas, from the standpoint of farming-based cultures, the lands of the hunter-gatherers – or those totally uninhabited – have been regarded as being lands with no owner and without law (known in international law as *res nullius*) and therefore available for appropriation in accordance with an internationally accepted set of rules surrounding legal title. These have enabled states to acquire new territories and to enact laws concerning their governance and the public and private

---

*The ultimate betrayal of that unity will be an illusory unity and brotherhood of de-ranged peoples scientifically enforced within one man-made world.

† There were now splinter groups of people de-ranged and separated from the main body of law-abiding hunter-gatherers, putting their own interests above those of that mysterious entity, the kingdom of nature. These people were outcasts and outlaws. They were isolated, aliens in a foreign land. They could only 'make-it' while remaining the outcasts and outlaws – that is, people without the natural law – that they had become. It was these outcasts and outlaws who acquired respectability by becoming themselves the law-makers within each enclave and who eventually dubbed the law-abiding hunter-gatherers lawless.

ownership of the land. Such ownership has not only forced hunter-gatherers off the land into oblivion but inevitably and inexorably given rise to landed and landless people within any one state, often forcing those deprived of land to seek it elsewhere as economic migrants, as revealed in the three centuries of emigration to North America. Now, with all the lands lawfully – that is, according to man-made law – appropriated by states, and innumerable people within those states expropriated or alienated from the land, we are seeing new waves of economic migrants knocking at the doors of states such as the UK and USA and being turned away, exacerbating friction between the 'haves' and the 'have-nots' and turning the words 'economic migrant' into a pejorative phrase. In short, whereas the absence of land-ownership amongst hunter-gatherers made for order, the ownership of land by some and the expropriation of others is one of the principal causes of disorder, while the denuding of the lands of wildlife makes for disorder within the kingdom of nature. The change from natural law to man-made law was a change from the profoundly human to the fundamentally inhuman. 'The harmless people' had become the harmful people.

Appendix vii

The Fall of Man

The blood-dimmed tide is loosed, and everywhere
The ceremony of innocence is drowned
(W.B. Yeats, *The Second Coming*)

It is important to understand how the myth of a Fall from a State of Nature developed, and how it in turn relates to the hypothesis of the two-fold fall of man that I have expounded.

The Greeks and Romans believed in a 'State of Nature' that existed on Earth in some long-lost Golden Age. It was a state of affairs in which no one was exploited by anyone else, and which was characterized by universal good faith and brotherly love. According to the Roman poet Ovid:

Golden was that first age, which, with no one to compel, without a law, of its own will, kept faith and did the right. There was no fear of punishment, no threatening words were to be read on brazen tablets... The earth herself, without compulsion, untouched by hoe or plowshare, of herself gave all things needful...' But in time 'modesty and truth and faith fled the earth, and in their place came tricks and plots and snares, violence and cursed love of gain... And the ground, which had hitherto been a common possession like the sunlight and the air, the careful surveyor now marked out with long-drawn boundary-line... And now baneful iron had appeared, and gold more baneful still; war came... Men lived on plunder...'[1]

The Roman Stoic philosopher Seneca wrote of a similar Golden Age in which all the products of nature were enjoyed in common and where no man lived in poverty. Then Avarice invaded the land, bringing property to some and penury to others.

550

But – and this was central to his whole argument – Seneca was convinced that the old egalitarian order was not only lost but necessarily lost. As time passed, men had become vicious; and once that happened, institutions such as private property, coercive government, differentiation of status, even slavery were not only inevitable but also needful; not only consequences of but also remedies for the corruption of human nature. And it was in this form, and saddled with these qualifications, that the notion of the primal egalitarian State of Nature was adopted by the Fathers (of the Church) and incorporated into the political theory of the Church...

At the centre of this theory stands the distinction between the State of Nature, which was based on Natural Law and expressed directly the divine intention, and the conventional state, which has grown out of and is sanctioned by custom. It was agreed by most of the later Fathers that inequality, slavery, coercive government and even private property had no part in the original intention of God and had come into being only as a result of the Fall. Once the Fall had taken place, on the other hand, a development began which made such institutions indispensable. Corrupted by Original Sin, human nature demanded restraints which would not be found in an egalitarian order; inequalities of wealth, status and power were thus not only consequences of but also remedies for sin.[2]

The Golden Age here envisaged by Seneca and the subsequent adoption by the Church Fathers of the theory of a 'State of Nature, which was based on Natural Law and expressed directly the divine intention', was a State of Nature ostensibly created and governed by God, that is, God as envisaged and invoked by domesticated farming peoples, the Farmer God. It was an imaginary world conjured up by Graeco-Roman and Christian myth which was the antithesis of the real world of the hunter-gatherers governed by the Great Spirit – and the Fall was a Fall away from that imaginary world.

Similar concepts arose in India. According to the Hindu texts there have been four Ages, of which this is the fourth. The first was the Golden Age, when people were happy and equal: there was no distinction between high and low, no law of separate classes. This was followed, as in Christianity, by the Fall. Having lost the ground of eternity – which was, in reality and unbeknownst to them, the immortality inherent in the evolutionary status of *Homo sapiens* as hunter-gatherer – they remained in a perfectionless void, to be rigidly segregated into castes. The second Age (Treta yuga) and third Age (Dwapara yuga) have led them to their present Age (Kali yuga), morally the poorest of them all. Like Christianity, Hinduism has a sense of degeneration. The highest Brahmin caste, for instance, so understands the frailty of its claim on virtue that it has to perform elaborate, protective rituals concerning what it eats and touches and to whom it relates with 'relentlessly fierce fastidiousness'. Similarly the Untouchables* created fine gradations within their own pariah group.

The Christian and Hindu views of themselves and other peoples were therefore derived from the story of a Fall from a Golden Age – from a Garden of Eden, from paradise – according to which humanity, originally created innocent and perfect by their Farmer God or gods, has fallen into decline. There are, in the Christian story, two separate peoplings of the Earth – one by Adam and Eve after their disobedience to God and expulsion from paradise, and another by Noah after the Flood. So, apart from those considered to be antediluvian remnants, the various different peoples on Earth are presumed to be descendants of Noah's sons. All, as a result of the Fall, are tainted with Original Sin. The Golden Age, the primal egalitarian State of Nature, the Fall and Original Sin are all concepts conceived by de-ranged people to explain the corrupt state of humankind. They are concepts both arising in the absence of knowledge of the true sequence of events as I have tried to portray them, and falsifying and concealing that true sequence. And the consequences of the Fall (inequalities of wealth, private property, coercive government, status and power) came in time to be seen as sanctioned by God as the remedies for Original Sin – a truly remarkable rationalization of the existing stratified structure!† And although groups within the Churches have attempted, from time to time, to establish some measure of equality amongst people, the entrenched stratification and avarice of societies, and of the Churches themselves, has been too strong for them. So not only have the concepts enumerated above falsified and concealed the true sequence of events, but the sanctified growth of stratified societies – revolution upon revolution – as wealth-creating entities has further concealed that true sequence.

The fall and original sin of de-ranged people that each generation inescapably inherits as the component part of a stratified society lies in their degenerative loss of a hunting ability and obedience to the universal Great Spirit and natural law that guided them as an integral part of the

---

*Now known as Dalit.

†The Hindus rationalized the gross inequalities of their stratified societies as the outcome of behaviour in an earlier life: good behaviour has been rewarded with high caste and bad behaviour with untouchability.

grand symbiotic system of nature; in their coherence in rudimentary stratified societies and consequent imprisonment in an inhuman life-style around agriculture; and in their subsequent belief – as exemplified in the Middle Eastern myths – that the world had been created by their God and that their corrupt state was due to Original Sin on the part of their antediluvian ancestors. The Middle Eastern myths of a Fall and Flood falsified and overlaid the natural cause and effect with a supernatural cause and effect, and in so doing also reversed the order of events. So what was in fact a deluge followed by a fall and failure to re-adapt later became mythologized as a Flood due to Original Sin on the part of their antediluvian ancestors.

Hence a major part of the evil surrounding their condition and behaviour has stemmed from the mythopoeic knowledge of their anti-evolutionary agricultural/industrial ways of life and nations as God-given, Providential and Good and of their antediluvian ancestors, the hunting way of life and wilderness as savage, unregenerate and evil, fit only for domination, exploitation or extirpation. In such ways de-ranged people have perverted the real order of the world. When the Revd Dr Edward Norman was interviewed prior to giving the 1978 Reith Lectures, he intimated that the idea of original sin was important to him:

> Our innate corruption spills out into our best intentions and highest altruism. Left to ourselves, we will make a desert of the universe. I believe in the supremacy of God. And I also believe in Providence.

Yet it is precisely such beliefs that lie at the heart of the corruption! It was ostensibly at the behest of their Farmer God of Providence – as in Genesis 1:28 – that de-ranged people originally went out to lay waste and subdue a wilderness they could neither live in nor understand. (Only in the last few centuries have naturalists been fashioning our eleventh-hour awareness of the wild world about us.) The corruption is not innate, but arises from the 6–8,000 year long perversion of the individual psyche and physique to serve the collective institutions and beliefs of stratified societies, which includes their belief in a God of Providence. In other words, the priestly concepts of a Fall, original sin and new Creation both hide the real cause of the corruption and compound that corruption.

The modern equivalent of original sin (a priestly concept) is the doctrine of original violence (a scientific concept), and mankind is pictured as growing away from the Darkness of original sin and original violence towards the Light, an Ascent of Man towards the Heavens and Perfection. Yet that Darkness, and the primitiveness and savagery that are now everywhere apparent, only fell across the land with the two-fold fall of man. Violence does not stem, as is commonly supposed, from our animal nature, the legacy of inherited biological impulses – i.e. 'the beast in man', an idea that parallels the Christian doctrine of original sin – but from that nature frustrated and made fearful and void within captive de-ranged states of humankind, and thereafter perverted to serve the cold-blooded natures of nations. (Most sins and evil are the fruit of ignorance and fear, and it was from point zero of a primitive and ignorant savagery that de-ranged people first began to acquire their knowledge of a world from which they were essentially alienated and estranged, and of which they have therefore remained essentially ignorant and fearful.) De-ranged man's inhumanity to man and to nature – and the basic passions of aggression allied to domination and exploitation are the common inheritance of de-ranged peoples, no matter whether living in a primitive or a highly civilized state – is inseparably combined with the origin and growth of stratified societies, and now with the social, political and economic circumstances affecting nations. Sin, violence and evil originated with the fall of de-ranged people from the graceful state of all humankind as hunter-gatherers. Original goodness and virtual absence of intraspecific strife are the characteristics of the hunter-gatherer culture, whereas nations are killers by nature.

It will be appreciated that the priestly and scientific myths of original sin and original violence respectively relate to one another, and in the same way, as do all those priestly-scientific relationships to which I draw attention in Appendix viii. They also reinforce one another. Just as the development of institutions of the stratified society were seen by Christianity as consequences and remedies for original sin, so in turn has the development of scientific institutions been seen as a remedy for the original violence of humankind. Christianity and Science have combined to acquire dominion over nature, though it is the sciences which, under biblical authority, have given de-ranged people the means to exercise dominion over and to subdue nature, which the Bible had promised but which had hitherto remained conceptual rather than actual. It is science-based technology that is today the ultimate expression of violence as it sweeps aside all obstacles to development in the name of development, of progress, of the Ascent of Man.

Appendix viii

Language, and the Relatedness of Myth and Science

Before the catastrophe of the Mesolithic, the languages of all people were founded in an understanding of the secret language of nature: the human mind was in great part created by the hunter-gatherer's use of language in relation to an ecological understanding of nature. It has been estimated that there were some 10,000 languages spoken by the 10 million hunter-gatherers living 10,000 years ago. Such a diversity of language was based on the diversity of climate, landscape, animals and plants experienced by each hunter-gatherer band. Though each group of hunter-gatherers may have had its own different tongue – as different as the many tongues spoken by Australian Aborigines and San today – all of them grew out of and reflected their world-loving ecological understanding. Their languages were all descended from, and united in, their understanding of the secret language of nature, and integrated with other art forms of interpretive communication such as painting, sculpture, drama, music, song and dance. Information conveyed in so many verbal and non-verbal sentient, visual and aural forms was socially cohesive and assured freedom, equality and stability within the one kingdom of nature. Their languages epitomized the secret language of nature, of perfect transparency and truth. With the loss of their stability and *raison d'être* as hunter-gatherers, these voided people lost their ability to speak, to interpret and to understand the secret language of nature. They awoke in a world which they could no longer interpret nor understand; they had lost their evolved way of perceiving the world. With their adaptation to a primitive agriculture, these people began to develop related languages that gave meaning, albeit illusory, to an otherwise meaningless world. For example, a prototype Indo-European language now began to grow up and to spread outwards from S.W. Asia (see figure App. viii.i).

Evidence suggests that the early farmers, who originated in the Near

Fig App. viii.i

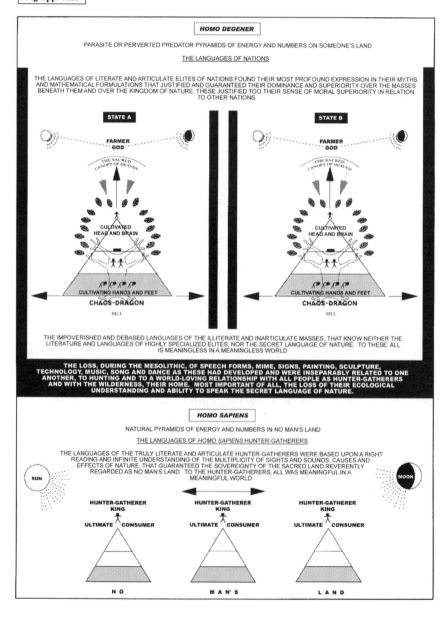

East circa 10000 BC, then spread from Turkey to Greece around 8500 BC, and thence spread west and north towards Britain and Scandinavia, brought with them to Europe languages such as Etruscan and Basque. They were followed, several thousand years later, by a second wave of farmers arising in the Black Sea area and spreading west into Europe and east towards India. They bore with them a proto-Indo-European language from which all Indo-European languages are descended. Their language changed first into dialects as populations separated and then into the different Indo-European languages we know today. For example, Celtic and Germanic languages originated from the language that groups of Indo-European-speaking farmers introduced into northern Europe. Their languages were, of course, directly related to the stratified structures that were now growing up throughout Europe and elsewhere.

A noteworthy relationship between language and the stratified societies that were growing up was the imposition of socio-economic order by means of daily, weekly, monthly and yearly rituals and religious festivals relating to human, animal and plant fertility, death, rebirth, etc. This was achieved with the aid of astronomical observations by priest-scientists of the Sun, Moon, Mars, Mercury, Jupiter, Venus and Saturn. Linguistic evidence of their importance and use survives in the form of the days of the week, whose names in most Indo-European languages, including Sanskrit, German, French and Welsh, refer to their respective deities in association with those heavenly bodies.*

Language thus became expressive of a self-consciousness self-created by dominant élites, a self-consciousness heightened by their close proximity to, and special relationship with, self-created or illusory deities, and the distancing of themselves from the wilderness, home of the illusory chaos-dragon. Given that a function of their language is to justify and cement the power relations and socio-economic order within stratified societies, it is axiomatic that any other state, such as that of *Homo sapiens* living in the wilderness, would be spoken of as something less orderly, greatly inferior, degenerate and less good. So, like the art of the hunter-gatherers buried deep in caves, lost to mankind for 10,000 years and then denigrated when first discovered,† a co-operative past and relative perfection of all

---

*It is important to note that the effect of their myths was to place a static vertically oriented construction upon every happening – a God's eye view, as it were – thereby disguising and essentially falsifying the truth of any event.

† Experts believed they were fakes, presuming primitive people incapable of producing such beautiful images. Primitive agricultural people were indeed so incapable. But these images were the products of highly developed, profoundly intelligent hunter-gatherers whom the primitive farming communities have destroyed.

people as hunter-gatherers was, with the aid of myths such as those of a Fall and Flood, covered over, falsified and made to appear evil. Meanwhile, the stratified societies and fertility cults that grew up on the mass of primary producers were presented as Providential and good. This was a process of double-think and double-talk that has made language ambiguous and action ambivalent ever since. What was originally light was made to appear Dark; what was now dark was made to appear Light, growing lighter with every agricultural-industrial revolution on the original re-evolution. This falsification of language, and so of understanding, is surely one of the most profound consequences of the two-fold fall of humankind.

Language changed from being a principal means of communication and expression of a natural self-consciousness to the co-operative survival in equality of all humans as hunter-gatherers, to being a principal means to the exploitative power of dominant élites over subservient masses of each stratified society, and over wild nature. Language also became a principal means to the competitive expansion and growth of nations in the Northern Hemisphere, as they bulldozed the languages of weaker peoples out of existence. The growth of the Word has been central to the growth of stratified societies.

This re-evolutionary change in the development and use of language is well illustrated in the case of the contemporary migrant worker. As increasing numbers of people have been forced to seek work outside their countries, and so outside the cultural bounds of their own language, they are cast adrift in a hostile-seeming world. As George Steiner pointed out, the migrant worker from Turkey or North Africa, adrift in a German factory, learns a pidgin from his employers suitable for accepting and carrying out orders, but insufficient for the expression of ideas: it is a language of servitude. The situation of the migrant worker is similar to that of the original primitive and ignorant subsistence farmers made helpless and apart in the seemingly hostile world of nature. The pidgin of migrant workers in a hostile-seeming world by comparison with the cultured speech of their employers at home in that world is similar to the primitiveness of the early Indo-European language of the subsistence farmers made helpless in an alien land by comparison with the highly developed language of *Homo sapiens* at home in that land. As their stratified societies have grown, head over hands and feet, their languages have reflected that growth and division of labour. The languages of stratified societies and the information they convey, whether written or by word of mouth, are socially divisive. They are no longer expressive of a coherence of all people as kings of natural food pyramids, but of increasing specialization and division within and between stratified societies.

Language has come to represent a statement of power of élites over the masses, and over wild nature, reinforcing and perpetuating the hierarchical order and division of labour. Such a division has been greatly exacerbated by the invention and development of the esoteric, arcane language of mathematics. That artificial language helped de-ranged élites aspire to grandeur and achieve a measure of predictive power and security in relation to the masses and to wild nature. This was initially achieved in the ancient world with the aid of astronomical information which, when gathered and recorded, enabled buildings to be erected and accurately aligned to accord with cosmological myth. Within them were performed religious ritual and recitations of myth, whose predictive value as the Word, when combined with that of the cleverly aligned architecture, served as an impressive display and justification of priestly-scientific power and prestige. The language of mathematics grew out of these early beginnings as a key to unlock the secrets of nature. Subsequent revolutions on the original re-evolution have seen the accretion of arcane mathematical knowledge by the scientific community: the language of mathematics, when combined with that of the Word (and with that of money, which speaks louder than words), has given immeasurable power to élites of stratified societies, power to control and exploit the masses and wild nature to secure their ascent to the skies.

The relatedness of myth and science to that end, and their independence of the ordinary laws of life, is well brought out by W.B. Stanford:

> First of all, there is the curious fact that myths and legends (which I take to be primary elements in the poetic process) have often anticipated future scientific inventions. To take a few examples out of many: flying-machines are anticipated in the story of Daedalus and Icarus, Aristophanes in *The Frogs* adds the idea of chemical warfare from the air, and Lucian describes a journey to the Moon. Underwater exploration and life under the sea are suggested in legends about the sea-divinities and about Theseus...[1]

Stanford asks how myth-makers and poets create their centaurs and chimeras and suggests that the mythopoeic process is ultimately very similar to higher mathematics:

> Both the poets and the mathematicians choose, or invent, symbols – centaurs and minotaurs or X's or alphas – and make their compositions out of these. Both sets of symbols are independent of the ordinary laws of life. And then axioms often are, too: Euclid's

point which has position but no magnitude is just as chimerical and non-factual as Homer's chimera; $pi = 3.14159$ and so on for ever is just as much an open-ended fantasy, in a way, as Aristophanes' Cloud-Cuckoo-Land. In what practical sense is it true that $(a + b)^2 = a^2 + 2ab + b^2$, or that 'the Snark was a Boojum, you see'? Further, both the poet and the mathematician manipulate these fact-free symbols according to principles of symmetry and design which are not operative in the natural world...

Now I come to something that I find quite amazing. The spectacular space flights which have been so widely acclaimed recently depended ultimately on mathematical formulations unconnected with the technological processes involved. It was pure mathematics and her sister, theoretical physics – aided, of course, by practical engineering – which enabled men to reach the Moon, as Lucian had predicted they would. In other words, from a system of symbols as fanciful as any in *Alice in Wonderland* or *Through the Looking Glass*, such epoch-making events as those at Cape Kennedy became feasible. And similarly, on the poetic side, the fantastic symbols of Bunyan's *Pilgrim's Progress* or Dante's *Inferno* or the Revelation of St John the Divine have caused total revolutions, morally and spiritually, in the lives of many men and women.[2]

Stanford concludes that the truths of pure poetry and of pure science are essentially the same and are based on a similar use of symbolic language. Both the poet and the mathematician manipulate fact-free symbols 'according to principles of symmetry and design which are not operative in the natural world'. By the manipulation of the fact-free myths of a superior Creation, made visible in mathematically beautiful temple and pyramid, the early priestly-scientific poet-cum-mathematician – the Master of, and Minister to, the Mysteries – was able to manipulate and mould the sedentary society in accordance with principles of symmetry and design quite independent of, and at variance with, the principles operative within nature. Myth (the Sacred Word) and mathematics (the Sacred Number) were combined in Egypt to raise the Pharaoh and Pyramid to the sun. The Space Age may be said to have opened, not in October 1957 when the Russians astounded the world by launching Sputnik 1, the pioneer artificial satellite, but when the Pharaohs were launched as the Sons of Ra in Chariots of the Sun into the presence of the Sun God Father. The relationship between the Pharaoh immured within a pyramid in preparation for a journey to another world and the astronaut immured within a space capsule bound for other worlds is direct. Not only was Tutankhamun's tomb, for instance, equipped with a life-support system similar to that of a space capsule, but the journey by space capsule is the technological end-product of the imaginary journey of a Pharaoh across the skies. Civilization has had to wait upon a further series of revolutions – the Industrial Revolutions – before technology has caught up with the ritually displaced imaginations of people, enabling them actually to ascend to the sun, the moon and the stars.*

The relatedness of myth – as of religion generally – and science lies in their similar personal and social functions. The early priestly-scientific experts, ministers of Farmer Gods and Goddesses, attempted to resolve the problems of primitive and emergent de-ranged societies by reference to their Gods and Goddesses, the founts of all knowledge. They hoped, by means of prayer, propitiatory rites and sacrifice so to dominate and manipulate their environments in their favour as to guarantee the wealth and stability of their stratified structures. To that end, science, in ancient and medieval times, was the servant of religion, which was itself the constitutional bedfellow of the State – creating, as in Ancient Egypt, the Theocratic Stable State.

Science began to fight its way forward as a secular movement when Galileo, the forerunner of the new age, directly challenged the Church, which then represented both authority and religion. Science has now largely taken over from the Farmer Gods as the hoped-for solver of the problems, and guarantor of the stability and wealth, of nations. Scientists are functionally the priests of our industrial societies, obtaining and establishing a body of reliable knowledge about the material world from which good answers to particular questions about any phenomenon or process in nature may ultimately be derived. But, whereas in previous centuries priest-scientists could only imaginatively manipulate nature by invoking their Farmer Gods, since the middle of the 19th century the body of knowledge established by science has enabled scientific experts actually to dominate and to manipulate nature. Science ostensibly enables men to gain more control over their destinies by becoming somewhat less dependent on the whim of the gods, on Fate – a control which they lost as debased hunter-gatherers 10,000

---

*It is noteworthy that the mythical launching into space of the Pharaohs and the actual launching into space of moon rockets had their grim origins in the sacrifice of thousands of workers who built the pyramids and rocket launch sites. Space travel in the modern world originated with the building of V2 rocket sites at La Coupole in northern France and at Dore in Germany during the Second World War. Altogether some 20,000 enslaved Russian and Polish workers died in the construction of these rockets, and a further 16,500 people – mostly in London and Antwerp – were killed when V2s and an earlier version, the V1s, struck their cities. After the war, the architects of the V2 went on to design the American launch sites for moon rockets. Russia in turn adapted V2 technology to the same ends, giving rise to a space race between the superpowers.

years ago. Like religion, science is preoccupied with freeing humanity from exigencies of an environment which has dominated them for nigh on 10,000 years, achieving control of natural processes and using nature, and the natures of *Homo sapiens non sapiens*, to produce all the material benefits that technology can provide. A strong base in fundamental science and high technology is now the key to national advancement. Science has thus largely replaced religion in its social rôle, the domination of nature and the natures of subservient *Homo sapiens non sapiens* producers to raise *Homo sapiens sapiens* to the skies. Or, put another way, scientists have largely replaced the earlier bishops, priests and scholars as the *Homo sapiens sapiens* doctors and professors of faith in the civilized way of life, in the Ascent of Man to the heavens. Today science is the new authority and religion. Science has developed quite extraordinary powers, which in turn have given immense authority to scientists and their ideas.* This authority, like that of a religion, has already in some instances hardened into a doctrine. For example, a basic proposition of molecular biology is called 'the central dogma'. The scientific establishment has taken over from the Church as preserver of the faith, as the guardian of delivered truth. It has replaced the Church as the constitutional bedfellow of the State – so creating the Technocratic Stable State.

An example of this rôle of science is that of the science of toxicology, the study of poisons, which affects virtually every area of modern life.

> Today, the subject and practice of toxicology has become exalted to the eminence and influence of a religion. It is, moreover, an established form of worship, actively supported by the State. It has its creeds and its commandments, and its hierarchy of high-priests, worshippers, adherents and novitiates. Again, like a religion, it relies rather more on faith than reason.[4]

An awareness of this direct relationship between religion (myth) and science may help place the observations of W.B. Stanford in perspective. If the relatedness of myth and science lies in their similar personal and social functions, both the personal and the social levels are vitally concerned with self-aggrandizement. The motivation of self-aggrandizement (to achieve significance for one's own de-ranged existence, whether the vehicle is religion or science) has in no way changed since the days of the Pharaohs of the second millennium BC in Ancient Egypt.

---

*'Our passive acceptance of the admonitions of anyone claiming scientific status mirrors the servility of medieval peasants towards anyone claiming divine authority.'[3]

They built their pyramids to last forever, so that people would not forget them. 'The king whose achievements are talked about does not die', wrote Sesostris I, and the inscribed annals of Thutmose III were placed in his sanctuary 'that he might be given life forever'.

Today, belief in some form of pharaonic immortality is widely accepted. In the 20th century, scientists, and everyone else, are trying to build personal pyramids...

We tell everyone repeatedly that science, or whatever else we do, is exciting for its own sake. We tell students that science should be pursued in a spirit of disinterested inquiry, with a view to advancing the frontiers of knowledge. But most people are not deceived and can see what really excites us: prestigious prizes and honorific titles. Most scientists nurse a secret ambition to win in their lifetime the highest awards. Thus will they attain pharaonic immortality.[5]*

Pharaonic immortality further extended to the sun itself in its daily progression across the skies, in its power to give Eternal Light and Life. In Egypt, the power to ascent and collective security reached an initial climax in the Pharaoh both circling the heavens in the Chariot of the Sun and immured within a pyramid: omniscient, omnipotent and omnipresent *Homo sapiens super sapiens* Controller of all the peoples and the lands of Egypt, Gateway to Heaven and promise of Resurrection into eternal after-life. That power will yet reach a final climax in scientists circling the heavens in space stations and on the moon, exploiting therefrom the power of the sun the better to ensure an environmentally sustainable future for the world: omniscient, omnipotent and omnipresent *Homo sapiens super sapiens* guardians of the globe. Like the Pharaoh lying athwart the threshold to an imaginary after-life and world beyond the grave, scientific guardians will stand at the threshold to actual worlds beyond worlds in outer space. They will encourage and enable a *Homo sapiens sapiens* few to escape the suffering and anarchy of this world by the medical prolongation of their lives so that they may reach up to other worlds in space, seeking a new Jerusalem, a new Paradise, an Eternal City, a New World somewhere out in space – and seeking eventually to

---

* 'Winning a Nobel Prize is perhaps the closest thing to deification that a scientist can expect in this life. That might explain why the ceremonies surrounding the presentation of the 1994 Nobel prizes in Stockholm ... bordered on the religious.

At the start of the Nobel banquet, the year's prizewinners were led arm-in-arm with the King and Queen of Sweden and members of the royal family down the huge marble staircase that leads into the Blue Hall of Stockholm's Stadshus. Above them a massed choir sang from the balcony. Behind them, lights projected a fan of diverging rays, making it look as though the procession was truly descending from heaven. In the darkness below, 1,500 guests waited to pay homage.'[6]

conquer the whole Galaxy.* This will be the technical actualization of what was only a sacerdotal dream in Ancient Egypt, albeit a dream which held the people of Egypt in thrall: Resurrection into a Paradisial Peace, Perfection and Immortality. But these were actually lost with the loss of their individual perfection and specific immortality as *Homo sapiens* hunter-gatherers moving freely through the world a paradisial land. The indefinite prolongation of the lives of a chosen few, and their actual raising-up (or resurrection) to worlds without end, will likewise be at the expense of the remainder and of the world itself: the whole Earth in thrall.

---

*There are already organizations offering those who can afford it the chance of life after death, and, in the event of science discovering the means of repairing damaged cells and reversing the process of ageing, eternal life or immortality. In preparation for such scientific advances, bodies are being placed in what is known as 'cryonic suspension'. After having their blood pumped out and replaced with glycerine, bodies are flown to Scottsdale, Arizona USA. There they are stored in liquid nitrogen at a temperature of minus 196°C inside a giant vacuum flask, to await resurrection by tomorrow's scientists, who will by then, it is hoped, have discovered the secrets of bodily immortality.

Appendix ix

The Shadow Beneath the Ice

What originally made for the real and for reality were the perceptions of *Homo sapiens* hunter-gatherers arising from the five senses and brain functioning in an integrated fashion in loving movement through an ever-changing natural environment. More importantly, the way they experienced the world was the way most useful to natural selection for them to perceive it. Because the natural flux and selection are fundamental processes behind the evolutionary reality of the living world, the way the hunter-gatherers experienced the world was the way it really was and is.

With the disintegration of their five senses and brains from their integrated function within the wilderness, and the loss of their wilderness home, ground of their evolutionary reality, *Homo degener* peoples dreamt new realities into existence commensurate with the exigencies of their double deprivation and incarceration in stratified societies. These new realities found their spiritual expression and justification in the Farmer God creators and destroyers peculiar to each de-ranged society; they found their concrete expression in solid structures devoted to the variety of activities which constituted the cultural backgrounds to their de-ranged lives. Their fantasies were thus made actual in solid structures, to form for them, together with farming, the ground of reality. Their brains, I have argued, were now wired so differently from those of *Homo sapiens* that they had what have been described as object-recognition modules, colour-perception systems, grammar and linguistic modules, etc., that were entirely different from those of their hunter-gatherer forbears. The way they experienced the world was no longer the way most useful to natural selection for them to perceive it, but the way most beneficial to stratified societies, each operating its own perverted cultural selection. One of the basic changes relates to the view of the land: the change from *Homo sapiens'* view that 'we belong to the land' to that of *Homo degener* that 'the land belongs to us'. They regarded their domestic environments under the protection of their Farmer Gods as holy and good, and their former home, the wilderness, as unregenerate, disorderly and evil. Hence they blackened what to their hunter ancestors had been, as it were, white – the wilderness – and whitewashed what was, from an evolutionary standpoint, black. They have consistently sworn, generation after generation, that black was white and white was black. This has not only constituted a collective falsehood but, in diagnostic terms, the essence of a collective madness, or what I have described as a collective primary schizophrenia. They were now separated from their original evolutionary path, and so from reality, by what I have described as a double skin of ice, a frozen sea. With the spread of *Homo degener* populations throughout the world, and the consequent despoliation of the wilderness, the skin of ice has grown thicker and *Homo degener's* grasp on reality ever more tenuous.

For instance, for some of a religious bent, reality has lain with God alone, in a life hereafter; for others, reality is the immediate actual environment and daily round, which forms their present situation. Both are man-made, artificial worlds; they are unnatural and unreal worlds which are nonetheless seen by their protagonists as real. While the supernatural has the dubious merit of remaining virtually unchanged to believers down the millennia, the domesticated world of *Homo degener* has become increasingly unreal with every agricultural/industrial revolution on the original re-evolution, for each has further abstracted *Homo degener* from contact with the real world. Our reality – including our ideas of right and wrong and how to behave – is now profoundly affected by the media, and by élites who have privileged access to the media. When President George Bush of the USA was re-elected in 2004, he said:

We are an empire now and when we act we create our own reality.

Today, most people's experience of what remains of the wilderness, true ground of reality, is through television, which mediates images of the natural world through a camera lens. It is fundamentally a vicarious experience. We are now faced with what is described as virtual reality. This technology gives the users the sensation of being inside a computer-generated world – in which they can be and do what, and where, they like – encouraging them to enter ever more deeply into the surreal and to draw even further away from the real.

Virtual reality aims to provide sedentary *Homo degener* people with an artificial electronically generated environment, a computer-generated virtual environment which changes as it would if their bodies were in motion, enabling them from the comfort and safety of a virtual world to explore the universe with the aid of probes bearing the electronic equivalents of their five senses. Thus probes to Mars, for instance, would relay the sights, sounds, feelings, tastes and smells of the Martian environment to deranged beings who have lost all sense and meaning of the real wilderness and whose senses and brains have been perverted over thousands of years out of a freedom of movement in the horizontal into the virtual movement in the vertical of imprisoned beings – and that includes climbing the social ladder and spiritual ascent into the presence of their Farmer God. Just as *Homo degener* people believe that the social world that surrounds them today (or a life hereafter) is the real world, tomorrow they may live out a computer-generated virtual life while all the time believing that to be reality. Such a situation could become widespread, particularly amongst those who have little or no contact with a fast disappearing wilderness. For under group pressure and deprived of all external reality testers, people tend to conform in their behaviour and eventually their beliefs, even if it means departing further from reality to do so. This process will be reinforced by what Andrew Marr has described as

> ...a new class-system of the mind ... not so different from the mental divisions of the medieval world. At the top are the illuminati, the great teachers and visionaries who tell stories about the way the world is. In the digital age...computing power is making these scientific narratives ever more compelling, intricate and exciting...
>
> Below the illuminati are a huge new class of well-informed digital workers and users who will enjoy that enlightenment – the guild-members of the system, the stone-scratchers, the people getting degrees in virtual reality programming. And below them, I fear, the digital peasants, consuming the same old vivid hokum that people have always enjoyed.[1]

The proliferation of virtual reality environments – including the experience of a digital forest as though it were alive, an experience of both being and seeing – will inevitably help people forget the need to protect the natural environment around them, in which their hunter-gatherer forbears had their real seeing, being and becoming. Bereft of what originally made them human, a profound irony pervades *Homo degener*'s search for truth, reality, identity and eventual brotherhood in harmony of humans and nature, because their very search has involved the destruction of that which is sought!

Is it not ironical that the cartoonist Trog[2] should have represented the new South Africa in a flag signposted *Blacks, Whites & Coloureds Only*, united in a land which only yesterday Archbishop Tutu proclaimed was a land stolen, with the aid of the Bible, from the Blacks? For how did the Blacks come by that land if not by its violent seizure from the San (Bushmen), the original inhabitants? The new flag unwittingly celebrates robbery with violence from the San – robbery with violence from which no good can possibly come, ever. And why? Because the only truly human and good peoples are hunter-gatherers like the San who obey the natural law enjoining peaceful non-exploitative relationships with other humans and with the land. Nelson Mandela forgave the Whites, but who can forgive the Blacks and the Whites their destruction of the San and his wilderness home, the true home of humankind? Their reconciliation is illusory, precisely because it leaves out of account one whole dimension: *Homo sapiens* and wild nature. Such an unwitting omission nullifies their reconciliation, for that reconciliation is itself irreconcilable with, implacably hostile to, their relationship with *Homo sapiens*, that is, to their own real identities as human beings.*

Ever since *Homo degener* took 'a wrong turn' in that 'dark and sacred wood', forcing him 'to labour, socially, psychologically, against the natural grain of being',[3] he has been subconsciously aware of having lost something invaluable, irreplaceable – an awareness of a paradise lost. He has never ceased to search for and lament lost innocence, the lost path, the golden time, the natural grain of being. The search is still pursued in the individual life and in literature today. John Steinbeck, for instance, wrote this of his friend Ed Ricketts ('Doc'):

> He was walled off a little, so that he worked at his philosophy of 'breaking through', of coming out through the back of the mirror into some kind of reality which would make the day world dreamlike. This thought obsessed him. He found the symbols of 'breaking through' in *Faust*, in Gregorian music, and in the sad, drunken poetry of Li Po. Of the *Art of the Fugue* he would say, 'Bach nearly made it. Hear now how close he comes, and hear his anger when he cannot. Every time I hear it I believe that this time he will come crashing through into the light. And he never does – not quite.'

> And of course it was he himself who wanted so desperately to break through into the light.[4]

---

*The return, in 1999, of 100,000 acres of land to the Khomani Bushmen by President Mbeki of South Africa can be seen as a first step in a deeper and more meaningful reconciliation.

Hermann Hesse wrote in similar vein, evinced in the thoughts of his Dionysian character, the artist Goldmund. He mused that people travelled through the world without really knowing anything, meeting with many challenges and promises, and with so much natural beauty, yet always there was something missing, something longed for,

> ...as though a veil would be pulled back off the world; till the feeling passed, and there had been nothing. The riddle was still unsolved, the hidden magic unrevealed...[5]

Or there is Colin Thubron, novelist and travel writer, who acknowledged within himself

> ...a congenital sense of alienation, immutable since childhood, but unexplained... Even self-knowledge, it seems, he equates with pain. 'Some people accommodate very well to what you would call reality; their present situation. There seems to be no argument in them, no dream, no anything. I think those people are what you would call mature, and I think a lot of artists are rather naive, because they are unreconciled, because they still have some kind of questing which goes on as if they haven't exactly come to terms with the world... You could say that any of our dissatisfactions as human beings stems from a feeling of being cut off from some primal happiness.'[6]*

That primal happiness is to be found only within the real world of wilderness. Novelists are well aware of the illusory nature of 'reality'. However, it is not, as many of them believe, the ultimate illusion. This is reserved for *Homo degener* peoples themselves, who are neither real nor true in any evolutionary sense, but an artefact of their own anti-evolutionary design. This book, *The Human Reality*, is itself the end product of a search for reality, an attempt to tear aside the mask – to break through the ice – concealing and distorting the truth of humankind. The situation of civilized people is akin to that of the skater mentioned by Coleridge who sees, through the transparent ice, his shadow in the water:

> There's the figure, scudding along, yet not intent upon the scene before him: rather his eyes are fixed on the flimsy skin of ice over

---

*We all have within us a deep core of sadness, and poetry and music call to it.

which he skates. Yet it's not *at* the ice he's looking, but *through* the ice, and what he's looking at with so much concentration is his own shadow mirrored in the water underneath. The object of his fascination is separated from him by the ice over which he slides: if it were otherwise, he'd be in the water, drowning. To embrace that shadow would be to die, and yet this it is – a shadowy counterpart – to which he feels drawn.[7]

Philip Hobsbaum suggests this imagery affords a useful clue to the nature of Coleridge's malady – that paralysis of the will that froze one part of his being off from another, and an agonizing dichotomy between potential and achievement. In the same way it affords a clue to the nature of *Homo degener*'s malady – the freezing off of the civilized part of *Homo degener*'s being from the natural, of an anti-evolutionary being isolated and imprisoned apart from an evolutionary being moving freely within nature, and an equally agonizing dichotomy between potential and achievement. In terms of Coleridge's imagery, the skater is the civilized human being, the skin of ice all the paraphernalia of several agricultural and industrial revolutions separating civilized people from their original evolutionary selves, and the skater's shadow in the water is that real evolutionary self moving most vivifyingly in concert with all other life within the wilderness.* Though they might take apart, analyse or observe the primates and other animals to discover signs of their true selves, they are nonetheless separated by the veils and concrete products of those agricultural and industrial revolutions from the objects of their fascination. Coleridge attempted to kill the pain of the ever-present shadow by recourse to drugs, while in his poem of that name he caused The Ancient Mariner to kill the albatross – a seaman's symbol of freedom, purity and perfection – that was shadowing him. Civilized people, meanwhile, have killed the pain of the shadow behind the veil of floodwater of the Mesolithic in myths of a Fall and euphoric new Creation and in a variety of other physical and psychical drugs, displacement activities and conflict behaviour, including the destruction of the albatross, primary habitats and primary hunter-gatherer kings, all symbols of freedom, purity and perfection. All

---

*The attempt to rejoin that self in the wilderness – or, in terms of Coleridge's imagery, 'To embrace that shadow would be to die' – has indeed caused the deaths of many who have felt compelled to trek into such as the Alaskan wilderness to 'find themselves' without the support of its true hunter-gatherer inhabitants. One person who did find herself with such support was Marlo Morgan, who depicted her epic journey across Australia into her real self in company with an Australian Aborigine group (described as 'The Real People') in her book *Mutant Message Down Under* (HarperCollins, 1995).

thereafter are haunted by that self-same shadow: a crime committed – and a penalty exacted for it.

The urge to 'break through into the light' (Steinbeck), the hope that 'a veil would be pulled back off the world' (Hesse), the 'feeling of being cut off from some primal happiness' (Thubron) are instinctive responses to the echoes of the 'deep concordance between man and the natural setting' (Steiner) that once existed, echoes of the music of the symphony of life of the kingdom of nature, conducted by the Great Spirit, to which all human beings once danced. *Homo degener* peoples are now divided by a deepening barrier of pain – the frozen sea of a primary collective schizophrenia that each generation inherits – from their real inheritance, evolutionary path and destiny under the natural flux and law. Franz Kafka said:

A book must be an axe for the frozen sea within us…

and this book is my attempt to break through that ice, to immerse myself, metaphorically speaking, in the waters beneath the ice – the ice that is formed by the artefacts and illusions of civilized society – to find my other half, my true potential drowning beneath those waters. This book is an invitation to others to do the same, to bring them to a truer knowledge of themselves. Armed with an understanding of the past, and so of the present, they will be able to answer the perennial questions: who and what am I, where have I come from, why am I here and where am I going?

The Spanish poet, Garcia Lorca, rightly suggested that lost innocence can only be found through 'duende', the spirit of the Earth, 'the mysterious power everyone feels but no philosopher has explained'. That innocence – which may be described as a world-loving wholeness of vision, a unity of psyche and physique within the wilderness – is only to be found amongst *Homo sapiens* hunter-gatherers immersed in the spirit of the Earth. Every generation of *Homo degener* children suffers a primary disillusionment as their innocence is subverted by the adult world around them. *Homo degener* can only recover an innocence lost 12,000 years ago by giving back the Earth to its rightful inheritors and by humbly offering himself to them as pupil.

Appendix x

A Return to the Way of the Ancestors

The second main form of revolution called for by certain members of the scientific community in order to solve our problems is the antithesis of the first (outlined earlier in Part I, Chapter 8). It involves the return to a simpler life-style within a world of self-sufficient village communities living in accordance with an ecological world view that embraces the Way of the ancestors and renounces the way to the stars. While the latter is less a revolution and more a logical development from earlier agricultural and industrial revolutions, the former requires a paradigm shift, a revolution both in thought and in deed. It too would involve the attainment of a sustainable environment, but by a quite different route: by invoking the science of Deep Ecology that would sustain life at the community-based village level. Those who advocate this ecology-based revitalist movement believe it necessary to reverse the impoverishment and degradation of rural life by multinational corporations by encouraging and enabling people to become, or to remain, small farmers and artisans; by satisfying local needs through local markets, while at the same time encouraging the phasing out of multinational corporations, together with the science and technology which they employ to develop society and the natural world along lines most profitable to themselves. The University of Plymouth and Schumacher College in England, the Earth First movement in the USA and Living Lightly* are among those teaching and practising sustainability through holistic science. In this connection, Mahatma Gandhi

---

*Living Lightly pioneers agree on a range of practical solutions to escape the global consumer culture, including eco-villages, urban living and working through co-operatives, local exchange trading systems, etc. They believe 'that the emerging global market is in effect a new world empire worshipping false gods of consumerism and greed. They think the empire will disintegrate, as other empires have done. In anticipation of that collapse, islands of refuge must be prepared. Whether a worldwide financial crash or an ecological catastrophe happens or not, these experiments will serve as beacons lighting a route into the next century'.[1]

attempted to stem the rising tide of the globalization of industry and commerce as it affected village India, but with little success. This is the major difficulty with this idealistic revolution: it is bucking a trend which has involved societies world-wide over many millennia reaching up to the stars in order to escape their wretched earth-bound existence.

This second main form of revolution does not take into account the primary re-evolution that has already occurred and which makes revolution into World Government and continuing ascent to the skies a logical progression. Even though many people in the Third World are involved in ecology-based revitalist movements, such movements do not allow for the fact that many people down the millennia have surely been only too keen to escape the hard – even harsh – conditions of the small farmer's and village artisan's existence, making their emigration from the land a major factor in the growth of cities and states. They are undergoing what has been described as a 'world revolution of human expectations'.

> This revolution is part of the homogenization of taste and attitude – which is stressing many societies (note the current debate in China about the respective importance of *spiritual* and *material* values), but which can only have one eventual outcome.[2]

Furthermore, nationalism, and the need to modernize and industrialize along the lines of European states, and thereby to avoid humiliating eclipse on the international stage, are powerful forces that defeated the likes of Gandhi. Islamic and Hindu fundamentalists, while seeming to react against Western economic imperialism and the disorientation of their cultures by Western technology and industrial development, are nevertheless only too keen to embrace the latest nuclear technology. Even the most profound implication of a return to the Way of the ancestors – that it would enable people to realize that they are an integral part of nature – is wrong unless such a return embraces a return to the hunter-gatherer way of life. A state of being integrated within nature can only pertain amongst those who are primarily hunter-gatherers. Sedentary small farmers, gardeners and artisans are already unavoidably disintegrated and divorced from wild nature, if only because their sedentary occupations necessitate keeping wild nature at bay. So the second main form of revolution – while being infinitely more commendable than the first, and even offering islands of refuge in the event of catastrophe – is, I believe, as inherently self-defeating and must, like the former, fail.

Appendix xi

A Composite Animal

Examples of what may be described as composite animals in nature are the marine creature *Siphonophora* and the termitary. Eugene N. Marais writes of *Siphonophora*:

> The great peculiarity of these creatures is that every full-grown specimen is a composite animal composed of hundreds of individuals. The single individual is born by a budding process from the generative group of the composite animal. These newly born individuals swim round freely and are able to continue life singly and reproduce themselves. Each is a perfect marine creature with mouth, stomach, swimming apparatus and sexual organs. If by chance a group of *Siphonophora* happen to meet, they cling to each other. In some species organic union takes place immediately, in others something less than this. But apart from this small difference the final result is the same. Immediately after the union the single individuals undergo a curious change. One group forms a complicated swimming apparatus; another group becomes the stomach and digestive system; and yet another group develops into the sexual organs of the composite animal. One group even takes on hepatic functions and becomes the liver. Each individual of such a group loses all its separate organic functions. Those of the stomach group, for instance, forget they ever sought food or had a sexual life of their own. The new organism is a perfect whole animal. Were you to see it in its perfect stage you would not dream that it had been formed in this way from separate individuals.[1]

Likewise the founding individuals of a termitary undergo extraordinary changes in order to form group organs.

In every termitary there is a brain, a stomach, a liver and sexual organs which ensure the propagation of the race. They have legs and arms for gathering food; they have a mouth...

Another fact one should constantly remember is that, if there is the least grain of truth in this theory of development, then just as certainly the termite was originally a perfect flying individual insect, of which the queen and king are the prototypes. The union of these individuals and the wonderful changes which resulted from it is a late development in the history of the race. If the blind, wingless, sexless soldiers and workers are not a degeneration of the perfect king and queen type, then the opposite conclusion will have to be accepted: the perfect king and queen must be a development from one or other of the sexless types, and that cannot be the case. There are other biological facts which indicate that the imperfect types are the result of degenerative change of the perfect insect. The rudiments of wing buds and of sexual organs in the sexless types show clearly the way development, or rather degeneration, has gone.[2]*

Compare the origins and growth of rudimentary nations of deranged farming peoples with those of the composite animals exemplified above. Just as the wingless and blind worker and soldier termites would appear to be degenerate descendants of a perfect flying individual insect, the deranged gregarious worker, civil servant and soldier members of nations are also the result of a degenerative change of a relatively perfect human being. Like the individuals making up the composite *Siphonophora*, which lost all their separate organic functions, many *Homo sapiens* individuals lost their integrated organic functions as hunter-gatherers. Those organic functions were thereafter disintegrated and perverted to the growth of organisms resembling giant human beings, whose members became specialized as head and intellect, fighting arms, stomach and hands and feet. They formed composite animals – comprising people, domestic animals, plants and machinery – as different from the perfect individual as the camel from the whale. Their members were in effect grossly imperfect, just as they are today.

---

*From the standpoint of the termitary itself, all its inhabitants are, of course, relatively perfect and perfectly adapted to their rôles, just as is the termitary to its rôle within the natural environment. Such is not the case with members of nations, although it is the intent of Science, with the aid of genetic engineering, eventually to perfect them.

The Human Locusts

So extraordinary a change has taken place amongst humans in the last 12,000 years as to make them the subject, not of evolution as one species amongst many others within nature, but of convergent evolution of separate Sacred Species of composite animal divorced from nature. The appearance and behaviour of

Homo sapiens sapiens

Homo sapiens non sapiens

so differs from that of *Homo sapiens* as not only to make them seem to be different species but as actually to cause *Homo degener* to treat *Homo sapiens* as though he *were* nonhuman, a different species. Their different appearance and behaviour may be compared with those that exist between the gregarious and the solitary locust, which until recently were regarded as different species because of the remarkable differences in their appearance and behaviour. For the behaviour of *Homo degener* is sufficiently like that of the gregarious locust as to warrant comparison – the word *locust* has long been applied to persons 'of devouring or destructive propensities'; while *to locust* is 'to swarm and devour as locusts do'.[1] These phrases neatly describe the behaviour of the waves of *Homo degener* farmers and land developers down the millennia as they spread over the face of the Earth. In this connection, it is noteworthy that the Native Americans said of the invading white man that 'They were everywhere like locusts'.

The most peculiar characteristic of the desert locust (*Schistocerca gregaria*) is its two forms or phases, solitary and gregarious, which are entirely different in appearance and in habit. As juveniles, solitary locusts vary in colour between dark green and brown. They resemble typical grasshoppers, and show no desire whatsoever to gather in swarms. They are relatively inactive and only come together as adults when mating. They fly mainly at night. Gregarious juveniles, on the other hand, are yellow with black markings. Their dominant motivating drive is the urge to mass together.

They develop into adults that gather in swarms of millions of insects. The swarm flies by day and can daily devour 2,000 tons of vegetation.

These phases are so different that the locusts were long considered entirely separate species. The two are indeed identical genetically, but the adult form assumed by any individual is determined by the conditions under which it grew up. The critical factor is population density combined with a chemical affecting the eggs. A few young locusts kept in a large cage during the period of growth will emerge as solitary grasshoppers. But if a large number of the same young are crowded into a small cage, they develop into the gregarious locust.

The solitary form of locust is widely distributed throughout the desert areas of the Middle East and North Africa. If, however, a large group of eggs happens to be deposited in a locality where a lush growth of vegetation follows the desert rains, a gregarious migratory swarm may start to form. 'Outbreak areas' include the reed beds along river valleys in the Middle East, and in the arid hills of North Africa following heavy rain.

Now it might appear that the migratory locust is unique in its ecological relationships, since the conditions in which a generation of young grows up regulate not only the number of individuals in a population, but even dictate their physical form and their pattern of behaviour. Indeed it is unique, though the ecological relationship of population size, physical form and behaviour of gregarious deranged people to the greenhouse conditions of their birth and growth, in contrast with those born free as hunter-gatherers, is sufficiently like that favouring migratory locusts as to warrant their comparison.

Emerging from a probable genesis in the heart of Africa, the whole essence of the evolution of *Homo sapiens* lay in a slow movement of small groups and solitary hunter-gatherers across a land treated as no man's land. Like a few young locusts, kept in a very large cage, which emerge as solitary locusts, each generation of people emerged as hunter-gatherers and explorers, apparently evincing no desire whatsoever during their hundreds of thousands of years evolution as hunter-gatherers permanently to congregate and settle around agriculture. On the contrary, hunter-gatherers were very much a part of the natural system. They depended on nature for food and individual fulfilment, while their numbers, like those of all other creatures subordinate to the natural flux and law, were regulated and controlled by an evolutionary process involving survival of the fittest. Nature fostered *Homo sapiens* impartially, as it did all other species, and was therefore in full control of an extremely delicate situation.

Following the primary fall of humankind, forcibly de-ranged hunter-gatherers, crowded like a large number of locusts into very small cages, eventually developed into the gregarious agricultural type, whose most dependable sources of food were their protected domestic environments, where surely were born the greatest number of children. Their cultural and reproductive behaviour, which went out of control with the loss of their hunter-gatherer skills and obedience to the Great Spirit, remained essentially irresponsible and out of control as their subsequent conflict behaviour became ritualized and institutionalized under the authority of their Farmer fertility Gods and Goddesses. Thereafter, the great river valleys became the main 'outbreak areas', in which originated what have come to be known as civilizations, where main critical factors were population density, a plentiful supply of food and fertility cults encouraging the fecund growth of populations, together with what may be described as a chemical affecting each generation of children – the collective memetic inheritance of the nation. The reproduction of similar greenhouse conditions down the ages has ensured not only the rapid growth of populations, but dictated too their physical form and parasitical behaviour.

The urge to congregate and mass together in great numbers, like gregarious locusts, and to consume daily hundreds of thousands of tons of vegetation in their voracious advance through the land, have been dominant motivating drives of civilized peoples. This gregarious instinct and mass behaviour have been principle elements in the development of

Homo sapiens sapiens
Homo sapiens non sapiens

– their most recent by-products are mass meetings, mass education, mass entertainment, mass production and mass destruction – and, as such, are entirely foreign to the real nature of humankind. Their behaviour more closely resembles that of insects generally than that of *Homo sapiens.*

Homo degener members of composite landowning animals are as different in their collective appearance and behaviour from *Homo sapiens* as are the gregarious members of the migratory locust swarm from the solitary locust, so different in fact as to appear to be different species. *Homo degener* and *Homo sapiens* are not different species, but, like the migratory locust as compared with the solitary locust, they are made to appear and behave as though they were by reason of *Homo degener* people's dominant deranged motivating drive to mass together in great numbers, their incorporation and growth within the regulated greenhouse conditions and atmosphere of the nation, and their treatment of *Homo sapiens* as though they were nonhuman, a different species to the extent that *Homo degener* has driven *Homo sapiens* to the brink of extinction. The vast majority of humankind is no longer the subject of evolution as individual *Homo sapiens* men and women, but of convergent evolution as

<u>*Homo sapiens sapiens*</u>
Homo sapiens non sapiens

members of nations. It is as though the gregarious locust swarm had entirely replaced the solitary locust as the norm of locust evolution. The consequences would be equally terrible.

Appendix xiii

The Neuropathology of the Nation

Human beings underwent an extraordinary change in learned behaviour when they were forced out of their rôle as hunter-gatherers. No longer attuned to the natural creative potential and needs of the individual integrated as a king of natural food pyramids within the nervous system and flux of nature, they and their behaviour were ritually redirected and bent to the nervous system and all-consuming drive to vertical growth of nations. It is my contention that this ritual change in outlook and behaviour was so fundamental as to constitute a change in the nervous structure of those affected, a biochemical change affecting the whole nervous system of the deranged individual.

Niko Tinbergen has pointed out that ritualization not only results in making the movement more conspicuous; it also makes it more specific, in the sense of the characteristic of the species. The process of ritualization, making the derived movement more conspicuous and more specific as a signal, therefore tends to obscure the origin of the movement. But even more important is the fact that ritualization causes the movement to become increasingly different from its original, in turn causing the underlying central nervous structure to change.

> With progressing ritualisation, the displacement-activity loses its displacement character and becomes incorporated into the pattern of its 'new boss'.[1]

In the case of

Homo sapiens sapiens
Homo sapiens non sapiens

the new boss was the nervous system and Life-Force to ascent of the nation itself. The creative nervous system and life-force of the individual

580

were ritually displaced, redirected and made subservient to the nervous system and Life-Force of the nation. The activities of

<u>Homo sapiens sapiens</u>

Homo sapiens non sapiens

began to assume an obsessive up and down movement in the vertical. They began to build physical and psychical edifices and stairways up to the sun, the moon and the stars, and down underground and to the Underworld, a displacement movement up and down, bearing overtones respectively intimidating and submissive, against the ever-present threat of the wilderness. Each nation was fundamentally a stage for the ritualized displacement display of élites against the wilderness seen as a hostile environment. Each élite has been judged on its stage performance, not by any impartial objective standards related to the original evolutionary behaviour and true needs of *Homo sapiens* unpossessively immersed in and attuned to universal laws, but by its own highly partial peers attuned to laws surrounding the rights of possession of each nation, and rewarded or punished accordingly. The masses, meanwhile, have unthinkingly provided the stages and applauded the performances. As displacement movements are essentially illusionary and incomplete movements, serving mainly as outlets for repressed and pent-up emotions, the ritualized displacement activities of élites oriented in the vertical had to be prolonged by means of myth into an illusory after-life and immortality, else their transitory lives of suffering would have remained entirely meaningless and unsatisfactory. How much more impressive the display if, as in the case of the Pharaoh, it is projected into an after-life!

I have stated that the individual nervous system and life-force of deranged men were ritually suppressed and redirected following the Mesolithic. But how does this tie in with what we actually know about the nervous system? How might the change that has occurred be expressed in terms of neurology? The change referred to has already been described as a biochemical response to a position of checkmate: deranged men were the victims of a collective primary schizophrenia, which in the main also describes the pathology of their ritualized conflict behaviour and redirected responses.

Jonathan Miller[2] has argued that until quite recently students of the nervous system believed in a vertical model of nervous organization in the human being. Prior to Darwin, Herbert Spencer had elaborated an evolutionary notion of the nervous system in which he posited a double animal, as it were, in every living creature. Within the higher, well-integrated, organized animal at the summit of its own evolutionary branch was an older, more incoherent animal which represented its ancient incapable ancestry. This theory was later developed by a clinician, John Hughlings Jackson. The papers in which Jackson expressed his fundamental ideas of evolution and dissolution in the nervous system appeared between 1860 and 1870. Forty years later his theories were developed by Sir Henry Head, a consultant neurologist at the London Hospital, and his colleague W.H.R. Rivers, a psychiatrist and anthropologist, who together undertook an experiment on the sensory nerves to the skin, with Head as the guinea-pig. This involved severing the nerve supplying Head's forearm, then joining together the cut ends of this nerve with silk sutures. In other words, the nerve was put back again in physical continuity. The fibres, however, had been interrupted. Living nerve fibres will grow together again after they have been severed, providing anatomical continuity is maintained. Thereafter, Head submitted himself to a series of minutely detailed investigations on the recovering sensation in his own arm, involving a series of graduated assaults on his skin. From their observations Head and Rivers went on to elaborate a theory of the central nervous system which they used as an explanation.

They claimed to have uncovered an earlier stage in the evolutionary development of the nervous system prior to its refinement in human beings. In the crude early stage of recovery – which Head and Rivers described as the protopathic stage of recovery – they revealed the more primitive stage of the nervous system, and in the subsequent stage of recovery – which they described as the epicritic stage or final varnishing of the recovered area of skin with normal, precise, accurate, graduated sensation – they returned to the fully-evolved condition of the human that we know.

Miller suggests that the idea that the human being is in some respects a double animal forms a part of the fundamental theory of Romantic poetry. Byron, for instance, wrote that poetry is the lava of the imagination, whose eruption prevents an earthquake.

Behind that proposal is the notion that there is something split about the nature of the human being, that there is a crust of higher or more familiar function beneath which are fluid incandescent levels of activity held in by this crust. There are two ways of interpreting this duplicity. You could simply propose that all individuals are fundamentally and inexplicably duplex. This makes no reference either to our ancestry or to our individual development in the womb: it simply asserts that human nature is ranked in some way, that there is a familiar surface of highly-organised public, rather decorous function, and that underneath there is some other level. It may be conceived as a rather dangerous, violent level, or it may be conceived rather more favourably, as the Romantics conceived it, as the source of some higher, inspirational level of organisation. In neither case is any reference made to the source of this duplicity.[3]

I have already argued that a dangerous, violent level exists just below the civilized veneer, while below that again is the level of hunter-gatherer. Either or both levels may contribute to the higher, inspirational level of organization. The source of duplicity is, of course, the fall from a state of relative perfection as hunter-gatherer.

The idea of ranking, of organization based on levels, is extremely old, going back at least to Aristotle. The historian of ideas, Arthur Lovejoy, devoted his book, *The Great Chain of Being*, to the subject, referring to the history of the idea that life was arranged in a scale of organization from the least complex to the most elaborate, from the lowly to the most exalted. With the arrival of Darwin, the assertion is made that not only is nature ranked in a series of scales of being, but that life itself has passed through these scales of being and has proceeded from one to the other. Furthermore, that in proceeding upwards on the scale of being, in evolving from one stage to another, the animal successively conceals residues of its older self. This raises the idea of inhibition in the nervous system as an essential feature of nervous function.

The nervous system is now conceived in terms of two sorts of neurological function. On the one hand, there is the excitatory action of the nervous system, through which it responds to stimuli from the outside world and negotiates with them more or less successfully, and behind it there's a level of concealed inhibition, active neurological inhibition, which is keeping down the dynamic, springy, antique version of the animal which is concealed under this evolutionary heap of subsequent development... We can see that both Jackson's and Head's and Rivers's results flow from the basic idea of a restraining higher level holding down some old animal. They were in fact proposing that the epicritic level – that refined, delicate, well-located, graduated function of the intact nerve – was exerting two functions within the nervous system. One was its positive function of providing accurate information about the outside world, and the other was a domestic, internal affair of suppressing the older protopathic animal that was crouched like a monster, like a dog beneath the skin, like something older which had had to be suppressed, which the injury had released and which for the moment was running rampant.[4]

Head and Rivers were criticized for claiming that the protopathic stage of recovery was a picture of an earlier stage of evolution, because this meant that the older animal was incoherent, ungraduated in its response, gross, unlocalized, savage and vague. Yet what sort of animal could survive with such gross, incoherent and vague responses to the outside world? Although this criticism may rightly be levelled against their theory in relation to the human being, in the light of what I have tried to show concerning the nation as a giant human being their theory can be seen to be very relevant. Though Head and Rivers had no appreciation of this aspect of society, their work was nonetheless inevitably influenced by the social environment of the time. As members of a nation, they had unwittingly revealed, not the nervous organization of the human being, but that of the nation, a giant human being that could only survive in the world by changing the environment to suit its own protopathic condition; behind or below that again lay the true neurological function of the individual as hunter-gatherer – altogether a state of affairs that was entirely unknown both to Head et al. and to Miller. Miller continues:

> It's profitable to look at some of the sources of inspiration which are not declared overtly in Head's and Rivers's work, or indeed in Jackson's. It's important to remember that at the time when Jackson was writing his 'Theory of Evolution in the Nervous System', England has passed through a series of social upheavals in which riot and public disorder has alarmed a large number of middle-class intellectuals. It was, moreover, less than a hundred years since the French Revolution had produced a sense of enormous anxiety about the incoherent, violent, ungraduated energies of the mob. It's interesting to note in this respect that when Jackson came to use a metaphor for describing the double symptoms of the central nervous system, he actually made reference to a social model: 'If the governing body of this country were destroyed suddenly, we should have two causes of lamentation. The loss of services of eminent men and the anarchy of the now uncontrolled people'. And this paper was written within a few years of the Hyde Park Riots in 1867.[5]

Again it is important to note that this is precisely the model of the nervous system of the nation as a composite animal, of a *Homo sapiens sapiens* élite (head) governing and suppressing a potentially anarchical *Homo sapiens non sapiens* majority (hands and feet), the whole established against a threatening external world, while at the same time suppressing and perverting the true neurological function of each member as *Homo sapiens* hunter-gatherer.

> It's now nearly seventy years since the formulation of Head's and Rivers's great notion of the protopathic and epicritic nervous system, and the idea has undergone a great deal of modification in that time. However, it still exerts a considerable influence...
>
> Competing with this notion is a theory of nervous function which is beginning to replace it. No one wishes to repudiate the notion that we have in fact climbed up an evolutionary ladder and have arrived at our excellent current condition through previous states. But what I think we would quarrel with now is the idea that evolution consists of a concentric series of restraints upon these older conditions, and that you can reveal these older conditions by injury or assault or by special procedures of one sort or another. It's quite possible that this vertical model of nervous organisation is no longer useful for examining the nervous system that we now know.[6]

Although the vertical model may be outmoded when applied to the individual, it is nonetheless applicable to the nation regarded as a giant human being. In contrast, the true evolutionary development of the individual nervous system was argued by Patrick Wall, then Professor of Anatomy at University College, London, who suggested that when Henry Head proposed that a newer brain had developed, suppressing and supplanting an older one – a 'dog beneath the skin' or a frog beneath the man – he presented a highly unlikely picture of the brain, and of an evolutionary process.

> Isn't it far more likely that evolution would build on rather than suppress a system which is already capable of achievements of remarkable delicacy, such as the frog's ability to catch flies, and wives?
>
> We need to look on our own brains as marvellously expanding the capability of the frog's brain by adding not just complexity but new abilities, such as the ability to set up in our heads a model of the outer world on which we can try experiments to see what happens. An ability like that, which you can call 'mind' if you wish to give it a label, seems to be a far more efficient use of an evolutionary process than the hierarchical development of a higher system which will suppress a lower system.[7]

With regard to the nervous system of the individual human being, evolution certainly built on rather than suppressed a system which was already capable of remarkable delicacy. As I pointed out earlier, the evolutionary path leading to humankind and the real freedom of humans lay in absorbing more and more of the natural world, both past and present, into the self the better to express and fulfil the self. Human freedom and understanding lay in adapting to the present in the light of the past, not in denying and falsifying the past, as did *Homo degener*. What Head and Rivers have done – however unwittingly – is to formulate a theory of the nervous system which precisely describes that of the nation as a composite animal (see figure App. xiii.i).

From 10–5000 BC, generations of deranged men were forced to undergo an experience similar to that undergone by Henry Head under experimental conditions, when the nervous system and life-force joining many hunter-gatherers to the wilderness and Great Spirit were severed by natural catastrophic conditions and culture loss similar in their anxiety-producing effects to the deluge-like social conditions during and following the French Revolution, that so impinged upon the imagination of Jackson. As in the case of Sir Henry Head, the cut ends were artificially joined together – in the case of early deranged people, the silk sutures were a primitive agriculture and primitive religion. But the nerve fibres had been interrupted. However, unlike the experimental case of Head where anatomical continuity was maintained, in the case of early *Homo degener* a physical anatomical and psychical continuity integrated within the kingdom of nature was broken. The fibres, after the acute phase of the injury had worn off, were forced to recover sensation, not in hunter-gatherer movement in the horizontal as heretofore, but in static cultivation in the vertical. It was an artificial sensation, a collective memetic inheritance, which began to be transmitted. Once the decision was made as to how to behave in this new and painful situation, and the behaviour was started, information no longer relevant to sustaining that behaviour was excluded – including any information and ecological understanding previously stored in their memories as hunter-gatherers. They now 'paid attention', not to the real call of the Great Spirit, but to the illusory call of a Farmer God. A nervous system and fibres that had evolved harmoniously integrated in a freedom of movement within the whole body of the kingdom of nature were now reconnected to that body as though they did not belong, as though deranged people were trying to veneer over and escape the pain of that body, seeking a new nervous pathway, system and body in stasis away from the natural world.

A nervous system and fibres that had 'sung for joy' within the paradisial

Fig App. xiii.i

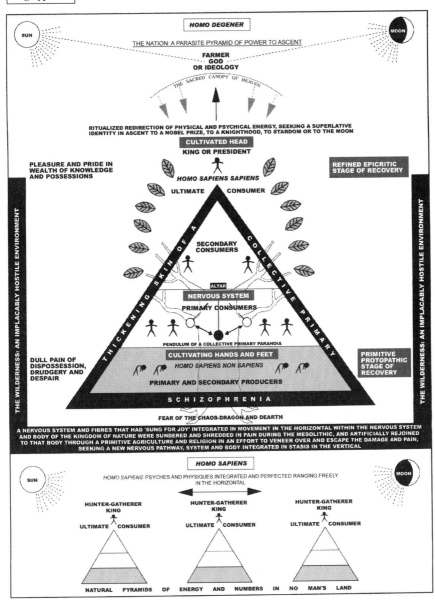

nervous system and body of the kingdom of nature were now sundered and shredded in pain. The world-loving extrovert in no man's land became a world-fearing introvert on someone's land, whose pain required the constant ministration of priest-scientists. For just as pain is the most common driving force to bring patients and doctors together, the pain of the Mesolithic first brought deranged men directly under the power of magicians, medicine-men and priest-scientists who specialized in developing measures to minister to the insecurities and pains of *Homo degener* societies. Slowly the protopathic stage of recovery gave way to the epicritic stage of the sensitive refined few, when the priest-scientists varnished over the injury with cultural innovations, myth and ritual. But in doing so, of course, the varnishers became permanently ensconced as the élite makers of theories and fictionalized history in both East and West – the *Homo sapiens sapiens* priest-scientists at the summit of parasite trees of knowledge – while the primitive *Homo sapiens non sapiens* labourers and slaves remained at the coarse protopathic stage of recovery. Compensatory pleasures and pride in a wealth of knowledge and possessions in more elegant and graceful surroundings became the permanent prerogative and inheritance of those standing head and shoulders out of the water on the backs of those below them, while pain became the permanent inheritance of those only just managing to survive at the bottom of the heap. Pain, not the immediate physical pain that all of us experience, but the special pain of humiliating degradation, disease, dirt and dearth has been the life-long experience of the poor. It is this collective condition of deranged people, epicritic at one end and protopathic at the other, that makes for a composite animal whose behaviour is that of an animal at war both within itself and with the world without. It is a protopathic composite animal that suffers constant pain arising from the two-fold fall of humankind.

Here was a protopathic composite animal that stood little chance of ordinary biological success – unless it walled itself in, manufactured its own food, armed itself and changed the environment to suit its own deranged diseased condition. It follows, in agreement with the processes outlined by Jonathan Miller, that the nervous system of the nation, working upon the nervous systems of its members, has exerted three main functions of its own. First, there were its excitatory actions and movements towards the outside world, the 'positive' (though in reality negative) function of providing and responding to totally inaccurate information about, and misinterpreted stimuli from, the outside world regarded as a hostile environment. Secondly, there was the domestic, internal affair of suppressing the older protopathic animal, like a 'dog beneath the skin', which was the primitive incoherent stage in the development of deranged men. Lastly, by the back door or through its own basement, there was the level of concealed inhibition, active neurological inhibition affecting all the members, the inhibiting function of the collective memetic inheritance of the nation that helped it to sit on and suppress the dynamic, springy, true version of *Homo sapiens* attuned to truly positive memetic functions of the evolved nervous system – the jack-in-the-box of the previous evolutionary condition of *Homo sapiens*, which is concealed under the heap of subsequent anti-evolutionary development.

In the light of Patrick Wall's argument quoted above, this multi-layered suppression of a system is further evidence that

<u>*Homo sapiens sapiens*</u>
Homo sapiens non sapiens

is not an evolutionary descendant of *Homo sapiens*, but an anti-evolutionary one. Furthermore, this argument reinforces, and is reinforced by, that relating to the physiology of

<u>*Homo sapiens sapiens*</u>
Homo sapiens non sapiens.

I argued earlier that because the brain of the individual is no longer integrated in movement with the sensorium in a true experience of the natural world, but is subservient to the collective brain of a composite animal at war with that world, a physiological change must have taken place in the brains of those concerned. This change is all the more likely to have taken place in the light of the redirection and multi-layered suppression of individual nervous systems by those of composite animals over a period of some 12,000 years.

Appendix xiv

Environmental Degradation

It was argued in Part I that the hunter-gatherers prior to the Mesolithic must have been important in restructuring food chains, and had thus become highly significant variables in their own environments. Such modifications as they might have effected as hunter-gatherers would have been generally life-enhancing. Other modifications of their environments resulted from natural causes such as vagaries of weather, fluctuations in the quality and supply of food, and local catastrophes such as flood, earthquake or volcanic eruption. The degeneration of the hunter-gatherer into primitive farmer turned people into destroyers of Earth environments. Their domestication of other animals to produce their food and fibre, and the parallel domestication of plants for food and fabric had an immediate deleterious impact on the quality of the environment (see figure App. xiv.i)

The farmers' domesticated herbivores, like the deranged farmers themselves, no longer ranged widely in search of food. Like them, the herds were restricted in their movements, and consequently destroyed the vegetation in their immediate vicinity rather than living in harmony with it. Overgrazing of the vegetation led to erosion of soils that had been evolving through millions of years. Dr W. Frank Blair[1] points out that primitive man made two serious mistakes in the domestication of his herbivores.* First, he domesticated too few species and moved these around the world, with the result that they used the resources of environments to which they were not especially adapted and hence had a major detrimental impact on the plants they ate. Dr Blair instances the very different effects of the native red kangaroo and the introduced sheep on vegetation in arid lands of Australia. The adapted kangaroo *clips* the grass; the sheep pulls it up by the roots, destroying it. Primitive

---

*This is not to forget that domestication itself was the most serious mistake of all.

Fig App. xiv.i

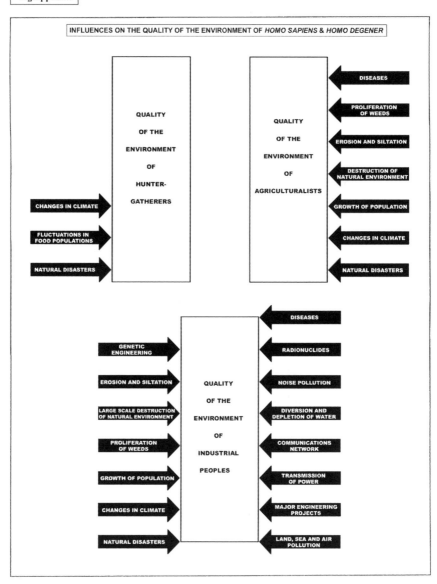

INFLUENCES ON THE QUALITY OF THE ENVIRONMENT OF *HOMO SAPIENS* & *HOMO DEGENER*

people's second mistake was in domesticating the goat as well as the sheep. Both are highly destructive of the vegetation on which they feed, but goats destroy not only the grass but woody vegetation as high as they can reach. Goat 'deserts' exist today in much of the Mediterranean region, in northern South America and in parts of North America. Goats rank second only to *Homo degener* as destroyers of environmental quality.

As regards the parallel domestication of plants for food and fabric, Dr Blair has this to say:

> As man learned to cultivate and harvest domesticated plants, his agricultural practices provided greater insults to the environment than did his herds of grazing animals. Breaking of the soil increased the amount of erosion and his crops depleted the nutrients in the soil. Environment-wise, there were again mistakes as well as unavoidable changes in ecological systems. Two important features of natural ecological systems were altered – stability and diversity. An undisturbed interaction of animals to their environment (ecosystem) has stability; the plants and animals exist together in what ecologists refer to as a climax condition. Each ecological niche is filled. It would be very difficult for an exotic species to establish itself in such a system because the ecological niches are occupied. Farm lands, on the other hand, are in a continual state of ecological imbalance. The natural tendency is for flora and fauna to change toward the steady state of the ecological climax but cultivation and cropping prevent this. The result is that certain hardy, pioneer species have followed agricultural and other man-made disturbances around the world. These hardy plants are the weeds about us. They are the product of man's agriculture.[2]

It will be appreciated that agriculture and its related pioneer species of plant (weeds) are themselves the products, not of true human beings, but of exotic pioneer species of composite animal.

> Perhaps the most far reaching agricultural practice in its adverse environmental effects has been the planting of crops in monocultures. High diversity of species promotes stability in ecological systems, as there are many checks and balances and alternate routes with respect to predator and prey. A well-tended field crop, on the other hand, is maintained as a system that is as simple as possible, and weeds and all plants other than the crop in question are periodically removed. Instead of stability there is now an erratic system in which things such as insect pests flourish.

Having upset the balance of ecological systems by his agricultural practices, man turned naturally to the control of weeds and insect pests that his practices had created or encouraged. This led to further unwanted ecological effects.[3]

The impact of farming people on the quality of the environment had greatly increased over that of the hunter-gatherers, turning humans into destroyers of Earth environments. But it was still slight by comparison with the impact of industrial or technological people.

Homo degener's technology took a giant step forward with the arrival of organized agriculture combined with organized religion and organized war, as in the Egypt of the Pyramids. While the Church effectively prevented any further advance between the years 500–1500 AD, the relative freedom of the Renaissance encouraged a new flowering of the sciences and of technology. But it encouraged too the flowering of the Protestant Ethic of individual salvation. With the renewal of the alliance between technology, religion and war under the canopy of a Messianic Protestant Christianity, and more recently still under the canopy of a Messianic Stalinism, technology in the past few hundred years has undergone explosive growth.

Dr Blair points out that technological people represent at most two to four thousand of humankind's millions of years on Earth; that much of the technology that we take for granted – motor cars, aircraft, radio, television, computers – has all come within less than 100 years; that the by-products of this technology have exceeded all of humankind's past mistakes in their adverse effect on world environments; and that this 100-year explosion of technological advance, together with the damage done to Earth environments through the production of food and fibres and the provision of housing, has greatly multiplied the number of pressures on technological people's world environment over those of farming people, to create the present environmental crisis:

The major pressures on the world's environments today fall into four broad categories. Firstly, there are those that result from efforts to use technology for the control of agricultural pests, both plant and insect, and for the control of the carriers (vectors) of disease organisms. Secondly, those that stem from the use of the internal-combustion engine in automobiles and aircraft. There are those related to the fact that there are just too many people in too many places in the world and finally, there are those that accompany man's major feats of engineering – dams, irrigation systems, highways, power distribution systems.[4]

If the steam engine was the principal engine of economic growth in the 18th century, and the railroad in the 19th, the automobile was in the 20th. As pointed out by Mark Hertsgaard,

> Manufacturing cars is the biggest industry in the world; fueling them is the second biggest.[5]

Yet the cost has been staggering. Up to a million people a year worldwide are killed in car accidents, while environmental costs include air pollution, destruction of farmland and wilderness, and the intensification of the greenhouse effect.

> The world's five hundred million cars are responsible for between 20 and 25 percent of current greenhouse emissions; only electric power plants, with 25 percent, and deforestation, with 25 percent, are as damaging. But the car's share of global emissions is growing rapidly, as more and more people around the world join the auto economy. With motor traffic expected to increase by 60 percent over the next twenty years, the UN Population Fund has projected that, by 2025, 'developing countries could be emitting four times as much carbon dioxide as the industrialized countries do today.'[6]

However,

> If the automobile was the most economically important technology of the century, nuclear fission was the most important technology, period, because it raised the question of whether there would *be* any human life beyond this century... The embrace of atomic energy not only threatened the end of human civilization, it condemned humanity to environmental and health injuries that would take decades if not centuries to heal, and it saddled us with waste disposal responsibilities that for all intents and purposes will last forever.[7]

As regards the latter, and as I argued in the main text, physicists may build what are called transmutation reactors to destroy plutonium and reduce the amount of radioactive waste.

Homo sapiens' technology enabled them to adapt and survive in the wild world, whereas *Homo degener* peoples have pursued technological mastery over that world.* The cumulative effects of agriculture and

---

*Their respective religions have complemented their technological development.

industry on the world's environments are extraordinary and overwhelming. *Homo degener* peoples now possess the ability to make the Earth uninhabitable. They can do this quickly through nuclear holocaust, or more slowly – but just as surely – through the adverse effects of their past and present agricultural practices and technology.

Appendix xv

An Allegory of Challenge and Response

Situations reminiscent of the humiliating, survival-threatening and voiding circumstances surrounding the origins of *Homo degener* peoples challenge them to respond in ways similar to their original response, and so on down the millennia. Nowhere has this similarity been more apparent than in Europe since the Second World War.

When *Homo degener* peoples lost their self-governing abilities and character as hunter-gatherers during what may be described as the Great Depression of the Mesolithic/early Neolithic, their kind eventually united under the government of élites of rudimentary composite animals. Subsequent humiliating, survival-threatening conditions have occurred when collective government and the framework of normal life have broken down. This was, for instance, the situation in Germany following the Great Depression which gave rise to Hitler, and again after Hitler had laid waste Europe, forcing the inhabitants to unite. European unity was in the air because all the defeated peoples of the area felt dwarfed by the super-powers and saw unity as the only way to regain some power over their own destinies – just as the original cohesion of primitive farmers in rudimentary composite animals occurred, I believe, because these humiliated and defeated peoples were dwarfed by the all-powerful presence of the wilderness. The following extract from an article on Europe after the Second World War provides an example of the operation of challenge and response at a secondary historical level following the collapse of government. It may also, with the aid of my italics, be read at the deeper primary level, as the story of the loss of a *Homo sapiens* hunter-gatherer structure and security following the Mesolithic, with Hitler and the German armies personifying the chaos of waters, marching forests and desiccation overrunning the land.

> Over a large part of the Continent – Germany, France, Italy, the Low Countries, Poland, Yugoslavia – *the framework of normal life*

in an organised society had broken down. It took time to re-create this, to restore the authority of the state, to get the processes of administration and law working again, to eliminate the black market and inflation, the habits of illegality and violence. *It took even longer to restore people's sense of security and confidence, which had been destroyed by seeing the institutions on which these depended swept away or turned against them.* [my italics]

I lay stress on this because it is too often forgotten that the recovery of Europe was not simply a question of making good material shortages and getting its economy to work again: there had to be political and social as well as economic recovery, and until these had gone far enough to restore at least a measure of confidence, *Europe was deeply troubled by insecurity and fear – as great a source of weakness as lack of supplies and low production. I lay stress on this feeling of insecurity for another reason. Insecurity was the background to the quarrel between Russia and the Western powers who had been her allies during the war.*[1] [my italics]

Similar situations arose more recently in the aftermath of war in the former Yugoslavia and in Rwanda and Burundi. Every anarchical situation caused and suffered by *Homo degener* is a reflection of the deluge, desiccation and crisis of the Mesolithic, when the framework of normal life of certain of their organized societies broke down, and the natural structures and laws on which *Homo sapiens* originally depended were lost to them. It took time to create new sources of authority. Just as humiliating fear, uncertainty and insecurity formed the background to the quarrel between Russia and the Western powers who had been her allies during the war, they formed the background to the quarrel between deranged peoples and wild nature that had previously been their ally and friend. Their humiliating sense of insecurity and fears arising from the ever-present threat of invasion by the wild environment – an all-pervading threat of extinction – were likewise an inescapable part of the context in which decisions had to be made, in which unity in rudimentary composite animals occurred, and in which relations with other composite animals grew up. Thereafter they began to take the initiative against the wild environment, and eventually against each other. By their failure to readapt, a 'machinery of suspicion and counter-suspicion, action and counter-action'[2], came into full operation.

More precisely, their suspicions have led nations to fear that unless a particular territory was expropriated, or a particular technical development took place, or a pre-emptive strike was made, the enemy would get there first. An example was America's fear in general, and Robert Oppenheimer's in particular, that the Germans were developing the atom bomb and that therefore they must develop one first. The threat of humiliating eclipse forces technical development.

Later, during the Cold War with Russia, it was suggested that Polaris was an answer to a Soviet threat that had not then developed. Its success produced the response with which it had been intended to deal. In general, under the historical imperative of challenge and response, the US did what encouraged the Soviet response, and in turn they did what encouraged the US response, in each case threatening the other with humiliating eclipse, such as when US politicians

> ...spoke of the 'devastating humiliations' of the Soviet Union's achievements in space. They urged that scientific resources in the US be 'mobilised to a wartime basis because we are at war.'[3]

Appendix xvi

Aspirations to Ascent

While the trait of hope amongst *Homo degener* peoples may appear to control the future, that trait derives from and is subordinate to the primary driving force of the historical imperative, the oft-repeated challenge of the humiliating threat to survival that originated in the profound void of the Mesolithic, when dreams both lie in the dust (challenge) and are born (response).

Hope amongst deranged people lies at the opposite pole to hopelessness and despair. Both form part of the Life-force to ascent of the nation, but both originated in the profound void of the Mesolithic. In other words, both hope and despair on the part of *Homo degener* are expressive of an escape or failure to escape respectively from the humiliating void of meaninglessness and fear of wild nature. The hopes of deranged people, especially as they find an ultimate expression in a Farmer God of Hope of everlasting life in a world hereafter, are essentially delusional, arising as they do out of the void created when the real hopes and dreams of *Homo sapiens* hunter-gatherers were destroyed.

Hope, all the hopes of *Homo degener* – including the hopes and dreams of all those throughout history escaping Darkness towards the Light of a Promised Land, including too the apotheosis of Hope, dreams and ideas, the Farmer God of the community, divine embodiment of the fatal tendency of *Homo degener* to go on hoping – are in fact delusive, discounting as they do the experience of past history and concealing the present personal and national abyss, behind and below which lies the yet greater abyss, the profound void of the Mesolithic. There is now a world-wide phenomenon, which psychiatrists call the 'existential vacuum', of people complaining of 'a sense of total meaninglessness in their lives'. As someone paraphrased Paul Valéry, if God made everything out of nothing, the nothing shows through. Yet we must go on hoping, dreaming, for without such hopes and dreams our world would indeed be meaningless.

'I have a dream,' said Martin Luther King: but that dream is broken. As other dreams have been, time and time again: the dream of the French Revolution, of the British Empire, of the 'war to end war', of the Communist Utopia. Most resounding of all for our time – Jefferson's dream of an America which accepts that all men are created equal. That dream is broken. But must I stop singing, like Hölderlin, because of the fragility of all aspiration? I do not think this is in fact what happens. We celebrate – even in outdated forms at times – because we must.[1]

It is the compulsion to go on hoping – even the cry of a baby born to a destitute woman is heard as a cry of hope – that constitutes the outward and visible psychical expression of the underlying threat of eclipse, the humiliating abyss in which delusional hopes are born and into which they are inexorably and inevitably cast down. The delusion of hope amongst *Homo degener* peoples is dangerous precisely because it distorts and conceals the past, and hence the present, for the sake of a brighter future. Notwithstanding mounting evidence that scientists are leading mankind towards an ultimate abyss, the delusion of hope remains firmly to the forefront of the Ascent of *Homo degener* to the skies, whether it be in the Christian expectation of the life of the world to come or the scientific hope of a genetically engineered immortality amongst the stars.

John Steinbeck speculated on a mutated humankind which is either progressing towards extinction – when the mutation described by Steinbeck as corresponding 'to the thickening armor of the great reptiles' will see us destroyed – or marching into the forehead of God. Steinbeck suggests that, on the basis of the overwhelming evidence, extinction is the more likely outcome. However, despite such evidence,

> ...the trait of hope still controls the future, and man ... will approach perfection, and, finally, tearing himself free, will march up to the stars and take his place where, because of his power and virtue, he belongs: on the right hand of the $^{\pi}\sqrt{-1}$. From which majestic seat he will direct with pure intelligence the ordering of the universe.[2]

Appendix xvii

Living in the Clouds

In Western developed nations in particular people residing at or near the top of society see little of the poorer bottom half who, because they are separated geographically, culturally and economically from the wealthier, have all but disappeared from sight. This situation is exacerbated as the world is increasingly turned into a playground for the well-heeled businessman and tourist. The effect world-wide of establishing air-conditioned staging posts for travellers from the developed nations has been to emphasize most cruelly the distance between the tops and bottoms of parasite pyramids, between what Paul Fussell has described as 'top out-of-sight' and 'bottom out-of-sight'. This distance is vividly conveyed by the following report of an arrival by air in a city in the Indian sub-continent which, although written in 1970, is nevertheless ubiquitous and timeless in its application. It portrays the extraordinary disparity in living standards between voyaging 'haves' and the imprisoned 'have-nots' – a gap which, despite aspirations and efforts to the contrary, has been steadily widening on a global scale – and the isolation of the voyaging 'haves' from the common herd.

> ...indeed one might, I think, without ambiguity, have described the view as 'underdeveloped'. Or rather it was typical of the sort of development which the West has imposed over the years on most of the urban East. The road, the whole landscape, was as flat and characterless and depressing as the sum total of all airport roads everywhere. But as well, it was poverty-stricken – literally. A plague land in mud and corrugated iron. Ferocious pot-holes and a cynically optimistic population count were the most obvious impressions. It was Ramadan and people were hawking vigorously in the gutters, following the Prophet implicitly in not allowing even their own saliva to break their daylight fast. It was a cliché of despair: basement department, lower depths.

Then an immense white building, a splendid example of late Hilton-Moorish, reared up in front of us through the clutter of huts and kerosene flares. In its imposition over the city it would have disgraced any hostelry of the same sort in New York or London... In the four days I was in the hotel no one seemed to leave the place at all. They arrived all right, by the score, unsteady but grateful, like the survivors of some frightful accident: a convention dealing with the problems of the Third World, a Japanese TV crew, German salesmen, UN officials and men from the Chase Manhattan Bank... The fairly beautiful people streamed around the shopping concourse on the ground floor – the beauty salons, the gift shops and airline offices – chatting and laughing, sticking close to the lift banks and intuitively avoiding the area round the swing-doors, as though a sudden drop in the air-conditioning might drag them screaming into the real weather outside.[1]

The Americans, as the inheritors of the Victorian tradition, have built staging posts across the world so that their people will find a Little America wherever they go. Whether at home or abroad, together with other prosperous peoples of the world, they live as sheltered from the noise, dust and disturbance of modern life as if they dwelt on the summit of a mountain. Theirs is a structured isolation, maintained even on the great highways on land, at sea and in the sky. They travel in a rarefied atmosphere in air-conditioned cars, trains, ships and planes between points of known safety, avoiding contact with the real weather outside. They live and move cocooned in a rarefied atmosphere from mountain top to mountain top, indifferent to, if not unaware of, the wretchedness and plight of the moiling mass of hands and feet below them, and to the plight of the wilderness that lies beyond the ghettos of rich and poor alike.*

---

*Such a scenario may also be likened to that of monkeys moving transversely through the leaf canopy of a rain forest at a level high above the forest floor.

Appendix xviii

The Convergent Evolution of the
Eco-computer

Corporate growth is leading inevitably to an increasing globalization of commercial and industrial activity. Multinational corporations are concerned with the development and distribution of myriad products – including the development and distribution of energy, the growth and distribution of food, and the mining and transport of minerals – and with the supervision of the flow of capital and information. In their monitoring and regulation of the economic structure of the planet, multinational corporations are heavily underwritten by the World Bank and International Monetary Fund (IMF). The economic infrastructure thus created is a Global Market (or Global Shopping Centre) supplied by the processes of Global Production (or Global Factory) and run by the world managers. As well as manufacturing and supplying the necessities of modern life, multinational corporations have a deep commitment to the development and use of weapons and propaganda to sustain the global economic order. Companies and nations need to collect and process data in order to survive and to prosper in an increasingly competitive and hostile world. To that end they rely more and more on the collection and dissemination of information through the use of computers linked with sensors of many different types established in all areas of what Geoff Simons, in his book *Eco-Computer*, describes as the ecosphere – in the sea, on land, in the sky and in space – monitoring environmental phenomena and environmental changes that might either assist or hinder the sustained growth and globalization of the economic order.

As I argued in Part II, those organizations or people who disseminate and control knowledge or information have power – over individuals, over the nation and over world resources. Moreover, computers have been developed to gather and control information. The digital computer developed as a convergent mixture of mathematics, logic and engineering. As machines that mimic people, computers perform such 'mental' tasks as knowledge generation, decision making and artistic creation. Increasingly they are taking over as the brain, as the storage place and disseminator of the collective memetic inheritance of each nation. Computers store, analyse, disseminate and communicate information through electronic networks linking factories, laboratories, offices, schools, military complexes and government departments throughout the world.

> Today computing, communications and other linked technologies have converged to define IT – information technology, a central shaping force in modern society.[1]

Such technology increasingly not only shapes buildings and affects the geography of towns, but is also uniting the world into a unified IT-based global culture.

> Today it is often said that Information Technology is the required ticket to economic and political development – but increasingly a few countries, or a few multinational corporations, will dominate the world in IT terms. It is no accident that the emerging world culture is being framed by the countries with the largest IT presence. Countries *lacking* such an IT element – and this means the vast majority of the countries of the world – can only serve as recipients of products, attitudes and values generated elsewhere.[2]

The developed world is already suffering from an information overload, while the developing countries will continue to suffer an information underload. A Global Market, sustained by IT, supplied by the processes of Global Production and run by world managers will generate an international consumer community of the affluent and influential concentrated mainly in the developed world. (Already, according to 1998 United Nations statistics, the 358 richest people in the world, headed by Bill Gates of Microsoft, had more wealth, and so more power to influence events, than the poorest 45 per cent of the world's population.)

> We can envisage a *stratified* global community in which old divisions have broken down and new ones have been erected. The criteria for high status, we may judge, will be the qualities needed for management of the Global Shopping Centre. The world managers

will be the new élite, an unremarkable development in the light of current political and commercial attitudes.[3]

Such a stratified global community is what I have already described as a super-organism comprising an integrated hierarchy of all the nations governed by an élite that includes scientists and technocrats, whom I have described as guardians of the globe, whose task in monitoring the ecosphere will be greatly assisted – and perhaps even eventually supplanted – by what Geoff Simons describes as a world eco-computer, an intelligent electronic matrix. Such a global artificial intelligence will not be deliberately devised like a predetermined blueprint; rather it will emerge as the inevitable outcome of the growing needs on the part of the world economy in general, and of the multinational corporations in particular, for the accumulation and processing of global data collected by means of computer-based systems that will be increasingly linked in global electronic networks. A host of new (converging) technologies are accelerating the pace of movement towards the establishment of a global intelligence.

The eco-computer is emerging, and will continue to do so over this century, from the convergence of many disparate though linked technologies: in particular, the convergence of computing, communications and sensor-based artefacts. Computation, communications via electronic highways – using a mixture of submarine cables, land lines and artificial satellites – and a complex array of artificial sensors have converged in a revolutionary fashion to form an electronic matrix that will become established as an autonomous global system. It is the evolution of a complex array of artificial sensors that will give the eco-computer its autonomy, an increasingly autonomous global intelligence.*

As well as having implications for the monitoring and control of society at large – in the studies of traffic flows, market research, demographic change, land use, etc. – remote sensing, with the aid of geostationary and orbiting satellites, is becoming most important in the study of environmental areas such as oceanography,† forestry, meteorology and air pollution. Millions of sensors – many associated with robots – sited in

---

* See Part III, Fig 3.1 I describe the Computer Bank Centres as a termitary-like Central Intelligence.

† As reported by Tom Clarke ('Neptune's Net], New Scientist, Vol. 168, No. 2269, 16 December 2000, p. 33):

A European, American and Japanese initiative called Deep Earth Observing System aims to network the world's oceans with cabled or moored observatories.

There are systems under development for the Atlantic, the waters around Japan as well as the Mediterranean.

It is expected that the entire ocean will be wired in 50 to 100 years.

the seas, on land, in the sky and in outer space in artificial satellites will be the eyes and the ears of the eco-computer, providing the data for computer processing and transmission over communication routes for storage and analysis, enabling the evolving eco-computer to monitor, 'understand' and 'regulate' the global environment. Geoff Simons has likened the eco-computer to an intelligent or 'smart' building, in which there are computer-based systems, communications links and sensors: the latter are concerned with regulating air-conditioning, temperature and fire prevention mechanisms, thus revealing an 'ecological' concern. The eco-building is using an eco-computer to secure its survival in an optimum state.* Such a building will also contain a variety of expert systems concerned with market trends, government regulations, company law, etc. Smart buildings are then connected to one another locally or across the world. The neural links grow and interconnect, and smart buildings become connected in nodes in local networks which in turn become nodes on international arrangements. Thus the systems of the eco-computer are established.

> 'Smart buildings' – of one sort or another – are being developed and installed all over the planet; and each may be seen as analogous to a subsection of the human brain. Pons, medulla, visual cortex, hypothalamus – all are linked together in networks to provide the total entity with a unified structure and purpose (perhaps the hypothalamus is a metaphor for the smart building).[4]

Simons argues that the eco-computer may usefully be regarded '*as an emerging person*.'[5] In terms of my argument relating to the development of nations as giant human beings, the eco-computer may be seen as the nervous system and brain of a giant human being, or superorganism, comprising the multinational corporations and nations hierarchically ordered in one global culture. Such a hierarchy is already being created by the globalization of consumption and production, as the affluent and influential developed nations stand on the backs of the poorer developing nations in their efforts to reach up to the stars. As the nervous system and brain of the resultant giant human being, the eco-computer will concentrate in itself what I have described as the five-fold concentration of power to the vertical self-aggrandizement of élites. To that end it will also concentrate in itself the

---

*Cf. Part II, Chapter 5, in which I argued that the predicted city of the future, linked by 'glass nerves' that 'feel' their environment and condition in a way analogous to a termitary, will warn of adverse changes through a neural network of computers.

collective memetic inheritance of nations. People, as cells within the superorganism, will tap into, and be governed by, the eco-computer brain (and its collective memory and memetic inheritance) via the Internet.

Simons argues that the eco-computer will be helped to develop its own autonomy and evolve strategies for eco-initiative on a global scale – such as control of the weather, using cloud seeding and other techniques – with the aid of artificial intelligence (AI). Artificial intelligence will be developed in conjunction with expert systems that draw on specialist knowledge contained in massive databases. These will contain all current knowledge relating to particular fields – such as farming, medicine, geology, finance and law. Such specialist programmes, which will be able to think using high-level AI techniques, will be found in every field. As computers learn to think like people, though on a far greater scale and at an enormously faster rate, computational activity will be progressively transferred from human beings, *Homo degener*, to artificial machines functioning as centres of AI. This will create a computer dominated global village in which both the mental and physical activities of *Homo degener* will be increasingly marginalized. As the eco-computer processes policies and judgements, its decisions will increasingly be arrived at in ways beyond the comprehension of human beings, thereby assuring the autonomy of the eco-computer and the increasing impossibility of challenging such decisions. There will be no way for *Homo degener* to check whether the global system is performing erroneously. Yet it cannot but be a fractured and imperfect system that is liable to error.

According to Geoff Simons, the eco-computer will be a fractured intelligence:

This means that the eco-computer will evolve as a fractured personality... It will embody no single overriding objective: there will be no single purpose to which all the system elements will unambiguously work. There is some significance in the emergence of a world culture. Many differences will melt away as a common (global) value system, stimulated by international communications, impinges on every national culture. But national and corporate differences – of attitude, aim and interest – will continue to influence the shape of the emerging global intelligence. The developing global culture will not be sufficiently influential to provide the global eco-computer with a single coherent objective.[6]*

---

*'(We do not need to dwell on the interesting paradox of many communications networks helping to sustain and improve human life on Earth while an equal number of global networks are used to lay plans for the total destruction of the human race.)'[7]

Simons speculates that, because the emerging world intelligence will not be a coherent, unified system,

> The eco-computer ... *will have multiple personalities.* Perhaps, in such circumstances, it will also evince other signs of mental illness. How apposite if Man's persistent derangement came to trap him in the interstices of an artificial global insanity![8]

This most insightful observation is entirely in keeping with my findings relating to the psychotic condition of nations seen as giant human beings.

In the absence of global catastrophe, the emerging eco-computer will come to evolve a host of local, as well as global, intelligences dedicated to particular purposes. Regarding its multiple personalities,

> We can well imagine a situation in which particular subsystems sets are vying for supremacy against other configurations: a particular region of artificial intelligence may use high-level techniques to incapacitate another configuration – so allowing one 'personality' to become dominant. But then the disabled configuration, with a host of AI-linked back-up systems, will search for survival strategies, and in due course manage to assert a (temporary) dominance. In such a fashion, following the characteristic modes of true multiple-personality types, key areas in the eco-computer will swing from control by *one* subsystem intelligence to control by another. We can speculate in such a way about how other forms of derangement might come to characterize the behaviour of the global electronic intelligence. In a few centuries from now, *Homo sapiens* may well be trapped in the nodes of a mad machine![9]

And not only *Homo sapiens* – or rather *Homo degener* – but also the entire natural world. Planet Earth was one world before and following the advent of the human race. Now the global economy, and the globalization of the economy, has overlaid the ecosphere, while technology is turning the planet into a vastly different unified world, in which a cloak of highly artificial structures lies over the natural environment. This comprises an emerging global nervous system, where the natural nervous system governed by the natural flux is transmuted into wires, electrical pulses and computer programmes. The evolution of machine sensors is analogous to the evolution of the senses of biological systems. Just as bacteria evolved throughout the world and developed senses whose world-wide integration has helped maintain the stability of the biosphere, so the integration of computer-based systems and sensors will ostensibly help maintain the stability of *Homo degener* societies while at the same time overlaying and destroying the integrity of natural systems throughout the world.

> It is clear that the eco-computer defines one of the futures that we can envisage, and perhaps we can say more – that this is the most likely future of them all.[10]

However, a future determined by the convergent evolution of electronic and biological technology, which is increasingly in competition with one determined by the natural flux and law,* is, on the evidence, a self-defeating and self-destructive future – one that is no future at all.

---

*Or what I describe in Part III, Chapter 4, as a direct confrontation between an artificial world ordered primarily as a vertically orientated superorganism and the biosphere ordered primarily as a horizontally orientated superorganism.

Appendix xix

The Black Sun

The story of civilization is a tragedy in the classic sense of the word. It is the story of the loss of the kingdom of the hunter-gatherer kings, of *Homo degener's* subsequent awareness of loss – as intimated in the myths of a Fall and a Paradise lost – but of their blindness as to its cause and full extent, and of their tragic struggle to replace that loss with Kingdoms of their imaginations,* destroying their true kingdom and its true kings in the process, thereby creating the circumstances of their own entrapment and destruction. It is an absolute tragedy, a tragedy above and beyond all others, encompassing all history and the whole world.

George Steiner once undertook a detailed exposition of absolute tragedy, particularly as portrayed in drama and poetry. He pointed out that amongst the absolute Greek tragedies – plays that end in human destruction or self-destruction – Sophocles' *Antigone* in particular offers 'a profoundly black vision of man as a kind of threatened guest and stranger on this earth'. At the end of *Antigone*, repentance on the part of Creon leads him to the right action that 'brings upon himself the hideous, annihilating vengeance which destroys Antigone, his son and, of course, himself'. White and black: the white of repentance turns to the black of annihilation.

Again, as Steiner points out of the Judaic world of the Bible, 'there are insights into the self-destructive nullity of human life', which are, however, 'hedged about within the Bible by constant and eloquent elements of reassurance, of the unalterable belief that finally, even in its anguish, the universe makes sense and that the punishments which God visits upon us are justified or deserved. Above all, and contrary to the world of Creon, there is the assurance that if we repent there will be reparation.'

---

*The Kingdoms they have struggled for are the man-made parasite pyramidal Kingdoms on Earth, and their quintessence, the Heavenly Kingdom above. Both deny and destroy the true kingdom of humankind – a no man's land of natural food pyramids – on Earth.

610

However, while drawing attention to the contrast between Athens and Jerusalem – 'between the vision of man as an alien or even unwanted guest in this world, and of man finally at home with God in the universe which must make ethical sense' – Steiner argues that, as Russian and European Jewry in the 20th century entered an age of catastrophic destruction, of self-destruction, across large areas of the world, major elements in the Jewish imagination seem to have been directed back to that black world of Hippolytus and the *Antigone*. Steiner instances three visions – those of Osip Mandelstam, Franz Kafka and Paul Celan – which not only seem to deny the Messianic gates of Jerusalem, but to speak instead of that black possibility which dominates Greek tragic drama. He quotes Mandelstam as writing:

At Jerusalem's gate a black sun has risen;

and as writing of his own birth:

I awoke in my cradle blinded by a black sun.

These observations entirely negate both the traditional place of entrance into the Messianic hope and kingdom, and the cradle as the place of dawn and new beginning. Mandelstam himself was eventually removed to one of the Soviet Russian death camps where he 'died in anonymous abjection in indifferent darkness'.

Steiner then writes of Kafka anticipating, in *The Trial* and *In the Penal Colony*, an all-embracing world of imprisonment, torture and execution, a world in which man is rushing headlong towards self-annihilation, a world to which God is totally indifferent.

Steiner goes on to quote from a poem of Paul Celan called 'The Death Fugue', in which is the famous line:

I have drunk the milk of blackness.

'Notice again,' says Steiner, 'the reversal we met with in the *Antigone*. White and black: milk, which should be, which usually is, the very symbol of new life, of nurture, of growth, has become venom and death, the brew of night.' Similarly, Mandelstam, both in his writings and in his life, is pursued by 'a black sun'. Steiner sums up:

For the first time, perhaps, since the central chapters in the Book of Job, since the wry sadness of Ecclesiastes, Judaic thought proclaims

the finding, so crucial to the *Antigone* of Sophocles, to Euripides'
Bacchae, that man is not a very welcome guest in the house of
being.[1]

My view of the subject concurs with those of the dramatists and poets
cited by Steiner as subscribing to a black vision of humankind. *Homo
degener* peoples have indeed become threatened guests, unwelcome strangers
on this Earth, for two main reasons. First, because they are no longer
Homo sapiens, true human beings, but *Homo degener*, subhuman degenerate
people, who yet believe themselves to be truly human. Secondly, because
they have destroyed the wilderness, the beloved home of *Homo sapiens*,
which became a place of evil to *Homo degener*. White became black;
black became white. In other words, those who may be described as
white evolving as *Homo sapiens* at home in the wilderness – all together,
in Steiner's phraseology, 'the very symbol of new life, of nurture, of
growth' – were perceived as black by *Homo degener*, as 'venom and death,
the brew of night'. Yet in thus blackening and destroying both their
hunter-gatherer forebears and the place of their evolutionary being and
becoming – and so, in effect, blackening the sun whose energy enabled
the wilderness to evolve – it was *Homo degener* peoples who became the
purveyors of 'venom and death, the brew of night' while whitewashing
themselves as milk-white, as true human beings. In all this *Homo degener*
peoples have been aided and abetted by the illusory Farmer God(s) whom
they have raised up as their ultimate authority, as the divine justification
of their rectitude and whiteness. (Paul Celan struggled in some of his
poems with the evil of the Holocaust and the silence of God, as well
he might. Likewise, would such a God have stood by and condoned the
destruction of a wild world it had taken him four billion years to create?
The answer lies in what is perhaps the ultimate irony: that God's silence
is as eternal as his non-existence.) Is it any wonder, therefore, that *Homo
degener* 'is not a very welcome guest in the house of being'? The alien
outcast farmers (outcast both in myths of a lost Eden and in fact) have
in turn caused the wilderness and wildlife to become outcast; they have
turned wild nature, that had been the hunter-gatherer's friend and home,
into an implacable enemy. They are thus involved in a tragic drama, the
outcome of hubris, of disastrous arrogance on the part of degenerate
subhumans who believe themselves to be human. Because they have
blackened and terrorized the whole wild world, *Homo degener* peoples
unwittingly reside under, and are pursued by, 'a black sun'. They have
indeed created the circumstances of their own entrapment and destruction.

Appendix xx

A Cancer Called Progress

In the Prologue I questioned whether the whole idea of progress was not a mental refuge, a comforting myth, in the face of an apparent historical inevitability. I have tried to show that this is the case, and that *Homo degener* is an anti-evolutionary cancer in the body of nature. It is the inexorable growth of this cancer that is promoted as progress, in direct opposition to a true progress of humankind.

From a biological standpoint, progress may be described as improvement that allows for or facilitates further improvement, leading to increased efficiency in dealing with the challenges of the wild environment, and to greater independence of changes in that environment. This was helped by improvement in the brain and subsequent improvement of mental capacity and the acquisition, organization and accretion of knowledge. This made possible a more harmonious integration of the individual organism as a whole within the wilderness. Such a progression of our animal ancestors resulted in the appearance of *Homo sapiens* in diverse varieties of hunter-gatherer and the efflorescence of their artistic and scientific potential harmoniously integrated within the climax ecosystem of the wilderness. (Such integration is a specific requirement of evolutionary progress). With the two-fold fall of *Homo degener*, biological progress and relative perfection turned into regression and imperfection. Prevented from growing to their full stature or adulthood as hunter-gatherers, every generation of *Homo degener* peoples has remained in a state of retarded or arrested development, 'developing' only and always as doubly deprived delinquent adolescents.

They can never attain true adulthood – unless, that is, they were to readapt to their original evolutionary path. Such development as has taken place has been of the nature of a perverted memetic selection, perverting the adolescent nature of *Homo degener* to serve – whether in the capacity of agent or worker – the growth of stratified societies within an increasingly devastated wilderness. What is today described as progress is in reality a progressive scientific and technological improvement of the life conditions of *Homo degener* which yet overlays the original cultural and biological degeneration, evodeviation or regression, and furthers that regression.

The concept of progress, as it concerns *Homo degener*, is succinctly presented by Ludovico Settembrini, a character in Thomas Mann's novel, *The Magic Mountain*:

> Technical progress, he said, gradually subjugated nature, by developing roads and telegraphs, minimizing climatic differences; and by the means of communication which it created proved itself the most reliable agent in the task of drawing together the peoples of the earth, of making them acquainted with each other, of building bridges to compromise, of destroying prejudice; of, finally, bringing about the universal brotherhood of man. Humanity had sprung from the depths of fear, darkness, and hatred; but it was emerging, it was moving onward and upward, toward a goal of fellow-feeling and enlightenment, of goodness and joyousness; and upon this path, he said, the industrial arts were the vehicle conducive to the greatest progress.[1]

Indeed *Homo degener* sprang 'from the depths of fear, darkness, and hatred', moving ever upwards in a search for enlightenment. With the exponential growth of technology, some scientists, particularly physicists, see the ascension of humankind to the stars as not only possible but as essential both to the pursuit of intellectual enlightenment and to the preservation of the species in the event of the death of Earth, by which time humanity 'hopefully, will have found its rightful place among the stars'.[2] Yet the idea that humankind's rightful place is among the stars is as delusive as is the description of their ascent as progress. From an evolutionary standpoint, there is only one rightful place for humankind and that is the wild world; the belief in progress, though necessary to psychological well-being, has meant nothing more nor less that the rationalization of the drive of *Homo degener* peoples to improve their social and economic conditions by the total subjugation of that world. That means the total subjugation of all the evolutionary processes of nature to the anti-evolutionary processes of *Homo degener*: the overlaying and destruction of the diversity of natural ecosystems by a homogeneity of parasite pyramidal domestic ecosystems. That is not progress but an infinite regression, or a progressive degeneration.

The idea of progress, as it relates to *Homo degener*, may also be shown to embrace yet another delusion: the hope of the eventual perfection of mankind.

The Church and many adherents both of Christianity and of other religions believe that the perfection of humans will take place in Heaven, in a life hereafter; Science, on the other hand, with the aid of genetic engineering, will attempt to adapt *Homo degener* more perfectly to his artificial environment. But such perfection would be a universal perfection in degeneration. In reality, every day takes *Homo degener* peoples further away from the evolutionary circumstances and ground of their true perfectibility as hunter-gatherers.

As delusive is *Homo degener*'s search for a universal brotherhood of man. For not only do the parasite pyramidal structures which they inhabit preclude any possibility of equality, but, in destroying the wilderness and *Homo sapiens*, *Homo degener* peoples have destroyed the only possible ground of a true brotherhood in equality of humankind. More than that, they have destroyed the only ground on which humans can be truly described, and live, as such.

The greatest delusion of all is that *Homo degener* is truly human. In reality, all *Homo degener* peoples are degenerate members of composite animals who are fundamentally driven by the profound humiliations suffered in the two-fold fall of man. Every subsequent revolution on the original re-evolution, which gave rise to the dark veil between *Homo degener* peoples and their hunter-gatherer past, has deepened that darkness between them, adding successive layers of humiliation to the initial humiliations and self-hatred suffered by *Homo degener* peoples. These layers are in turn concealed beneath layers of narcissism and self-glorification, which persuade *Homo degener* peoples to view their dazzling ascent as progress, while blinding them to the fact that the growth and ascent of *Homo degener* nations constitute an anti-evolutionary cancer spreading over the face of the Earth.

References and Bibliography

PROLOGUE

1 Kennedy, Paul, *The Rise and Fall of the Great Powers* (London: HarperCollins, 1989)
2 Koestler, Arthur, 'The Brain Explosion', *The Observer*, 15 January 1978 (© *Guardian/Observer*)
3 Steiner, George, 'In Bluebeard's Castle – Some Notes Towards the Re-Definition of Culture', *The Listener*, Vol. 85, No. 2190, 18 March 1971, p. 327

PART I

Chapter 1

1 Margulis, Lynn, and Sagan, Dorion, *Microcosmos: Four Billion Years of Evolution from our Microbial Ancestors* (London: HarperCollins, 1987)
2 Long, John, 'The extraordinary fishes of Gogo', *New Scientist*, Vol. 120, No. 1639, 19 November 1988, p. 44
3 Margulis, Lynn, and Sagan, Dorion, *Microcosmos: Four Billion Years of Evolution from our Microbial Ancestors* (London: HarperCollins, 1987), pp. 32–4
4 Mayr, Ernst, *Populations, Species, and Evolution* (Cambridge, Massachusetts: Belknap Press of Harvard University, 1975), p. 363. (Copyright © 1963, 1970 by the President and Fellows of Harvard College. Reprinted by permission of Harvard University Press)
5 Margulis, Lynn, and Sagan, Dorion, *Microcosmos: Four Billion Years of Evolution from our Microbial Ancestors* (London: HarperCollins, 1987), p. 152
6 Geist, Valerius, 'The Biology of Health', *New Scientist*, Vol. 81, No. 1143, 22 February 1979, p. 581

Chapter 2

1 *The World At 18,000 BP, Vol. 1: High Latitudes*, Ed. Olga Soffer, Clive Gamble (London: Unwin Hyman, 1990), pp. 335–6

2 Read, Herbert, *The Meaning of Art* (London: Penguin, 1966), p. 55 (Reprinted by permission of David Higham Associates)

3 Brody, Hugh, *The Other Side of Eden* (London: Faber & Faber, 2002), p. 147

4 Boyden, Stephen, *Western Civilization in Biological Perspective* (Oxford: Oxford University Press, 1989), p. 62 (By permission of Oxford University Press)

5 Boyden, Stephen, op. cit. p. 62

6 Brody, Hugh, *The Other Side of Eden* (London: Faber & Faber, 2002), p. 308

7 Brody, Hugh, op. cit. p. 262

8 Brody, Hugh, op. cit. pp. 263–4

9 Turnbull, Colin, *Wayward Servants: The Two Worlds of the African Pygmies* (London: Eyre & Spottiswoode, 1966), p. 109

10 Thomas, Elizabeth Marshall, *The Harmless People* (London: Penguin, 1969), p. 21

11 Brown, Dee, *Bury My Heart at Wounded Knee* (London: Barrie & Jenkins, 1971), p. 316 (Reprinted by permission of Peters Fraser & Dunlop Group Ltd)

12 Brown, Dee, op. cit., p. 242

13 Lopez, Barry Holstun, *Of Wolves and Men* (London: J.M. Dent, 1978), pp. 90–1

14 Turnbull, Colin, *The Forest People* (London: Jonathan Cape, 1974), p. 116

15 van der Post, Laurens, *The Lost World of the Kalahari* (London: Penguin, 1968), p. 238

16 Lopez, Barry Holstun, *Of Wolves and Men* (London: J.M. Dent, 1978), pp. 86–7

17 Thomas, Elizabeth Marshall, *The Harmless People* (London: Penguin, 1969), p. 21

18 Thomas, Elizabeth Marshall, op. cit., p. 98

19 Ed. Phillip Tobias, *The Bushman* (Cape Town: Human and Rousseau, 1978), Foreword and p. 148

20 Beston, Henry, *The Outermost House* (London: Selwyn and Blount, 1928), p. 40

21 Turnbull, Colin, *Wayward Servants: The Two Worlds of the African Pygmies* (London: Eyre & Spottiswoode, 1966), p. 259

22 McLuhan, T.C., *Touch the Earth* (London: Sphere Books, 1982), p. 23

23 McLuhan, T.C., op. cit., p. 6

24 van der Post, Laurens, *The Lost World of the Kalahari* (London: Penguin, 1968), pp. 236–7

25 Morgan, Marlo, *Mutant Message Down Under* (London: HarperCollins, 1995), p. 61

26 Morgan, Marlo, op. cit., p. 189

27 Schaller, George B., *The Year of the Gorilla* (Chicago: University of Chicago, 1964), p. 43 (© 1964 by The University of Chicago Press)

28 Brody, Hugh, *The Other Side of Eden* (London: Faber & Faber, 2002), p. 309

29 Boyden, Stephen, *Western Civilization in Biological Perspective* (Oxford: Oxford University Press, 1989), p. 79

30 Vogel, Virgil J., 'Indian Health and Disease', *The Ecologist*, Vol. 5, No. 7, Aug/Sept 1975, p. 257

31 Reader, John, and Croze, Harvey, *Pyramids of Life* (London: HarperCollins, 1977), p. 198 (Reprinted by permission of Peters Fraser & Dunlop Group Ltd)
32 Herbert, Read, *The Meaning of Art* (London: Penguin, 1966), p. 253 (Reprinted by permission of David Higham Associates)
33 Leopold, Aldo, *Sand County Almanack* (Oxford: Oxford University Press, 1953), pp. 86, 97 (Copyright © Aldo Leopold, by permission of Oxford University Press)
34 Player, Ian, *Zululand Wilderness* (Cape Town: David Philip Publishers, 1997), p. 15

Chapter 3

1   Tudge, Colin, *New Scientist*, Vol. 109, No. 1490, 9 January 1986, p. 58
2   *The World At 18,000 BP, Vol. 1: High Latitudes*, ed. Olga Soffer, Clive Gamble (London: Unwin Hyman, 1990), p. 19
3   Hughes, Robert, *The Fatal Shore* (London: Pan Books, 1988), p. 8 (Copyright © Robert Hughes, 1986. Reproduced by permission of The Harvill Press)
4   Sandars, N.K., *Prehistoric Art in Europe* (London: Penguin, 1968) p. 75
5   *Politics and History in Band Societies*, ed. E. Leacock and R. Lee (Cambridge: Cambridge University Press, 1989), p. 15
6   *Hunters in transition*, ed. Marek Zvelebil (Cambridge: Cambridge University Press, 1990), pp. 148–9
7   Fagan, Brian, *The Long Summer* (London: Granta Books, 2004)
8   Howell, John M., 'Early Farming in Northwestern Europe', *Scientific American*, Vol. 257, No. 5, November 1987, pp. 98, 100)
9   Howell, John M., op. cit., p. 105
10 *Hunters in transition*, ed. Marek Zvelebil (Cambridge: Cambridge University Press, 1990), p. 12
11 Boyden, Stephen, *Western Civilization in Biological Perspective* (Oxford: Oxford University Press,1989), p. 89 (By permission of Oxford University Press)
12 Mostert, Noel, *Frontiers* (New York: Alfred A. Knopf, 1992), p. 52
13 Bunney, Sarah, 'Desperate times forced rise of farming', *New Scientist*, Vol. 142, No. 1931, 25 June 1994, p. 17
14 Fagan, Brian, *The Long Summer* (London: Granta Books, 2004), p. 87
15 Hemmer, Helmut, *Domestication: The Decline of Environmental Appreciation* (Cambridge: Cambridge University Press, 1990), p. 182
16 Sandars, N.K., *Prehistoric Art in Europe* (London: Penguin, 1968), pp. 77–8
17 Sandars, N.K., op. cit., p. 77
18 Thomas, Elizabeth Marshall, *The Harmless People* (London: Penguin, 1969), p. 31
19 Hemmer, Helmut, *Domestication: The Decline of Environmental Appreciation* (Cambridge: Cambridge University Press, 1990)
20 Clark, Grahame, *Mesolithic Prelude* (Edinburgh: Edinburgh University Press, 1980), p. 67
21 Delbrück, Max, *Mind From Matter?* (Oxford: Blackwell Scientific Publications, 1986), pp. 122, 125

22 Boyden, Stephen, *Western Civilization in Biological Perspective* (Oxford: Oxford University Press, 1989), p. 21 (By permission of Oxford University Press)

23 'Paradise Lost', *Earthlife* (in association with The Observer, 2 February 1986) p. 21 (© *Guardian/Observer*)

24 Fisher, H.A.L., *A History of Europe* (London: Edward Arnold, 1961), Preface, p. v

Chapter 4

1 Tinbergen, Niko, *The Herring Gull's World* (London: HarperCollins, 1965), p. 119

2 Cohen, M.N., *The Food Crisis in Prehistory* (New Haven: Yale University Press, 1977)

3 Piotrowska, Agnieszka, 'Hope for a nation', *Radio Times*, Vol. 263, No. 3443, 2–8 December 1989, p. 18

4 Braudel, Fernand, *The Mediterranean and the Mediterranean World in the Age of Philip II* (London: HarperCollins, 1975), pp. 185–6

5 Wilson, Edward O., *On Human Nature* (Cambridge, Massachusetts: Harvard University Press, 1978) p. 119 (Copyright © 1978 by the President and Fellows of Harvard College. Reprinted by permission of Harvard University Press)

6 Wilson, Edward O., op. cit., p. 119

7 Fromm, Erich, *The Anatomy of Human Destructiveness* (London: Jonathan Cape, 1974), p. 186 (Copyright 1973 by Erich Fromm. Reprinted by permission of Henry Holt and Company, LLC)

8 Turnbull, Colin, *The Forest People* (London: Jonathan Cape, 1974), p. 19

9 Sandars, N.K., *Prehistoric Art in Europe* (London: Penguin, 1968), p. 73

10 Turnbull, Colin, *The Forest People* (London: Jonathan Cape, 1974), p. 18

11 Cohn, Norman, *The Pursuit of the Millennium* (London: Granada Publishing, 1978), p. 52

12 Sparks, Allister, *The Mind of South Africa* (London: Heinemann, 1990), pp. 293–4

13 'Middle America', Supplement to *National Geographic*, Vol. 134, No. 4, October 1968.

14 Barbu, Zevedei, 'Social conflict and natonal myth', *The Listener*, Vol. 78, No. 2000, 27 July 1967, p. 116

15 Foster, Richard, 'St George and the Dragon', *The Listener*, Vol. 116, No. 2982, 16 October 1986, p. 13

16 Boyden, Stephen, *Western Civilization in Biological Perspective* (Oxford: Oxford University Press, 1989), p. 139 (By permission of Oxford University Press)

17 Hooke, S.H., *Middle Eastern Mythology* (London: Penguin, 1963), p. 131

18 Davis, Mike, *Late Victorian Holocausts* (London: Verso, 2001), p. 179

19 Sandars, N.K., *Prehistoric Art in Europe* (London: Penguin, 1968), p. 73

20 Sandars, N.K., op. cit., p.153

21 Thackeray, W.M., *Vanity Fair* (London: Signet Classics, 1962), p. 205

22 Margulis, Lynn, and Sagan, Dorion, *Microcosmos: Four Billion Years of Evolution from our Microbial Ancestors* (London: HarperCollins, 1987), p. 95

23 Schaller, George B., *The Year of the Gorilla* (Chicago: University of Chicago Press, 1964), p. 14 (© 1964 by The University of Chicago Press)
24 Lopez, Barry Holstun, *Of Wolves and Men* (London: J.M. Dent, 1978), pp. 140–1

Chapter 5

1   Tudge, Colin, *New Scientist*, Vol. 105, No. 1445, 28 February 1985, p. 2
2   Atkinson, R.J.C., *Stonehenge and neighbouring monuments* (Historic Buildings and Monuments Commission for England, 1965), p. 36 [Reproduced from Atkinson, R.J.C., *Stonehenge* (London: Hamish Hamilton, 1956)] (Reproduced by permission of Penguin Books Ltd. Copyright © R.J.C. Atkinson)
3   Renfrew, Colin, 'The builder of Stonehenge', *The Listener*, Vol. 115, No. 2964, 12 June 1986, p. 15
4   Carver, Martin, *Underneath English Towns: Interpreting Urban Archaeology* (London: Batsford, 1987), p. 36
5   Kennedy, Paul, *The Rise and Fall of the Great Powers* (London: Fontana, 1989), p. 16
6   Boorstin, Daniel J., 'The future of exploration', *The Listener*, Vol. 94, No. 2437, 18 December 1975, p. 821
7   Barnes, T. [et al.], *People Making History, Book 3. O Level History* (Harare: Zimbabwe Publishing House, 1991), p. 13 (Fig. 1.5)
8   Jacob, François, *The Statue Within* (London: HarperCollins, 1988), p. 192 (English translation copyright ©1988 by Basic Books, Inc)
9   Jacob, François, op. cit., pp. 273–4
10 Barnes, T. [et al.], *People Making History, Book 3: O Level History* (Harare: Zimbabwe Publishing House, 1991), p. 14 (Fig. 1.6), p. 38 (Fig. 3.8)
11 Kennedy, Paul, *The Rise and Fall of the Great Powers* (London: Fontana, 1989), p. xvi (Reprinted by permission of HarperCollins Publishers Ltd © Paul Kennedy 1988)
12 Bayley, Stephen, 'Say it with Buildings', *The Listener*, Vol. 100, No. 2582, 19 October 1978, p. 514
13 Bullock, Alan, *Hitler, A Study in Tyranny* (London: Penguin, 1969), p. 387 (Reprinted by permission of Reed Consumer Books)
14 Tafuri, Manfredo, *Theories and History of Architecture* (New York: Harper and Row, 1979), p. 185
15 Pearce, Fred, 'Hit and run in Sarawak', *New Scientist*, Vol. 126, No. 1716, 12 May 1990, p. 49
16 Fromm, Erich, *The Anatomy of Human Destructiveness* (London: Jonathan Cape, 1974), p. 142 (Copyright 1973 by Erich Fromm. Reprinted by permission of Henry Holt and Company, LLC)

Chapter 6

1   Sivanandan, A., *When Memory Dies* (London: Arcadia, 1997), p. 235
2   Alexander, Frank, *Fundamentals of Psychoanalysis* (London: Allen and Unwin, 1949), p. 256
3   Hemmings, Gwynneth, *What Causes Schizophrenia* (The Schizophrenia Association of Great Britain, 2001)
4   Hemmings, Gwynneth, *Disability in the Courtroom* (The Schizophrenia Association of Great Britain, 1999)
5   Howe, Gwen, *The Reality of Schizophrenia* (London: Faber and Faber, 1991), p. 23
6   Howe, Gwen, op. cit., pp. 28, 31
7   Howe, Gwen, op. cit., p. 41
8   Howe, Gwen, op. cit., pp. 36, 39
9   Young, Stephen, and Concar, David, 'Secret Life of the Brain', *New Scientist*, Vol. 136, No. 1848, 21 November 1992, p. 8
10 Klein, Melanie, *The Selected Melanie Klein* (Penguin, 1991), p. 195 (With acknowledgement to The Melanie Klein Trust)
11 Howe, Gwen, *The Reality of Schizophrenia* (London: Faber and Faber, 1991), p. 41
12 Shlain, Leonard, *The Alphabet versus the Goddess* (London: Viking, 1998), pp. 267, 390
13 Levi, Primo, *If This Is A Man* (London: Sphere Books, 1987), p. 277
14 Howe, Gwen, *The Reality of Schizophrenia* (London: Faber and Faber, 1991), p. 152
15 Hooke, S.H., *Middle Eastern Mythology* (London: Penguin, 1963), p. 29
16 Hooke, S.H., op. cit., pp. 29–30
17 Horrobin, David, *The Madness of Adam and Eve* (London: Bantam Press, 2001), p. 189 (Reproduced by permission of The Random House Group, Ltd)

Chapter 7

1   Calder, Nigel, *Timescale* (London: Chatto and Windus, 1984), p. 90
2   Steiner, George, 'In Bluebeard's Castle – Some Notes Towards the Re-Definition of Culture', *The Listener*, Vol. 85, No. 2190, 18 March 1971, p. 327
3   McLuhan, T.C., *Touch the Earth* (London: Sphere Books, 1982), p. 67
4   Caufield, Catherine, *In the Rainforest* (London: Pan Books, 1986), pp. 86–7
5   Gordimer, Nadine, 'The Witwatersrand: A Time and Tailings', *Optima*, Vol. 18, No. 1, March 1968, p. 23
6   Hemmer, Helmut, *Domestication: The Decline of Environmental Appreciation* (Cambridge: Cambridge University Press, 1990), p. 181
7   Merson, John, 'The Sacred Tree that Died', *The Listener*, Vol. 94, No. 2421, 28 August 1975, p. 270
8   Smith, Anthony, *Mato Grosso* (London: Michael Joseph, 1971), p. 53
9   Sparks, Allister, *The Mind of South Africa* (London: Heinemann, 1990), p. 28
10 Hughes, Robert, *The Fatal Shore* (London: Pan Books, 1988), p. 324 (Copyright © Robert Hughes, 1986. Reproduced by permission of The Harvill Press)

11 Thomas, Hugh, *An Unfinished History of the World* (London: Hamish Hamilton, 1979), p. 192

12 Thomas, Hugh, op. cit., p. 110

13 Bales, Kevin, *Disposable People* (Berkeley, California: University of California Press, 1999)

14 Fromm, Erich, *The Anatomy of Human Destructiveness* (London: Jonathan Cape, 1974), pp. 198–9 (Copyright 1973 by Erich Fromm. Reprinted by permission of Henry Holt and Company, LLC)

15 Thomas, Hugh, *An Unfinished History of the World* (London: Hamish Hamilton, 1979), pp. 40, 69)

16 *Dictionary of War Quotations*, Ed. J. Wintle (London: Hodder and Stoughton, 1989), p. 126 (© 1989 by Justin Wintle)

17 Arlacchi, Pino, *Mafia Business* (Oxford: Oxford University Press, 1988), pp. 227–8 (By permission of Oxford University Press)

18 Hawkes, Jacquetta, *Man on Earth* (London: Cresset Press, 1954), pp. 154–5

Chapter 8

1 Ward, Barbara, *Five Ideas that Change the World* (London: Hamish Hamilton, 1959), p. 12

2 Bradley, Richard, 'Precedents, power and prehistory', *The Listener*, Vol. 101, No. 2610, 10 May 1979, p. 642

3 Saunders, Nick, 'The ancient sky at night', *New Scientist*, Vol. 123, No. 1679, 26 August 1989, p. 58

4 Chatwin, Bruce, *The Songlines* (London: Pan Books, 1988), p. 226

5 Charbonnier, Georges, *Conversations with Claude Lévi-Strauss* (London: Jonathan Cape, 1969), pp. 29–30 (© 1969 by Jonathan Cape)

6 Hooke, S.H., *Middle Eastern Mythology*, (London: Penguin 1963), p. 28

7 Hooke, S.H., op. cit., p. 29

8 Boyden, Stephen, *Biohistory: The Interplay between Human Society and the Biosphere* (Park Ridge, New Jersey: Parthenon Publishing, 1992), p. 190

9 Karlen, Arno, *Plague's Progress: A Social History of Man and Disease* (London: Victor Gollancz, 1995), pp. 71–2

10 Mumford, Lewis, *The Pentagon of Power* (London: Secker and Warburg, 1971)

11 Shlain, Leonard, *The Alphabet versus the Goddess* (New York: Viking, 1998)

12 Pelz, Werner and Lotte, *God is No More* (London: Victor Gollancz, 1963)

13 Shlain, Leonard, *The Alphabet versus the Goddess* (New York: Viking, 1998), p. 272 (Copyright © Leonard Shlain, 1998. Reproduced by permission of Penguin Books (UK) and of Viking Penguin, a division of Penguin Group (USA) Inc)

14 Shlain, Leonard, op. cit., p. 275

15 Shlain, Leonard, op. cit., pp. 267, 390

16 Hughes, Pennethorne, *Witchcraft* (London: Pelican Books, 1965), pp. 59–60

17 Hughes, Pennethorne, op. cit., p. 61

18 Hughes, Pennethorne, op. cit., p. 164

19 Hughes, Pennethorne, op. cit. p. 104

20 Hughes, Pennethorne, op. cit., p. 48

21 Hughes, Pennethorne, op. cit., p. 195

22 Shlain, Leonard, *The Alphabet versus the Goddess* (New York: Viking, 1998), pp. 323–4 (Copyright © Leonard Shlain, 1998. Reproduced by permission of Penguin Books (UK) and of Viking Penguin, a division of Penguin Group (USA) Inc)

23 Hughes, Pennethorne, *Witchcraft* (London: Pelican Books, 1965), p. 187

24 *The Times Illustrated History of the World*, Ed. Geoffrey Parker (London: Times Books, 1995), p. 185

25 Shlain, Leonard, *The Alphabet versus the Goddess* (New York: Viking, 1998), p. 375 (Copyright © Leonard Shlain, 1998. Reproduced by permission of Penguin Books (UK) and of Viking Penguin, a division of Penguin Group (USA) Inc)

26 Bacon, Francis, *The Physical and Metaphysical Works of Lord Bacon,* Ed. Joseph Devey (London: George Bell and Sons, 1911), p. 17

27 Shlain, Leonard, *The Alphabet versus the Goddess* (New York: Viking, 1998), p. 379 (Copyright © Leonard Shlain, 1998. Reproduced by permission of Penguin Books (UK) and of Viking Penguin, a division of Penguin Group (USA) Inc)

28 Williams, Heathcote, *Whale Nation* (London: Jonathan Cape, 1988), pp. 69, 78

29 Landes, David S., *The Unbound Prometheus: Technological Change and Industrial Development in Western Europe from 1750 to the Present* (Cambridge: Cambridge University Press, 1969), p. 41

30 Jones, Gareth Stedman, *Outcast London* (Oxford: Oxford University Press, 1971), pp. 162, 170–1

31 Gordimer, Nadine, 'The Witwatersrand: A Time and Tailings', *Optima*, Vol. 18, No. 1, March 1968, p. 23

32 Montgomery of Alamein, *A Concise History of Warfare* (William Collins, Sons and Company Ltd, 1972), p. 11

33 Arlacchi, Pino, *Mafia Business* (Oxford: Oxford University Press, 1988), pp. 227–8 (By permission of Oxford University Press)

34 Cocker, Mark, *Rivers of Blood, Rivers of Gold* (London: Jonathan Cape, 1998), p. xiii

35 Kennedy, Paul, *The Rise and Fall of the Great Powers* (London: Fontana, 1989), p. 192 (Reprinted by permission of HarperCollins Publishers Ltd © Paul Kennedy, 1988)

36 Shlain, Leonard, *The Alphabet versus the Goddess* (New York: Viking, 1998), p. 401 (Copyright © Leonard Shlain, 1998. Reproduced by permission of Penguin Books (UK) and of Viking Penguin, a division of Penguin Group (USA) Inc)

37 Shlain, Leonard, op. cit., p. 402

38 Shlain, Leonard, op. cit., p. 420

39 Hertsgaard, Mark, *Earth Odyssey* (London: Abacus, 2000), p. 241

40 Shlain, Leonard, *The Alphabet versus the Goddess* (New York: Viking, 1998), p. 145 (Copyright © Leonard Shlain, 1998. Reproduced by permission of Penguin Books (UK) and of Viking Penguin, a division of Penguin Group (USA) Inc)

PART II

Chapter 1

1 Cohen, M.N., *The Food Crisis in Prehistory* (New Haven: Yale University Press, 1977), p. vii (Copyright © 1977 by Yale University)

2 Hosking, Geoffrey, *Russia: People and Empire 1552–1917* (London: HarperCollins, 1997), p.206

3 Hemmer, Helmut, *Domestication: The Decline of Environmental Appreciation* (Cambridge: Cambridge University Press, 1990), p. 102

4 Hemmer, Helmut, op. cit., p. 182

5 Sparks, Allister, *The Mind of South Africa* (London: Heinemann, 1990), pp. 11–12

6 Dawkins, Richard, *The Selfish Gene* (Oxford: Oxford University Press, 1989), pp. 189–201

7 Blackmore, Susan, *The Meme Machine* (Oxford: Oxford University Press, 1999), p. 17 (© Susan Blackmore 1999, by permission of Oxford University Press)

8 Blackmore, Susan, op. cit., p. 74

9 Blackmore, Susan, op. cit., pp. 170–1

10 Dawkins, Richard, *The Selfish Gene* (Oxford: Oxford University Press, 1989), pp. 197, 199 (© Richard Dawkins 1989, by permission of Oxford University Press)

11 Mayr, Ernst, *Populations, Species, and Evolution* (Cambridge, Massachusetts: Belknap Press of Harvard University, 1975), p.363 (Copyright © 1963, 1970 by the President and Fellows of Harvard College. Reprinted by permission of Harvard University Press)

12 Mayr, Ernst, op. cit., p. 331

13 Mayr, Ernst, op. cit., p. 67

14 Mayr, Ernst, op. cit., p. 43

Chapter 2

1 Thornton, A.P., *The Habit of Authority* (London: HarperCollins, 1966), p. 35

2 Fromm, Erich, *The Art of Loving* (London: Unwin Paperbacks, 1979), pp. 18–19

3 Fromm, Erich, *The Anatomy of Human Destructiveness* (London: Jonathan Cape, 1974), p. 207 (Copyright 1973 by Erich Fromm. Reprinted by permission of Henry Holt and Company, LLC)

4 Wilson, Edgar, *The Myth of British Monarchy* (London: Journeyman Press, 1989), pp. 145, 148, 154

5 Fromm, Erich, *The Art of Loving* (London: Unwin Paperbacks, 1979), p. 20

6 Hitler, Adolf, *Mein Kampf,* Trans. Ralph Manheim (London: Pimlico, 1992), p. 528

7 Bullock, Alan, *Hitler, A Study in Tyranny* (London: Penguin, 1969), p. 278 (Reprinted with permission of Curtis Brown Ltd, London, on behalf of the Estate of Alan Bullock © Alan Bullock 1952, 1962)

8   Wilson, Edgar, *The Myth of British Monarchy* (London: Journeyman Press, 1989), pp. 127, 143

9   Fromm, Erich, *The Anatomy of Human Destructiveness* (London: Jonathan Cape, 1974), p. 199 (Copyright 1973 by Erich Fromm. Reprinted by permission of Henry Holt and Company, LLC)

10 Jones, David, *In Parenthesis* (London: Faber and Faber, 1961), pp. 204–5

11 Junger, Ernest, *Storm of Steel* (London: Chatto and Windus, 1929), p. ix

12 Carrington, Charles, *Soldier From the Wars Returning* (London: Hutchinson, 1965), p. 87

13 Thomson, David, *Europe Since Napoleon* (London: Longmans, 1962)

14 Barnett, Correlli, 'The locusts began eating during the War Years,' *The Observer*, 2 March 1986 (© *The Guardian/Observer*)

15 Giliomee, Hermann, 'The Elusive Search For Peace', *Optima*, Vol. 36, No. 3, September 1988, p. 128

16 Morris, Desmond, *The Human Zoo* (London: Corgi Books, 1971), p. 33

17 Kennedy, Paul, *The Rise and Fall of the Great Powers* (London: Fontana, 1989), pp. 89–90 (Reprinted by permission of HarperCollins Publishers Ltd © Paul Kennedy 1988)

18 Braudel, Fernand, *The Identity of France* (London: Fontana, 1988)

19 Steiner, George, 'In Bluebeard's Castle – Some Notes Towards the Re-Definition of Culture', *The Listener*, Vol. 85, No. 2190, 18 March 1971, p. 327

20 Zuckerman, Solly, *Scientists and War: The Impact of Science on Military and Civil Affairs* (London: Hamish Hamilton, 1966), p. viii

21 Chain, Ernst, 'Defence and the Scientist', *The Listener*, Vol. 86, No. 2213, 26 August 1971, pp. 267–8

22 Fromm, Erich, *The Anatomy of Human Destructiveness* (London: Jonathan Cape, 1974), p. 187 (Copyright 1973 by Erich Fromm. Reprinted by permission of Henry Holt and Company, LLC)

23 Fromm, Erich, op. cit., p.187

24 Trotter, W., *Instincts of the Herd in Peace and War* (London: Ernest Benn, 1942), p. 174

25 Bradford, William, 'The Mayflower Compact', 11 November 1620

26 Wilson, James, *The Earth Shall Weep* (London: Macmillan, 1998), p. 157

27 Kennedy, Paul, *The Rise and Fall of the Great Powers* (London: Fontana, 1989), p. 373 (Reprinted by permission of HarperCollins Publishers Ltd © Paul Kennedy 1988)

Chapter 3

1   *Black's Medical Dictionary*, 37th Edn, Ed. Gordon Macpherson (London: A. & C. Black, 1992), pp. 441, 369

2   Brown, Dee, *Bury My Heart at Wounded Knee* (London: Barrie and Jenkins, 1971), p. 6 (Reprinted by permission of Peters Fraser & Dunlop Group Ltd)

3   Bullock, Alan, *Hitler and Stalin: Parallel Lives* (London: HarperCollins, 1992), p. 428

4   Bullock, Alan, op. cit., p. 428

5 Fromm, Erich, *The Anatomy of Human Destructiveness* (London: Jonathan Cape, 1974), p. 187 (Copyright 1973 by Erich Fromm. Reprinted by permission of Henry Holt and Company, LLC)

6 Norman, Edward, 'Latin America's Radical Clergy', *The Listener*, Vol. 104, No. 2671, 24 July 1980, p. 104

7 Norman, Edward, op. cit., p. 103

8 Sheppard, David, 'The poverty that imprisons the spirit', *The Listener*, Vol. 111, No. 2854, 19 April 1984, pp. 8–9

9 Mark, Sir Robert, *The Observer*, 13 March 1977 (© *The Guardian/Observer*)

10 Maddock, Sir Ieuan, 'Any Questions?' *The Listener*, Vol. 104, No. 2668, 3 July 1980, p. 15

11 O'Brien, Conor Cruise, 'The Reith Lectures', *The Listener*, Vol. 103, No. 2660, 1 May 1980, p. 577

12 Young, John Russell, *Around the World with General Grant* (American News Company, n.d.), pp. 447–8

13 Ignatieff, Michael, 'A rich nation is tearing itself apart', *The Observer*, 9 June 1991, p. 21 (© *The Guardian/Observer*)

14 Kennedy, Paul, *The Rise and Full of the Great Powers* (London: Fontana, 1989), p. 479 (Reprinted by permission of HarperCollins Publishers Ltd © Paul Kennedy 1988)

15 Craib, I., 'Social construction as a social psychosis', *Sociology*, 31/1, 1997

16 Morris, Desmond, *The Naked Ape* (London: Corgi Books, 1969), p. 153

Chapter 4

1 Kanner, Leo, *Child Psychiatry* (Springfield, Illinois: Charles C. Thomas, 1957), p. 739

2 Hudson, Liam, *Contrary Imaginations* (London: Methuen, 1966), p. 128

3 Hughes, Robert, *The Fatal Shore* (London: Pan Books, 1988), p. 3 (Copyright © Robert Hughes, 1986. Reproduced by permission of The Harvill Press)

4 Steiner, George, 'In Bluebeard's Castle – Some Notes Towards the Re-Definition of Culture', *The Listener*, Vol. 85, No. 2194, 15 April 1971, p. 472

5 Delahaye, Michael, 'Louis XIV', *The Listener*, Vol. 109, No. 2815, 30 June 1983, p. 11

6 Leading Article, *The Observer*, 4 July 1976 (© *The Guardian/Observer*)

7 Shepherd, Jack, *The Observer*, 27 May 1990 (© *The Guardian/Observer*)

8 Hackett, John, 'Illusion and Reality', *The Listener*, Vol. 83, No. 2134, 19 February 1970, p. 245

Chapter 5

1 Carr, Archie, and the Editors of Time-Life Books, *The Land and Wildlife of Africa* [in 'Life Nature Library' series] (New York: Time-Life Books, 1964), p. 114 (© 1964 Time-Life Books Inc)

2 Overy, Paul, 'The Green Crown', *The Listener*, Vol. 103, No. 2649, 14 February 1980, p. 218

3 Jay, Antony, *Corporation Man* (London: Jonathan Cape, 1972), p. 132
4 Horrobin, David, *The Madness of Adam and Eve* (London: Bantam Press, 2001), p. 25 (Reprinted by permission of The Random House Group Ltd)
5 Humphrey, Nicholas, 'The Bronowski Memorial Lecture: "Four Minutes to Midnight"', *The Listener*, Vol. 106, No. 2733, 29 October 1981, p. 498
6 Lyon, Peter, 'Commonwealth sense and sentiment', *The Listener*, Vol. 102, No. 2621, 26 July 1979, p. 100
7 Carr, Archie, and the Editors of Time-Life Books, *The Land and Wildlife of Africa* [in 'Life Nature Library' series] (New York: Time-Life Books, 1964), p. 113 (© 1964 Time-Life Books Inc)
8 Rappaport, Roy A., 'Forests and Man', *The Ecologist*, Vol. 6, No. 7, Aug/Sept 1976, p. 241
9 Marais, Eugene, *The Soul of the White Ant* (London: Methuen, 1950)
10 Reader, John, and Croze, Harvey, *Pyramids of Life* (London: HarperCollins, 1977), p. 60 (Reprinted by permission of Peters Fraser & Dunlop Group Ltd)
11 Kullas, H. and Ayer, G., *What the Elders of Ashanti Say* (Kumasi, Ghana: University Press, 1967)
12 McCamley, N.J., *Secret Underground Cities* (London: Leo Cooper, 1998)

Chapter 6

1 Farb, Peter, and the Editors of Time-Life Books, *Ecology* [in 'Life Nature Library' series] (New York: Time-Life Books, 1965), pp. 40–1 (© 1965 Time-Life Books Inc)
2 Smith, Adam, *Lectures on Jurisprudence*, Ed. R.L. Meek and others (Oxford: Oxford University Press, 1978), p. 208
3 Disraeli, Benjamin, *Sybil: or The Two Nations* (Oxford: Oxford University Press, 1967), p. 67
4 Dando, W.A., *The Geography of Famine* (London: Edward Arnold, 1980)
5 Davis, Mike, *Late Victorian Holocausts* (London: Verso, 2001)
6 Dando, W.A., *The Geography of Famine* (London: Edward Arnold, 1980), p. 154
7 Dando, W.A., op. cit., p. 17
8 Ascherson, Neal, 'The end of an old song', *The Observer*, 26 March 1989, p. 13 (© *The Guardian/Observer*)
9 Evans, Ivor H., *Brewer's Dictionary of Phrase and Fable*, 14th Edn (London: Cassell, 1989), p. 1173
10 Evans, Ivor H., op. cit., pp. 118, 255
11 Pakenham, Thomas, *The Scramble for Africa* (London: Weidenfeld and Nicolson, 1991), p. 607
12 Blythe, Ronald, *The View in Winter: Reflections on Old Age* (London: Allen Lane, 1979), p. 114
13 Malcolm Muggeridge talks to David Ben-Gurion *The Listener*, Vol. 79, No. 2040, 2 May 1968, p. 570
14 Ibn Khaldun (1332–1406): Arab philosopher, historian and politician
15 Teilhard de Chardin, Pierre, *The Phenomenon of Man* (London: Collins, 1960)

16 Bales, Kevin, *Disposable People* (Berkeley, California: University of California Press, 1999)

17 Owen, Wilfred, 'Anthem for Doomed Youth', in *Poetry of the English-Speaking World*, Ed. Richard Aldington (London: Heinemann, 1947), p. 893

18 Bower, Tom, *The Paperclip Conspiracy* (London: Michael Joseph, 1987)

19 Naughton, John, 'Knowledge at too high a cost', *The Listener*, Vol. 117, No. 3000, 26 February 1987, p. 32

20 Woudhuysen, James, 'Danger: pods at work', *The Listener*, Vol. 116, No. 2986, 13 November 1986, p. 22

21 *New Scientist*, Vol. 167, No. 2254, 2 September 2000

22 Hertsgaard, Mark, *Earth Odyssey* (London: Abacus, 2000), p. 139

23 Margerison, Tom; Wallace, Marjorie and Hallenstein, Dalbert, *The Superpoison* (London: Macmillan, 1981), p. 226

24 Sunday Times Insight Team, *Suffer the Children: the story of thalidomide* (London: André Deutsch, 1979)

25 *Understanding Chimpanzees*, Ed. Paul Heltne and Linda Marquardt (Cambridge, Massachusetts: Harvard University Press, 1989)

26 Carson, Rachel, *Silent Spring* (London: Penguin, 1965), p. 167

27 van der Post, Laurens, and Taylor, Jane, *Testament to the Bushman* (London: Viking, 1984), p. 159

28 Bradford, William, *Of Plymouth Plantation (1620–1647)*, Ed. Harvey Wish (New York: Capricorn Books, 1962)

29 Brown, Dee, *Bury My Heart at Wounded Knee* (London: Barrie and Jenkins, 1971), p. 176 (Reprinted by permission of Peters Fraser & Dunlop Group Ltd)

30 Lopez, Barry Holstun, *Of Wolves and Men* (London: J.M. Dent, 1978), p. 139

31 Lopez, Barry Holstun, op. cit., p. 233

32 Maccoby, Hyam, *The Listener*, Vol. 112, No. 2879, 11 October 1984, p. 26

33 Grierson, P.J. Hamilton, *The Silent Trade* (Edinburgh: William Green and Sons, 1903), p. 33

34 Browning, C.R., *Ordinary Men: Reserve Police Battalion 101 and the Final Solution in Poland* (London: HarperCollins, 1993 – HarperPerennial ed.), p. 132

Chapter 7

1 Glubb, John, *The Course of the Empire* (London: Hodder and Stoughton, 1965)

2 Glubb, John, op. cit., p. 57

3 Kennedy, Paul, *The Rise and Fall of the Great Powers* (London: Fontana, 1989), pp. xv, xvi, 698 (Reprinted by permission of HarperCollins Publishers Ltd © Paul Kennedy 1988)

4 Kennedy, Paul, op. cit., pp. 61–2

5 Kennedy, Paul, op. cit., p. 666

6 Kelly, David Victor, *The Ruling Few* (London: Hollis and Carter, 1952), p. 5

7 Glubb, John, *The Course of the Empire* (London: Hodder and Stoughton, 1965)

8 Lamb, David, *The Africans* (London: Mandarin, 1990), p. xv (Copyright © David Lamb 1982. Reprinted by permission of Brandt and Hochman Literary Agents, Inc.)

9 Oppenheimer, Harry, *Four Steps to Democracy* (Johannesburg: Anglo American Corp., 1989), [Speech given at The World Economic Forum conference in Davos, Switzerland, on 31 January 1989]

10 Kennedy, Paul, *The Rise and Fall of the Great Powers* (London: Fontana, 1989), pp. 567, 592 (Reprinted by permission of HarperCollins Publishers Ltd © Paul Kennedy 1988)

11 Ashby, Eric, 'The murky history of Father Thames', *New Scientist*, Vol. 111, No. 1521, 14 August 1986, p. 43

Chapter 8

1 Mayr, Ernst, *Populations, Species, and Evolution* (Cambridge, Massachusetts: Belknap Press of Harvard University, 1975), p. 390 (Copyright © 1963, 1970 by the President and Fellows of Harvard College. Reprinted by Permission of Harvard University Press)

2 *The Life of Thomas Holcroft, Vol. 2*, Ed. Elbridge Colby (London: Constable, 1925), p. 82

3 Marais, Eugene, *The Soul of the White Ant* (London: Methuen, 1950)

4 Russell, W.M.S., 'Men and Women', *The Listener*, Vol. 88, No. 2264, 17 August 1972, p. 194

5 Tudge, Colin, 'Are human beings still evolving?', *New Scientist*, Vol. 119, No. 1630, 15 September 1988, p. 71

6 Huxley, Julian, *Evolution in Action* (London: Chatto and Windus, 1953), pp. 150–1 (Copyright © Julian Huxley 1953) (Reprinted by permission of PFD on behalf of the Estate of Julian Huxley)

7 Hegel, G.W.F., *Lectures on the Philosophy of History* (London: George Bell and Sons, 1902), pp. 70, 34

8 Brown, Dee, *The Westerners* (London: Michael Joseph, 1974), p. 8 (Reprinted by permission of PFD)

9 McLuhan, T.C., *Touch the Earth* (London: Sphere Books, 1982), p. 67

10 Russell, Bertrand, *In Praise of Idleness and Other Essays* (London: Allen and Unwin, 1935), p. 12

11 Brown, Dee, *Bury My Heart at Wounded Knee* (London: Barrie and Jenkins, 1971), p. 316 (Reprinted by permission of Peters Fraser & Dunlop Group Ltd)

12 Tinker, Jon, 'Nor any drop to drink', *New Scientist*, Vol. 173, No. 1043, 17 March 1977, p. 637

13 Taylor, Gordon Rattray, *The Doomsday Book* (London: Panther Books, 1972), p. 237 (Copyright © Gordon Rattray Taylor 1970)

14 Brown, J.A.C., *The Social Psychology of Industry* (London: Penguin, 1961), p. 59

15 Kennedy, Paul, *Preparing for the 21st Century* (London: HarperCollins, 1993), p. 26

16 Calder, Peter Ritchie (Baron Ritchie-Calder), *Hell Upon Earth* (Potters Bar: The

Conservation Society, 1968 [Presidential Address to The Conservation Society] (© *The Guardian/Observer*)

17   Hanlon, Joseph, 'Mercury and trees', *New Scientist*, Vol. 72, No. 1024, 28 October 1976, p. 229

18   Tudge, Colin, 'The Best Medicine', *New Scientist*, Vol. 172, No. 2317, 17 November 2001, p. 43

19   Pearce, Fred, 'The great dam scam', *New Scientist*, Vol. 168, No. 2265, 18 November 2000, p. 6

20   Inglis, Brian, *Drugs, Doctors and Disease* (London: HarperCollins, 1965), p. 231 (© Brian Inglis 1965)

21   Grant, Michael, 'Roman Myths', *The Listener*, Vol. 87, No. 2232, 6 January 1972, p. 12

22   Bullock, Alan, *Hitler, A Study in Tyranny* (London: Penguin, 1969), p. 380 (Reproduced with permission of Curtis Brown Ltd, London, on behalf of the Estate of Alan Bullock © Alan Bullock 1952, 1962)

23   Snyder, Solomon H., *Drugs and the Brain* (New York: W.H. Freeman, 1987)

24   Lewin, Roger, 'Total ban sought on genetic engineering', *New Scientist*, Vol. 73, No. 1042, 10 March 1977, p. 571

25   *The Lancet*, June 1988

26   Bullock, Alan, *Hitler and Stalin: Parallel Lives* (London: HarperCollins, 1992), p. 1003

27   Sample, Ian, 'Small Visions, Grand Designs', *New Scientist*, Vol. 172, No. 2311, 6 October 2001, p. 35

28   Kennedy, Paul, *The Rise and Fall of the Great Powers* (London: HarperCollins, 1989)

29   Fromm, Erich, *The Anatomy of Human Destructiveness* (London: Jonathan Cape, 1974), p. 10 (Copyright 1973 by Erich Fromm. Reprinted by permission of Henry Holt and Company, LLC)

Chapter 9

1   Blakely, Denis, 'Goodbye to Moscow', *The Listener*, Vol. 84, No. 2161, 27 August 1970, p. 264

2   Blainey, G., *The Causes of War* (London: Macmillan, 1988), pp. 149–50

3   Kennedy, Paul, *The Rise and Fall of the Great Powers* (London: Fontana, 1989), p. xix (Reprinted by permission of HarperCollins Publishers Ltd © Paul Kennedy 1988)

4   Kennedy, Paul, op. cit., p. 592

5   Bullock, Alan, *Hitler and Stalin: Parallel Lives* (London: HarperCollins, 1992), p. 456

6   Bullock, Alan, op. cit., pp. 456–7

7   Bullock, Alan, op. cit., pp. 414–5

8   Bullock, Alan, op. cit.

9   Bullock, Alan, op. cit., p. 815

10   Breuer, G., *Weather Modification* (Cambridge: Cambridge University Press, 1980)

11 Kissinger, Henry, *The Observer*, 30 September 1979 and 18 October 1981 (© *The Guardian/Observer*)

12 Klevemann, Lutz, 'The New Great Game: Blood and Oil in Central Asia', *Atlantic Monthly*, 2003

13 *Radio Times*, 8 November 1980

14 *The Forests*, Ed. Geoffrey Lean (Godalming: World Wide Fund for Nature and *The Observer*, 1992) (© *The Guardian/Observer*)

15 Caufield, Catherine, *In the Rainforest* (London: Pan Books, 1986), p. 42

16 Caufield, Catherine, op. cit., p. 40

17 Holmes, Bob, 'Destruction follows in trawlers' wake', *New Scientist*, Vol. 154, No. 2086, 14 June 1997, p. 4

18 Fry, Colin, 'Marxism versus Ecology', *The Ecologist*, Vol. 6, No. 9, November 1976, p. 329

19 Pearce, Fred, 'All polluted on the Eastern front', *New Scientist*, Vol. 136, No. 1841, 3 October 1992, p. 42

20 Pearce, Fred, op. cit., p. 42

21 Komarov, Boris, *The Destruction of Nature in the Soviet Union*, Trans. Michel Vale and Joe Hollander (London: Pluto Press, 1978), p. 16

22 *The Forests*, Ed. Geoffrey Lean (Godalming: World Wide Fund for Nature and *The Observer*, 1992) (© *The Guardian/Observer*)

23 Dutton, Diana, *Worse than the Disease* (Cambridge: Cambridge University Press, 1988), p. 223

24 Marder, Arthur J., *From the Dreadnought to Scapa Flow, Vol. 5: Victory and aftermath* (Oxford: Oxford University Press, 1970), p. 247 (© Arthur J. Marder 1970, by permission of Oxford University Press)

25 Hsiao Ch'ien, *Traveller Without a Map*, Trans. Jeffrey C. Hinkley (London: Hutchinson, 1990), p. 134

PART III

Chapter 1

1 Steinbeck, John, *The Log from the Sea of Cortez* (London: Heinemann, 1958), p. 88 (Copyright © John Steinbeck, 1951. Reproduced by permission of Penguin Books Ltd)

2 Gould, Stephen Jay, 'Another Look at Lamarck', *New Scientist*, Vol. 84, No. 1175, 4 October 1979, p. 40

3 Huxley, Julian, *Evolution in Action* (London: Chatto and Windus, 1953)

4 *The Observer*, in association with Concern Worldwide, 16 October 1994, p. 12 (© *The Guardian/Observer*)

5 Sale, Kirkpatrick, 'Five Facets of a Myth', *Resurgence*, No. 192, Jan/Feb 1999, p. 22 (www.resurgence.org)

6 Figures from UN Department for Economic and Social Information

7 Ralph, Bob, 'Now you see it, now you don't', *New Scientist*, Vol. 122, No. 1669, 17 June 1989, p. 77

8 Figures from UN Department for Economic and Social Information

9   Hogan, Jenny, 'Global Warming: the new battle', *New Scientist*, Vol. 179, No. 2412, 13 September 2003, p. 6

10   Pearce, Fred, 'Will a seachange turn up the heat?', *New Scientist*, Vol. 152, No. 2058, 30 November 1996, p. 16

11   Lynas, Mark, 'At the end of our weather', *The Observer*, 5 October 2003

12   *The Forests*, Ed. Geoffrey Lean (Godalming: World Wide Fund for Nature and *The Observer*, 1992) (© *The Guardian/Observer*)

13   Cameron, James, 'The plight of the New Diaspora', *The Listener*, Vol. 103, No. 2666, 19 June 1980, p. 791

14   *New Scientist*, Vol. 122, No. 1668, 10 June 1989, p. 25

15   Leading Article, *New Scientist*, Vol. 123, No. 1673, 15 July 1989

16   Fagan, Brian, *The Long Summer* (London: Granta Books, 2004), pp. xv, xvi

17   Fagan, Brian, op. cit., p. xvi

Chapter 2

1   Taylor, Stephen, *Shaka's Children* (London: HarperCollins, 1994), pp. 39–40

2   Tsai Chin, *The Observer*, 5 November 1989 (© *The Guardian/Observer*)

3   Bullock, Alan, *Hitler, A Study in Tyranny* (London: Penguin, 1969), p. 591 (Reproduced with permission of Curtis Brown Ltd, London, on behalf of the Estate of Alan Bullock © Alan Bullock 1952, 1962)

4   *The Listener*, Vol. 102, No. 2637, 15 November 1979, p. 667

5   Campbell, James, *Talking At The Gates* (London: Faber and Faber, 1991), p. 213

6   Wells, H.G., *The Outline of History* (London: Cassell, 1966), pp. 1015–6 (Reprinted by permission of AP Watt Ltd on behalf of the Trustees of H.G. Wells deceased)

7   *Britannia Royal Naval College: New Defence Studies Course* (Royal Navy Broadsheet, 1987)

8   Dunbar, Sir George, *A History of India*, 3rd Edn (London: Nicholson and Watson, 1943), pp. 92–3

9   Kennedy, Paul, *Preparing for the 21st Century* (London: HarperCollins, 1993), p. 243

10   Hamilton, Adrian, *The Observer*, 17 September 1989 (© *The Guardian/Observer*)

11   Churchill, W.S., speech in the House of Commons, 16 February 1922

12   Sumner, Gordon ('Sting'), *The Observer*, 16 April 1989, p. 14 (© *The Guardian/Observer*)

Chapter 3

1   Thomas, Hugh, *An Unfinished History of the World* (London: Hamish Hamilton, 1979), p. 609

2   Sampson, Anthony, *The Observer*, 23 November 1980 (© *The Guardian/Observer*)

3   Rose, Steven, 'Beyond 1984', *New Scientist*, Vol. 82, No. 1160, 21 June 1979, p. 1024

4   Bohm, David, 'Can science save the fragmenting Universe?' [review of *God and*

the New Physics by Paul Davies (London: Dent, 1983)], *New Scientist*, Vol. 99, No. 1367, 21 July 1983, p. 217

5 Siebker, M.H., 'Industrial and post-industrial images of Man' *The Ecologist*, Vol. 7, No. 4, 25 May 1977, p. 1

6 Medawar, Peter, *The Hope of Progress* (London: Methuen, 1972), p. 125

7 Hughes, Robert, *The Shock of the New: Art and the Century of Change* (London: British Broadcasting Corporation, 1980), p. 108 (Reproduced with the permission of BBC Worldwide Limited. Copyright © Robert Hughes 1980)

8 Breuer, G., *Weather Modification* (Cambridge: Cambridge University Press, 1980)

9 'Poverty and Corruption' (Leading Article), *New Scientist*, Vol. 180, No. 2416, 11 October 2003, p. 3

10 Monbiot, George, 'Enslaved by free trade', *New Scientist*, Vol. 178, No. 2397, 31 May 2003, p. 25

11 *New Scientist*, Vol. 133, No. 1805, 25 January 1992, p. 19

12 Greenpeace, Campaign Report, August 1991, No. 6

13 *New Scientist*, Vol. 134, No. 1816, 11 April 1992, p. 3

14 Carson, Rachel, *Silent Spring* (London: Penguin, 1965), pp. 225–6

15 Cornwell, John, 'Just following orders?', *New Scientist*, Vol. 179, No. 2414, 27 September 2003, p. 25

16 'A new heaven and a new earth: Thomas Paine on space habitats', *The Listener*, Vol. 96, No. 2465, 8 July 1976, p. 10

17 Ridpath, Ian, and O'Neill, Gerard K., 'Living out there', *New Scientist*, Vol. 74, No. 1057, 23 June 1977, p. 720

18 *New Scientist*, Vol. 166, No. 2239, 20 May 2000

19 Hawking, Stephen, *A Brief History of Time* (London: Bantam Press, 1996), p. 233

20 Teilhard de Chardin, Pierre, *The Phenomenon of Man* (London: Collins, 1959)

21 *New Scientist*, Vol. 176, No. 2362, 28 September 2002, p. 56

22 Steiner, George, 'In Bluebeard's Castle – Some Notes Towards the Re-Definition of Culture', *The Listener*, Vol. 85, No. 2194, 15 April 1971, p. 476

Chapter 4

1 Hardy, Thomas, 'The Convergence of the Twain', *Complete Poems* (London: Macmillan, 1981), pp. 306–7

2 Roszak, Theodore, 'Leave the wilderness alone!', *New Scientist*, Vol. 118, No. 1615, 2 June 1988, p. 63

3 Roszak, Theodore, op. cit., p. 64

4 *Politics and History in Band Societies*, Ed. E. Leacock and Richard Lee (Cambridge: Cambridge University Press, 1989), p. 442

5 Horne, Gabrielle, 'Why be a scientist?', *New Scientist*, Vol. 83, No. 1171, 6 September 1979, p. 719

6 Margulis, Lynn, and Sagan, Dorion, *Microcosmos: Four Billion Years of Evolution from our Microbial Ancestors* (London: HarperCollins, 1987), pp. 228–9

7 Huxley, Julian, *Evolution in Action* (London: Chatto and Windus, 1953), p. 37 (Copyright © Julian Huxley 1953. Reprinted by permission of PFD on behalf of the Estate of Julian Huxley)

8 *New Scientist*, Vol. 176, No. 2373, 14 December 2002, p. 6

9 Ascherson, Neal, [review of *The Age of Empire, 1875–1914* by E.J. Hobsbawm (London: Weidenfeld and Nicolson, 1987)], *The Observer*, 18 October 1987 (© *The Guardian/Observer*)

Chapter 5

1 Brody, Hugh, *The Other Side of Eden* (London: Faber & Faber Ltd, 2002), p. 314

2 Bintliff, John, 'Leaky and Co.', *The Listener*, Vol. 106, No. 2719, 9 July 1981, p. 53

3 Bintliff, John, op. cit., p. 53

4 Mandela, Nelson, *Long Walk to Freedom* (London: Abacus, 1995), p. 664

5 *Investigations on Cetacea*, Ed. George Pilleri (Berne: Brain Anatomy Institute, 1969–94), 25 vols and 5 supplements

6 Maxwell, Nicholas, 'Wanted: a new way of thinking', *New Scientist*, Vol. 114, No. 1560, 14 May 1987, p. 63

7 Reddy, Amulya K.N., 'Science v. deprived humanity', *New Scientist*, Vol. 80, No. 1126, 26 October 1978, p. 270

8 Schaller, George B., *The Year of the Gorilla* (Chicago: University of Chicago Press, 1964), p. 85 (© 1964 by The University of Chicago Press)

9 Leakey, L.S.B., *Animals in Africa* [photographed by Ylla, text by Leakey] (London, Harvill Press, 1953), p. 51

10 Larkin, Philip, 'This be the Verse', *High Windows* (Faber and Faber, 1979), p. 30

11 Morris, Desmond, *The Naked Ape* (London: Corgi Books, 1969), pp. 155–6

12 Gall, Sandy, *The Bushmen of Southern Africa* (London: Chatto and Windus, 2001) (Used by permission of The Random House Group Limited)

Epilogue

1 Greer, Germaine, *Whitefella Jump Up* (London: Profile Books, 2004), p. 129

2 *Man the Hunter*, Ed. Richard B. Lee and Irven DeVore (New York: Aldine Publishing Company, 1979), p. 3

3 *Politics and History in Band Societies*, Ed. E. Leacock and Richard Lee (Cambridge: Cambridge University Press, 1989), p. 405

4 *Man the Hunter*, Ed. Richard B. Lee and Irven DeVore (New York: Aldine Publishing Company, 1979), p. 345

5 Greer, Germaine, *Whitefella Jump Up* (London: Profile Books, 2004), p. 128

APPENDICES

Appendix i

1 Hemmer, Helmut, *Domestication: The Decline of Environmental Appreciation* (Cambridge: Cambridge University Press, 1990), pp. 40, 42
2 Hemmer, Helmut, op. cit., p. 92
3 Hemmer, Helmut, op. cit., pp. 110–1
4 Hemmer, Helmut, op. cit., p. 113

Appendix ii

1 Steiner, George, 'In Bluebeard's Castle – Some Notes Towards the Re-Definition of Culture', *The Listener*, Vol. 85, No. 2193, 8 April 1971, p. 446
2 Steiner, George, 'In Bluebeard's Castle – Some Notes Towards the Re-Definition of Culture', *The Listener*, Vol. 85, No. 2192, 1 April 1971, p. 408
3 Sandars, N.K., *Prehistoric Art in Europe* (London: Penguin, 1968), p. 73
4 McLuhan, T.C., *Touch the Earth* (London: Sphere Books, 1982), p. 106

Appendix iii

1 Mithen, Steven, *The Prehistory of the Mind* (London: Phoenix, 1998) (Copyright © 1996 Thames and Hudson Ltd, London)
2 Mithen, Steven, op. cit., p. 240
3 Shlain, Leonard, *The Alphabet versus the Goddess* (London: Viking, 1998) (Copyright © Leonard Shlain, 1998. Reproduced by permission of Penguin Books (UK) and of Viking Penguin, a division of Penguin Group (USA) Inc)
4 Shlain, Leonard, op. cit., p. 33
5 Shlain, Leonard, op. cit., p. 81

Appendix iv

1 Zuckerman, Solly, *The Social Life of Monkeys and Apes* (London: Routledge and Kegan Paul, 1981), p. 217
2 Russell, Claire and W.M.S., 'The Sardine Syndrome', *The Ecologist*, Vol. 1, No. 2, August 1970, p. 7
3 Turnbull, Colin, *The Mountain People* (London: Jonathan Cape, 1973)

Appendix v

1   Iremonger, Lucille, *The Fiery Chariot* (London: Secker and Warburg, 1970)
2   Iremonger, Lucille, op. cit., p. 14
3   Iremonger, Lucille, op. cit., p. 309
4   James, Oliver, *The Larkin Syndrome* [*The Observer* Pamphlet No. 2], p. 18 (© *The Guardian/Observer*)
5   Iremonger, Lucille, *The Fiery Chariot* (London: Secker and Warburg, 1970), p. 20
6   Iremonger, Lucille, op. cit., p. 21
7   Wilson, David, 'The Paradox of Dr Alfred Nobel', *The Listener*, Vol. 82, No. 2105, 31 July 1969, p. 149
8   Wilson, David, op. cit., p.149
9   Wilson, David, op. cit., p.149
10 'Chief Enaharo on Biafran casualties', *The Listener*, Vol. 79, No. 2047, 20 June 1968, p. 807

Appendix vi

1   'The Lord Chancellor, Lord Hailsham, talks to Robin Day', *The Listener*, Vol. 88, No. 2259, 13 July 1972, p. 42
2   Gabriel Josipovici, *Tempo*, July 1972

Appendix vii

1   Ovid, *Metamorphoses*, Trans. Frank Justus Miller (London: Heinemann, 1916), pp. 9, 11, 13
2   Cohn, Norman, *The Pursuit of the Millennium* (London: Granada Publishing, 1978), pp. 190–2 (Reprinted by permission of Peters Fraser & Dunlop Group Ltd)

Appendix viii

1   Stanford, W.B., 'Poetic Truth and Scientific Truth', *The Listener*, Vol. 87, No. 2247, 20 April 1972, pp. 511–2
2   Stanford, W.B., op. cit., pp. 511–2
3   Naughton, John, 'The menace of expertise', *The Observer*, 8 April 1979 (© *The Guardian/Observer*)
4   Balls, Michael, 'Time to reform toxic tests', *New Scientist*, Vol. 134, No. 1819, 2 May 1992, p. 33
5   Harrison, Edward, 'Glittering prizes that can tarnish science', *New Scientist*, Vol. 106, No. 1457, 23 May 1985, p. 42
6   *New Scientist*, Vol. 144, No. 1956, 17 December 1994, p. 3

Appendix ix

1 Marr, Andrew, 'As I was walking up the stairs I saw a future that wasn't there', *The Observer*, 17 January 1999 (© *The Guardian/Observer*)
2 *The Observer*, 1 May 1994 (© *The Guardian/Observer*)
3 Steiner, George, 'In Bluebeard's Castle – Some Notes Towards the Re-Definition of Culture', *The Listener*, Vol. 85, No. 2190, 18 March 1971, p. 327
4 Steinbeck, John, *The Log from the Sea of Cortez* (London: Heinemann, 1958), pp. liii
5 Hesse, Hermann, *Narziss and Goldmund*, Trans. Geoffrey Dunlop (London: Penguin, 1971), p. 72
6 McNamara, Sheila, 'A Solitary Quest', *The Observer Magazine*, 15 September 1991, pp. 24–5 (© *The Guardian/Observer*)
7 Hobsbaum, Philip, 'Coleridge the Ice-Skater', *The Listener*, Vol. 87, No. 2244, 30 March 1972, p. 417

Appendix x

1 Schwarz, Walter and Dorothy, 'Living Lightly', *Resurgence*, No. 192, January/February 1999, p. 45
2 Simons, Geoff, *Eco-Computer: The Impact of Global Intelligence* (Chichester: John Wiley and Sons, 1987), p. 109 (Copyright 1987 © John Wiley & Sons Limited. Reproduced with permission)

Appendix xi

1 Marais, Eugene, *The Soul of the White Ant* (London: Methuen, 1950), pp. 78–80
2 Marais, Eugene, op. cit., pp. 80–1

Appendix xii

1 *Shorter Oxford English Dictionary*

Appendix xiii

1 Tinbergen, Niko, *The Herring Gull's World* (London: HarperCollins, 1965), p. 119
2 Miller, Jonathan, 'Are hierarchies necessary? – The Dog Beneath the Skin', *The Listener*, Vol. 88, No. 2260, 20 July 1972, pp. 74–6
3 Miller, Jonathan, op. cit., pp. 74–6
4 Miller, Jonathan, op. cit., pp. 74–6
5 Miller, Jonathan, op. cit., pp. 74–6
6 Miller, Jonathan, op. cit., pp. 74–6
7 Wall, Patrick, 'Are hierarchies necessary? – Is there a higher nervous system?', *The Listener*, Vol. 88, No. 2262, 3 August 1972, pp. 139–41

Appendix xiv

1   Blair, Dr W. Frank, 'Protecting the human environment', *Optima*, Vol. 20, No. 1, March 1970, pp. 9, 11
2   Blair, Dr W. Frank, op. cit., pp. 9, 11
3   Blair, Dr W. Frank, op. cit., pp. 9, 11
4   Blair, Dr W. Frank, op. cit., pp. 9, 11
5   Hertsgaard, Mark, *Earth Odyssey* (London: Abacus, 2000), p. 109
6   Hertsgaard, Mark, op. cit., p. 94
7   Hertsgaard, Mark, op. cit., pp. 124, 141

Appendix xv

1   Bullock, Alan, 'Europe since Hitler', *The Listener*, Vol. 85, No. 2196, 29 April 1971, pp. 538, 540
2   Bullock, Alan, op. cit., pp. 538, 540
3   *New Scientist*, Vol. 123, No. 1674, 22 July 1989, p. 54

Appendix xvi

1   Tippett, Michael, 'Poets in a Barren Age', *The Listener*, Vol. 87, No. 2255, 15 June 1972, p. 800
2   Steinbeck, John, *The Log from the Sea of Cortez* (London: Heinemann, 1958), pp. 88, 89 (Copyright © John Steinbeck, 1951. Reproduced by permission of Penguin Books Ltd)

Appendix xvii

1   Hone, Joseph, 'Sunny Dacca', *The Listener*, Vol. 83, No. 2151, 18 June 1970, pp. 830–1

Appendix xviii

1   Simons, Geoff, *Eco-Computer: The Impact of Global Intelligence* (Chichester: John Wiley and Sons, 1987), p. xiii (Copyright 1987 © John Wiley and Sons Limited. Reproduced with permission)
2   Simons, Geoff, op. cit., p. 123
3   Simons, Geoff, op. cit., p. 109
4   Simons, Geoff, op. cit., p. 158
5   Simons, Geoff, op. cit., p. 175
6   Simons, Geoff, op. cit., pp. 173–4
7   Simons, Geoff, op. cit., p. 106
8   Simons, Geoff, op. cit., p. 176
9   Simons, Geoff, op. cit., p. 178
10 Simons, Geoff, op. cit., p. 187

Appendix xix

1   Steiner, George, 'Tragedy: remorse and justice', *The Listener*, Vol. 102, No. 2633, 18 October 1979, pp. 508–11

Appendix xx

1   Mann, Thomas, *The Magic Mountain,* Trans. H.T. Lowe-Porter (London: Penguin, 1960), p. 155
2   Kaku, Michio, *Hyperspace* (Oxford: Oxford University Press, 1994), p. 302 (By permission of Oxford University Press)

Index